Florida
Course 3

interactive
SCIENCE

PEARSON

...assachusetts
...dler, Arizona
...enview, Illinois
Upper Saddle River, New Jersey

AUTHORS

You're an author!

As you write in this science book, your answers and personal discoveries will be recorded for you to keep, making this book unique to you. That is why you are one of the primary authors of this book.

✎ **In the space below, print your name, school, town, and state. Then write a short autobiography that includes your interests and accomplishments.**

YOUR NAME

SCHOOL

TOWN, STATE

AUTOBIOGRAPHY

Your Photo

Acknowledgments appear on pages 515–519, which constitute an extension of this copyright page.

ISBN-13: 978-0-13-252512-1
ISBN-10: 0-13-252512-7
2 3 4 5 6 7 8 9 10 V011 15 14 13 12 11

ON THE COVER
A Big Repair Job
How do you repair the outside of a space shuttle in orbit? With a robotic arm, of course! This astronaut was anchored to a foot restraint on the International Space Station's Canadarm2, and carried out repairs on the exterior of the Space Shuttle Discovery.

Program Authors

DON BUCKLEY, M.Sc.
Information and Communications Technology Director, The School at Columbia University, New York, New York
Mr. Buckley has been at the forefront of K–12 educational technology for nearly two decades. A founder of New York City Independent School Technologists (NYCIST) and long-time chair of New York Association of Independent Schools' annual IT conference, he has taught students on two continents and created multimedia and Internet-based instructional systems for schools worldwide.

ZIPPORAH MILLER, M.A.Ed.
Associate Executive Director for Professional Programs and Conferences, National Science Teachers Association, Arlington, Virginia
Associate executive director for professional programs and conferences at NSTA, Ms. Zipporah Miller is a former K–12 science supervisor and STEM coordinator for the Prince George's County Public School District in Maryland. She is a science education consultant who has overseen curriculum development and staff training for more than 150 district science coordinators.

MICHAEL J. PADILLA, Ph.D.
Associate Dean and Director, Eugene P. Moore School of Education, Clemson University, Clemson, South Carolina
A former middle school teacher and a leader in middle school science education, Dr. Michael Padilla has served as president of the National Science Teachers Association and as a writer of the National Science Education Standards. He is professor of science education at Clemson University. As lead author of the *Science Explorer* series, Dr. Padilla has inspired the team in developing a program that promotes student inquiry and meets the needs of today's students.

KATHRYN THORNTON, Ph.D.
Professor and Associate Dean, School of Engineering and Applied Science, University of Virginia, Charlottesville, Virginia
Selected by NASA in May 1984, Dr. Kathryn Thornton is a veteran of four space flights. She has logged over 975 hours in space, including more than 21 hours of extravehicular activity. As an author on the *Scott Foresman Science* series, Dr. Thornton's enthusiasm for science has inspired teachers around the globe.

MICHAEL E. WYSESSION, Ph.D.
Associate Professor of Earth and Planetary Science, Washington University, St. Louis, Missouri
An author on more than 50 scientific publications, Dr. Wysession was awarded the prestigious Packard Foundation Fellowship and Presidential Faculty Fellowship for his research in geophysics. Dr. Wysession is an expert on Earth's inner structure and has mapped various regions of Earth using seismic tomography. He is known internationally for his work in geoscience education and outreach.

Understanding by Design Author

GRANT WIGGINS, Ed.D.
President, Authentic Education, Hopewell, New Jersey
Dr. Wiggins is coauthor of *Understanding by Design®* (UbD), a philosophy of instructional design. UbD is a disciplined way of thinking about curriculum design, assessment, and instruction that moves teaching from covering the content to ensuring understanding. Dr. Wiggins is one of today's most influential educational reformers, and consults with schools, districts, and state education departments.

Planet Diary Author

JACK HANKIN
Science/Mathematics Teacher, The Hilldale School, Daly City, California Founder, Planet Diary Web site
Mr. Hankin is the creator and writer of Planet Diary, a science current events Web site. Mr. Hankin is passionate about bringing science news and environmental awareness into classrooms. He's offered numerous Planet Diary workshops at NSTA and other events to train middle school and high school teachers.

ELL Consultant

JIM CUMMINS, Ph.D.
Professor and Canada Research Chair, Curriculum, Teaching and Learning department at the University of Toronto
Dr. Cummins's research focuses on literacy development in multilingual schools and the role of technology in promoting student learning across the curriculum. The *Interactive Science* program incorporates essential research-based principles for integrating language with the teaching of academic content based on Dr. Cummins's instructional framework.

Reading Consultant

HARVEY DANIELS, Ph.D.
Professor of Secondary Education, University of New Mexico, Albuquerque, New Mexico
Dr. Daniels serves as an international consultant to schools, districts, and educational agencies. Dr. Daniels has authored or coauthored 13 books on language, literacy, and education. His most recent works include *Comprehension and Collaboration: Inquiry Circles in Action* and *Subjects Matter: Every Teacher's Guide to Content-Area Reading.*

REVIEWERS

Contributing Writers

Edward Aguado, Ph.D.
Professor, Department of Geography
San Diego State University
San Diego, California

Elizabeth Coolidge-Stolz, M.D.
Medical Writer
North Reading, Massachusetts

Donald L. Cronkite, Ph.D.
Professor of Biology
Hope College
Holland, Michigan

Jan Jenner, Ph.D.
Science Writer
Talladega, Alabama

Linda Cronin Jones, Ph.D.
Associate Professor of Science and Environmental Education
University of Florida
Gainesville, Florida

T. Griffith Jones, Ph.D.
Clinical Associate Professor of Science Education
College of Education
University of Florida
Gainesville, Florida

Andrew C. Kemp, Ph.D.
Teacher
Jefferson County Public Schools
Louisville, Kentucky

Matthew Stoneking, Ph.D.
Associate Professor of Physics
Lawrence University
Appleton, Wisconsin

R. Bruce Ward, Ed.D.
Senior Research Associate
Science Education Department
Harvard-Smithsonian Center for Astrophysics
Cambridge, Massachusetts

Content Reviewers

Paul D. Beale, Ph.D.
Department of Physics
University of Colorado at Boulder
Boulder, Colorado

Jeff R. Bodart, Ph.D.
Professor of Physical Sciences
Chipola College
Marianna, Florida

Joy Branlund, Ph.D.
Department of Earth Science
Southwestern Illinois College
Granite City, Illinois

Marguerite Brickman, Ph.D.
Division of Biological Sciences
University of Georgia
Athens, Georgia

Bonnie J. Brunkhorst, Ph.D.
Science Education and Geological Sciences
California State University
San Bernardino, California

Michael Castellani, Ph.D.
Department of Chemistry
Marshall University
Huntington, West Virginia

Charles C. Curtis, Ph.D.
Research Associate Professor of Physics
University of Arizona
Tucson, Arizona

Diane I. Doser, Ph.D.
Department of Geological Sciences
University of Texas
El Paso, Texas

Rick Duhrkopf, Ph.D.
Department of Biology
Baylor University
Waco, Texas

Alice K. Hankla, Ph.D.
The Galloway School
Atlanta, Georgia

Mark Henriksen, Ph.D.
Physics Department
University of Maryland
Baltimore, Maryland

Chad Hershock, Ph.D.
Center for Research on Learning and Teaching
University of Michigan
Ann Arbor, Michigan

Jeremiah N. Jarrett, Ph.D.
Department of Biology
Central Connecticut State University
New Britain, Connecticut

Scott L. Kight, Ph.D.
Department of Biology
Montclair State University
Montclair, New Jersey

Jennifer O. Liang, Ph.D.
Department of Biology
University of Minnesota–Duluth
Duluth, Minnesota

Candace Lutzow-Felling, Ph.D.
Director of Education
The State Arboretum of Virginia
University of Virginia
Boyce, Virginia

Cortney V. Martin, Ph.D.
Virginia Polytechnic Institute
Blacksburg, Virginia

Joseph F. McCullough, Ph.D.
Physics Program Chair
Cabrillo College
Aptos, California

Heather Mernitz, Ph.D.
Department of Physical Science
Alverno College
Milwaukee, Wisconsin

Sadredin C. Moosavi, Ph.D.
Department of Earth and Environmental Sciences
Tulane University
New Orleans, Louisiana

David L. Reid, Ph.D.
Department of Biology
Blackburn College
Carlinville, Illinois

Scott M. Rochette, Ph.D.
Department of the Earth Sciences
SUNY College at Brockport
Brockport, New York

Karyn L. Rogers, Ph.D.
Department of Geological Sciences
University of Missouri
Columbia, Missouri

Laurence Rosenhein, Ph.D.
Department of Chemistry
Indiana State University
Terre Haute, Indiana

Sara Seager, Ph.D.
Department of Planetary Sciences and Physics
Massachusetts Institute of Technology
Cambridge, Massachusetts

Tom Shoberg, Ph.D.
Missouri University of Science and Technology
Rolla, Missouri

Patricia Simmons, Ph.D.
North Carolina State University
Raleigh, North Carolina

William H. Steinecker, Ph.D.
Research Scholar
Miami University
Oxford, Ohio

Paul R. Stoddard, Ph.D.
Department of Geology and Environmental Geosciences
Northern Illinois University
DeKalb, Illinois

John R. Villarreal, Ph.D.
Department of Chemistry
The University of Texas–Pan American
Edinburg, Texas

John R. Wagner, Ph.D.
Department of Geology
Clemson University
Clemson, South Carolina

Jerry Waldvogel, Ph.D.
Department of Biological Sciences
Clemson University
Clemson, South Carolina

Donna L. Witter, Ph.D.
Department of Geology
Kent State University
Kent, Ohio

Edward J. Zalisko, Ph.D.
Department of Biology
Blackburn College
Carlinville, Illinois

REVIEWERS

Florida Content Reviewers

Phillip Allman, Ph.D.
Department of Biological Sciences
Florida Gulf Coast University
Fort Myers, Florida

Jeff R. Bodart, Ph.D.
Professor of Physical Sciences
Chipola College
Marianna, Florida

Joshua Cohn, Ph.D.
Department of Physics
University of Miami
Coral Gables, Florida

Fred Hamann, Ph.D.
Department of Astronomy
University of Florida
Gainesville, Florida

Linda Cronin Jones, Ph.D.
Associate Professor of Science
and Environmental Education
University of Florida
Gainesville, Florida

T. Griffin Jones, Ph.D.
Clinical Associate Professor of Science
Education
College of Education
University of Florida
Gainesville, Florida

Thomas Juster, Ph.D.
Department of Geology
University of South Florida
Tampa, Florida

Stephen Kucera, Ph.D.
Department of Biology
University of Tampa
Tampa, Florida

Margaret Lowman, Ph.D.
Division of Natural Sciences
New College of Florida
Sarasota, Florida

Kurt Winkelmann, Ph.D.
Department of Chemistry
Florida Institute of Technology
Melbourne, Florida

Ping Zhu, Ph.D.
Department of Earth Sciences
Florida International University
Miami, Florida

Built especially for

Florida

Florida *Interactive Science* covers 100 percent of the Next Generation Sunshine State Standards with no extraneous content. Built on feedback from Florida educators, *Interactive Science* focuses on what's important to Florida, creating a personal, relevant, and engaging classroom experience.

Florida Middle Grades Teacher Advisory Board

Roy Bernstein
Polo Park Middle School
Wellington, Florida

Marla Blair
Deerlake Middle School
West Tallahassee, Florida

Tracey Kumm
Lakeside Junior High School
Orange Park, Florida

Jan Plym
C.H. Price Middle School
Interlachen, Florida

Denise Skinner
Buddy Taylor Middle School
Palm Coast, Florida

Guytri Still
McNair Magnet School
Rockledge, Florida

Tania Studer
Bridgewater Middle School
Winter Garden, Florida

Gina Triboletti
Creekside Middle School
Port Orange, Florida

CONTENTS

my science ONLINE.com

Go to MyScienceOnline.com to interact with this chapter's content. **Keyword:** The Tools of Science

> UNTAMED SCIENCE
• Measuring Up

> PLANET DIARY
• The Tools of Science

> INTERACTIVE ART
• Inquiry Diagram • The Need for Numbers

> VIRTUAL LAB
• What Is Scientific Inquiry?

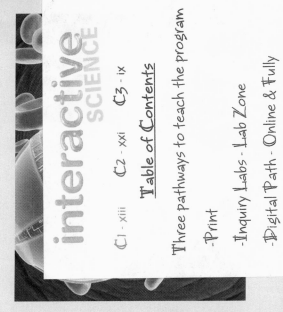

Lab zone® Enter the Lab zone
for hands-on inquiry.

Chapter Lab Investigations:
• Directed Inquiry: Selecting Models
• Open Inquiry: Selecting Models

Inquiry Warm-Ups: • Developing a Theory
• Models in Science • Developing Scientific
Theories • Science and Society's Interactions

Quick Labs: • Activities of Science
• Scientific Thinking • Science and Its Methods
• Working With Models • Characteristics
of Systems • Testing a Scientific Theory
• Modifying Theories • How Science Affects
Society • Science, Society, and You

my science ONLINE.com

Go to MyScienceOnline.com to
interact with this chapter's content.
Keyword: Scientific Understanding

> UNTAMED SCIENCE
• Principles of Scientific Principles

> PLANET DIARY
• Scientific Understanding

> INTERACTIVE ART
• Scientific Stumbling Blocks • Why Make a
Model? • Building a Theory

> REAL-WORLD INQUIRY
• When Science Sparks Controversy

CONTENTS

Lab zone ® **Enter the Lab zone for hands-on inquiry.**

△ **Chapter Lab Investigations:**
• Directed Inquiry: Chemical Composition and the Spectrum
• Open Inquiry: Chemical Composition and the Spectrum

△ **Inquiry Warm-Ups:** • Stringing Along • Why Does the Milky Way Look Hazy? • What Factors Affect Gravity? • How Stars Differ • What Determines How Long Stars Live? • How Can You Safely Observe the Sun?

△ **Quick Labs:** • How Far Is That Star? • Measuring the Universe • Planets Around Other Stars • A Spiral Galaxy • What's Doing the Pulling? • Around and Around We Go • Star Bright • Interpreting the H-R Diagram • Life Cycle of Stars • Death of a Star • Layers of the Sun • Viewing Sunspots

my science ONLINE.com

Go to MyScienceOnline.com to interact with this chapter's content. Keyword: Stars, Galaxies, and the Universe

▷ **ART IN MOTION**
• Formation of the Solar System

▷ **INTERACTIVE ART**
• Universe at Different Scales • Lives of Stars
• Anatomy of the Sun

▷ **REAL-WORLD INQUIRY**
• How Can Light Help You Find Life?

▷ **VIRTUAL LAB**
• What Affects Gravity?

CHAPTER 4

The Solar System

Lab zone®
Enter the Lab zone for hands-on inquiry.

Chapter Lab Investigations:
• Directed Inquiry: Speeding Around the Sun
• Open Inquiry: Speeding Around the Sun

Inquiry Warm-Ups: • How Big Is Earth?
• Why Do Craters Look Different From Each Other? • Ring Around the Sun • How Big Are the Planets? • Collecting Micrometeorites
• What Is at the Center?

Quick Labs: • Clumping Planets
• Moonwatching • Characteristics of the Inner Planets • Greenhouse Effect • Density Mystery
• Make a Model of Saturn • Changing Orbits
• Going Around in Circles • A Loopy Ellipse

my science online.com

Go to MyScienceOnline.com to interact with this chapter's content.
Keyword: The Solar System

▷ **UNTAMED SCIENCE**
• 100 Meters to Neptune

▷ **PLANET DIARY**
• The Solar System

▷ **INTERACTIVE ART**
• Objects of the Solar System

▷ **ART IN MOTION**
• Formation of the Solar System

▷ **VIRTUAL LAB**
• Why Isn't Pluto a Planet? • Making Observations of Our Solar System

CONTENTS

Enter the Lab zone for hands-on inquiry.

Chapter Lab Investigations:
• Directed Inquiry: Reasons for the Seasons
• Open Inquiry: Reasons for the Seasons

Inquiry Warm-Ups: • What Causes Day and Night? • How Does the Moon Move? • When Is High Tide?

Quick Labs: • Sun Shadows • Moon Phases • Eclipses • Modeling the Moon's Pull of Gravity

my science ONLINE.com

Go to MyScienceOnline.com to interact with this chapter's content.
Keyword: Earth, Moon, and Sun

> UNTAMED SCIENCE
• Phased by the Moon

> PLANET DIARY
• Earth, Moon, and Sun

> INTERACTIVE ART
• Seasons and Earth's Revolution • Solar and Lunar Eclipses

> ART IN MOTION
• Cause of Tides

CHAPTER 6

Exploring Space

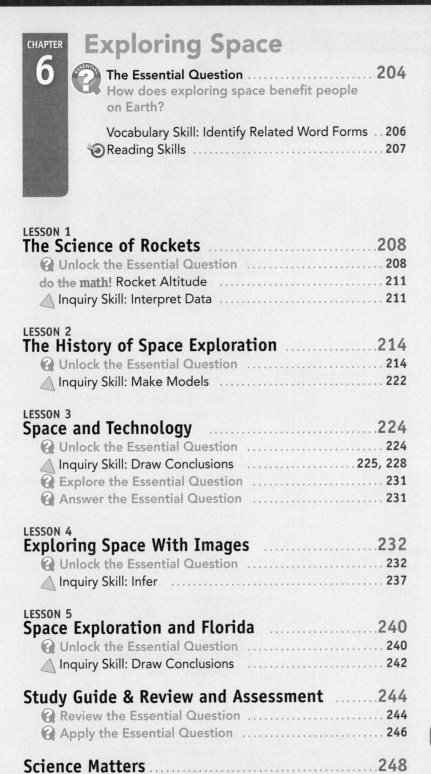

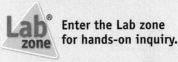 Enter the Lab zone for hands-on inquiry.

Chapter Lab Investigations:
• Directed Inquiry: Space Spinoffs, Design and Build a Telescope
• Open Inquiry: Space Spinoffs, Design and Build a Telescope

Inquiry Warm-Ups: • What Force Moves a Balloon? • Where on the Moon Did the Astronauts Land? • Using Space Science • How Does Distance Affect an Image? • Space Jobs

Quick Labs: • History of Rockets • Be a Rocket Scientist • Modeling Multistage Rockets • Humans in Space • Which Tool Would You Use in Space? • Remote Control • What Do You Need to Survive in Space? • Useful Satellites • Observing a Continuous Spectrum • Reading Satellie Images • Space and Florida

my science online.com

Go to MyScienceOnline.com to interact with this chapter's content.
Keyword: Exploring Space

> **INTERACTIVE ART**
• Build an Orbiter • Space Spinoffs
• Refracting and Reflecting Telescopes

> **VIRTUAL LAB**
• Get a Rocket Into Orbit

CONTENTS

Enter the Lab zone for hands-on inquiry.

△ **Chapter Lab Investigations:**
• Directed Inquiry: Melting Ice
• Open Inquiry: Melting Ice

△ **Inquiry Warm-Ups:** • Differences in Compounds • What Are Solids, Liquids, and Gases? • What Happens When You Breathe on a Mirror?

△ **Quick Labs:** • Modeling Atoms and Molecules • Modeling Particles • As Thick as Honey • How Do the Particles in a Gas Move? • What Is a Physical Change? • Observing Sublimation

my science online.com

**Go to MyScienceOnline.com to interact with this chapter's content.
Keyword: Introduction to Matter**

▷ **UNTAMED SCIENCE**
• Building a House of Snow

▷ **PLANET DIARY**
• Introduction to Matter

▷ **INTERACTIVE ART**
• States of Matter

▷ **VIRTUAL LAB**
• Solid to Liquid to Gas: Changes of State

CHAPTER 8 Properties and Changes of Matter

Lab zone® Enter the Lab zone for hands-on inquiry.

Chapter Lab Investigations:
• Directed Inquiry: Making Sense of Density
• Open Inquiry: Making Sense of Density

Inquiry Warm-Ups: • Which Has More Mass? • How Do You Describe Matter? • Is a New Substance Formed?

Quick Labs: • Calculating Volume • Observing Physical Properties • Physical and Chemical Changes

my science ONLINE .com

Go to MyScienceOnline.com to interact with this chapter's content.
Keyword: Properties and Changes of Matter

> **UNTAMED SCIENCE**
• What's the Matter?

> **PLANET DIARY**
• Properties and Changes of Matter

> **INTERACTIVE ART**
• Properties of Matter • Physical or Chemical Change?

> **VIRTUAL LAB**
• How Do You Measure Weight and Volume? • Will It Float? • Density of Solids and Liquids

CONTENTS

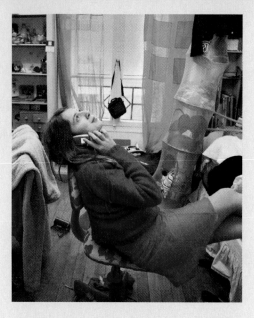

Enter the Lab zone for hands-on inquiry.

Chapter Lab Investigations:
• Directed Inquiry: Copper or Carbon? That Is the Question
• Open Inquiry: Copper or Carbon? That Is the Question

Inquiry Warm-Ups: • Which Is Easier?
• Why Use Aluminum? • What Are the Properties of Charcoal? • What's in the Box?

Quick Labs: • Classifying • Using the Periodic Table • Expanding the Periodic Table • Finding Metals • Carbon—A Nonmetal • Finding Nonmetals • Visualizing an Electron Cloud • How Far Away Is the Electron?

my science ONLINE.com

Go to MyScienceOnline.com to interact with this chapter's content. Keyword: **Elements and the Periodic Table**

PLANET DIARY
• Elements and the Periodic Table

INTERACTIVE ART
• Periodic Table • Investigate an Atom

VIRTUAL LAB
• Which Element Is This?

Lab zone® **Enter the Lab zone
for hands-on inquiry.**

△**Chapter Lab Investigations:**
• Directed Inquiry: Shedding Light on Ions
• Open Inquiry: Shedding Light on Ions

△**Inquiry Warm-Ups:** • What Are the Trends
in the Periodic Table? • How Do Ions Form?
• What Color Does Litmus Turn?

△**Quick Labs:** • Element Chemistry • How
Do You Write Ionic Names and Formulas?
• Sharing Electrons • What Do Metals Do?
• pHone Home

my science.com

**Go to MyScienceOnline.com to
interact with this chapter's content.
Keyword:** Bonding and Chemical
Compounds

▷ **UNTAMED SCIENCE**
• The Elements of Hockey

▷ **PLANET DIARY**
• Bonding and Chemical Compounds

▷ **INTERACTIVE ART**
• Periodic Table • Table Salt Dissolving in
Water • Investigate Ionic Compounds

▷ **VIRTUAL LAB**
• Will It React?

CONTENTS

**Enter the Lab zone
for hands-on inquiry.**

Chapter Lab Investigations:
• Directed Inquiry: Speedy Solutions
• Open Inquiry: Speedy Solutions

Inquiry Warm-Ups: • What Is a Mixture?
• What Makes a Mixture a Solution? • Does It
Dissolve?

Quick Labs: • Recognizing Pure Substances
• Separating Mixtures • Scattered Light
• Predicting Rates of Solubility

my science online.com

**Go to MyScienceOnline.com to
interact with this chapter's content.
Keyword: Mixtures and Solutions**

UNTAMED SCIENCE
• What's the Solution?

PLANET DIARY
• Mixtures and Solutions

INTERACTIVE ART
• Table Salt Dissolving in Water • Classifying
Solutions

REAL-WORLD INQUIRY
• Is It Pure?

Enter the Lab zone for hands-on inquiry.

Chapter Lab Investigations:
• Directed Inquiry: Where's the Evidence?
• Open Inquiry: Where's the Evidence?

Inquiry Warm-Ups: • What Happens When Chemicals React? • Did You Lose Anything? • Can You Speed Up or Slow Down a Reaction?

Quick Labs: • Observing Change • Information in a Chemical Equation • Is Matter Conserved? • Modeling Activation Energy • Effect of Temperature on Chemical Reactions

MY SCIENCE online.com

Go to MyScienceOnline.com to interact with this chapter's content.
Keyword: Chemical Reactions

UNTAMED SCIENCE
• Chemical Reactions to the Rescue

PLANET DIARY
• Chemical Reactions

INTERACTIVE ART
• Balancing Equations • Conservation of Matter • Physical or Chemical Change?

ART IN MOTION
• Activation Energy

VIRTUAL LAB
• Energy and Chemical Changes

CONTENTS

Lab zone ® Enter the Lab zone for hands-on inquiry.

Chapter Lab Investigations:
• Directed Inquiry: Exhaling Carbon Dioxide
• Open Inquiry: Exhaling Carbon Dioxide

Inquiry Warm-Ups: • Where Does the Energy Come From? • Cellular Respiration • Are You Part of a Cycle?

Quick Labs: • Energy From the Sun • Looking at Pigments • Observing Fermentation • Following Water • Modeling the Carbon Cycle • Conservation in Living Systems

my science online.com

Go to MyScienceOnline.com to interact with this chapter's content. **Keyword:** Energy, Matter, and Living Things

UNTAMED SCIENCE
• Tracking Your Carbon Atoms

PLANET DIARY
• Energy, Matter, and Living Things

INTERACTIVE ART
• Photosynthesis • Cellular Respiration • Water Cycle

ART IN MOTION
• Opposite Processes

REAL-WORLD INQUIRY
• Alert: Matter Disruption!

° Video Series: Chapter Adventures

Untamed Science created this captivating video series for interactive SCIENCE featuring a unique segment for every chapter of the program.

Featuring

interactive SCIENCE

This is your book. You can write in it!

Get Engaged!

At the start of each chapter, you will see two questions: an Engaging Question and the Essential Question. Each chapter's Essential Question will help you start thinking about the Big Ideas of Science. Look for the Essential Q symbol throughout the chapter!

HOW CAN AN ELEPHANT FLOAT, BUT A PENNY SINK?

How do scientists investigate the natural world?

Scientists are constantly asking questions about elephants, oceans, planets—you name it! They're curious about the world around them, and they're looking for answers. Every scientist has their own interests that lead to different observations and investigations about the natural world. *Pose Questions* What question do you have about this elephant that you would like to investigate?

How long can this elephant swim?

> **UNTAMED SCIENCE** Watch the **Untamed Science** video to learn more about scientific inquiry.

2 Practicing Science

Follow the Untamed Science video crew as they travel the globe exploring the Big Ideas of Science.

Interact with your textbook.   **Interact with inquiry.**   **Interact online.**

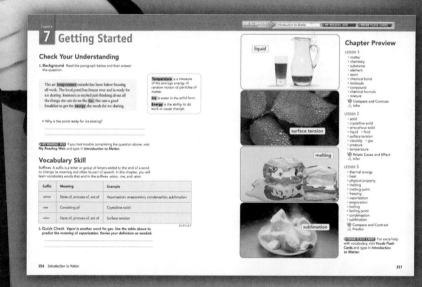

Build Reading, Inquiry, and Vocabulary Skills

In every lesson you will learn new ⟲ Reading and ▲ Inquiry skills. These skills will help you read and think like a scientist. Vocabulary skills will help you communicate effectively and uncover the meaning of words.

Go Online!

Look for the MyScienceOnline.com technology options. At MyScienceOnline.com you can immerse yourself in amazing virtual environments, get extra practice, and even blog about current events in science.

Florida Standards!

Look for your Next Generation Sunshine State Standards throughout every chapter to see the interesting concepts you will be exploring.

Explore the Key Concepts.

Each lesson begins with a series of Key Concept questions. The interactivities in each lesson will help you understand these concepts and Unlock the Essential Question.

My PLANET DiaRY
for Florida

At the start of each lesson, My Planet Diary will introduce you to amazing events, significant people, and important discoveries in science or help you to overcome common misconceptions about science concepts.

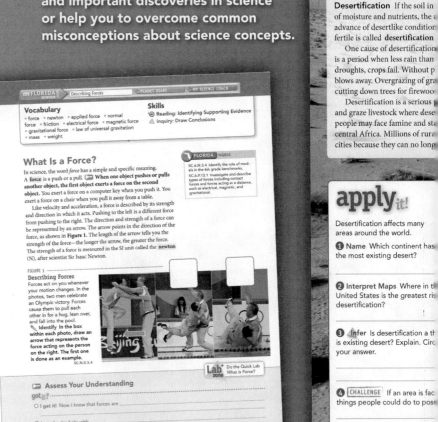

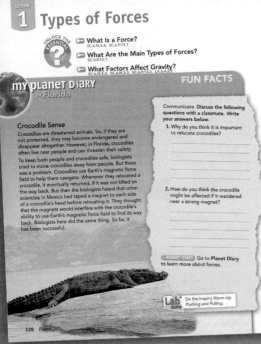

Explain what you know.

Look for the pencil. When you see it, it's time to interact with your book and demonstrate what you have learned.

apply it!

Elaborate further with the Apply It activities. This is your opportunity to take what you've learned and apply it to new situations.

Lab Zone

Look for the Lab zone triangle. This means it's time to do a hands-on inquiry lab. In every lesson, you'll have the opportunity to do many hands-on inquiry activities that will help reinforce your understanding of the lesson topic.

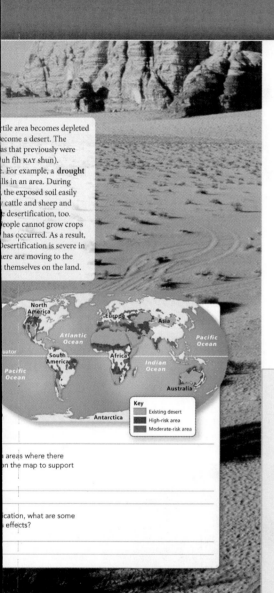

tile area becomes depleted
ecome a desert. The
as that previously were
uh fih KAY shun).
. For example, a **drought**
lls in an area. During
the exposed soil easily
y cattle and sheep and
e desertification, too.
eople cannot grow crops
has occurred. As a result,
Desertification is severe in
ere are moving to the
themselves on the land.

areas where there
on the map to support

ication, what are some
effects?

Land Reclamation Fortunately, it is possible to replace land damaged by erosion or mining. The process of restoring an area of land to a more productive state is called **land reclamation**. In addition to restoring land for agriculture, land reclamation can restore habitats for wildlife. Many different types of land reclamation projects are currently underway all over the world. But it is generally more difficult and expensive to restore damaged land and soil than it is to protect those resources in the first place. In some cases, the land may not return to its original state.

FIGURE 4 ⋯⋯⋯⋯⋯⋯

Land Reclamation
These pictures show land before and after it was mined.

✎ **Communicate** Below the pictures, write a story about what happened to the land.

Lab zone | Do the Quick Lab *Modeling Soil Conserv...*

🖰 Assess Your Understanding

1a. Review Subsoil has (less/more) plant and animal matter than topsoil.
SC.7.E.6.6

b. Explain What can happen to soil if plants are removed?
SC.7.E.6.6

c. Apply Concepts W
that could preve
land reclama

got it? ⋯⋯⋯⋯⋯⋯⋯⋯⋯⋯⋯⋯⋯⋯⋯⋯⋯⋯⋯⋯⋯

○ **I get it!** Now I know that soil management is important becaus

○ **I need extra help with**

Go to MY SCIENCE 🄢 COACH *online for help with this subject.*

got it?

Evaluate Your Progress.

After answering the Got It question, think about how you're doing. Did you get it or do you need a little help? Remember, MY SCIENCE ⒮ COACH is there for you if you need extra help.

Explore the Essential Question.

At one point in the chapter, you'll have the opportunity to take all that you've learned to further explore the Essential Question.

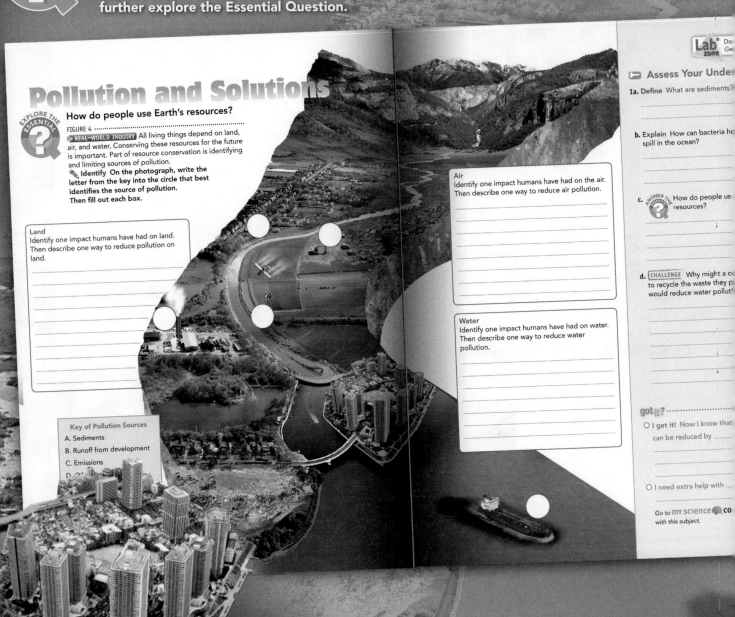

Pollution and Solutions

How do people use Earth's resources?

FIGURE 4 ....

REAL-WORLD INQUIRY All living things depend on land, air, and water. Conserving these resources for the future is important. Part of resource conservation is identifying and limiting sources of pollution.

Identify On the photograph, write the letter from the key into the circle that best identifies the source of pollution. Then fill out each box.

Land
Identify one impact humans have had on land. Then describe one way to reduce pollution on land.

_____
_____
_____
_____
_____
_____

Key of Pollution Sources

A. Sediments

B. Runoff from development

C. Emissions

D. Oil

Air
Identify one impact humans have had on the air. Then describe one way to reduce air pollution.

_____
_____
_____
_____
_____
_____

Water
Identify one impact humans have had on water. Then describe one way to reduce water pollution.

_____
_____
_____
_____
_____

Lab zone Do Ge

Assess Your Under

1a. Define What are sediments

_____

b. Explain How can bacteria he spill in the ocean?

_____

c. How do people us resources?

_____
_____

d. **CHALLENGE** Why might a ce to recycle the waste they p would reduce water pollut

_____

got it? ....

○ I get it! Now I know that can be reduced by _____

_____

○ I need extra help with ____

Go to MY SCIENCE CO with this subject.

Answer the Essential Question.

Now it's time to show what you know and answer the Essential Question.

Review What You've Learned.

Use the Chapter Study Guide to review the
Essential Question and prepare for the test.

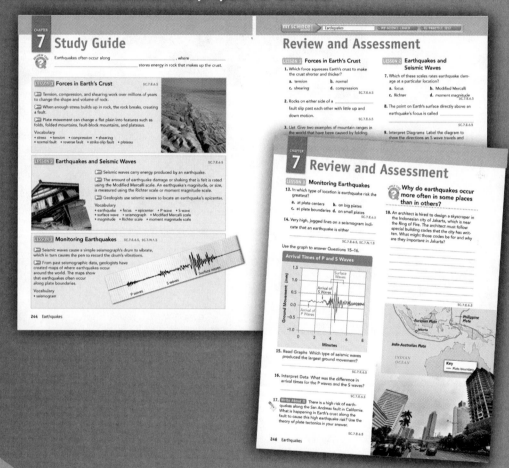

Practice Taking Tests.

Apply the Essential Question
and take a practice test in
standardized test format.

INTERACT... WITH YOUR TEXTBOOK...

Go to **MyScienceOnline.com** and immerse yourself in amazing virtual environments.

ESSENTIAL QUESTION

Each online chapter starts with a Essential Question. Your mission is to unlock the meaning of this Essential Question as each science lesson unfolds.

Unit 4 > Chapter 1 > Lesson 1

Ask | Unlock | Explore | Answer | Apply

Essential Question | Untamed Science | Check Your Understanding | Vocabulary Skill | Vocabulary Flashcards

How do living things affect one another?

Tools

Unit 2 > Chapter 4 > Lesson 1

Engage & Explore | Explain

Planet Diary

my planet diary

VOCAB FLASH CARDS

Practice chapter vocabulary with interactive flash cards. Each card has an image, definitions in English and Spanish, and space for your own notes.

Unit 4 > Chapter 1 > Lesson 1

Ask | Unlock | Explore | Answer | Apply

Essential Question | Untamed Science | Check Your Understanding | Vocabulary Skill | Vocabulary Flashcards

Vocabulary Flashcards

Tools

Card List | Create-a-Card | 10 Cards Left | Test Me

Lesson Cards | My Cards

Birth Rate
Carrying Capacity
Commensalism
Community
Competition
Death Rate
Ecology
Ecosystem
Emigration
Habitat
Host
Immigration
Limiting Factor

Science Vocabulary

Term: Community

Definition: All the different populations that live together in a particular area.

View Spanish

Add Notes

Card 5 of

Unit 6 > Chapter 1 > Lesso

Engage & Explore

Apply It | Directed Virtual La

Color in Light

Unit 6 > Chapter 1 > Lesson 1

Engage & Explore | Explain | Elaborate | Evaluate

Apply It | Do the Math | Art in Motion | Interactive Art | Real World Inquiry

The Nebraska Plains

▶ Bald Eagle

Information | Media

Haliaeetus leucocephalus
Bald Eagles are 80-95 cm tall with a wingspan of 180-230 cm. These birds are born with all brown feathers but grow white feathers on their head, neck, and tail.

Layers List | ▲ Show

Next

22 of 22

Back

INTERACTIVE ART

At MyScienceOnline.com, many of the beautiful visuals in your book become interactive so you can extend your learning.

⟳ + 🌐 http://www.myscienceonline.com/

▷ PLANET DIARY

My Planet Diary online is the place to find more information and activities related to lesson topics.

Elaborate   Evaluate

Everest

Tools

Still Growing! Mount Everest in the Himalayas is the highest mountain on Earth. Climbers who reach the peak stand 8,850 meters above sea level. You might think that mountains never change. But forces inside Earth push Mount Everest at least several millimeters higher each year. Over time, Earth's forces slowly but constantly lift, stretch, bend, and break Earth's crust in dramatic ways!

▷ Planet Diary Go to Planet Diary to learn more about forces in the Earth's crust.

Next
22 of 22
Back

Elaborate   Evaluate

Tools

0:35 / 1:30

Next
22 of 22
Back

▷ VIRTUAL LAB

Get more practice with realistic virtual labs. Manipulate the variables on-screen and test your hypothesis.

Find Your Chapter

1 Go to www.myscienceonline.com.

2 Log in with username and password.

3 Click on your program and select your chapter.

Keyword Search

1 Go to www.myscienceonline.com.

2 Log in with username and password.

3 Click on your program and select Search.

4 Enter the keyword (from your book) in the search box.

Other Content Available Online

▷ **UNTAMED SCIENCE** Follow these young scientists through their amazing online video blogs as they travel the globe in search of answers to the Essential Questions of Science.

▷ **MY SCIENCE COACH** Need extra help? My Science Coach is your personal online study partner. My Science Coach is a chance for you to get more practice on key science concepts. There you can choose from a variety of tools that will help guide you through each science lesson.

▷ **MY READING WEB** Need extra reading help on a particular science topic? At My Reading Web you will find a choice of reading selections targeted to your specific reading level.

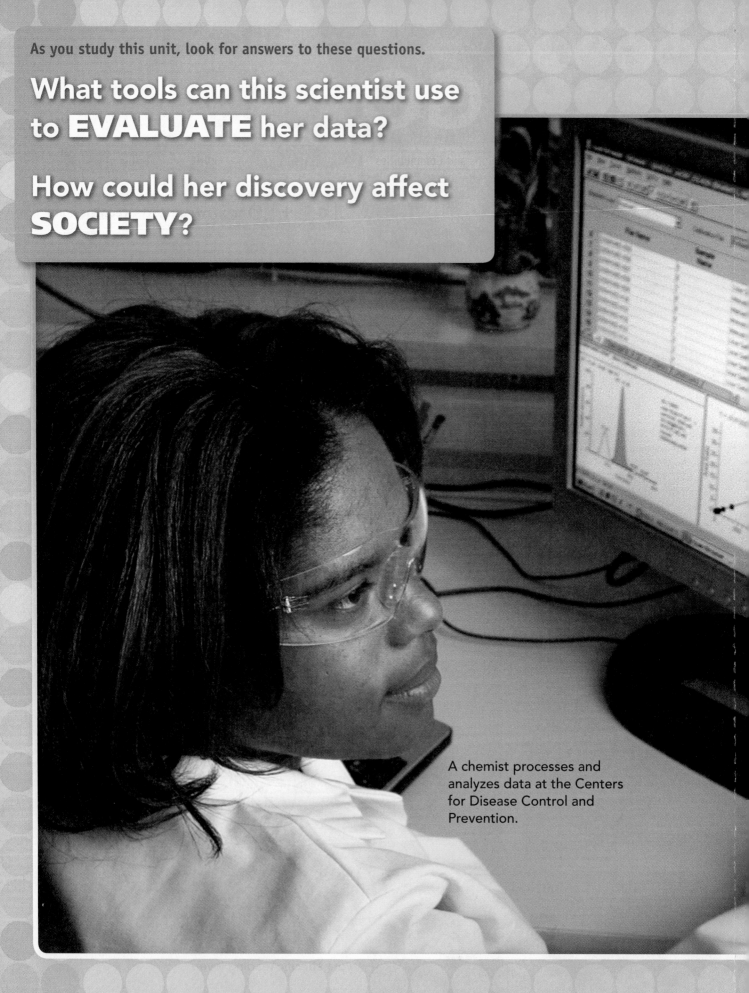

As you study this unit, look for answers to these questions.

What tools can this scientist use to **EVALUATE** her data?

How could her discovery affect **SOCIETY**?

A chemist processes and analyzes data at the Centers for Disease Control and Prevention.

Introducing

Big Ideas and Essential Questions

Nature of Science

 Florida Big Idea 1

The Practice of Science

A: Scientific inquiry is a multifaceted activity; the processes of science include the formulation of scientifically investigable questions, construction of investigations into those questions, the collection of appropriate data, the evaluation of the meaning of those data, and the communication of this evaluation.

B: The processes of science frequently do not correspond to the traditional portrayal of "the scientific method."

C: Scientific argumentation is a necessary part of scientific inquiry and plays an important role in the generation and validation of scientific knowledge.

D: Scientific knowledge is based on observation and inference; it is important to recognize that these are very different things. Not only does science require creativity in its methods and processes, but also in its questions and explanations.

 What tools do scientists use to investigate the natural world?

 How does science change society?

 Florida Big Idea 2

The Characteristics of Scientific Knowledge

A: Scientific knowledge is based on empirical evidence, and is appropriate for understanding the natural world, but it provides only a limited understanding of the supernatural, aesthetic, or other ways of knowing, such as art, philosophy, or religion.

B: Scientific knowledge is durable and robust, but open to change.

C: Because science is based on empirical evidence it strives for objectivity, but as it is a human endeavor, the processes, methods, and knowledge of science include subjectivity, as well as creativity and discovery.

 How does science change society?

 Florida Big Idea 3

The Role of Theories, Laws, Hypotheses, and Models

The terms that describe examples of scientific knowledge, for example; "theory," "law," "hypothesis," and "model" have very specific meanings and functions within science.

 How does science change society?

 Florida Big Idea 4

Science and Society

As tomorrow's citizens, students should be able to identify issues about which society could provide input, formulate scientifically investigable questions about those issues, construct investigations of their questions, collect and evaluate data from their investigations, and develop scientific recommendations based upon their findings.

 How does science change society?

1

WHY ARE THESE SCIENTISTS WEIGHING A POLAR BEAR?

What tools do scientists use to investigate the natural world?

Scientists weighed this small female polar bear while she was asleep. They also measured the bear's body and skull. They observed her sleeping habits, as well as those of other bears throughout the Beaufort Sea of Alaska. The bears live on a frozen portion of the ocean called sea ice. Scientists are also measuring the sea ice to determine how much the ice is shrinking. Scientists can use the data they collected to make predictions, analyze information, and draw conclusions about how the bears are affected by their environment.

Develop Hypotheses **Write a hypothesis that could be tested with these scientists' measurements.**

_____

_____

_____

> UNTAMED SCIENCE Watch the **Untamed Science** video to learn more about how tools help scientists.

The Tools of Science

interactive SCIENCE

C1-188   C2-472   C3-48

Engaging Question

An engaging question starts off each chapter to hook students and get them thinking about the Essential Question

Essential Question

Students develop initial hypotheses to the Essential Question and write them in their book or type them online

②

interactive SCIENCE

C1-86-87   C2-372-373   C3-xxx-1

Big Ideas & Essential Questions

C1-188

-The Florida Big Ideas

-Essential Question(s) found in the upcoming chapters that will help students develop a thorough & deep understanding of each Big Idea.

2b

interactive SCIENCE

C1-188   C2-472   C3-48

Untamed Science

-Engaging videos Online and CD-ROM allow students to make early connections to Essential Questions

-Students can watch these videos from school or home.

FLORIDA Next Generation Sunshine State Standards

Big Idea 1: SC.8.N.1.1, SC.8.N.1.2, SC.8.N.1.3, SC.8.N.1.4, SC.8.N.1.5

Language Arts: LA.8.2.2.
Mathematics: MA.6.A.3.

1 Getting Started

Check Your Understanding

1. Background Read the paragraph below and then answer the question.

> Emi studied hard to prepare for her science lab investigation. She was concerned because her **research** was complex. However, it was also well **organized**. Emi also wanted to use her lab report as a **sample** of her science work.

> **Research** is information collected from careful study of a subject.
>
> To be **organized** is to be arranged in an orderly way.
>
> A **sample** is a portion of something that is used to represent the whole thing.

- Why would being organized help Emi prepare for her lab investigation?

  _____

  _____

  _____

> **MY READING WEB** If you have trouble completing the question above, visit **My Reading Web** and type in *The Tools of Science.*

Vocabulary Skill

High-Use Academic Words High-use academic words are words that are used frequently in academic reading, writing, and discussions. These words are different from key terms because they appear in many subject areas.

Word	Definition	Example
trend	*n.* a general tendency or direction	An increase in song downloads shows a *trend* in the way people purchase music.
periodically	*adv.* at regular intervals	Scientists update their research *periodically* throughout their experiments.

LA.8.1.6.3

2. Quick Check Complete each sentence with the correct high-use academic word.

- Melting glaciers show a _____ toward rising temperatures.

- Birds return to the nest _____ to tend to their chicks.

science

weight

estimate

controlled experiment

Chapter Preview

LESSON 1
* science • observing
* quantitative observation
* qualitative observation
* classifying • inferring
* predicting • analyzing

↪ **Identify Supporting Evidence**
△ **Observe**

LESSON 2
* metric system
* International System of Units (SI)
* mass • weight • volume
* meniscus • density

↪ **Ask Questions**
△ **Measure**

LESSON 3
* estimate • accuracy • precision
* significant figures • mean
* median • mode • range
* anomalous data • percent error

↪ **Identify the Main Idea**
△ **Calculate**

LESSON 4
* graph • linear graph
* nonlinear graph • outlier

↪ **Relate Cause and Effect**
△ **Graph**

LESSON 5
* scientific inquiry • hypothesis
* independent variable
* dependent variable
* controlled experiment • bias
* repeated trial • replication
* scientific explanation

↪ **Summarize**
△ **Develop Hypotheses**

> VOCAB FLASH CARDS For extra help with vocabulary, visit **Vocab Flash Cards** and type in *Tools of Science.*

How Scientists Work

UNLOCK THE ESSENTIAL

🔑 **How Do Scientists Explore the Natural World?**
SC.8.N.1.1, MA.6.A.3.6

my PLANET DiARY

The Road to Discovery

Today, paclitaxel is one of the most effective drugs against cancer. But it was not well known until Dr. Susan Horwitz's work drew attention to it. Horwitz went to college to study history, but after taking a biology class, she became fascinated with how scientists form and test their ideas. After graduating with a biology degree, she went on to a graduate program in biochemistry. At the time, there were very few women in graduate schools, but that didn't stop Dr. Horwitz. Armed with a doctorate degree, Horwitz eventually moved to her current position at Albert Einstein School of Medicine. It was there that she discovered how paclitaxel stopped the growth of cancer cells. Her work convinced pharmaceutical companies to turn paclitaxel into a medicine that now saves many lives.

BIOGRAPHY

Model of the paclitaxel molecule

Write your answers to each question below.

1. Why did Susan Horwitz decide to become a scientist?

_____

_____

_____

_____

_____

2. What do you think is the difference between the way historians and scientists think?

_____

_____

_____

_____

▶ PLANET DIARY Go to **Planet Diary** to learn more about how scientists work.

Lab zone Do the Inquiry Warm-Up
How Does a Scientist Think?

Vocabulary
- science • observing • quantitative observation
- qualitative observation • classifying • inferring
- predicting • analyzing

Skills
- Reading: Identify Supporting Evidence
- Inquiry: Observe

How Do Scientists Explore the Natural World?

Paclitaxel is one of the many great success stories of science. **Science** is a way of learning about the natural world. Science is also the knowledge gained through this exploration. **Scientists explore the natural world by using skills such as observing, classifying, making models, inferring, and predicting. They form and test their ideas through scientific investigation.**

Observing Paclitaxel is a drug made from the bark of the Pacific yew tree, shown in **Figure 1.** The seeds and leaves of all yew trees are poisonous, but Native Americans found that they could make teas from the bark and needles. They observed that drinking the tea sometimes made people who were sick feel better. **Observing** means using one or more of your senses to gather information. Native Americans observed the effects of the tea on sick people and decided that the tea could help treat headaches and other health problems. Observing also means using tools, such as a microscope, to help your senses.

Observations can be quantitative or qualitative. A **quantitative observation** deals with numbers, or amounts. For example, seeing that a person has a fever of 101 degrees Fahrenheit is a quantitative observation. A **qualitative observation** deals with descriptions that cannot be expressed in numbers. Feeling that a person's head is warm is a qualitative observation.

FLORIDA NGSSS

SC.8.N.1.1 Define a problem from the eighth grade curriculum using appropriate reference materials to support scientific understanding, plan and carry out scientific investigations of various types, such as systematic observations or experiments, identify variables, collect and organize data, interpret data in charts, tables, and graphics, analyze information, make predictions, and defend conclusions.

MA.6.A.3.6 Construct and analyze equations to describe simple relations using common language.

FIGURE 1
What Do You Observe?
The photo shows the berries and bark of the slow-growing and ancient Pacific yew tree.
Observe Write one quantitative observation and one qualitative observation about the tree.

Organizing Data

In 1962, plant biologists collected samples of different types of trees. They were searching for a cure to cancer. They sent the samples back to a laboratory that ran tests to see what affect these samples had on cancer cells. Then the samples were classified according to their results. **Classifying** is grouping together items that are alike in some way. Paclitaxel, from the yew tree sample, was classified as having anticancer effects. **Figure 2** shows a test that can be used to classify samples.

Making Models

Once people realized that paclitaxel had an effect on cancer cells, they needed to figure out what it was made of. They built a model that showed the arrangement of atoms in a molecule of paclitaxel. Making models involves creating representations of complex objects or processes. Some models can be made of actual objects, such as balls and sticks. Others are in the form of drawings or mathematical equations. Models help people study things that can't be observed directly. By using models, scientists were able to better understand the properties of paclitaxel.

Inferring

Susan Horwitz examined how paclitaxel affected cancer cells. The invention of the electron microscope allowed scientists to observe how cells divide. From her observations, Horwitz inferred that paclitaxel stopped cancer cells from dividing.

When you explain or interpret things that you observe, you are **inferring.** Making an inference is not guessing. Inferences are based on reasoning from your prior knowledge and from what you observe. By making inferences about how paclitaxel worked, Horwitz was able to show that paclitaxel could be an effective anticancer drug.

FIGURE 2 ·······

Classifying Cancer Colonies

Scientists observed the effects of different tree samples on cancer cells. Each petri dish began with 10 colonies of cancer cells. The diagrams show the results after being treated with the tree samples.

1. **Observe** Count and record the number of cancer cell colonies below each petri dish.

2. **Infer** What can you infer about each of the samples from the petri dishes that were treated?

_____

_____

_____

3. **Classify** Which sample(s) should be classified as possible cancer treatment(s)? Explain.

_____

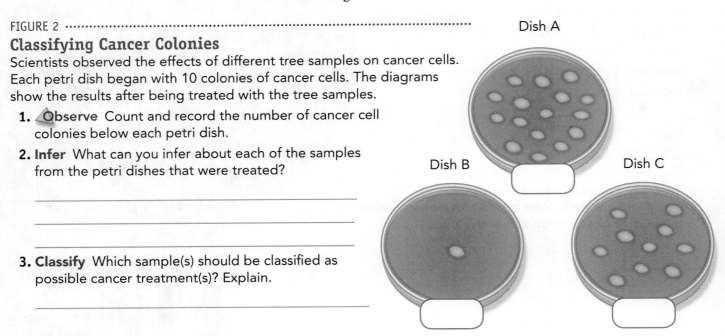

Predicting Paclitaxel only kills some kinds of cancer cells. After running tests on mice, scientists made predictions about what types of human cancer paclitaxel might treat. **Predicting** means making a statement or a claim about what will happen in the future based on past experience or evidence.

Scientists planted human tumors onto mice. Then they gave the mice paclitaxel. The mice with breast tumors showed signs of recovery. From this observation, scientists predicted that paclitaxel could help treat breast cancer.

Predictions and inferences are related. While inferences are attempts to explain what has already happened, predictions are forecasts about what will happen. If you see a puddle of water on the floor, you might infer that a glass spilled. If, however, you see someone bump into a glass, you can predict that it's about to make a mess.

Identify Supporting Evidence Determine if the statement below is a prediction or an inference. Then underline the sentence in the text that supports your answer. "The alarm clock is blinking 12:00 because the electricity went out temporarily."

do the math!

Only a small amount of paclitaxel can be produced from the bark of a single Pacific yew. It requires 120 kilograms of paclitaxel to treat 60,000 patients with 2 grams each of the drug per year.

1 Calculate If 1 kilogram of bark can produce about 0.015 kilogram of paclitaxel, how much bark is needed to make 120 kilograms of paclitaxel?

2 CHALLENGE You need to cut down 3 trees to get about 5 kilograms of bark. About how many trees do you have to cut down each year to make enough paclitaxel for 60,000 patients?

3 Evaluate the Impact on Society Some people think that the destruction of so many trees and the habitat of forest animals was too high a price to pay for paclitaxel. Explain why you agree or disagree with this opinion.

MA.6.A.3.6, MA.8.A.6.4

This scientist places a sample under a microscope in order to see objects she can't see with her eyes alone.

- ● Observing
- ● Inferring
- ● Predicting
- ● Classifying
- ● Making a model
- ● Analyzing

Analyzing Before paclitaxel could be sold as a medicine, scientists had to run experiments on people. They measured the size of individual's cancerous tumors throughout the experiment. They also recorded any side effects they observed. Then they analyzed this data. **Analyzing** involves evaluating observations and data to reach a conclusion about them. Scientists compared the data and concluded that paclitaxel was a very effective treatment for women with cancer in their ovaries.

Scientific Investigations The story of paclitaxel involves many scientific investigations. A scientific investigation is the forming and testing of ideas about the natural world. When people carry out scientific investigations, they use all the skills discussed above. These include observing, making models, classifying, inferring, predicting, and analyzing. Scientists use these skills when they investigate questions in science. **Figure 3** shows people using these skills.

FIGURE 3 ···

▶ INTERACTIVE ART **Scientific Investigations**
Scientific investigations involve observing, making models, classifying, inferring, predicting, and analyzing.

✎ **Interpret Photos** Determine which skill is being described in each box in the lab photo.

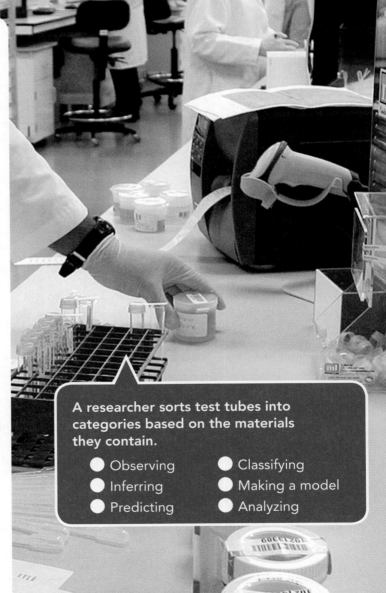

A researcher sorts test tubes into categories based on the materials they contain.

- ● Observing
- ● Inferring
- ● Predicting
- ● Classifying
- ● Making a model
- ● Analyzing

Scientists often use whiteboards to draw sketches of molecules or other objects they observe in order to study them more closely.

- ● Observing
- ● Classifying
- ● Inferring
- ● Making a model
- ● Predicting
- ● Analyzing

After data has been collected, this researcher examines it to find results and draw conclusions.

- ● Observing
- ● Classifying
- ● Inferring
- ● Making a model
- ● Predicting
- ● Analyzing

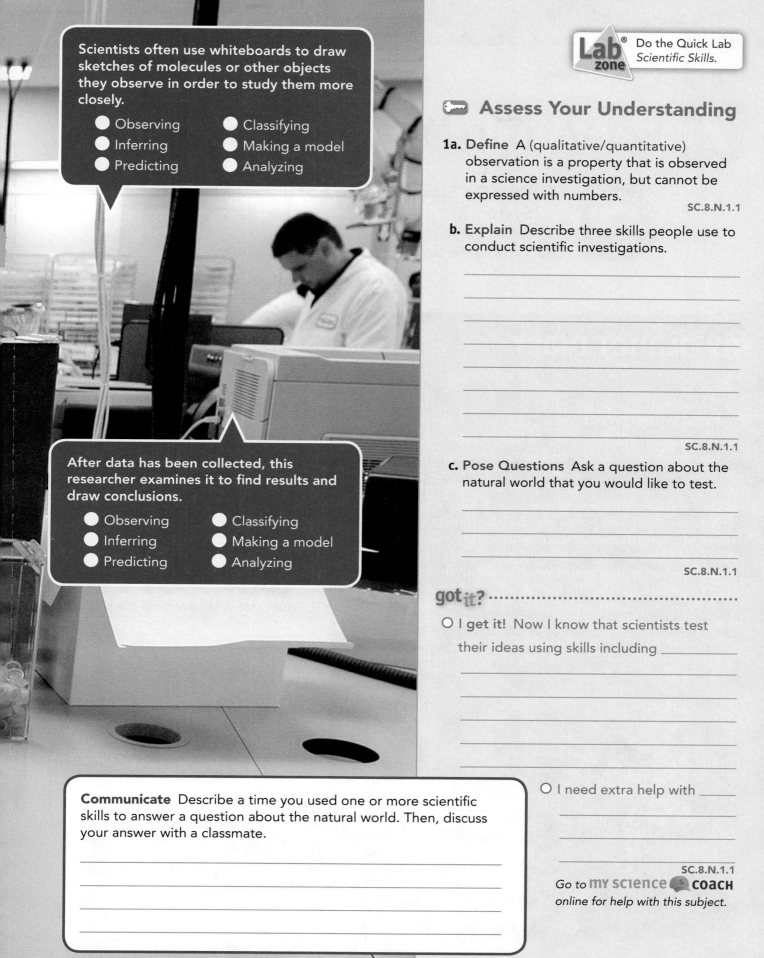

Communicate Describe a time you used one or more scientific skills to answer a question about the natural world. Then, discuss your answer with a classmate.

_____

_____

_____

_____

Lab® zone Do the Quick Lab *Scientific Skills.*

🔑 Assess Your Understanding

1a. Define A (qualitative/quantitative) observation is a property that is observed in a science investigation, but cannot be expressed with numbers.

SC.8.N.1.1

b. Explain Describe three skills people use to conduct scientific investigations.

_____

_____

_____

_____

_____

_____

_____

SC.8.N.1.1

c. Pose Questions Ask a question about the natural world that you would like to test.

_____

_____

_____

SC.8.N.1.1

got it? ....

○ **I get it!** Now I know that scientists test their ideas using skills including _____

_____

_____

_____

_____

○ **I need extra help with** _____

_____

_____

SC.8.N.1.1

Go to **MY SCIENCE Ⓢ COACH**
online for help with this subject.

Scientific Measurement

🔑 **Why Do Scientists Use a Standard Measurement System?**
SC.8.N.1.1

🔑 **What Are Some SI Units of Measure?**
SC.8.N.1.1

MY PLANET DIARY

Fancy Footwork

You probably know how long an inch, a foot, or a mile is. But do you know where these units of measure came from? An inch was originally the length of three dried grains of barley, lined up end to end. A foot was the length of the foot of the king who was in power. In Rome, a mile was the length of a thousand paces marched by Roman soldiers. These old units of measure were difficult to use because they could change. An inch could get shorter during a drought when barley grains were smaller. When a new king came into power, the length of a foot would change. With every new battalion of soldiers, the length of a mile would change. Now we have standard values for these and other units of measurement. Standard units allow people to understand each other when they describe measurements.

FUN FACTS

Communicate Write your answer to each question below. Then discuss your answers with a partner.

1. What are some nonstandard ways that you could measure the length of a dog?

_____

_____

_____

2. Why is it important for scientists to have a standard measurement system that is used around the world?

_____

_____

_____

_____

_____

> **PLANET DIARY** Go to **Planet Diary** to learn more about scientific measurement.

Lab zone® Do the Inquiry Warm-Up
What Is Scientific Measurement?

Vocabulary
- metric system • International System of Units (SI)
- mass • weight • volume • meniscus • density

Skills
- Reading: Ask Questions
- Inquiry: Measure

Why Do Scientists Use a Standard Measurement System?

Suppose you decided to measure length using your foot. Your friend decided to measure length using her hand. How would you be able to compare the length of a 5-foot object to a 7-hand one? Without a standard measurement system, it would be hard to share information about the world.

A standard measurement system is very important to scientists. It enables them to share information or repeat experiments done by other scientists. The **metric system** is a standard measurement system based on the number 10. Modern scientists use a version of the metric system called the **International System of Units (SI).** **Using SI as the standard system of measurement allows scientists to compare data and communicate with each other about the results of scientific investigations.** Mass, length, and many other properties are measured using SI units. All SI units use the same set of prefixes. For example, a paper clip has a mass of about 1 gram. An object with ten times more mass than a paper clip has a mass of 10 grams, or 1 dekagram. A child could be 1 meter tall. A tree that is ten times taller than the child has a height of 10 meters, or 1 dekameter. **Figure 1** shows some common SI prefixes.

FLORIDA NGSSS

SC.8.N.1.1 Define a problem from the eighth grade curriculum using reference materials to support scientific understanding, carry out scientific investigations, such as systematic observations, identify variables, collect and organize data, interpret data, analyze information, make predictions, and defend conclusions.

✎ **Ask Questions** Write a question you want to know about the SI system.

_____

_____

_____

FIGURE 1 ··························

Prefixes of SI Units
The man in this photo is one of the tallest men in the world at 2.46 meters, or 246 centimeters.

✎ **Name** Complete the column in the table using a meter as the base, which is the SI unit for length.

Common SI Prefixes		
Prefix	**Meaning**	**Example**
kilo- (k)	1,000	_____
deka- (da)	10	_____
no prefix	1	meter
centi- (c)	0.01 (one hundredth)	_____
milli- (m)	0.001 (one thousandth)	_____
micro- (µ)	0.000001 (one millionth)	_____
nano- (n)	0.000000001 (one billionth)	_____

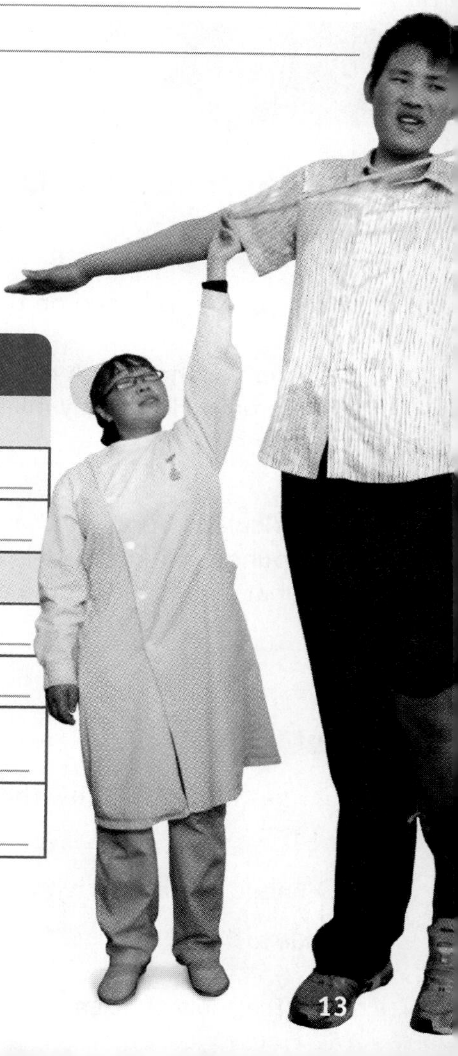

do the math!

SI prefixes show how measurements increase or decrease by powers of 10. Use the table of SI prefixes in **Figure 1** to answer the questions.

1 **Calculate** A picnic blanket is 1 meter across. An ant is 1 centimeter in length. How many ants of the same length would fit end-to-end across the length of the picnic blanket?

_____

2 **Explain** The length of the grassy park where the ant lives is 1 kilometer. How much longer than the ant is the park? Explain your answer.

_____

_____

_____

3 [CHALLENGE] How could you use decimals to represent the length of the ant compared to the length of the park?

_____

_____

_____

_____

MA.8.G.5.1

 Do the Quick Lab
Measuring With SI.

🔑 Assess Your Understanding

1a. Review The International System of Units, or

_____ , is based on the _____ system.

SC.8.N.1.1

b. Apply Concepts A nickel coin weighs 5 grams. How many milligrams does it weigh?

_____

SC.8.N.1.1

c. Calculate Suppose the mass of a dog is 90 pounds. If 1 kilogram is equal to 2.2 pounds, what is the mass of the dog in kilograms?

_____

SC.8.N.1.1

d. Make Generalizations What might occur if the scientists in one country started to use a different system of measurement than the system used by scientists in the rest of the world?

_____

_____

_____

_____

_____

_____

SC.8.N.1.1

got it? ....

○ **I get it!** Now I know that scientists use SI to _____

_____

○ **I need extra help with** _____

Go to **MY SCIENCE** ⓢ **COACH** online for help with this subject.

SC.8.N.1.1

What Are Some SI Units of Measure?

Scientists measure length, mass, weight, volume, density, temperature, and time using SI units.

Length Length is the distance from one point to another.
🔑 **The basic SI unit for measuring length is the meter (m).**
One meter is about the distance from the floor to a doorknob. A meterstick is used to measure lengths that are close to a meter. Metric rulers are used to measure lengths smaller than a meter, such as a centimeter (cm) or millimeter (mm). A kilometer (km) is 1,000 times longer than a meter. **Figure 2** shows how organisms can be measured.

FLORIDA NGSSS

SC.8.N.1.1 Define a problem from the eighth grade curriculum using reference materials to support scientific understanding, carry out scientific investigations, such as systematic observations, identify variables, collect and organize data, interpret data, analyze information, make predictions, and defend conclusions.

Conversions for Length

1 km	= 1,000 m
1 m	= 100 cm
1 m	= 1,000 mm
1 cm	= 10 mm

FIGURE 2 ·······································

Wing Length

You can use a metric ruler to measure the length of small objects. Line up one end of the object with the zero mark. Read the number at the other end of the object to find the length.

✏️ **Use the rulers to find the lengths of the bird and butterfly wings. Then complete the activities below.**

1. **Measure** What is the length of each wing?

   _____

   _____

   _____

2. **Apply Concepts** Using the table in Figure 1, convert the length of each wing from centimeters to micrometers (μm).

   _____

   _____

15

Mass

Mass is the measure of the amount of matter in an object. **The basic SI unit for measuring mass is the kilogram (kg).** The mass of people, cars, and other large objects is measured in kilograms. The mass of mice, cell phones, and other small objects is measured in grams (g) or milligrams (mg). The triple-beam balance shown in **Figure 3** is used to measure mass in grams.

Weight

When you step on a scale, you are measuring your weight. **Weight** is the measure of the force of gravity acting on an object. **The basic SI unit for measuring weight is a measure of force called the newton (N).** The pound is a non-SI unit commonly used in the United States to measure weight. When you stand on a scale, gravity pulls down on you and the springs in the scale compress. Gravity has a greater pull on objects with more mass, so these objects weigh more than objects with less mass. Weight changes as gravity changes, so you would weigh less on the moon since it has less gravity than Earth. However, an object's mass does not change with a change in gravity. **Figure 3** shows tools for measuring an object's mass and weight.

Conversions for Mass	
1 kg	= 1,000 g
1 g	= 1,000 mg

FIGURE 3 ··

Comparing Apples and Oranges

Triple-beam balances use weights to determine an object's mass. A spring scale is used to measure an object's weight.

1. **Measure** Find the mass of the apple by adding the masses of each weight on the balance.

   _____

2. **Define** The spring scale measures the weight of the oranges, which is a measure of _____ on the oranges.

3. **Infer** Suppose the oranges weigh 16.7 newtons on Earth. How would their weight change if they were on the moon?

   _____

   _____

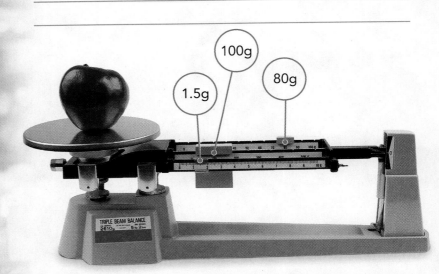

Volume

Volume A microwave oven takes up space on a countertop. A jug of milk takes up space in the refrigerator. Air spreads out to take up space in a room. **Volume** is the amount of space taken up by an object or substance. 🔑 **Scientists use liters (L) and cubic centimeters (cm³) to measure volume.** Liters are used to measure liquids. Cubic centimeters are used to measure solid objects. Use this page to practice measuring volume.

Conversions for Volume	
1 L	= 1,000 mL
1 L	= 1,000 cm³
1 mL	= 1 cm³

Volume of Liquids

Use a graduated cylinder or beaker to measure the volume of liquids. Pour the liquid into one of these containers and read the level at the bottom of the **meniscus,** or curve of the liquid.

✏️ **Measure What is the total volume of the liquid and berry in this photo?**
_____

Volume of Rectangular Solids

Use a ruler or meterstick to find the volume of rectangular solids. Measure the length, width, and height of the solid. Multiply these three values to get the volume.

✏️ **Calculate What is the volume of the crate?**
_____

30 cm
28 cm
42 cm

Volume of Irregular Solids

You can use the displacement of water to measure the volume of an irregular solid, like a rock or a berry. Fill a graduated cylinder partially full with water. Measure the volume of the water. Now place the berry in the water. Measure the volume of the water again. To get the volume of the berry, subtract the original volume of the water from the volume of water that included the berry.

✏️ **Infer Why would you get a more accurate measure of the volume of an irregular solid by using displacement instead of measuring with a ruler?**

_____
_____
_____

Density A foam brick and a clay brick can be the same size. If you pick them up, the clay brick feels heavy and the foam brick feels light. This is because the clay brick has a higher density than the foam brick. **Density** is the measure of how much mass is contained in a given volume. Units of mass are divided by units of volume to express the density of objects. 🔑 **The SI unit for density is kilograms per cubic meter (kg/m³), but scientists commonly use grams per milliliter (g/mL) or grams per cubic centimeter (g/cm³) to express density.** Look at **Figure 4** to compare the density of the balls in the picture.

FIGURE 4 ·······················

Predicting Density
Density determines if an object floats or sinks.

✏️ **Predict Circle the ball you think has the lower density. Explain your choice.**

_____

_____

_____

_____

_____

_____

Table tennis ball

Golf ball

To find the actual value of an object's density, you can use a mathematical formula for calculating density. Once you have taken measurements to find both the mass and volume of an object, calculate its density using the following formula.

$$\text{Density} = \text{Mass} \div \text{Volume}$$

apply it!

Once you find the volume and mass of an object, calculate its density using the formula.

❶ **Identify** Draw a line from the word *Meniscus* to the meniscus of each graduated cylinder.

❷ **Observe** What is the volume of water in each graduated cylinder? What is the volume of the bolt?

_____

_____

❸ **Calculate** The mass of the bolt is 101 grams. Find its density.

_____

_____

_____

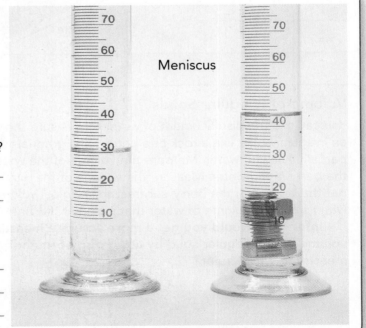

Meniscus

Using Density The density of a pure substance is always the same, no matter how much of the substance you have. For example, the density of fresh water is always 1.0 g/cm³, whether you have a drop of water or a whole lake. **Figure 5** shows the density of some common substances.

When you know the density of an object, you also know whether it will sink or float in water. If an object's density is less than 1.0 g/cm³, it will float. If its density is greater than 1.0 g/cm³, the object will sink. If you have an object made out of an unknown substance, you can tell whether its density is greater than or less than 1.0 g/cm³ by dropping the object in water!

FIGURE 5 ··
Using Density
The planet Saturn could float in water because its density is less than 1.0 g/cm³.

✎ **Infer** In the table, circle the liquids or solids that would float in water. Put a star next to those that would sink in water.

Densities of Common Substances	
Substance	**Density (g/cm³)**
Gold	19.3
Gasoline	0.7
Milk	1.03
Water	1.0
Iron	7.8
Air	0.001
Ice	0.9
Aluminum	2.7

✎ **CHALLENGE** Find the density of the surfboard and determine if the board should float. The surfboard's mass is 14 kg and its volume is 0.0875 m³. (*Hint:* The density of water is equal to 1,000 kg/m³.)

_____

_____

Time
How long would it take you to run 100 meters? Did you know that the fastest time recorded for running 100 meters is under 10 seconds? ☞ **The second (s) is the SI unit used to measure time.** Seconds can be divided into smaller units, such as milliseconds. Sixty seconds make up a minute. Sixty minutes make up an hour. So there are 3,600 seconds in an hour ($60 \times 60 = 3{,}600$).

Time is measured by clocks or stopwatches. A clock can measure time to the nearest second. Stopwatches like the one shown in **Figure 6** can measure time to the nearest hundredth of a second. The official timers used in the Olympics and other sports events can measure time to the nearest thousandth of a second!

FIGURE 6 ⋯⋯⋯⋯⋯⋯⋯⋯⋯⋯⋯⋯⋯⋯⋯⋯⋯

The Race Is On
The stopwatch shows the winning time in the last race at a school swim meet.

✎ **Answer the following questions about the race times.**

1. **Calculate** Jessica swims the last race in 22.56 seconds. By how much time did she lose the race?

   _____

   _____

2. **Analyze Sources of Error** Why would machine-operated stopwatches be used at sports events instead of hand-operated stopwatches?

   _____

   _____

   _____

   _____

   _____

Temperature

Did you need a jacket today, or could you wear shorts? You probably checked the temperature to find out. Temperature is a measure of the energy of motion of the particles in a substance. When molecules in air are moving fast and bouncing into each other, temperature is high and you feel hot. When these molecules slow down, temperature is lower and you feel cooler. Temperature affects the properties of some substances. For example, rising temperature can change a substance from a solid to a liquid to a gas.

Thermometers are instruments that measure temperature. Thermometers can have different temperature scales. Scientists commonly use thermometers with the Celsius temperature scale to measure temperature. On this scale, water freezes at 0°C and boils at 100°C. Scientists also use thermometers with the Kelvin scale to measure temperature. **Kelvin (K) is the official SI unit for temperature. The Kelvin scale starts at 0 K (absolute zero) and only goes up.** Units on the Kelvin scale are the same size as units on the Celsius scale. Use **Figure 7** to compare the Celsius and Kelvin scales.

FIGURE 7 ·····················

Kelvin and Celsius Scales

Liquid in a thermometer moves up or down as temperature changes.

✎ **Use the thermometer diagrams to complete the tasks.**

1. **Identify** Color in the Celsius thermometer to show how it would look when immersed in boiling water.

2. **Predict** Color in the Kelvin thermometer to show how it would look when immersed in ice water.

3. CHALLENGE Use the conversion chart to label the Kelvin thermometer with temperatures that correspond to the boiling point and freezing point of water.

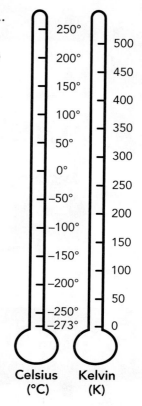

Celsius (°C) Kelvin (K)

Conversions for Temperature

0°C	= 273 K
100°C	= 373 K

Do the Quick Lab
A Unit of SI.

🔑 Assess Your Understanding

2a. Identify An SI unit used to measure volume is the (cubic centimeter/millimeter).

SC.8.N.1.1

b. Sequence What steps would you take to determine the density of a rubber eraser?

_____

_____

_____

_____

_____

SC.8.N.1.1

got it?

○ **I get it!** Now I know that the SI units for length, mass, weight, volume, density, time, and temperature are _____

_____

_____

○ **I need extra help with** _____

Go to MY SCIENCE ⓢ COACH *online for help with this subject.*

SC.8.N.1.1

Mathematics and Scientific Thinking

UNLOCK THE ESSENTIAL

🔑 **What Math Skills Do Scientists Use?**
SC.8.N.1.1, MA.6.A.3.6

🔑 **What Math Tools Do Scientists Use?**
SC.8.N.1.1, MA.6.S.6.2

my planet DiaRY

BLOG

Posted by: Mackenzye

Location: Redlands, California

Today I went to the mall to buy presents for my family. As I went into my favorite store, I saw a cute pair of jeans that I had to have. The price on the jeans was $59.99, but fortunately they were on sale for 30% off. In my head, I estimated that they would be about $18 off. I decided to buy them. I took them up to the counter to pay and they came out to $52.50. But that didn't seem right to me so I asked the cashier to check the price again. After he did, the pants came to $41.99 and I bought them.

Write your answers to the questions below.

1. How did Mackenzye's math skills save her money?

_____

_____

_____

2. Describe a time you used math to help you solve a problem in your daily life.

_____

_____

_____

▷ PLANET DIARY Go to **Planet Diary** to learn more about math in science.

Lab zone Do the Inquiry Warm-Up *How Do Math and Science Work Together?*

Vocabulary
- estimate • accuracy • precision
- significant figures • mean • median • mode
- range • anomalous data • percent error

Skills
↻ Reading: Identify the Main Idea
△ Inquiry: Calculate

What Math Skills Do Scientists Use?

Sizes, counts, and measurements are just a few of the interesting things that scientists investigate. Good math skills are essential as scientists collect and analyze data about their subject. ⟳ **When collecting data, scientists use math skills that include estimation, accuracy and precision, and significant figures.**

Estimation White blood cells help the human body fight disease. When a person has a blood test done, lab technicians count the number of white blood cells in a drop of the patient's blood. Doctors then use the count to estimate the total number of white blood cells in all of the patient's blood. An **estimate** is an approximation of a number, based on reasonable assumptions. The estimated white blood cell count helps a doctor determine if the patient has an infection. Estimation is useful when it is impossible to count every individual or object. It is also useful when the thing that is being estimated cannot be measured directly. Use **Figure 1** to practice estimation.

FLORIDA NGSSS

SC.8.N.1.1 Plan and carry out scientific investigations of various types, such as sytematic observations or experiments, identify variables, collect and organize data in charts, tables, and graphics, analyze information, make predictions, and defend conclusions.

MA.6.A.3.6 Construct and analyze equations to describe simple relations using common language.

FIGURE 1 ·······················

⟩ **INTERACTIVE ART** **Estimating**
Estimations are often used when it is impossible to count actual amounts.
✎ **Use the diagram to complete the activities about white blood cell (WBC) estimations.**

1. **Estimate** How many white blood cells are in the microscopic field?

   _____

2. △ **Calculate** This sample is 500 times smaller than a microliter. Estimate the number of white blood cells in a microliter of the patient's blood.

   Number of WBC counted × 500 = _____
   WBC per microliter

3. **Interpret Data** Patients with white blood cell counts higher than 10,500 WBC per microliter may have an infection. Could this patient have an infection? Explain.

   _____
   _____
   _____
   _____
   _____
   _____

Accuracy and Precision When scientists make measurements, they want to be both accurate and precise. Accuracy refers to how close the measurement is to the true or accepted value. Precision refers to how close a group of measurements are to each other.

Scientists try to use the highest quality tools to take measurements. They also measure the same object more than once. By repeating measurements with high-quality tools, scientists obtain the most accurate and precise results possible. Look at Figure 2 to determine the accuracy and precision of the measurements.

FIGURE 2 ···

Accuracy and Precision

Four teams measure the mass of the turtle below. The turtle's actual mass is 153.7 grams.

Interpret Diagrams Determine how accurate and precise each team's measurements were. Circle your answers in the boxes.

Team One	Team Two	Team Three	Team Four
Measurements	**Measurements**	**Measurements**	**Measurements**
1. 172.5 g	**1.** 154.5 g	**1.** 154.6 g	**1.** 153.7 g
2. 172.8 g	**2.** 121.7 g	**2.** 153.5 g	**2.** 153.6 g
3. 172.6 g	**3.** 177.0 g	**3.** 151.9 g	**3.** 153.9 g
This team was (accurate/not accurate).	This team was (accurate/not accurate).	This team was (accurate/not accurate).	This team was (accurate/not accurate).
This team was (precise/not precise).	This team was (precise/not precise).	This team was (precise/not precise).	This team was (precise/not precise).

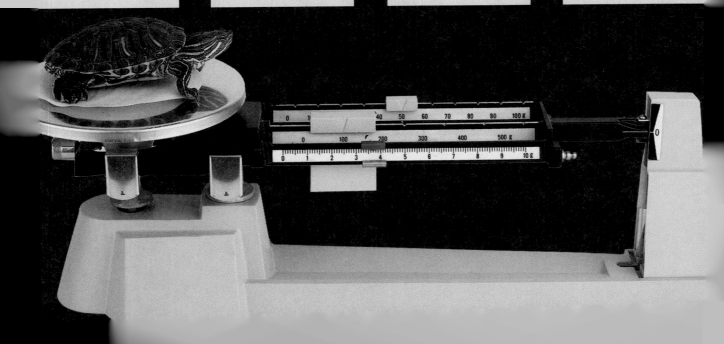

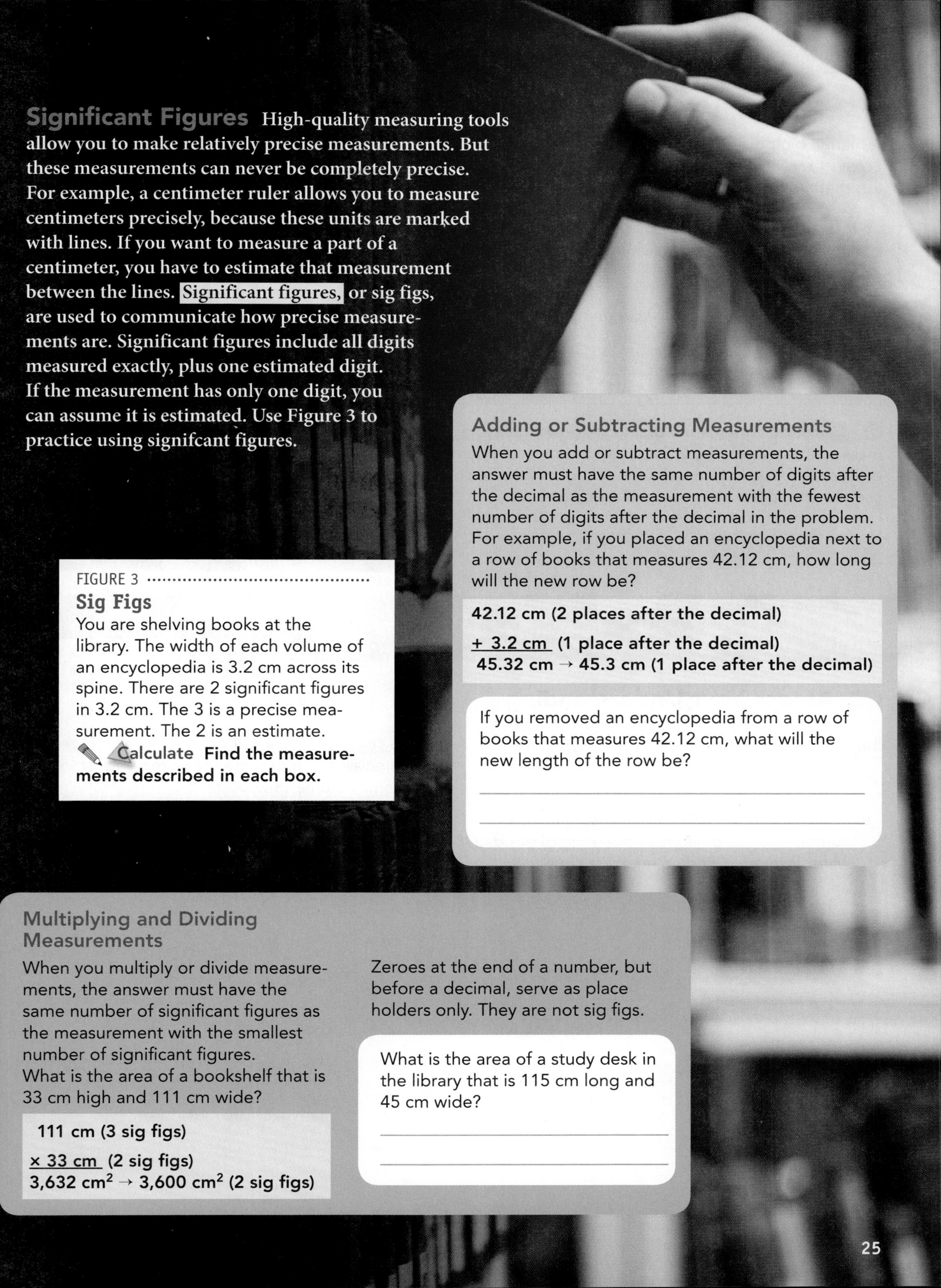

Significant Figures

High-quality measuring tools allow you to make relatively precise measurements. But these measurements can never be completely precise. For example, a centimeter ruler allows you to measure centimeters precisely, because these units are marked with lines. If you want to measure a part of a centimeter, you have to estimate that measurement between the lines. Significant figures, or sig figs, are used to communicate how precise measurements are. Significant figures include all digits measured exactly, plus one estimated digit. If the measurement has only one digit, you can assume it is estimated. Use Figure 3 to practice using significant figures.

FIGURE 3 ·····················
Sig Figs
You are shelving books at the library. The width of each volume of an encyclopedia is 3.2 cm across its spine. There are 2 significant figures in 3.2 cm. The 3 is a precise measurement. The 2 is an estimate.

✎ Calculate **Find the measurements described in each box.**

Adding or Subtracting Measurements

When you add or subtract measurements, the answer must have the same number of digits after the decimal as the measurement with the fewest number of digits after the decimal in the problem. For example, if you placed an encyclopedia next to a row of books that measures 42.12 cm, how long will the new row be?

42.12 cm (2 places after the decimal)

+ 3.2 cm (1 place after the decimal)
45.32 cm → 45.3 cm (1 place after the decimal)

If you removed an encyclopedia from a row of books that measures 42.12 cm, what will the new length of the row be?

_____

_____

Multiplying and Dividing Measurements

When you multiply or divide measurements, the answer must have the same number of significant figures as the measurement with the smallest number of significant figures.
What is the area of a bookshelf that is 33 cm high and 111 cm wide?

111 cm (3 sig figs)

× 33 cm (2 sig figs)
3,632 cm² → 3,600 cm² (2 sig figs)

Zeroes at the end of a number, but before a decimal, serve as place holders only. They are not sig figs.

What is the area of a study desk in the library that is 115 cm long and 45 cm wide?

_____

_____

do the
math!

A marine biologist is studying food webs in deep water ecosystems. She needs to estimate the total biomass of the fish that are part of the ecosystem.

❶ Interpret Photos Count the number of fish in the yellow boxed area. The number of fish in your sample is

_____

❷ Estimate Approximately how many fish are in the whole school shown in the photo?

_____

_____

❸ Calculate The marine biologist knows the average mass of these fish to be 2.5 kg. Use this measurement to estimate the total biomass of the school of fish. Be sure to use the correct number of significant figures.

_____

_____

MA.6.A.3.6, MA.8.A.6.4

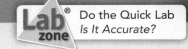

Lab zone® Do the Quick Lab
Is It Accurate?

🔑 Assess Your Understanding

1a. Identify There are _____ significant figures in the number 2.75.

SC.8.N.1.1

b. Explain Why would scientists estimate the number of cells of algae in a sample of pond water instead of finding an exact count?

_____

_____

_____

_____

_____

SC.8.N.1.1

c. CHALLENGE How is it possible to get three precise but inaccurate measurements of the same volume of water?

_____

_____

_____

_____

_____

_____

_____

SC.8.N.1.1

got it? ....

○ **I get it!** Now I know that, when scientists collect data, they use math skills that include _____

_____

○ **I need extra help with** _____

Go to **my science ⓢ coach** *online for help with this subject.*

SC.8.N.1.1

What Math Tools Do Scientists Use?

Math is used to analyze data so that scientists can draw conclusions about experimental results. 🔑 **Scientists use many math tools to analyze data, including mean, median, mode, and range. They also use percent error and other math tools to determine if the values of data points are reasonable.**

Mean, Median, and Mode The mean, median, and mode are called measures of central tendency. This means that all the data tend to center around each of these values. Use **Figure 4** to learn more about mean, median, and mode.

FLORIDA NGSSS

SC.8.N.1.1 Plan and carry out scientific investigations, collect and organize data, interpret data in tables and graphics, and analyze information.

LA.8.2.2.3 The student will organize information, such as comparing and contrasting, to show understanding.

MA.6.S.6.2 Select and analyze the measures of central tendency.

Mean
The **mean** is the numerical average of a set of data. To find the mean, add up all the numbers in the data set. Then divide by the total number of items that you added.
✏️ What is the mean wind speed of the strongest storms?

Median
The **median** is the middle number in an ordered set of data. To find the median, list all the numbers in order from least to greatest. If the list has an odd number of entries, the median is the middle entry. If the list has an even number of entries, the median is the mean of the two middle entries.
✏️ What is the median wind speed of the strongest storms?

Mode
The **mode** is the number that appears the most in a list of numbers.
✏️ What is the mode wind speed of the strongest storms?

Range
The **range** of a data set is the difference between the greatest value in the set and the least value. Scientists use the range to determine how far data points are from the average value of the data set.
✏️ What is the range of wind speeds during the strongest storms?

FIGURE 4 ·············
It Will Blow You Away
Winds can be fierce during a storm. You can use math to estimate the maximum wind speed of recent strong storms.
✏️ **Calculate** Use the data table below to answer the questions about the measures of central tendency.

MA.6.S.6.2

Maximum Wind Speed, Strongest Storms of Each Year, 2002–2009	
Year	Maximum Wind Speed (kilometers per hour)
2002	285
2003	280
2004	290
2005	295
2006	285
2007	280
2008	280
2009	240

Reasonable and Anomalous Data Scientists must always ask themselves whether their data make sense and are reasonable. For example, suppose that a scientist is studying the wind speed of a hurricane that appears very strong and is knocking down trees. The scientist sees that the hurricane's wind speed has been measured at 56 kilometers per hour, which is far lower than expected. The scientist is likely to check the equipment recording wind speed, to see if it is functioning properly.

Human or equipment error can produce **anomalous data,** or data that do not fit with the rest of the data set. If a scientist sees a data point that is different from others, he or she will examine it to see if an error was made. If no errors were made, the anomalous data might be due to an unknown variable. Investigating the reason for anomalous data can lead scientists to new discoveries.

 **apply** *it!*

Researchers measured the masses of five adult male Florida black bears. The bears were in their natural habitat during the summer months.

Adult Male Florida Black Bear Masses	
Bear	Mass (kg)
A	276
B	320
C	312
D	825
E	293

❶ Identify Which bear's mass is anomalous?

_____

❷ Draw Conclusions What probably produced the anomalous data?

_____

_____

❸ Select and Analyze Which measure of central tendency would you use to find the average mass of the bears? Exclude the anomalous data and calculate the measurement.

_____

MA.6.S.6.2

Percent Error

Percent Error Some properties of substances never change. For example, the density of pure silver is always 10.5 g/cm³. This value has been determined by extremely accurate lab equipment.

When you measure an object made of pure silver, you may find that you do not get a density of 10.5 g/cm³. The difference might be due to an error that you made when you measured the mass or volume of the silver. It could also be due to the accuracy of your measuring equipment. The percent difference between the known value of a substance and its measured value during an experiment is called the **percent error.** A low percent error means that the experimental results were accurate. A high percent error means the experimental results were inaccurate. Percent error is always considered positive even if the resulting calculation is negative.

$$\text{Percent Error} = \frac{\text{experimental value} - \text{true value}}{\text{true value}} \times 100\%$$

$$\% E = \frac{10.75 \text{ g/cm}^3 - 10.5 \text{ g/cm}^3}{10.5 \text{ g/cm}^3} \times 100\%$$

$$\% E = \frac{0.25 \text{ g/cm}^3}{10.5 \text{ g/cm}^3} \times 100\% = 2.38\%$$

FIGURE 5 ·······
Percent Error
Winners of a Nobel prize receive a medal plated with 24-karat pure gold.

◁ **Calculate** The density of gold is 19.3 g/cm³. A worker calculates the density of the Nobel medal's plating as 20.1 g/cm³. What is the percent error of his measurement?

_____

_____

_____

_____

_____

Lab zone® Do the Quick Lab
Math Tools in Science.

🔑 Assess Your Understanding

2a. Review To find the difference between the highest and lowest values in a data set, scientists calculate the (percent error/range).

SC.8.N.1.1

b. Compare and Contrast How is the mode different from the median?

_____

_____

_____

SC.8.N.1.1, LA.8.2.2.3

c. Apply Concepts Why wouldn't you throw out data points that appeared to be anomalous?

_____

_____

_____

_____

_____

_____

_____

_____

SC.8.N.1.1

got it? ···

○ **I get it!** Now I know that scientists analyze data using math tools that include _____

_____

_____

○ **I need extra help with** _____

    _Go to_ **MY SCIENCE** 🅢 **COACH** _online for help with this subject._

SC.8.N.1.1

🔑 **How Do Scientists Use Graphs?**
SC.8.N.1.1, LA.8.2.2.3, MA.6.A.3.6

my planet diary *for* Florida

SCIENCE STATS

Nesting Numbers

Imagine sitting around a campfire on the beach when suddenly a 2,000-pound, 6-foot-long turtle comes crawling out of the sea. You should be thankful to see such an event because leatherback sea turtles are an endangered species. They come ashore to lay eggs and their nesting numbers are crucial to the species' survival. The information in the graph shows the number of leatherback sea turtle nests on Juno Beach, Florida, between 2004 and 2009.

 **PLANET DIARY** Go to **Planet Diary** to learn more about graphs.

Answer the question below.

Describe the overall trend in the number of leatherback nests from 2004–2009.

_____

_____

_____

_____

 Do the Inquiry Warm-Up
What's in a Graph?

FLORIDA NGSSS

SC.8.N.1.1 Plan and carry out scientific investigations, such as identify variables, interpret data in tables and graphics, and analyze information.

LA.8.2.2.3 The student will organize information, such as comparing and contrasting, to show understanding.

MA.6.A.3.6 Construct and analyze tables and graphs to show relations.

How Do Scientists Use Graphs?

Have you ever been to an event that started off with a jet plane flyby? If so, you probably noticed that you could see the jets before you heard the roar of their engines. That is because sound travels slower than light. The speed of sound is also affected by the temperature of the medium it's traveling through, as shown by the data in **Figure 1.** To help understand what the data mean, you can use a **graph.** A graph is a "picture" of your data.

Vocabulary
• graph • linear graph • nonlinear graph • outlier

Skills
Reading: Relate Cause and Effect

Inquiry: Graph

Kinds of Data Graphs can illustrate different types of data. Scientists use graphs to identify trends, make predictions, and recognize anomalous, or inconsistent, data. Graphs display categorical and numeric data. Categorical data are information that can be grouped into categories. For example, the amounts of material in the universe can be grouped by element: hydrogen, helium, oxygen, carbon, nitrogen, and so on. Numerical data, such as time, temperature, and size, are continuous, ranging from small to large amounts. Different kinds of graphs are used to display these two kinds of data.

Relate Cause and Effect In the text, underline the cause and circle the effect of variables when scientists conduct experiments.

Kinds of Graphs Line graphs are used to display numerical data. They show how one variable (the dependent variable) changes in response to another variable (the independent variable). Scientists control changes in the independent variable. Then they collect data about how the dependent variable responded to those changes. The data in **Figure 1** show how the speed of sound changes in response to temperature. Bar graphs can be used to display both numerical and categorical data.

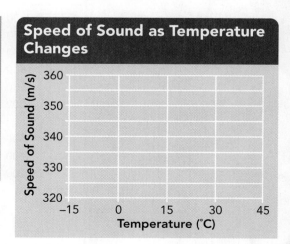

A "sonic boom cloud" can appear the moment a jet goes faster than the speed of sound.

FIGURE 1 ·········

Graphing the Speed of Sound

As temperatures rise, so does the speed at which sound travels through the air.

✎ **Use the data to complete the tasks below.**

1. **Graph** Create a line graph by plotting the data from the table on the grid.

2. **Identify** What is the independent variable? What is the dependent variable?

MA.6.A.3.6

Temp. (°C)	Speed of Sound (m/s)
–15	322
0	331
15	340
30	349
45	358

Speed of Sound as Temperature Changes

Speed of Sound (m/s) vs Temperature (°C)

(Graph grid: y-axis 320 to 360 m/s; x-axis –15 to 45 °C)

Linear and Nonlinear Graphs

Graphs are powerful tools because they show how different sets of data are related. A line graph in which the data points yield a straight line is a linear graph. A **linear graph,** for example, illustrates how the volume of a material changes with temperature. The graph of the speed of sound at different temperatures in **Figure 1** is a linear graph. A graph in which the data points do not fall along a straight line is a **nonlinear graph.** Population growth can be represented by a nonlinear graph.

Even though most points do not fall exactly along a line, a graph can still show a clear trend. When one point is clearly not part of the trend, it is considered an anomalous data point called an **outlier.** When a graph does not have any clear trend, it usually means the variables are not related.

FIGURE 2 ···

Sea Life Diving Data

The diving depths of several sea creatures were measured and recorded in the data table.

1. **Graph** Create a bar graph. Arrange the animals in order from shallowest to deepest divers. Label the x-axis with the animals' initials and title the graph.

2. **Draw Conclusions** Can you determine a trend between the size of the sea creature and the depth of the dive? Explain.

_____

_____

_____

Maximum Dive Depths of Sea Animals	
Animal	Dive Depths (meters)
Leatherback sea turtle (LST)	1200
Emperor penguin (EP)	565
Elephant seal (ES)	1529
Cuvier's beaked whale (CBW)	1900
King penguin (KP)	343

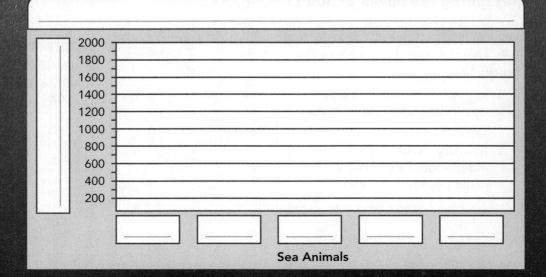

Sea Animals

apply it!

The data table shows the number of tourists visiting a Florida 4th of July celebration between 2006 and 2009.

Year	Number of Tourists (in thousands)
2006	40.5
2007	41.0
2008	42.3
2009	42.8

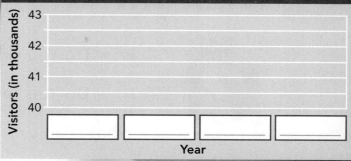

Visitors to 4th of July Celebration, 2006–2009

1 **Graph** Plot the data on the graph. Label the axes and connect the points.

2 **Read Graphs** The greatest increase in visitors was between _____

3 **CHALLENGE** Suppose the data for 2010 shows that 31,000 tourists visited Florida that year. How would you classify this data point? How would it be plotted on the graph?

_____

_____

_____

MA.6.A.3.6

Lab zone® Do the Quick Lab *Recognizing Trends.*

🔑 Assess Your Understanding

1a. Classify Observing that there are fewer hours of daylight in the winter is a (qualitative/quantitative) observation.
SC.8.N.1.1

b. Draw Conclusions What does a graph with no trend indicate about the variables?

_____
SC.8.N.1.1

c. Compare and Contrast How are linear and nonlinear graphs alike? How are they different?

_____

_____

_____

_____
SC.8.N.1.1, LA.8.2.2.3

got it?

○ **I get it!** Now I know that scientists use graphs to _____

_____

_____

○ **I need extra help with** _____

Go to **MY SCIENCE COACH** *online for help with this subject.*
SC.8.N.1.1

Designing an Experiment

🔑 **How Do You Conduct Scientific Inquiry?**
SC.8.N.1.2

🔑 **How Do You Test a Hypothesis?**
SC.8.N.1.2, SC.8.N.1.3, SC.8.N.1.4, LA.8.2.2.3

🔑 **What Is a Scientific Explanation?**
SC.8.N.1.5

MY PLANET DIARY

DISCOVERY

A Galactic Garden

Orbiting Earth is an amazing experience. But eating dehydrated space food can be boring and unappetizing. So, scientists conducted an experiment to see whether they could grow vegetables in space. They picked an old Thanksgiving favorite: sweet potatoes. They grew some cuttings onboard a shuttle and some cuttings on Earth. The cuttings were placed under similar conditions in space and on Earth for five days. They discovered that the number of roots that sprouted were the same in both places. But the roots of those in space actually grew faster! The cuttings that grew in space had more sugar and starch than those on Earth. Astronauts, however, hope that space potatoes taste just as good!

Write your answers to each question below.

1. What was the purpose of the experiment?

_____

_____

_____

2. Why do you think the scientists grew cuttings both in space and on Earth?

_____

_____

_____

_____

_____

▶ PLANET DIARY Go to **Planet Diary** to learn more about designing experiments.

Lab zone® Do the Inquiry Warm-Up *What's the Question?*

Vocabulary

- scientific inquiry
- hypothesis
- independent variable
- dependent variable
- controlled experiment
- bias
- repeated trial
- replication
- scientific explanation

Skills

- Reading: Summarize
- Inquiry: Develop Hypotheses

How Do You Conduct Scientific Inquiry?

It's Monday morning. You drag yourself out of bed and go to the kitchen. You pour yourself a bowl of cereal with milk. Yuck! Something tastes awful. The milk has gone sour. What happened? Your questioning is the beginning of the **scientific inquiry** process. **People conduct scientific inquiry by gathering evidence about the natural world and proposing explanations based on this evidence.**

FLORIDA NGSSS

SC.8.N.1.2 Design and conduct a study using repeated trials and replication.

Posing Questions and Defining a Problem

Scientific inquiry often begins with a question that leads to an observation. Your observation about the sour milk may lead you to ask a question: What made the milk go bad so quickly? Questions come from your experiences, observations, and natural curiosity. Look at **Figure 1** to pose a question about the strawberries.

Once you've posed your question, you should define a problem that can be tested. It is possible that others have already investigated the same problem. You can do research to find what information is known about the topic before you begin your investigation.

Using Reference Materials Scientists often begin researching a problem using reference materials. Newspapers, magazines, the Internet, and library books are all examples of reference materials. When using references, it is important to be skeptical and only use sources that are accurate and reliable. Appendix A, at the back of this book, explains how to find credible science reference material.

Look for the milk icon to follow the steps of the scientific inquiry.

✏ **Identify** In the text, circle the question posed about the sour milk.

FIGURE 1 ···

Posing Questions

Scientific inquiry starts with a question.

✏ **Pose Questions** Observe the photo. Then pose a question you could test about the strawberries.

_____

_____

_____

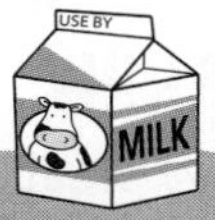

Developing a Hypothesis

How could you answer your question about the milk becoming sour? You start by developing a hypothesis. A **hypothesis** (plural: *hypotheses*) is a possible answer to a scientific question. You left the milk out overnight. So, you may suspect that the temperature at which the milk is kept contributes to how quickly the milk goes sour. Your hypothesis would be that milk turns sour more quickly if it is left at room temperature for too long. Use **Figure 2** to practice developing a hypothesis.

Hypotheses are not facts. In science, a fact is an observation that has been confirmed repeatedly. For example, that milk is a source of calcium is a fact. A hypothesis, on the other hand, is one possible answer to a question. For example, one explanation as to why milk goes sour might be that room temperature causes chemical changes in the milk that make it taste different.

In science, you must be able to test a hypothesis. Researchers perform investigations and collect data that either supports or fails to support a hypothesis.

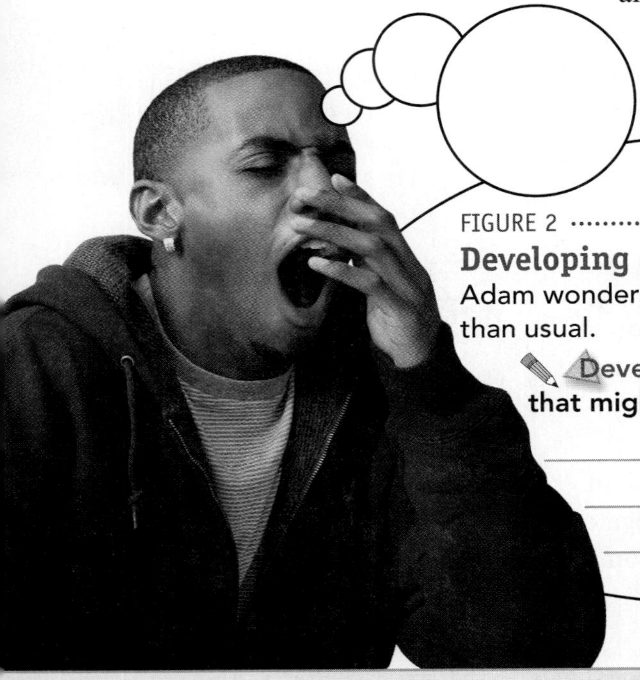

FIGURE 2 ....

Developing a Hypothesis
Adam wonders why he has been sleeping less than usual.

Develop Hypotheses Write a hypothesis that might answer Adam's question.

_____

_____

_____

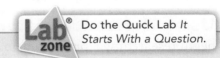
Do the Quick Lab *It Starts With a Question.*

🔑 Assess Your Understanding

1a. Pose Questions Write a question about what causes cavities that could be tested with a scientific investigation.

_____

_____

SC.8.N.1.2

b. Develop Hypotheses Write a hypothesis that might explain why some people get more cavities than other people.

_____

_____

_____

SC.8.N.1.2

got it?

O **I get it!** Now I know that people conduct scientific inquiry by _____

_____

_____

_____

_____

O **I need extra help with** _____

Go to **my science** **coach** *online for help with this subject.*

SC.8.N.1.2

How Do You Test a Hypothesis?

Once you have a hypothesis, you need to test it. **You test a hypothesis by designing an experiment that follows reliable scientific principles.** To test your hypothesis that milk will sour quicker if left out at room temperature, you need to smell the milk periodically when it is left out at room temperature. But how do you know that the milk wouldn't turn sour in the refrigerator? You cannot know unless you smell the milk periodically when it is left in the refrigerator, as well.

Controlling Variables To test your hypothesis, you will observe how milk smells when it is kept at different temperatures over a period of time. All other variables, or factors that can change in an experiment, must be the same. This includes variables such as the type of milk used and the container it's kept in. By keeping these variables the same, you will know that any differences in the odor of the milk are due to temperature alone.

The one factor that is purposely changed to test a hypothesis is the **independent variable.** In this experiment, the independent variable is air temperature. The factor that may change in response to the independent variable is the **dependent variable.** The dependent variable here is the time it takes the milk to sour.

FLORIDA NGSSS

SC.8.N.1.2 Conduct a study using repeated trials and replication.

SC.8.N.1.3 Use phrases such as "results support" or "fail to support."

SC.8.N.1.4 Explain how hypotheses are valuable even if they turn out not to be supported by the data.

LA.8.2.2.3 The student will organize information, such as summarizing, to show understanding.

✏️ **List** What are the independent and dependent variables in the milk experiment?

_____

_____

_____

FIGURE 3 ···

Controlling Variables

A student wants to test whether shampoo cleans oily hair better than water alone. The student mixes oil with water in one test tube and oil with soapy water in another test tube. She watches to see when the mixture separates.

✏️ **Use the data table to complete the activities.**

1. **Classify** What is the independent variable? What is the dependent variable?

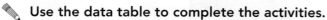

_____

_____

_____

2. **Identify** Name two other possible variables in this experiment.

_____

_____

3. **Draw Conclusions** Write a summary of what was observed in this experiment. What can you conclude?

_____

_____

Amount of Soap in Water (mL)	Time of Oil and Water Separation (seconds)
0	15
1.5	105

Designing a Controlled Experiment A scientific experiment in which only one variable is changed at a time is called a **controlled experiment.** You decide to test the milk at three different temperatures, as shown in **Figure 4.** All other variables should be kept the same. If your experiment were to have more than one independent variable, there would be no way to tell which variable influenced your results.

For example, in this experiment you are testing the effect of three temperatures on the time it takes milk to sour. You will keep all variables the same, except temperature. However, if you were to use different kinds of milk for each of your samples or kept each sample in a different kind of container, then you would not know which variable caused the milk to sour quickly. Was it temperature? Was it the type of milk? For this reason, you can only test one variable at a time in a controlled experiment.

Experimental Bias In any experiment there is a risk of introducing **bias,** an error in the design of the experiment. For example, without meaning to, you might use a carton of milk that is beyond its expiration date. Having a good sample size, or repeating your test with milk from different cartons and different brands, is also important.

FIGURE 4 ························

VIRTUAL LAB **A Controlled Experiment**

In this experiment, the temperatures must be different enough that your results can only be due to temperature.

✎ **Complete the activities.**

1. **Design Experiments** Label each milk sample with the temperature at which it could be tested. (*Hint:* Average room temperature is 22°C.)

2. **Apply Concepts** What is another variable that must be kept the same for each milk sample?

_____

_____

3. **Analyze Sources of Error** How could testing milk that is past its expiration date introduce bias?

_____

_____

_____

Collecting and Interpreting Data

Collecting and Interpreting Data You are almost ready to begin your experiment. You decide to test the milk every 12 hours. Before starting your experiment, determine what observations you will make and what data you will gather. Data (singular: *datum*) are the facts, figures, and other information gathered through qualitative and quantitative observations. A helpful tool to use while collecting data is a data table. A data table is an organized way to collect and record your observations.

After your data have been collected, they need to be interpreted. Tools such as diagrams, graphs, and models can help you interpret data. They can reveal patterns or trends. For example, you may observe that the shape of the moon changes from day to day. You can use a chart to draw the shape. After a couple of months, you would notice a pattern known as moon phases.

do the math!

Information organized in a data table can easily be made into a graph. This data table shows the percent of students who finished testing over a period of time.

❶ Graph Plot the data on the graph. Identify the independent and dependent data.

_____

_____

Students Finished (%)	Time (min)
0	30
2	45
50	60
98	75

_____

_____

_____

❷ Read Graphs Describe the difference in the percent of students finished testing between 30 and 45 minutes and between 45 and 60 minutes.

_____

_____

_____

_____

_____

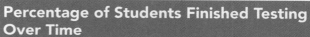

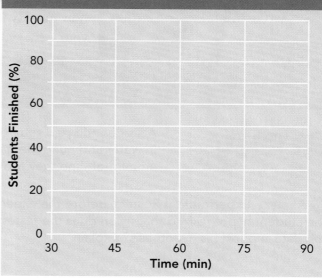

Percentage of Students Finished Testing Over Time

❸ CHALLENGE After how many minutes would you predict that all of the students will finish their testing?

_____

MA 6.A.3.6, MA.8.A.1.2

✏️ **Identify the Main Idea**
Underline the sentence(s) in the text that summarize what to consider when you draw a conclusion.

Drawing Conclusions

Once you've collected your data, you can draw a conclusion. A conclusion is a summary of what you have learned from an experiment. When drawing a conclusion, examine the data objectively to see if the results support or fail to support your hypothesis. Also, consider whether the data allow you to draw a conclusion at all based on the results.

You may decide that the data support your hypothesis. The milk at room temperature smelled sour sooner than the milk kept refrigerated. Now, repeat your experiment to see if you get the same results. A conclusion is unreliable if it comes from the results of one experiment. Many trials are needed before a hypothesis can be accepted as true. A **repeated trial** is a repetition of an experiment.

Sometimes your data won't support your hypothesis. When this happens, check your experiment for errors, or bias. Maybe you should have tested the milk every 6 hours. Sometimes you cannot draw a firm conclusion from your data. For example, you might discover that milk left at room temperature, 22°C, soured sooner than milk left at 35°C.

Hypotheses are valuable even when they are not supported by the data. They can lead to further investigation. For example, you may decide to test whether milk's exposure to light has an effect on how quickly it sours. How would you design an experiment to test your new hypothesis?

apply it!

A student dipped squares of nylon, polyester, and cotton in water and hung them up to dry. He then measured the amount of time they took to dry.

❶ **Analyze Experimental Results** Before the experiment, the student hypothesized that nylon dries the fastest. Do the data support his hypothesis? Explain.

_____

_____

Fabric	Trial 1	Trial 2	Trial 3	Trial 4
Nylon	28 min	25 min	27 min	33 min
Polyester	17 min	19 min	19 min	25 min
Cotton	44 min	45 min	45 min	51 min

❷ **Identify Experimental Bias** Are the results from one trial different from the others? If so, how might the student have introduced bias that resulted in anomalous data?

_____

_____

_____

❸ **Apply Concepts** Based on these results, what kind of socks would you want to wear on a fishing trip?

_____

_____

Communicating Scientists share their ideas and results with each other by giving talks at meetings, exchanging information on the Internet, or publishing articles in scientific journals.

When scientists share the results of their research, they describe their procedure so that others can repeat their experiments. A **replication** is an attempt by a different group of scientists to conduct the same experiment.

Scientists must keep detailed records of their procedures and results so that others can evaluate their accuracy. Other scientists review the experiment for sources of error, such as bias, data interpretation, and faulty conclusions, before the results can be published. Only after other scientists are able to conduct replications and obtain similar results, are the conclusions of an experiment accepted.

Sometimes, scientists from around the world work together on scientific inquiries that are part of a larger project. For example, the International Space Station is one of the largest international scientific projects in history. Sixteen nations participate in it. The goal is to conduct experiments in unusual conditions, such as near-weightlessness. On such a large project, scientists must share their ideas and results regularly.

✏️ **Communicate**
You conclude that milk left at room temperature (22°C) sours quicker than refrigerated milk. Write a catchy newspaper headline that communicates this to other scientists.

VOLUME 22, NO. 03

FLORIDA SCIENCE WEEKLY

MILK

Lab zone® Do the Lab Investigation
Become a Learning Detective.

🔑 **Assess Your Understanding**

2a. Identify At the beach, a student tests the effectiveness of three sunscreens, each with a different sun protection factor. What is the independent variable in her experiment?

_____

_____

SC.8.N.1.2

b. Explain Why is a hypothesis important even if evidence fails to support it?

_____

_____

_____

_____

SC.8.N.1.4

got it? ....

○ **I get it!** Now I know that you test a hypothesis by _____

_____

○ **I need extra help with** _____

Go to **MY SCIENCE COACH** *online for help with this subject.*

SC.8.N.1.2, SC.8.N.1.3, SC.8.N.1.4

FLORIDA NGSSS

SC.8.N.1.5 Analyze the methods used to develop a scientific explanation as seen in different fields of science.

What Is a Scientific Explanation?

If you are studying chemistry or physics, you can usually design and conduct controlled experiments. If you are studying astronomy or geology, however, it can be difficult or even impossible to carry out controlled experiments.

When you study astronomy or geology, you are often trying to understand how things happened in the past. You must make observations and then use what you already know to draw conclusions. Drawing a conclusion from an experiment is a way to develop a **scientific explanation.** 🔑 **A scientific explanation is a generalization that makes sense of observations by using logical reasoning.** For example, in 2000, workers digging a road in Tennessee discovered a layer of black soil filled with bones. Scientists examined the bones to find out what animals had lived at this site. Scientists knew these animals had lived in North America between 4 and 7 million years ago. Using this data, they reasoned that the site must be the same age! Things in the natural world that cannot be studied through a controlled experiment often rely on scientific explanation.

EXPLORE THE ESSENTIAL ❓

Think Pink

What tools do scientists use to investigate the natural world?

FIGURE 5 ·······························

▶ **REAL-WORLD INQUIRY** Baby flamingos are born with white feathers, but over time they turn bright pink. Sometimes the feathers of adult flamingos fade back to white. Why does this happen?

✎ **Design Experiments** Plan an investigation to determine if something in their diet causes flamingos' feathers to turn pink.

❶ Question

Does a flamingo's diet of shrimp affect the color of its feathers?

❷ Hypothesis

_____

_____

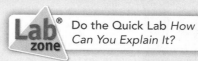

Lab zone ® Do the Quick Lab *How Can You Explain It?*

🔑 Assess Your Understanding

3a. Summarize How does a scientist explain something when a controlled experiment cannot be carried out?

_____

_____

_____

_____

SC.8.N.1.5

b. ANSWER THE ESSENTIAL **?** What tools do scientists use to investigate the natural world?

_____

_____

_____

_____

_____

_____

_____

_____

_____

_____

_____

_____

_____

SC.8.N.1.1, SC.8.N.1.2, SC.8.N.1.3,
SC.8.N.1.4, SC.8.N.1.5

③ Variables
Independent Variable

_____

_____

Dependent Variable

_____

_____

Factors to Control

_____

_____

_____

④ Procedure

_____

_____

_____

_____

_____

⑤ Analyze Information
Scientific Skills Used

_____

_____

_____

Possible Sources of Error

_____

_____

Alternative Explanations

_____

_____

got it? ....

O **I get it!** Now I know that a scientific explanation is _____

_____

_____

O **I need extra help with** _____

Go to **my science** s **coach** *online for help with this subject.* SC.8.N.1.5

1 Study Guide

To learn about the natural world, scientists form a(n) _____ and then test

this idea by conducting a(n) _____ .

LESSON 1 How Scientists Work
SC.8.N.1.1

🔑 Scientists explore the natural world by using skills such as observing, classifying, making models, inferring, and predicting. They form and test their ideas through scientific investigation.

Vocabulary
- science
- observing
- quantitative observation
- qualitative observation
- classifying
- inferring
- predicting
- analyzing

LESSON 2 Scientific Measurement
SC.8.N.1.1

🔑 The SI system allows scientists to compare data and communicate with each other about the results of scientific investigations.

🔑 SI units for length, mass, weight, volume, density, time, and temperature include meters, kilograms, newtons, cubic centimeters, grams per cubic centimeter, seconds, and kelvins.

Vocabulary
- metric system
- International System of Units (SI)
- mass
- weight
- volume
- meniscus
- density

LESSON 3 Mathematics and Scientific Thinking
SC.8.N.1.1

🔑 Scientists use math skills that include estimation, accuracy and precision, and significant figures.

🔑 Scientists use math tools including mean, median, mode, range, and percent error.

Vocabulary
- estimate
- accuracy
- precision
- significant figures
- mean
- median
- mode
- range
- anomalous data
- percent error

LESSON 4 Using Graphs in Science
SC.8.N.1.1

🔑 Scientists use graphs to identify trends, make predictions, and recognize anomalous data.

Vocabulary
- graph
- linear graph
- nonlinear graph
- outlier

LESSON 5 Designing an Experiment
SC.8.N.1.2, SC.8.N.1.3, SC.8.N.1.4, SC.8.N.1.5

🔑 People conduct scientific inquiry by gathering evidence about the natural world and proposing explanations based on this evidence.

🔑 Test a hypothesis by designing experiments that follow reliable scientific principles.

🔑 A scientific explanation is a generalization that makes sense of observations by using logical reasoning.

Vocabulary
- scientific inquiry
- hypothesis
- independent variable
- dependent variable
- controlled experiment
- bias
- repeated trial
- replication
- scientific explanation

Review and Assessment

LESSON 1 How Scientists Work

1. When scientists group information into categories, they are

   a. analyzing.

   b. making models.

   c. classifying.

   d. observing.

SC.8.N.1.1

2. Finding that the length of a caterpillar is 4.5 centimeters is a(n) _____ observation.

SC.8.N.1.1

3. Infer What inference might a scientist make if she observed an increase in her energy after eating an afternoon snack?

_____

_____

_____

_____

SC.8.N.1.1

4. Predict What would you predict will happen next in the scene below?

_____

_____

_____

SC.8.N.1.1

5. **Write About It** Scientists use models to help them study things they can't observe directly. Draw a model of your classroom to help you determine the best way to get out in case of a fire. On your model, include the pathway you would take from your desk to the exit.

SC.8.N.1.1

LESSON 2 Scientific Measurement

6. A newton is the SI unit for

   a. mass.

   b. density.

   c. volume.

   d. weight.

7. The SI system of measurement is based on the

_____

SC.8.N.1.1

8. Calculate Find the volume of the object at the right. Explain your method.

3 cm

2 cm

3 cm

7 cm

3 cm

_____

_____

_____

_____

SC.8.N.1.1

9. Apply Concepts Will an object with a volume of 77 grams per cubic centimeter and a mass of 65 grams float or sink in water? Explain.

_____

_____

SC.8.N.1.1

10. Write About It Your friend sends you an e-mail about an experiment that she read about. She mentions that the results from the experiment work best at −2 K. Write an e-mail back to your friend explaining why she must be mistaken about the temperature.

SC.8.N.1.1

1 Review and Assessment

Mathematics and Scientific Thinking

11. How close a measurement is to its true or accepted value is

    a. accuracy.   **b.** estimation.

    c. precision.   **d.** range.

SC.8.N.1.1

12. Nineteen is the _____ for the data set 25, 19, 18, 31, 19, 22.

SC.8.N.1.1

13. Interpret Data How many significant figures are in the measurement 230 kg?

_____

SC.8.N.1.1

14. Calculate You measure the mass of a model car to be 230 grams. The actual mass is 218 grams. What is your percent error?

_____

_____

SC.8.N.1.1

Using Graphs in Science

15. Anomalous data shows on a graph as a(n)

    a. nonlinear graph.   **b.** trend.

    c. linear graph.   **d.** outlier.

SC.8.N.1.1

16. In a linear graph, data points fall along a(n)

_____

SC.8.N.1.1

17. math! Plot a line graph using this data table from a summer science camp. Determine if the graph is linear or nonlinear and label any outliers.

Year	Number of Campers
1	52
2	60
3	63
4	41
5	70

SC.8.N.1.1, MA.6.A.3.6

Designing an Experiment

18. How do scientists draw conclusions when it is impossible to conduct an experiment?

    a. They run a replication of another experiment.

    b. They use logical reasoning to form a scientific explanation.

    c. They make random guesses.

    d. They accept never knowing the answer and move on to something else.

SC.8.N.1.5

19. The variable that is purposely changed in order to be tested is the _____

SC.8.N.1.2

20. Compare and Contrast How are repetition and replication of an experiment different?

_____

_____

_____

SC.8.N.1.3

APPLY THE ESSENTIAL **What tools do scientists use to investigate the natural world?**

21. Suppose you want to know if the color of people's hair affects how warm it can keep their heads. Describe the skills you would use to conduct an experiment to test your inquiry.

_____

_____

_____

_____

_____

_____

_____

_____

SC.8.N.1.1, SC.8.N.1.2, SC.8.N.1.3,
SC.8.N.1.4, SC.8.N.1.5

Florida Benchmarks Review

Circle the letter of the best answer.

1 Lia tested the effect of temperature on plant growth. Before the experiment, she hypothesized that plants grow better in warm temperatures. The results of the experiment are shown below.

How would you *best* describe the results of Lia's experiment?

A The results support the hypothesis.

B The results fail to support the hypothesis.

C No conclusion can be drawn from the results.

D The results are inaccurate.

SC.8.N.1.3, SC.8.N.1.4

2 Drew made observations while visiting the pet store. Which is a quantitative observation he may have made?

A The store sells hamsters.

B The dogs are fed at 4:00 in the afternoon.

C The store's employees wear blue aprons.

D There are ten more cats than rabbits.

SC.8.N.1.1

3 Nicole measured the height of her locker as 39.8 cm, 42.3 cm, 42.0 cm, and 43.1 cm. The locker is actually 45.5 cm. Which *best* describes Nicole's measurements?

A They were accurate.

B They were precise.

C They were both accurate and precise.

D They were neither accurate nor precise.

SC.8.N.1.1

4 Determining that the moon is the same age as Earth based on comparison of the age of moon rocks to the age of Earth rocks is an example of

A a scientific explanation.

B a qualitative observation.

C an estimate.

D anomalous data.

SC.8.N.1.5

5 A controlled experiment

A introduces bias.

B tests several variables at once.

C tests only one variable and is free of bias.

D changes no variables.

SC.8.N.1.2

Use the graph below to interpret data about an experiment.

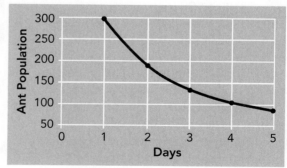

6 What kind of trend do the data show?

A A linear trend that the population is increasing.

B A linear trend that the population is decreasing.

C A nonlinear trend that the population is increasing.

D A nonlinear trend that the population is decreasing.

SC.8.N.1.1

47

WHAT
MIGHT THESE
TINY
ROBOTS
DO?

How does science change society?

This nanorobot has attached itself to a red blood cell using insectlike legs. Are nanorobots for real? Not yet, but engineers are working to design microscopic robots that may one day be able to perform tasks like injecting medicine into red blood cells.

Develop Hypotheses What might nanorobots be able to do in the future?

_____
_____
_____
_____
_____
_____
_____

> **UNTAMED SCIENCE** Watch the **Untamed Science** video to learn more about how science and society interact.

Scientific Understanding

FLORIDA | Next Generation Sunshine State Standards

Big Idea 1: SC.8.N.1.6
Big Idea 2: SC.8.N.2.1, SC.8.N.2.2
Big Idea 3: SC.8.N.3.1, SC.8.N.3.2
Big Idea 4: SC.8.N.4.1, SC.8.N.4.2

Language Arts: LA.8.2.2.3
Mathematics: MA.6.A.3.6

2 Getting Started

Check Your Understanding

1. Background Read the paragraph below and then answer the question.

> Jane worked as a scientific **researcher** in the field of genetics. She designed experiments that provided **evidence** certain families can be at higher risk for specific diseases. Joan learned that genetics has had a great impact on how **society** treats diseases.

A **researcher** is anyone who studies a scientific problem.

Evidence is any object or result that indicates a certain theory is true.

Society is an organization of individuals, forming a larger unit such as a city or town.

- What is one activity a scientific researcher does?

_____

> **MY READING WEB** If you have trouble completing the question above, visit **My Reading Web** and type in *Scientific Understanding.*

Vocabulary Skill

Identify Multiple Meanings Some familiar words have more than one meaning. Words you use every day may have different meanings in science. Look at the different meanings of the words below.

Word	Everyday Meaning	Scientific Meaning
model	*n.* A person who poses for an artist Example: Julio worked as a *model* for a sculptor in Daytona Beach.	*n.* A representation of an object or process Example: A globe is a *model* of Earth.
cost	*n.* The price paid by someone for a certain object or service Example: The *cost* of the train ticket was $35.	*n.* An undesirable outcome of a decision Example: Dirty air might be one *cost* of not using "clean" energy.

LA.8.1.6.9

2. Quick Check Circle the sentence below that uses the scientific meaning of the word *cost.*

- The cost of repairing the highway was $12 million.
- One cost of building a new highway might be more cars on the road.

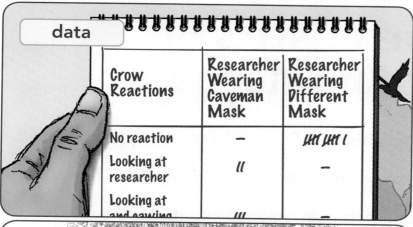

data

Crow Reactions	Researcher Wearing Caveman Mask	Researcher Wearing Different Mask
No reaction	–	ЖНТ ЖНТ I
Looking at researcher	II	–
Looking at and cawing	III	

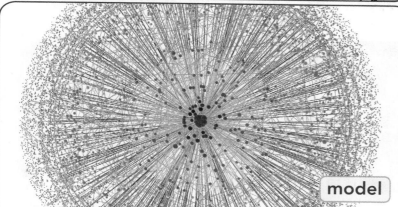

model

scientific theory

benefit

Chapter Preview

LESSON 1
- observing • data
- empirical evidence • inferring
- objective reasoning
- subjective reasoning
- opinion • pseudoscience
- ↻ Outline
- △ Interpret Data

LESSON 2
- model
- system
- input
- process
- output
- feedback
- ↻ Identify the Main Idea
- △ Make Models

LESSON 3
- scientific theory • scientific law
- ↻ Relate Text and Visuals
- △ Design Experiments

LESSON 4
- cost • benefit
- ↻ Sequence
- △ Pose Questions

▷ **VOCAB FLASH CARDS** For extra help with vocabulary, visit **Vocab Flash Cards** and type in *Scientific Understanding.*

The Characteristics of Scientific Knowledge

🔑 **What Activities Do Scientific Investigations Involve?**
SC.8.N.1.6

🔑 **What Are Scientific and Pseudoscientific Thinking?**
SC.8.N.2.1

🔑 **What Characterizes Science and Its Methods?**
SC.8.N.2.2, LA.8.2.2.3

my pLaNeT DiaRY

MYSTERY

Bittersweet

In 2007, scientists found they had a mystery on their hands. In some countries, commerical honeybees began dying off in very large numbers. Honeybees pollinate crops such as apples, nuts, celery, and squash. If the mystery went unsolved, basic foods might become scarce!

Scientists began to investigate. In 2009, they compared the genes in healthy honeybees to the genes in sick honeybees. They found evidence that certain viruses attack proteins in honeybees. The afflicted bees seem unable to produce proteins that can fight the viruses. So the bees die.

This study was one of the first to identify a cause for the mystery. But scientists still need to investigate further to find a cure for the sick bees.

Write your answers to the questions below. Then discuss your answers with a partner.

1. Why did scientists have to keep investigating even after they thought they had found a reason why honeybees were dying?

_____

_____

2. How might your life be affected if large numbers of honeybees kept dying?

_____

_____

_____

▶ PLANET DIARY Go to **Planet Diary** to learn more about scientific investigations.

Lab zone® Do the Inquiry Warm-Up *Developing a Theory.*

Vocabulary
- observing • data • empirical evidence
- inferring • objective reasoning
- subjective reasoning • opinion • pseudoscience

Skills
- Reading: Outline
- Inquiry: Interpret Data

What Activities Do Scientific Investigations Involve?

Researchers in Seattle wanted to learn if crows recognize specific faces. So they trapped some crows under a net. Then they wrapped bands around the crows' legs while wearing "caveman" masks, as shown in **Figure 1.** The crows cawed loudly while being caught and banded. The researchers let the crows go and later walked around the area where they had trapped the crows. When crows that had been trapped saw the caveman masks again, they again cawed loudly. The crows' cawing suggested that crows recognize faces.

Although the crow experiment seems simple, the researchers used many basic activities of scientific investigation. 🔑 **Scientific investigations involve observing, collecting empirical evidence, using logical reasoning, inferring, and applying imagination.**

Observing The crow researchers watched and listened to see which crows cawed at them. That is, they observed the crows. **Observing** means using one or more of your senses to gather information. 🔑 **Observing is the process of gathering information from which scientific conclusions are drawn.**

FLORIDA NGSSS

SC.8.N.1.6 Understand that scientific investigations involve the collection of relevant empirical evidence, the use of logical reasoning, and the applied application of imagination in devising hypotheses, predictions, explanations and models to make sense of the collected evidence.

FIGURE 1 ·······························
Counting Crows
Researchers wearing masks trapped crows (1). Then the researchers put bands around the crows' legs (2). Then they walked around, recording crows' reactions (3).

✏️ **Interpret Diagrams** Answer the questions.

What senses did the researchers use when observing the crows?

_____

_____

Why did the researchers wear masks when they put bands on the crows' legs?

_____

_____

_____

53

Collecting Empirical Evidence The crow researchers wrote their observations in notebooks. They recorded such facts as how many banded crows cawed at them at any one time. The specific information they wrote down is called data. **Data** are facts, figures, and other evidence collected during a scientific investigation. Look at **Figure 2**. Scientists use data to draw logical conclusions that explain their observations.

When data are collected in a precise, logical, and consistent manner, the data are called empirical evidence. **Empirical evidence** is data and observations that have been collected through scientific processes and that also explain a particular observation. ⚷ **All scientific investigations involve the collection of relevant empirical evidence to support researchers' conclusions.**

Using Logical Reasoning Scientists collect data. They then carefully review their figures, to look for patterns that explain their observations. Using logic and reason, they can then draw a conclusion based on the patterns that they see. ⚷ **Scientists use logical reasoning to examine their data and reach conclusions that explain their observations.** Use logical reasoning in **Figure 2** to determine whether crows recognize individual human faces.

FIGURE 2 ....
Conclusions and Empirical Evidence
While wearing a caveman mask, a researcher walked away from a particular crow in the area they were studying. A second researcher walked away from the same crow while wearing a different mask.

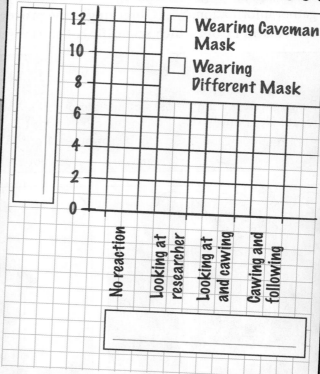

Crow Reactions	Researcher Wearing Caveman Mask	Researcher Wearing Different Mask
No reaction	—	ⵕⵕ ⵕⵕ ⵕ
Looking at researcher	ⵕⵕ	—
Looking at and cawing at researcher	ⵕⵕⵕ	—
Cawing and following researcher	ⵕⵕⵕⵕ ⵕ	—

✎ **Interpret Data** The table shows the number of trials during which each type of crow reaction was observed in the chosen crow at a certain site.

Use the data to draw a bar graph in the space above. Label the x- and y-axes of your graph.

12
10
8
6
4
2
0

☐ **Wearing Caveman Mask**
☐ **Wearing Different Mask**

No reaction
Looking at researcher
Looking at and cawing
Cawing and following

Inferring

The crow researchers studied the data they collected. They concluded that crows can recognize human faces. **Inferring** means explaining observations in a logical manner. It does not mean guessing wildly. 🔑 **Scientific investigations involve inferring, or basing conclusions on reasoning from what is already known.**

Applying Imagination

The crow researchers used scientific methods while making their observations and while drawing their conclusions. But by deciding to use caveman masks in their experiment, the researchers also made use of creative thinking. 🔑 **Applying imagination is an important element of scientific investigation. It helps scientists to design experiments. It also allows scientists to solve scientific problems and see patterns in data that no one else has noticed.**

Look at the graph you drew on the previous page. Now, draw a conclusion from your graph: Do you think crows can recognize human faces? Explain your reasoning.

Crow Study

Conclusion: _____

_____

Reasoning: _____

_____

_____

_____

_____

_____

_____

_____

_____

_____

Do the Quick Lab Activities of Science.

🔑 Assess Your Understanding

1a. Review (Empirical evidence/Logical reasoning) is data and observations collected through scientific research, indicating that a specific explanation is true.

SC.8.N.1.6

b. Understand In scientific investigations, how does empirical evidence help scientists devise hypotheses?

_____

_____

_____

_____

_____

SC.8.N.1.6

c. Identify Faulty Reasoning Review the empirical evidence collected in the crow experiment. Suppose a certain researcher used the evidence to conclude that all birds recognize human faces. Why would that be a faulty conclusion?

_____

_____

_____

_____

_____

SC.8.N.1.6

got it? ....

○ I get it! Now I know activities involved in scientific investigations include _____

_____

_____

○ I need extra help with _____

_____

Go to MY SCIENCE COACH online for help with this subject.   SC.8.N.1.6

 **FLORIDA** NGSSS

SC.8.N.2.1 Distinguish between scientific and pseudoscientific ideas.

What Are Scientific and Pseudoscientific Thinking?

Recall that the crow researchers used reasoning to review their observations. Then the researchers drew a logical conclusion from them. Scientific thinking requires a logical way of reasoning based on gathering and evaluating evidence. Look at **Figure 3.** Scientific thinking can be divided into two general types of reasoning: objective reasoning and subjective reasoning.

Objective and Subjective Reasoning

Objective reasoning is reasoning that is based on evidence. Because scientific reasoning relies on gathering and evaluating evidence, it is objective reasoning.

In contrast, **subjective reasoning** is reasoning that is based on personal feelings or personal values. For instance, you might think crows are ugly and stupid. As a result, you might conclude crows could not possibly recognize humans. If you based your conclusion on your **opinions,** or personal feelings, you could reach the wrong conclusion.

Look at the photograph in **Figure 3.** By being able to distinguish between objective and subjective reasoning, you can distinguish between strong scientific claims and less reliable assertions.

........................✎........................

🔁 **Outline** Read the text and complete the outline.

1. _____

   a. Based on evidence

   b. Example: _____

   _____

2. Subjective Reasoning

   a. _____

   b. Example: Crows are ugly.

FIGURE 3 ·····················

▷ **INTERACTIVE ART** **Subjective Reasoning**
Opinions can be misleading. In science, conclusions are based on objective reasoning.

✎ **Interpret Photographs** Look at the photograph of a horseshoe crab and answer the questions.

1. What words would you use to describe horseshoe crabs? Are your words based on opinion or on objective reasoning?

   _____

   _____

   _____

2. The blood of horseshoe crabs is often used to ensure that some vaccines do not contain potentially deadly contamination from bacteria. Knowing this, what new words would you use to describe this animal?

   _____

   _____

   _____

Science Versus Pseudoscience Look at **Figure 4.**

Perhaps you know that astronomers are scientists who study the stars. But do you know what astrologists are? They are people who use star charts to predict the course of human events. But astrology, or the use of the stars to predict human events, is not a science.

Astrologists claim that the course of human life in part depends on the stars. But scientists look for evidence of what causes human events. Astrology makes use of data regarding the positions of the stars. But it bases its predictions on personal interpretation rather than empirical evidence. So astrology is considered to be a pseudoscience. A **pseudoscience** is a set of beliefs that may make use of science but whose conclusions and predictions are not based on observation, objective reasoning, or scientific evidence.

🔑 **Science is based on empirical evidence and well-reasoned interpretation of data. Pseudoscience may make use of scientific data. But the conclusions of pseudoscience are based on either subjective reasoning or faulty beliefs rather than on careful examination of evidence.**

Taurus

Aldebaran

FIGURE 4 ·····

Starry-Eyed

Scientists make use of empirical evidence and relevant data to draw conclusions. People who practice pseudoscience do not.

✏️ **Distinguish** Look at the outline above of the star pattern called Taurus (also known as "the bull"). Identify whether each statement below is based on science (S) or on pseudoscience (P).

_____ People whose zodiac sign is Taurus tend to be loyal.

_____ Aldebaran is the brightest star in the constellation Taurus.

_____ Each year, Taurus reaches its highest point in the sky in January.

_____ Taurus is a constellation, or pattern of stars.

_____ Scientists know that bulls are colorblind. So many people whose zodiac sign is Taurus cannot tell green and red apart.

Nonscientific Ways of Knowing The study of science provides a logical, well-reasoned understanding of the natural world. But understanding other aspects of the world requires training outside of science. Look at **Figure 5.** Many artists apply their understanding of mathematics when they use points, lines, angles, shapes, and sizes to define spaces. But knowing mathematics would not provide you with a complete understanding of the meaning of an abstract painting. You would need training in the history and principles of art to fully understand the aesthetics, or beauty, of such a painting.

The study of science can also provide only a partial understanding of subjects such as philosophy and history. For example, scientists do not claim to be able to explain the meaning of life. Nor can science easily explain the causes of major historic events.

"Untitled" (1920) by George Grosz.
© 2009 VAGA

FIGURE 5 ···

Eyes of the Beholder
Many artists create beauty in their art by using the science of defining spaces in a series of lines, angles, and shapes.

✎ [CHALLENGE] Find three simple shapes in the painting and outline them. How does your appreciation of this piece of art relate to the science of shapes? How does it relate to your personal sense of beauty?

_____

_____

_____

_____

 Do the Quick Lab *Scientific Thinking.*

🔑 Assess Your Understanding

2a. Summarize The conclusions of (science/pseudoscience) are based on subjective reasoning.   SC.8.N.2.1

b. Distinguish Is palm-reading a science or a pseudoscience? Explain.

_____

_____

_____

_____

SC.8.N.2.1

got it?

○ **I get it!** Now I know that science is based on empirical evidence. Although pseudoscience makes use of scientific data, the conclusions of pseudoscience are based on _____

_____

○ **I need extra help with** _____

_____

Go to **MY SCIENCE** 🔊 **COACH** *online for help with this subject.*   SC.8.N.2.1

What Characterizes Science and Its Methods?

Scientists use their senses, along with specially designed instruments, to observe, gather information, and record data. They use reasoning to infer, or interpret what they observe. They also use experience to analyze data and draw logical conclusions. 🗝 **Science and its methods are characterized by an ordered approach to learning about the world. This approach relies on objective analysis of data obtained through careful observation. Because scientific investigations are well-reasoned, they can be repeated by other scientists to confirm results.**

interactive SCIENCE

C1 - 195   C2 - 479   C3 - 59

Apply It

An opportunity to see if students can transfer what they learned to another unique situation

TRANSFER
Heart of Unit

apply it!

Scientists once believed coral reefs thrive only in very shallow water, where sunlight can easily reach the reefs. But in 1999, scientists discovered a reef off Florida's southwest coast that lies at depths of up to 80 meters. Scientists believe this reef can thrive because the water around the reef is clear enough for sunlight to reach the reef.

1 Summarize How did scientists revise their original hypothesis to explain where reefs can thrive?

_____

_____

2 Discuss How does the scientists' new hypothesis illustrate the characteristics of science and its methods?

_____

_____

_____

Coral at Florida's Pulley Ridge

LA.8.2.2.3

Sometimes, scientific investigations produce new data that have not been explained by previous observations. If all previous data fit the current hypothesis, scientists do not need to reject the old hypothesis. Instead, scientists may simply need to revise their hypotheses only slightly to explain the new data. 🗝 **Although science is based on empirical evidence and objective reasoning, its results are open to new discoveries and change.** Sometimes, new data may be so unexpected that scientists rethink earlier hypotheses completely.

 Lab zone ® Do the Quick Lab *Science and Its Methods.*

🗝 **Assess Your Understanding**

got it? ....

○ **I get it!** Now I know that science and its methods are characterized by _____

_____

_____

○ **I need extra help with** _____

Go to my science ⓢ coach *online for help with this subject.*

SC.8.N.2.2

59

2 Models and Systems

UNLOCK THE ESSENTIAL **?**

🗝 **How Do Scientists Use Models?**
SC.8.N.3.1

🗝 **What Are the Characteristics of a System?**
SC.8.N.3.1, LA.8.2.2.3

🗝 **How Do Models Help Scientists Understand Systems?**
SC.8.N.3.1

MY PLANET DIARY

DISCOVERY

Model Moons

You have probably seen models that show the interior of Earth. But have you ever seen a model that shows the interior of one of the other planets? How about a model of one of the other planet's moons?

The spacecraft *Voyager* and *Galileo* sent back vast amounts of data to scientists about Jupiter's moons. The data helped scientists determine that the interiors of Jupiter's moons are layered. Scientists can use these observations to build models of Jupiter's moons. The models help us further understand how the interior of Jupiter's moons are structured.

✏ **Communicate** Write your answers to each question below. Then discuss your answers with a partner.

1. What does this model of Io, one of Jupiter's moons, show about its interior?

_____

_____

_____

2. If you could travel to Jupiter's moons, how might you check if the models are correct?

_____

_____

_____

_____

_____

_____

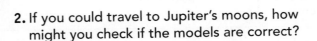

▲ Model of Jupiter's moon Io

Io

◄ Jupiter

> PLANET DIARY Go to **Planet Diary** to learn more about models.

Lab zone® Do the Inquiry Warm-Up *Models in Science.*

Vocabulary
- model - system - input
- process - output - feedback

Skills
↻ Reading: Identify the Main Idea
△ Inquiry: Make Models

How Do Scientists Use Models?

FLORIDA NGSSS

SC.8.N.3.1 Select models useful in relating the results of their own investigation.

Many department stores use mannequins to show customers how certain outfits might look. A mannequin is a model. A **model** is any representation of an object or a process. You use models in your daily life without even realizing it. For example, you might use a globe to find a country. A globe is a model of Earth.

Scientists work with models for a specific purpose. ☞ **Scientists use models to test their ideas about things they cannot observe directly.** Look at **Figure 1**. Scientists often build models to create a reasonable representation of things that are either very small or very large. These kinds of models are physical models—drawings or three-dimensional objects. But many models are not physical objects. For example, many models are models of a process. So a computer program might be used to model the movement of the stars as seen from Earth.

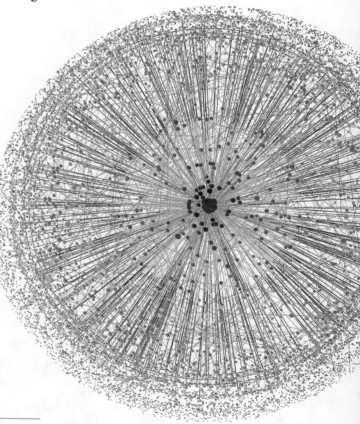

FIGURE 1 ···

> INTERACTIVE ART **Connecting the Dots**
This model shows how networks (drawn as dots) connect to each other on the Internet. The bigger the dot, the more Internet traffic the network handles.

✏ **Explain** Suppose all networks in the center of the model became unavailable for 24 hours. How can scientists use this model to predict how Internet traffic will be affected?

_____

_____

_____

Lab zone Do the Quick Lab
Working With Models

☞ Assess Your Understanding

got it? ···

○ **I get it!** Now I know that scientists use models to _____

_____

○ **I need extra help with** _____

Go to **my science** ⑤ **COACH** online for help with this subject.

SC.8.N.3.1

FLORIDA NGSSS

3.1 Select models useful
...ng the results of their own
...ation.

2.3 The student will organize
...ion to show understanding
...resenting key points within
...ough charting).

What Are the Characteristics of a System?

Models are often used to represent systems. A **system** is a group of parts that work together to carry out a function. You may recall that Earth is a system that consists of air, life, water, ice, and rock. But look at **Figure 2.** Many things you use in your daily life are systems. A bicycle pump, a toaster, and a flashlight all contain parts that work together while performing a function.

Systems have common characteristics. **All systems have at least one input, at least one process, and at least one output.** An **input** is a material or the energy that goes into the system. A **process** is an action or series of actions that happen within the system. An **output** is the material or energy that comes out of a system. To understand input, process, and output, think of a toaster. The input is electricity. The process is heating the bread. The output is hot toast.

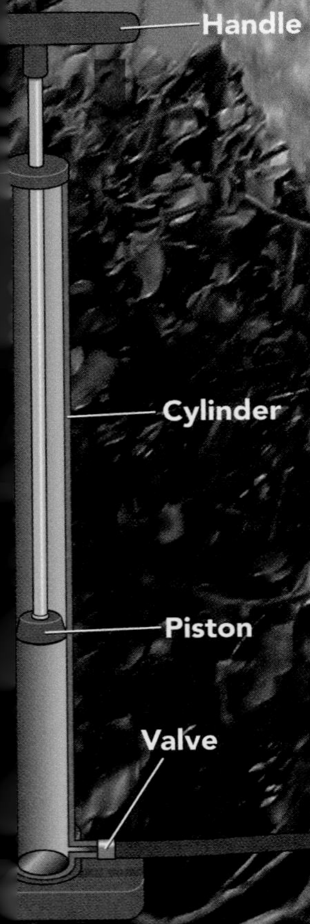

Handle

Cylinder

Piston

Valve

FIGURE 2·····

An Everyday System
In a bicycle pump, many parts work together as a system. Chart **Look at the pump and use what you know to fill in the chart.**
LA.8.2.2.3

...cle Pump as a System

	Inputs	Outputs

...entific Understanding

Look at **Figure 3.** The harder you ride a bike, the more oxygen your muscles need. As a result, your circulatory system provides information to your heart indicating that you need more oxygen. So your heart starts beating faster. By beating faster, your heart provides more oxygen to your muscles. **Feedback** is output that changes a system in some way. When you exercise, your heart receives feedback that makes your heart pump faster.

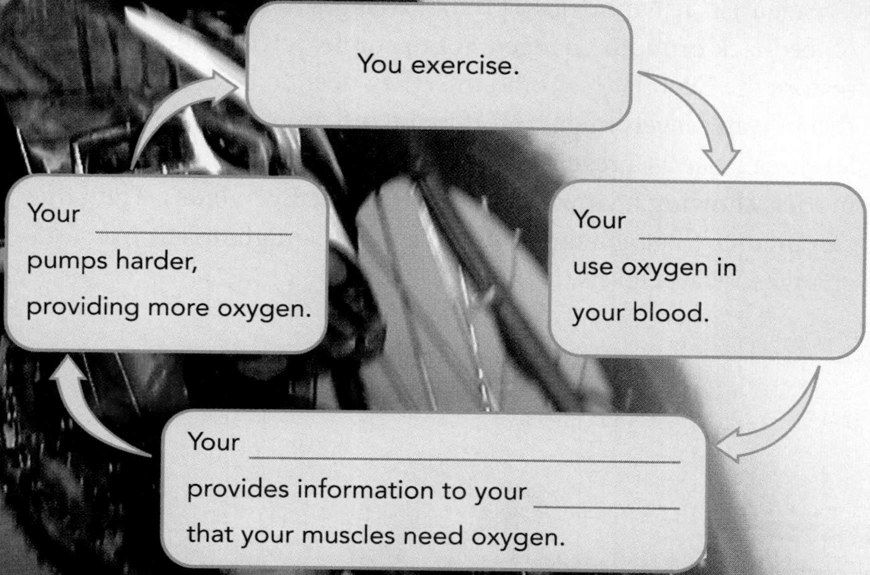

You exercise.

Your _____ pumps harder, providing more oxygen.

Your _____ use oxygen in your blood.

Your _____ provides information to your _____ that your muscles need oxygen.

FIGURE 3 ·······························

Feedback

When you exercise, your body's circulatory system feeds back information to your heart.

✎ **Fill in the blanks of the graphic organizer.**

Identify What is the input and output for this system?

_____
_____
_____
_____
_____

Lab® zone   Do the Quick Lab *Characteristics of Systems.*

🗝 Assess Your Understanding

1a. Identify A (model/system) is a group of parts that work together to perform a function.
SC.8.N.3.1

b. Apply Concepts Is a handheld can opener a system? Explain.

_____
_____
_____
_____
SC.8.N.3.1

c. Infer What is the input when you use a can opener?

_____
_____
_____
_____
_____
SC.8.N.3.1

got it?·······························

○ **I get it!** Now I know that all systems have _____ and some systems have feedback.

○ **I need extra help with** _____

Go to **my science** ⓢ **coach** *online for help with this subject.*
SC.8.N.3.1

How Do Models Help Scientists Understand Systems?

It's easy to identify the materials and energy that make up the inputs and outputs of a system. But observing a system's process can be difficult. Models can help scientists understand a system's process. **Scientists build models to represent a process. They test whether the input and output from the model match the input and output of the system in the natural world.**

Scientists use models to predict changes in a system as a result of feedback or input changes. For example, scientists have tried to restore the Everglades. To do this, they need to understand how a rise in water levels might affect plant and animal survival. Water levels can rise as a result of climate change. So scientists construct models showing how water levels affect the Everglades. Then they can predict what changes to the Everglades might result from a change in water levels.

apply it!

The Cape Sable seaside sparrow nests in certain areas of the Everglades. In one model of the sparrow's nesting habits, the sparrows start to mate when water levels drop to 5 cm. After they mate, the sparrows need approximately 43 consecutive days during which the water level is lower than 16 cm. If water levels rise to 16 cm or higher during this time, the sparrows will abandon their nest.

Nest not drawn to scale

Nest not drawn to scale

2 [CHALLENGE] How might scientists use the information from your model to save the species?

_____

_____

_____

_____

1 Make Models Make a model to show how Cape Sable seaside sparrow nests vary according to water levels. Shade in the water levels on each meterstick.

Modeling Simple and Complex Systems

Some systems that scientists study are simple. There may be only a few parts in the system or a few steps in the process. A toaster is one example of a system that is made up of only a few parts. **Figure 4** shows another example of a relatively simple system.

However, some systems are more complex. Many parts and many variables, or factors that can vary, interact in these systems. Often scientists may use a computer to keep track of the variables. For example, weather systems are very complex. Many factors affect weather, such as oceans, mountains and valleys, wind patterns, and the angle of the sun's rays. These factors can interact in many ways. As a result, scientists have a difficult time predicting when and where rain or snow might fall. Because such systems are difficult to model, scientists may model the specific part of the system that they wish to study. For instance, a hurricane is a complex system. To predict where a hurricane will make landfall, scientists might try to model winds that affect the hurricane's path.

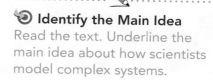

Identify the Main Idea
Read the text. Underline the main idea about how scientists model complex systems.

FIGURE 4 ···

The Mercury Cycle

Materials that contain the element mercury can be harmful to fish that eat them.

Look at the diagram and then complete the activities.

1. **Identify** On the diagram, label the inputs, outputs, and processes of the system.

2. **Predict** Suppose you want less mercury to end up in fish. How might you change the inputs of the system?

_____

_____

_____

_____

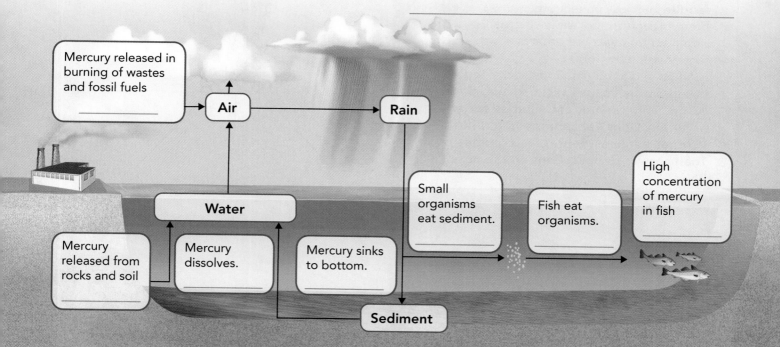

Mercury released in burning of wastes and fossil fuels
_____

Air

Rain

Water

Mercury released from rocks and soil
_____

Mercury dissolves.
_____

Mercury sinks to bottom.
_____

Small organisms eat sediment.
_____

Fish eat organisms.
_____

High concentration of mercury in fish
_____

Sediment

The lion is nicknamed the "King of the Jungle." But in open savannas, female lions do most of the hunting.

Testing Assumptions When scientists construct a model of a system, they begin with certain assumptions. For example, an astronomer might assume that in order for a planet to support life, the planet must have water.

Scientists check their assumptions. They compare the input and output of the model to the input and output in the natural world. If they match, then the assumptions are correct. If they do not match, scientists must change one or more assumptions. The revised model more accurately represents the natural world.

Sometimes scientists make assumptions to simplify the model. A scientist who wants to study how energy flows through a certain environment might use a model called a food chain. A food chain is a series of diagrams that shows what animals eat in a certain environment. For example, in a savanna, or grassy plain, a lion eats zebras and many other animals. Zebras eat grass. But the model may assume that lions eat only zebras. So the process that is shown in the model is somewhat simpler than the process that takes place in the natural world. Yet the model still accurately shows the relationship between the parts of the system. A food web, which you can draw in **Figure 5,** is a slightly more complex model of how energy flows through an environment.

FIGURE 5 ···

Food Webs

Scientists use food webs to model how energy flows through a particular environment. In a food web, lines connect organisms that eat other organisms. For any two organisms, the organism that eats the other is always shown higher up on the food web. ✎**Analyze Models and Systems** Construct a food web based on the images in the Picture Bank below. (*Hint:* Zebras and giraffes eat grass or leaves. Lions eat zebras and giraffes. Vultures eat lions, zebras, and giraffes.) Then answer the questions on the next page.

✎ **Infer** What are the assumptions of this model?

_____

_____

_____

_____

_____

CHALLENGE How could you test this model to see if your assumptions are correct?

_____

_____

_____

_____

_____

_____

 Lab zone® Do the Lab Investigation _Selecting Models._

🔑 Assess Your Understanding

2a. Review Scientists check _____ by comparing the inputs and outputs of a model to inputs and outputs of the natural world.

SC.8.N.3.1

b. Explain A certain astronomer assumes that a planet must have water to support life. How does the astronomer's assumption help the astronomer search for life in the universe?

_____

_____

_____

_____

_____

SC.8.N.3.1

c. Predict What might make the astronomer change the assumption made in the previous question?

_____

_____

_____

_____

_____

SC.8.N.3.1

got it? ···

○ **I get it!** Now I know models help scientists understand systems by allowing scientists to test _____

_____

and compare them to those of the natural world.

○ I need extra help with _____

Go to **MY SCIENCE** 🅢 **COACH** _online for help with this subject._ SC.8.N.3.1

Modifying Scientific Theories

UNLOCK THE ESSENTIAL

?

🔑 **What Is a Scientific Theory?**
SC.8.N.3.2

🔑 **Why Are Some Scientific Theories Modified?**
SC.8.N.3.2, LA.8.2.2.3

my planet Diary

DISCOVERY

One Leg to Stand On

You probably know that flamingoes often stand on one leg. But do you know why? For a long time, researchers had different explanations. Is it because flamingoes are better able to balance on one leg? Is it because fewer ducks bump into the flamingoes when they stand on one leg? Or is it for another reason? In 2009, researchers finally believed they had found the answer: Flamingoes are better able to control the temperature of their body when they stand on one leg.

✏️ **Evaluate Scientific Claims** Write your answers to each question below. Then discuss your answers with a partner.

1. Why do flamingoes stand on one leg?

_____

_____

_____

2. How could you confirm that flamingoes stand on one leg in order to better control their body temperature?

_____

_____

_____

_____

_____

> PLANET DIARY Go to **Planet Diary** to learn more about scientific theories.

Lab zone Do the Inquiry Warm-Up *Developing Scientific Theories.*

Vocabulary
- scientific theory
- scientific law

Skills
- ↻ Reading: Relate Text and Visuals
- △ Inquiry: Design Experiments

What Is a Scientific Theory?

FLORIDA NGSSS

SC.8.N.3.2 Explain why theories may be modified but are rarely discarded.

Your brother opens the cookie jar and demands, "Where have all the cookies gone?" You notice a trail of crumbs from the jar to your sister's bedroom. "Well," you say, "I have a theory about that." In everyday conversation, the word *theory* can be used loosely to describe an explanation of one or more events. In science, the word has a much more specific definition.

Sometimes a large set of related observations can be connected by a single explanation. This explanation can lead to the development of a scientific theory. 🔑 **A scientific theory is a well-tested explanation for a wide range of observations and experimental results.**

Look at **Figure 1.** According to the atomic theory, all substances are composed of particles called atoms. This single explanation helps to explain many observations. When the theory was first proposed, it helped explain how two elements, such as silver and gold, differ from each other. Later, scientists found that the theory could explain why iron nails rust when they are exposed to air and water. The nails rust because iron in the metal combines with oxygen and water in the air. A scientific theory becomes better accepted as it helps explain more and more observations.

FIGURE 1 ·········

A Scientific Theory
Atomic theory explains how elements differ from each other and how they combine together.

✏️ CHALLENGE Read the text. How does the rusting car illustrate the atomic theory?

_____

_____

_____

_____

_____

_____

Lab zone ® *Do the Quick Lab Testing a Scientific Theory.*

🔑 Assess Your Understanding

got it? ···

○ I get it! Now I know a scientific theory is _____

_____

○ I need extra help with _____

Go to **MY SCIENCE** s **COACH** *online for help with this subject.*   SC.8.N.3.2

FLORIDA NGSSS

SC.8.N.3.2 Explain why theories may be modified but are rarely discarded.

LA.8.2.2.3 The student will organize information to show understanding (e.g., representing key points within the text through summarizing).

Why Are Some Scientific Theories Modified?

You have learned that the word *theory* has a specific meaning in the field of science. Other words also have specific scientific meanings. In your daily life, the word *law* means a rule that must be followed. For example, you may not cross the street if the light is red. You must pay for things you get at a store. By contrast, a **scientific law** is a statement that describes what scientists expect to happen every time under a particular set of conditions. For example, the law of gravity explains that when you let go of a ball, it will fall to the ground. If it doesn't fall, some other condition has interfered.

Scientific laws and scientific theories each describe observed events. So you might think that the two words are synonyms. But there are key differences between these two words.

Scientific Law Versus Scientific Theory What is the difference between a scientific law and a scientific theory? Unlike a scientific theory, a scientific law describes an observed pattern in nature without attempting to explain it. How can you tell the difference between a scientific theory and a scientific law? You can do so by asking: "Does this statement provide an explanation for why an event or process is happening?" Try it in **Figure 2**.

✏️ **Relate Text and Visuals**
Look at **Figure 2**. How does the photograph of the three dogs illustrate the statement above it?

_____

_____

_____

_____

_____

_____

FIGURE 2 ....

> **INTERACTIVE ART** Scientific Law Or Scientific Theory?
Scientific laws describe observed patterns without trying to explain them. ✏️ **Classify** Label each idea given below as a scientific law or a scientific theory.

An object in motion tends to stay in motion.

Physical traits of animals are passed from parent to offspring through units called genes.

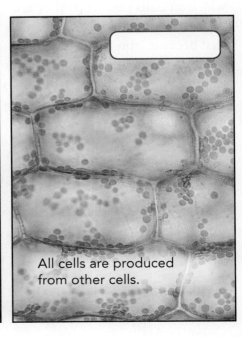

All cells are produced from other cells.

Modifying Scientific Theories

Scientific laws often explain easily observed events. So scientific laws become widely accepted relatively quickly. But scientists accept a theory only when it can explain important observations.

What happens if a theory cannot explain new observations about the original area of study? If the theory cannot explain new observations, then the theory is changed or even thrown out. But as long as a theory still explains a wide range of observations, it is revised rather than discarded.

🔑 **As scientists learn more about the natural world, their theories evolve to explain new observations.** The new observations can lead to new ideas that help us to understand the natural world. Theories also change because our ability to observe the natural world is improving. Why is our ability to observe the natural world improving? Because for centuries, people have been creating new technology to help us study the natural world. Technology is development of new instruments and methods to solve practical problems. 🔑 **Scientific theories change because new technology improves our ability to observe the natural world.**

apply it!

Scientists once believed dinosaurs became extinct because an asteroid struck Earth 65 million years ago. Later, scientists concluded that two asteroids struck Earth hundreds of thousands of years apart. They also found evidence that volcanic activity and climate change played a role in killing the dinosaurs.

❶ Infer What was the original theory to explain why dinosaurs became extinct?

_____

_____

❷ Summarize Why did scientists modify their theory about the extinction of the dinosaurs?

_____

_____

_____

LA.8.2.2.3

Lab zone Do the Quick Lab *Modifying Theories.*

🔑 Assess Your Understanding

1a. Summarize A scientific (theory/law) provides an explanation for why something happens.

SC.8.N.3.2

b. Classify Is the following statement a law or a theory? A dropped object will fall to the ground. Explain.

_____

_____

SC.8.N.3.2

c. Design Experiments How might you test the scientific law that two objects of different mass fall at the same speed?

_____

_____

_____

SC.8.N.3.2

got it? ....

○ **I get it!** Now I know that scientific theories may be modified because _____

_____

○ **I need extra help with** _____

Go to MY SCIENCE ⓢ **COACH** *online for help with this subject.*

SC.8.N.3.2

Understanding Science and Society

UNLOCK THE ESSENTIAL ?

🔑 **How Can Science Help Communities Make Decisions?**
SC.8.N.4.1, MA.6.A.3.6

🔑 **How Does Society Affect Science?**
SC.8.N.4.2

my PLANET DiARY

Racing With the Wind

Suppose you were an elite athlete but had unexpectedly lost a leg in an accident. You might still like to compete in your sport and continue as a productive member in your society. A need for prosthetic, or artificial, limbs has driven science to develop more and more complex artificial arms, legs, fingers, and toes.

HOT SCIENCE

Write your answer to the question below. Then discuss your answer with a partner.

How can scientists help people who have lost limbs in an accident?

_____

_____

_____

_____

_____

_____

▶ PLANET DIARY) Go to **Planet Diary** to learn more about science and society.

Lab zone® Do the Inquiry Warm-Up *Science and Society's Interaction.*

🏴 **FLORIDA** NGSSS

SC.8.N.4.1 Explain that science is one of the processes that can be used to inform decision making at the community, state, national, and international levels.

MA.6.A.3.6 Analyze graphs to describe simple relations using common language.

How Can Science Help Communities Make Decisions?

What steps should your school take to prevent an outbreak of the flu? Which cars should companies make and sell to help protect the environment? 🔑 **Understanding scientific research and thinking scientifically can help societies, groups, and individuals make good decisions and solve problems in everyday life.**

Vocabulary
- cost
- benefit

Skills
- Reading: Sequence
- Inquiry: Pose Questions

Science in Daily Life If you have ever bought an item in a store, you are a consumer. A consumer is anyone who buys or uses goods. To become an informed consumer, you need to know if the products you buy are safe. For example, you might want to know why some foods are recalled from grocery stores. When foods are recalled, manufacturers instruct stores to return products that may be defective or hazardous. Science can help you understand the reasons for a recall and help you protect yourself in the future.

As a consumer, you may also want to know how things work. Studying science can help you understand how products work. As a result, you can make better choices about the products you buy and use. For example, suppose you like to rollerblade. Look at **Figure 1**. How do you know the gear in the photograph is strong enough to protect you? Understanding what materials are made of is just one way science can help you as a consumer.

FIGURE 1 ·······································

Science in Everyday Life
✎ Learning science can make activities such as rollerblading safer and more fun for you.

1. **Observe** Circle the gear that can keep you safe when you rollerblade.

2. ◢**Pose Questions** List three science-related questions you might want to ask a shop-keeper before you buy safety gear for rollerblading.

_____

_____

_____

_____

_____

_____

Science and Decision Making for Society

🔑 **A knowledge of science helps individuals, communities, states, and nations analyze the costs and benefits of a decision.** A **cost** is an undesirable result of either taking or not taking an action. For example, a town might decide to preserve land that provides habitat for local wildlife. If the community had not made that decision, the cost might have been endangering the wildlife. A **benefit** is a desirable result of either taking or not taking a certain action.

States and nations might weigh the costs and benefits of large-scale projects. For example, a state might decide whether or not to build offshore wind farms, such as the offshore wind farm shown in **Figure 2**. Many nations might cooperate on scientific projects that are extremely complex. For example, before deciding whether to help build the International Space Station, countries around the world analyzed the costs, such as the amount of money they might be required to donate to the project. They also examined benefits, such as the pride they might feel in taking part in the project.

Vocabulary Identify Multiple Meanings Which sentence uses the scientific meaning of the word *benefit*?

- ◯ One benefit of preserving the Everglades is cleaner water.
- ◯ My sister played in a concert that was a benefit for Africa.

FIGURE 2 ·······························

Costs and Benefits

When individuals, groups, and societies make decisions, they often weigh the benefits that might be gained against the costs that may result. ✎ **Analyze Costs and Benefits** Identify one cost and one benefit of building offshore wind turbines.

Cost:

_____

_____

_____

Benefit:

_____

_____

_____

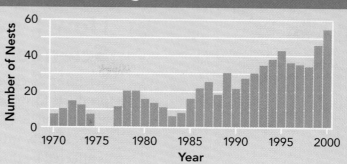

do the math!

Like many states, Florida uses science to help make decisions about protecting wildlife. For example, crocodiles are much more rare in Florida than alligators are. So scientists studied crocodiles closely. As a result, in 1975, the U.S. Fish and Wildlife Service listed Florida's population of American crocodiles as endangered. The graph shows the total number of American crocodile nests in Florida over time.

Crocodile Nesting in Florida

① **Read Graphs** In which years were there no American crocodile nests in Florida? In which years were there more than 50?

_____

_____

② **Interpret Data** Based on the graph, why might the wildlife service have listed American crocodiles as endangered in Florida in 1975?

_____

_____

③ [CHALLENGE] Some environmental groups removed the American crocodile from their "endangered" list in the mid-1990s. Why?

_____

_____

_____

_____

MA.6.A.3.6

Do the Quick Lab *How Science Affects Society.*

🔑 Assess Your Understanding

1a. Identify A (cost/benefit) is a negative result of either taking or not taking an action.

SC.8.N.4.1

b. Compare and Contrast What is the difference between a cost and a benefit?

_____

_____

_____

SC.8.N.4.1

c. Explain How can identifying costs inform decision making at the community level for a town debating whether to restrict water usage by homeowners during periods of drought?

_____

_____

_____

_____

SC.8.N.4.1

got it? ....

○ **I get it!** Now I know that understanding scientific research and thinking scientifically can help societies, groups, and individuals make _____

○ **I need extra help with** _____

Go to MY SCIENCE ⓢ COACH *online for help with this subject.*

SC.8.N.4.1

SC.8.N.4.2 Explain how political, social, and economic concerns can affect science, and vice versa.

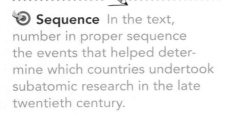

Sequence In the text, number in proper sequence the events that helped determine which countries undertook subatomic research in the late twentieth century.

How Does Society Affect Science?

Scientific discoveries have helped to bring computers and other products to society. But just as science can affect society, society can affect science. 🔑 **The work that scientists do changes society. In turn, society influences the work of scientists.** In general, science is affected by three main concerns of society: political concerns, social concerns, and economic concerns.

Political Concerns   Political concerns are concerns that governments have about how to use their money, power, and influence. For example, in the 1980s, scientists in the United States wanted to study subatomic particles. Subatomic particles are very small particles that make up atoms. They are even smaller than atoms! The scientists wanted to build a huge structure that would accelerate the particles to great speeds. Scientists could then smash the particles together. They hoped that the force of the collisions would split atoms into the subatomic particles that make them up.

The structure that the scientists wanted to build was called the Superconducting Supercollider (SSC). However, the U.S. Congress eventually decided the project cost too much money. So in 1993 Congress canceled the project. Europe later undertook subatomic research on its own. **Figure 3** shows the collider built by European countries.

Recall that the International Space Station is another example of a large project that governments around the world helped to support. Science can also focus international attention on very large problems affecting nations worldwide, such as climate change.

FIGURE 3 ·····································

Political Concerns

Scientists hope that the Large Hadron Collider near Geneva, Switzerland, will lead to discoveries about subatomic particles.

✏️ **Explain** How did political concerns help determine which countries undertook new subatomic research projects in the late twentieth century?

_____

_____

_____

_____

_____

_____

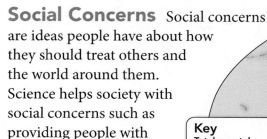

Tuberculosis Cases Worldwide

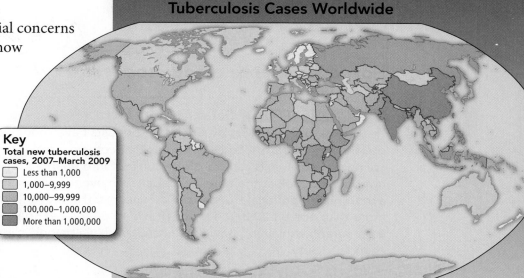

Key
Total new tuberculosis cases, 2007–March 2009
- [ ] Less than 1,000
- [ ] 1,000–9,999
- [ ] 10,000–99,999
- [ ] 100,000–1,000,000
- [ ] More than 1,000,000

Social Concerns Social concerns are ideas people have about how they should treat others and the world around them. Science helps society with social concerns such as providing people with housing, protecting the environment, treating and preventing disease.

In fact, many social concerns revolve around health issues. Look at **Figure 4.** Doctors know that tuberculosis is a disease that can be treated and prevented. This disease primarily affects the lungs. It also affects poor countries to a greater degree than it affects wealthy countries. By studying why the disease affects some countries more than others, scientists hope to stop the spread of the disease.

Economic Concerns Economic concerns are ideas people have about how people should make and spend money. How can science address these concerns? Science can help provide jobs. Science can also lower the costs of consumer goods as new methods and new technologies are developed.

Science can be used to weigh the costs and benefits of economic concerns. For example, in the early twentieth century, developers began to drain the Everglades. Draining this area would have provided jobs, affordable housing, and good farmland for growing crops. But development of the Everglades would have destroyed many wildlife habitats. Fewer tourists might also have visited the area. Businesses in nearby towns would have lost valuable customers. Also, the environment of the Everglades helps supply fresh water to much of southern Florida. So developing the area would have threatened its fresh water supply. After weighing the economic costs and benefits along with the scientific value of the Everglades, Florida decided to limit development of the area.

FIGURE 4 ....
Tuberculosis
✎ Tuberculosis is a treatable and preventable disease. It attacks the lungs and can cause death. It affects poor countries more severely than it affects wealthy countries.

1. Interpret Maps Which continent has the highest rates of tuberculosis?

_____

_____

2. Infer Identify one social concern that might drive scientists to try to stop the spread of tuberculosis.

_____

_____

_____

_____

_____

77

Seeing the Light

How does science change society?

FIGURE 5 ···

> **REAL-WORLD INQUIRY** **Solar Cell Society**

✎ **Evaluate the Impact on Society** Scientists have spent decades developing modern solar cells. Panels that contain a series of connected solar cells can transform sunlight into energy that does not pollute. Look at the timeline. Label each event as an example of **economic E**, **political P**, or **social S** concerns. (*Hint:* Events may be more than one type.) In the space provided on the next page, write a paragraph explaining how these concerns have helped science change society.

❶ 1954

The first practical solar cell is invented. It uses silicon to help produce power. Possible uses include providing remote power to improve telephone service.

E○ P○ S○

❷ 1962

Solar cells are used to power the first commercial communications satellites, improving communications around the world. Later, space stations such as SkyLab (shown here) also use solar panels.

E○ P○ S○

❸ 1979

The price of oil skyrockets. As a result, President Jimmy Carter installs solar panels on the roof of the White House to provide hot water and increase energy efficiency.

E○ P○ S○

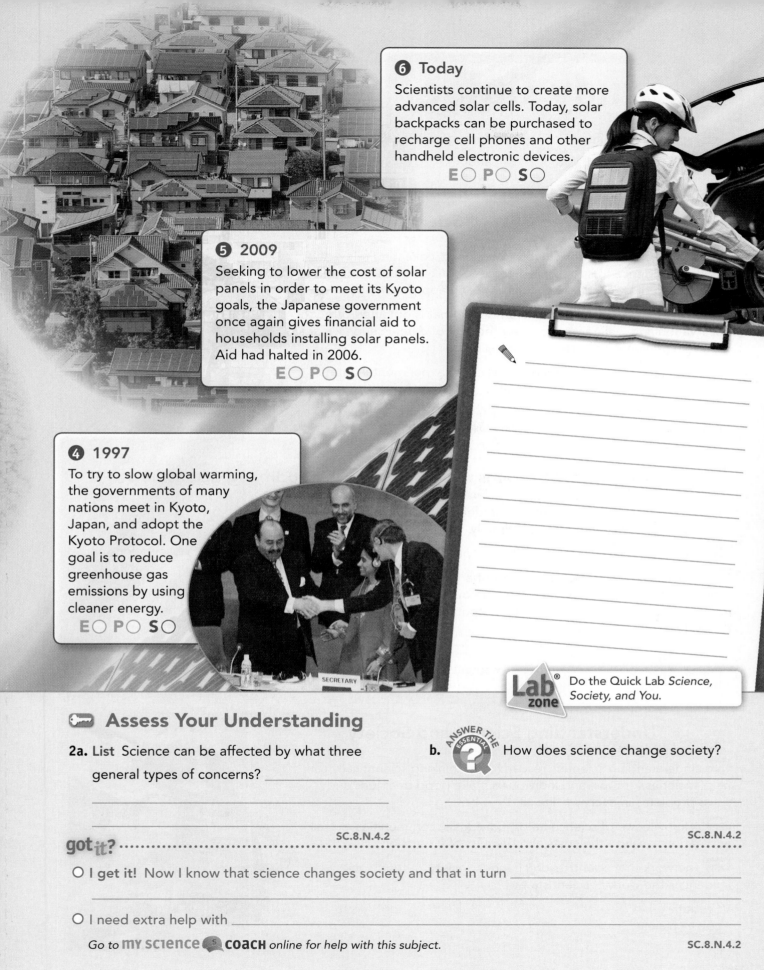

6 Today

Scientists continue to create more advanced solar cells. Today, solar backpacks can be purchased to recharge cell phones and other handheld electronic devices.

E○ P○ S○

5 2009

Seeking to lower the cost of solar panels in order to meet its Kyoto goals, the Japanese government once again gives financial aid to households installing solar panels. Aid had halted in 2006.

E○ P○ S○

4 1997

To try to slow global warming, the governments of many nations meet in Kyoto, Japan, and adopt the Kyoto Protocol. One goal is to reduce greenhouse gas emissions by using cleaner energy.

E○ P○ S○

Lab zone® Do the Quick Lab *Science, Society, and You.*

🔑 Assess Your Understanding

2a. List Science can be affected by what three general types of concerns? _____

_____

_____

SC.8.N.4.2

b. ANSWER THE ESSENTIAL ? How does science change society?

_____

_____

_____

SC.8.N.4.2

got it? ....

○ **I get it!** Now I know that science changes society and that in turn _____

○ **I need extra help with** _____

Go to **MY SCIENCE** ⬤ **COACH** *online for help with this subject.*

SC.8.N.4.2

Science affects society by allowing individuals, communities, and countries to analyze the
_____ and _____ of a decision.

LESSON 1 The Characteristics of Scientific Knowledge

SC.8.N.1.6, SC.8.N.2.1, SC.8.N.2.2

🔑 Scientific investigations involve observing, collecting relevant empirical evidence to support researchers' conclusions, using logical reasoning to draw conclusions, inferring, and applying imagination.

🔑 Science is based on empirical evidence that is obtained through observation and well-reasoned interpretation of data. Pseudoscience is based on personal interpretation or beliefs.

🔑 Science is based on objective analysis of experimental data.

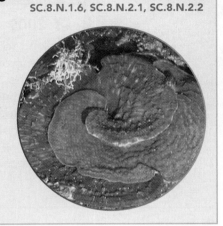

Vocabulary
• observing • data • empirical evidence • inferring • objective reasoning
• subjective reasoning • opinion • pseudoscience

LESSON 2 Models and Systems

SC.8.N.3.1

🔑 Scientists use models to test their ideas about things they cannot observe directly.

🔑 All systems have input, process, and output.

🔑 Scientists build models to represent a process. They test whether the input and output from the model match the input and output of the system in the natural world.

Vocabulary
• model • system • input • process • output
• feedback

LESSON 3 Modifying Scientific Theories

SC.8.N.3.2

🔑 A scientific theory is a well-tested explanation for a wide range of observations and experimental results.

🔑 As people learn more about the natural world, theories evolve to explain the new observations.

Vocabulary
• scientific theory • scientific law

LESSON 4 Understanding Science and Society

SC.8.N.4.1, SC.8.N.4.2

🔑 Understanding scientific research and thinking scientifically can help societies, groups, and individuals make good decisions and solve problems in everyday life.

🔑 A knowledge of science helps individuals, communities, states, and nations analyze the costs and benefits of a decision.

🔑 The work that scientists do changes society. In turn, society influences the work of scientists.

Vocabulary
• cost • benefit

Review and Assessment

LESSON 1 The Characteristics of Scientific Knowledge

1. Empirical evidence is data and observations that have been collected through

a. the Internet.   b. inferring.

c. scientific processes. d. the imagination.

SC.8.N.1.6

2. When you observe, you use one or more of your senses to _____.

SC.8.N.1.6

3. Compare and Contrast What is the difference between inferring and guessing wildly?

_____

_____

_____

_____

SC.8.N.1.6

4. Draw Conclusions In Lesson 1 you read about scientists who studied crows. At one point in their study, the scientists wore their caveman masks upside down. Some crows turned their heads upside down while looking at the researchers. Does this support the conclusion that crows recognize faces? Explain.

_____

_____

_____

_____

_____

_____

SC.8.N.1.6

5. Write About It Neurology is, in part, the study of the brain's functions to determine how the brain controls the human nervous system. Phrenology is the study of the shape of a person's skull to determine that person's personality. Both neurology and phrenology are based on evidence that specific areas of the brain control specific functions. Which is a science? Which is a pseudoscience? Explain.

SC.8.N.2.1

LESSON 2 Models and Systems

6. A model is any representation of an object or

a. an opinion.   b. a process.

c. an investigation.   d. data.

SC.8.N.3.1

7. A system is a group of parts that work together to _____.

SC.8.N.3.1

8. Define What is feedback?

_____

_____

_____

SC.8.N.3.1

Use the photograph to answer Question 9.

9. Make Models What is a classroom skeleton a model of?

_____

_____

_____

_____

SC.8.N.3.1

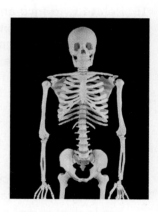

10. Infer A flashlight can be considered to be a system. What are the input and output of turning on a flashlight?

_____

_____

_____

_____

SC.8.N.3.1

11. Write About It A certain school teaches seven foreign languages. A different number of students elects to take each language. How might you model the relative popularity of each language?

SC.8.N.3.1

81

LESSON 3 **Modifying Scientific Theories**

12. A well-tested explanation for a wide range of observations and experimental results is a(n)

    a. scientific law.   **b.** scientific theory.

    c. model.   **d.** observation.

                                              SC.8.N.3.2

13. A _____ describes an observed pattern in nature without trying to explain it.

                                              SC.8.N.3.2

14. Classify Is the following statement a scientific law or a scientific theory? The planets in Earth's solar system revolve around the sun.

                                              SC.8.N.3.2

15. Relate Evidence and Explanation Before 2008, scientists thought that only emperor penguins spent significant parts of their lives on glaciers. What evidence might scientists have found that made them modify their belief?

                                              SC.8.N.3.2

16. **Write About It** Scientists used to believe that all ecosystems obtained energy from the sun. But look at the photograph. Small vents on the ocean floor emit hot, mineral-rich water from beneath the crust. No sunlight reaches these depths. But in the 1970s scientists found ecosystems thriving near the vents. How might scientists have modified their original theory regarding ecosystems and energy?

                                              SC.8.N.3.2

LESSON 4 **Understanding Science and Society**

17. Ideas that people have about how people should earn a living and spend money are called

    a. political concerns.   **b.** social concerns.

    c. economic concerns. **d.** artistic concerns.

                                              SC.8.N.4.2

18. In order to make decisions that are well informed, you should first analyze the

    _____ and _____.

                                              SC.8.N.4.1

19. Explain You are going to the beach and need to buy sunscreen. What are two pieces of information that the sunscreen manufacturer might include on the label to help you decide if the sunscreen will be effective?

                                              SC.8.N.4.1

How does science change society?

20. Scientists are studying the effects that melting ice might have on rising sea levels. Describe how the results of these studies might affect society. (*Hint:* Consider how cities on Florida's coasts might be affected by rising sea levels.)

                                              SC.8.N.4.2

Florida Benchmarks Review

Circle the letter of the best answer.

1 What might be one reason scientists would build a model of Earth like the one shown here?

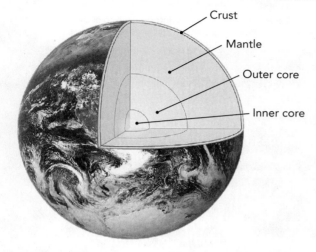

Crust
Mantle
Outer core
Inner core

A to show the color of the continents
B to show the depths of Earth's oceans
C to show the layers of Earth
D to show pressure inside Earth

SC.8.N.3.1

2 Which of the following statements best describes a scientific law?

A It is an educated guess.
B It is a statement that describes what might happen some of the time.
C It is a statement that describes what scientists expect to happen all of the time under a specific set of conditions.
D It is a statement that describes all procedures that scientists must follow.

SC.8.N.1.6

3 Dowsing is the process of searching for underground water by walking over land while holding a stick. When the person holding the stick determines that the stick is shaking, the person might be standing near water. Dowsing is an example of a(n)

A political concern.
B empirical evidence.
C pseudoscience.
D science.

SC.8.N.2.1

4 Which statement is an example of how political concerns have affected science?

A Doctors wash their hands before performing surgery on patients.
B In 1966, the U.S. Congress passed a law to help control how animals are treated in scientific research.
C The Everglades provide fresh water to southern Florida.
D Crows can recognize human faces.

SC.8.N.4.2

5 Many consumers want to be able to purchase cars that are safe. Which of the following is an example of a scientific invention that may have resulted from consumer concerns regarding automobile safety?

A fast cars   B cup holders
C clean gasoline   D air bags

SC.8.N.4.1

6 A scientist measured the distance that a stream of lava from a volcano flowed over 5 minutes. What is a logical conclusion you can draw from the graph of the scientist's data, shown below?

A Lava never changes speed.
B The speed of lava increases over time.
C The speed of lava decreases over time.
D All lava flows at the same rate of speed.

SC.8.N.1.6, SC.8.N.2.1

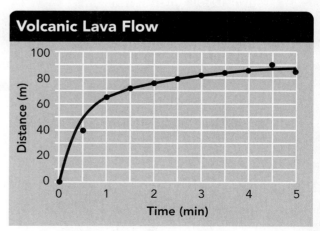

Volcanic Lava Flow

Science and Society

Something fishy

FLORIDA NGSSS

SC.8.N.4.1 Explain that science is one of the processes that can be used to inform decision making at the community, state, national, and international levels.

LA.8.2.2.3 The student will organize information to show understanding or relationships among facts, ideas, and events.

That delicious fish on your plate is full of nutrients. But it might also be full of the metal, mercury. Mercury damages the nervous system of humans. Recent research revealed that streams and wetlands across the United States, particularly in Florida, are contaminated with mercury. Most of the mercury comes from fossil fuels, such as coal. When coal is burned, mercury is released into the air. When it rains, the mercury atoms get trapped in raindrops. The rain falls and collects in streams, wetlands, and other bodies of water. From here, mercury enters the food chain.

Small fish contain the lowest levels of mercury. Suppose a bigger fish eats ten small fish. That big fish now has ten times the amount of mercury as one small fish. Now, suppose that a bird eats ten of the big fish. The mercury levels of the bird will be 100 times that of the small fish! The mercury levels will continue to rise in each animal as you move up through the food chain.

To help people avoid eating poisonous levels of mercury, the Florida Department of Health provides guidelines for eating fish. The Department developed these guidelines using data on mercury levels of different fish in different parts of Florida. The Florida Department of Environmental Protection (DEP) also uses the data. Informed by research, the DEP can make policies that help to protect Florida residents and ecosystems.

Research It Use the Internet to find *Your Guide to Eating Fish Caught in Florida* by the Florida Department of Health. Look through this reference material to locate the recommendations for your county. Make a pamphlet to inform residents of the guidelines for eating fish caught in your county.

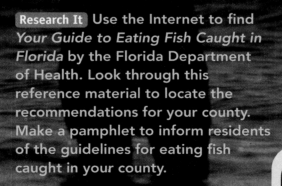

Data on mercury contamination helps the Florida Department of Health advise residents on the safety of eating different kinds of fish. ▶

WARNING

The Florida Department of Health and Rehabilitative Services has issued a health advisory urging limited consumption of largemouth bass and warmouth caught in certain portions of the Everglades due to excessive accumulation of the element mercury.

CAFFEINE CAUSES HALLUCINATIONS!

A new study reports that the equivalent of seven cups of coffee a day could cause people to see "ghosts."

Headlines grab your attention. That's their job—to get you to read more. Sometimes, though, when headlines promise interesting news, the report doesn't deliver accurate scientific data.

Recently, some newspapers reported that caffeine caused people to hallucinate. The report cited a study that showed that people who drank seven or more cups of coffee in a day saw things that weren't really there. However, the study had some flaws.

It had a small sample of only 219 people. Also, the sample came from a specific group of people—university students. The study took the form of a survey, which means the researchers did not directly observe the subjects. Finally, the researchers did not have a control group. There was no way for them to determine if other factors, besides the caffeine, had affected the subjects. Many scientists later agreed that more tests still needed to be done.

Science doesn't always make for interesting news. Most scientific discoveries happen slowly. They are the result of many trials performed over long periods of time. So be critical of catchy headlines that promise an interesting story. You may not be reading accurate science.

Analyze It Compare articles about science in two or three news sources. Are the headlines more eye-catching in one source? Identify the science claims that the articles make. Identify the evidence that supports these claims. Which source provides the clearest evidence? Which source relies mostly on opinions and assumptions? Create a table to compare the reporting in your sources.

FLORIDA NGSSS

SC.8.N.2.1 Distinguish between scientific and pseudoscientific ideas.

LA.8.4.2.2 The student will record information related to a topic and attribute sources of information.

A chemist processes and analyzes data at the Centers for Disease Control and Prevention.

Summarizing

 Big Ideas and Essential Questions

Nature of Science

In this Nature of Science unit, you learned about the characteristics of science and the ways in which scientists work. You learned about the skills and processes used in scientific investigations and how scientific theories lead to greater understanding of the natural world.

What tools can this scientist use to evaluate her data?

_____

_____

_____

_____

_____

_____

_____

_____

How could her discovery affect society?

_____

_____

_____

_____

_____

_____

_____

_____

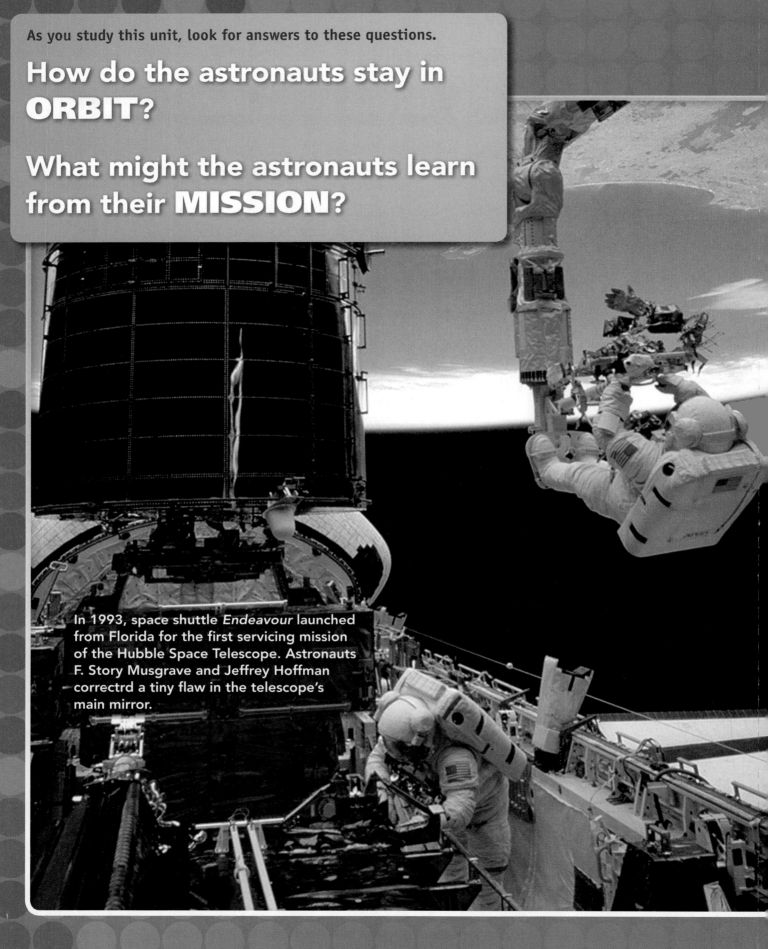

As you study this unit, look for answers to these questions.

How do the astronauts stay in ORBIT?

What might the astronauts learn from their MISSION?

In 1993, space shuttle *Endeavour* launched from Florida for the first servicing mission of the Hubble Space Telescope. Astronauts F. Story Musgrave and Jeffrey Hoffman correctrd a tiny flaw in the telescope's main mirror.

Introducing

Earth Science

 Florida Big Idea 5

Earth in Space and Time

The origin and eventual fate of the Universe still remains one of the greatest questions in science. Gravity and energy influence the formation of galaxies, including our own Milky Way Galaxy, stars, the planetary systems, and Earth. Humankind's need to explore continues to lead to the development of knowledge and understanding of the nature of the Universe.

? What astronomical objects exist in the universe?

? Why are objects in the solar system different from each other?

? How do Earth, the moon, and the sun interact?

? How does exploring space benefit people on Earth?

WHAT ELSE IS OUT THERE?

ESSENTIAL

What astronomical objects exist in the universe?

>UNTAMED SCIENCE Watch the **Untamed Science** video to learn more about the universe.

Two galaxies are colliding! It all started 40 million years ago and will take millions more for these two spiral galaxies to actually combine. Astronomers know that the galaxy on the left, NGC 2207, and the galaxy on the right, IC 2163, are 140 million light-years from Earth. A light-year is the distance light travels in one year, or 9.46 trillion kilometers. That makes these galaxies about 1,320,000,000,000,000,000,000 kilometers away. ◢Predict **Besides galaxies, what objects do you think might be pictured in this photograph?**

_____

_____

_____

_____

Stars, Galaxies, and the Universe

CHAPTER 3

FLORIDA Next Generation Sunshine State Standards

Big Idea 1: SC.8.N.1.5, SC.8.N.1.6
Big Idea 2: SC.8.N.2.2
Big Idea 5: SC.8.E.5.1, SC.8.E.5.2, SC.8.E.5.3,
SC.8.E.5.4, SC.8.3.5.5, SC.8.E.5.6

Language Arts: LA.8.2.2.3,
Mathematics: MA.6.A.3.6

3 Getting Started

Check Your Understanding

1. **Background** Read the paragraph below and then answer the question.

A room on Earth that seems to be empty is still full of air, which is a **gas.** If you got the air in a room cold enough, it would become a **liquid.** Even after becoming a liquid, the air would have the same **mass** as before.

A **gas** is a state of matter that has no definite shape or volume.

A **liquid** is a state of matter that has no definite shape but has a definite volume.

Mass is the amount of matter in an object.

- A balloon filled with helium gas floats. Does this mean it has no mass? Explain.

_____

_____

> MY READING WEB If you had trouble completing the question above, visit **My Reading Web** and type in *Stars, Galaxies, and the Universe*.

Vocabulary Skill

Greek and Latin Word Origins Many science words in English come from Greek and Latin. For example, *protostar* comes from the Greek word *proto*, meaning "earliest." A protostar is the earliest stage of a star's life.

Word	Language of Origin	Meaning	Example
chroma	Greek	color	chromosphere, *n.*
prominere	Latin	to jut forward	prominence, *n.*

LA.8.1.6.7

2. **Quick Check** Use the information in the chart to suggest a meaning for the vocabulary term below.

- prominence: _____

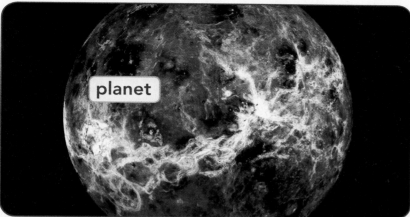

planet

supernova

spiral galaxy

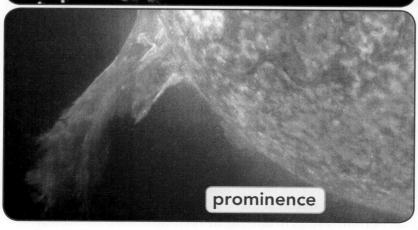

prominence

Chapter Preview

LESSON 1
- parallax • universe
- light-year • scientific notation
- ⟳ **Summarize**
- △ **Calculate**

LESSON 2
- star • planet • solar system
- binary star • galaxy
- spiral galaxy • elliptical galaxy
- irregular galaxy • quasar
- ⟳ **Outline**
- △ **Classify**

LESSON 3
- orbit • force • gravity
- law of universal gravitation
- mass • weight • inertia
- Newton's first law of motion
- accretion
- ⟳ **Ask Questions**
- △ **Draw Conclusions**

LESSON 4
- spectrograph
- apparent brightness
- absolute brightness
- Hertzsprung-Russell diagram
- main sequence
- ⟳ **Identify the Main Idea**
- △ **Infer**

LESSON 5
- nebula • protostar • white dwarf
- supernova • neutron star
- pulsar • black hole
- ⟳ **Compare and Contrast**
- △ **Predict**

LESSON 6
- core • nuclear fusion
- radiation zone • convection zone
- photosphere • chromosphere
- corona • solar wind • sunspot
- prominence • solar flare
- ⟳ **Relate Cause and Effect**
- △ **Interpret Data**

LESSON

1

The Scale of the Universe

UNLOCK THE ESSENTIAL ?

🔑 **How Do Astronomers Measure Distances to the Stars?**
SC.8.N.1.6, SC.8.E.5.1

🔑 **How Do Astronomers Describe the Scale of the Universe?**
SC.8.E.5.1, LA.8.2.2.3

my planet diary *for Florida*

FLORIDA SPACE HISTORY

Voyager Golden Record

Florida's location near the equator and the fact that it borders the Atlantic Ocean make it a good location for launching rockets, missiles, and spacecraft. Cape Canaveral has been the site of many launches since 1950. One spacecraft that was launched from Cape Canaveral in 1977, the *Voyager 1*, contains a gold-plated copper disk that is filled with images and sounds of Earth. *Voyager 1* is now sixteen billion kilometers away from the sun!

Communicate Discuss the Voyager Record with a partner. Then answer the question below.

What images and sounds would you put on a recording sent into space?

_____

_____

_____

_____

▶ **PLANET DIARY** Go to **Planet Diary** to learn more about the scale of the universe.

Lab zone® Do the Inquiry Warm-Up *Stringing Along.*

FLORIDA NGSSS

SC.8.N.1.6 Understand that scientific investigations involve the collection of relevant empirical evidence, the use of logical reasoning, and the application of imagination in devising hypotheses, predictions, explanations and models to make sense of the collected evidence.

SC.8.E.5.1 Recognize and apply knowledge of light and space travel to understand the enormous distances between objects in space.

How Do Astronomers Measure Distances to the Stars?

Standing on Earth looking up at the sky, it may seem as if there is no way to tell how far away the stars are. However, astronomers have found ways to measure those distances. 🔑 **Astronomers often use parallax to measure distances to nearby stars.**

Parallax is the apparent change in position of an object when you look at it from different places. Astronomers can measure the parallax of nearby stars to determine their distances.

Vocabulary
- parallax • universe
- light-year • scientific notation

Skills
- Reading: Summarize
- Inquiry: Calculate

FIGURE 1 ···

Parallax of Stars

The apparent movement of a star when seen from a different position is called parallax. Note that the diagram is not to scale.

CHALLENGE **Hold a finger about half an arm's length away from your face, as shown in the picture below. Switch back and forth between closing your left and right eye and watch how your finger appears to move against the background. Why does your finger seem to move? How is this related to the parallax of stars?** SC.8.N.1.6

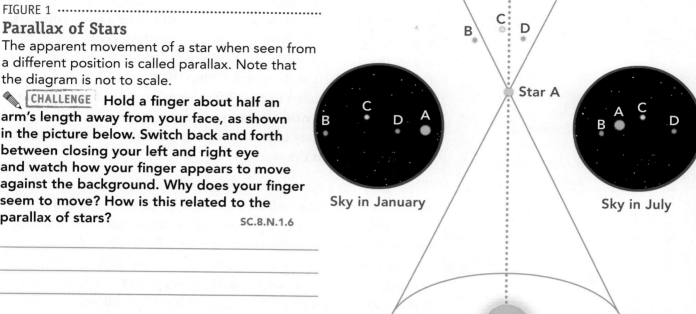

Star A

Sky in January

Sky in July

January

July

As shown in **Figure 1,** astronomers look at a nearby star when Earth is on one side of the sun. Then they look at the same star again six months later, when Earth is on the opposite side of the sun. Astronomers measure how much the nearby star appears to move against a background of stars that are much farther away. They can then use this measurement to calculate the distance to the nearby star. The less the nearby star appears to move, the farther away it is.

Astronomers can use parallax to measure distances up to a few hundred light-years from Earth. The parallax of any star that is farther away is too small to measure accurately.

Lab zone Do the Quick Lab
How Far Is That Star?

🔑 Assess Your Understanding

got it? ···

- ○ **I get it!** Now I know that astronomers often measure the distances to nearby stars using _____, which is _____
  _____
  _____

- ○ **I need extra help with** _____
  _____

Go to MY SCIENCE **COACH** *online for help with this subject.* SC.8.N.1.6, SC.8.E.5.1

95

 **FLORIDA** NGSSS

SC.8.E.5.1 Recognize that there are enormous distances between objects in space and apply our knowledge of light and space travel to understand this distance.

LA.8.2.2.3 The student will organize information to show understanding (e.g., summarizing).

✏️

🔵 **Summarize** Explain why astronomers use scientific notation to describe sizes.

_____

_____

_____

LA.8.2.2.3

do the math!

Scientific Notation

To express a number in scientific notation, first insert a decimal point in the original number so you have a number between one and ten. Then count the number of places that the decimal point moved. That gives you the power of ten.

1 ✏️ **Calculate** The sun takes about 220,000,000 years to revolve once around the center of the galaxy. Express this length of time in scientific notation.

_____

2 ✏️ **Calculate** The distant star Deneb is thought by some astronomers to be 3,230 light-years away. Write this distance in scientific notation.

_____

MA.8.A.6.1

How Do Astronomers Describe the Scale of the Universe?

Astronomers define the **universe** as all of space and everything in it. The universe is enormous, almost beyond imagination. Astronomers study objects as close as the moon and as far away as quasars. They study incredibly large objects, such as clusters of galaxies that are millions of light-years across. They also study the behavior of tiny particles, such as the atoms within the stars. 🔵 **Since the numbers astronomers use are often very large or very small, they frequently use scientific notation to describe sizes and distances in the universe. They use a unit called the light-year to measure distances between the stars.**

The Light-Year Distances to the stars are so large that meters are not very practical units. In space, light travels at a speed of about 300,000,000 meters per second. A **light-year** is the distance that light travels in one year, about 9.46 trillion kilometers.

The light-year is a unit of distance, not time. To understand this better, consider an example. If you bicycle at 10 kilometers per hour, it would take you 1 hour to go to a mall 10 kilometers away. You could say that the mall is "1 bicycle-hour" away.

Scientific Notation **Scientific notation** uses powers of ten to write very large or very small numbers in shorter form. Each number is written as the product of a number between 1 and 10 and a power of 10. For example: 1,200 is written as 1.2×10^3.

One light-year is about 9,460,000,000,000,000 meters. To express this number in scientific notation, first insert a decimal point in the original number so that you have a number between one and ten. In this case, the rounded number is 9.5. To determine the power of ten, count the number of places that the decimal point moved. Since there are 15 digits after the first digit, in scientific notation this number can now be written as 9.5×10^{15} meters.

The Immensity of Space The objects in the universe vary greatly in their distance from Earth. To understand the scale of these distances, imagine that you are going on a journey through the universe. Refer to **Figure 2** as you take your imaginary trip. Start on Earth. Now shift to the right and change the scale by 100,000,000,000, or 10^{11}. You're now close to the sun, which is located 1.5×10^{11} meters away. As you move from left to right across **Figure 2,** the distance increases. The nearest star to our sun, Alpha Centauri, is 4.2×10^{16} meters or 4.3 light-years away. The nearest galaxy to the Milky Way, the Andromeda galaxy, is about 2.4×10^{22} meters away.

FIGURE 2 ......

> INTERACTIVE ART **Scale of the Universe**
Scientists often use scientific notation to help describe the vast distances in space. The sun is 1.5×10^{11} m away from Earth, but the next star, Alpha Centauri, is 4.2×10^{16} m away, almost 300,000 times as far.

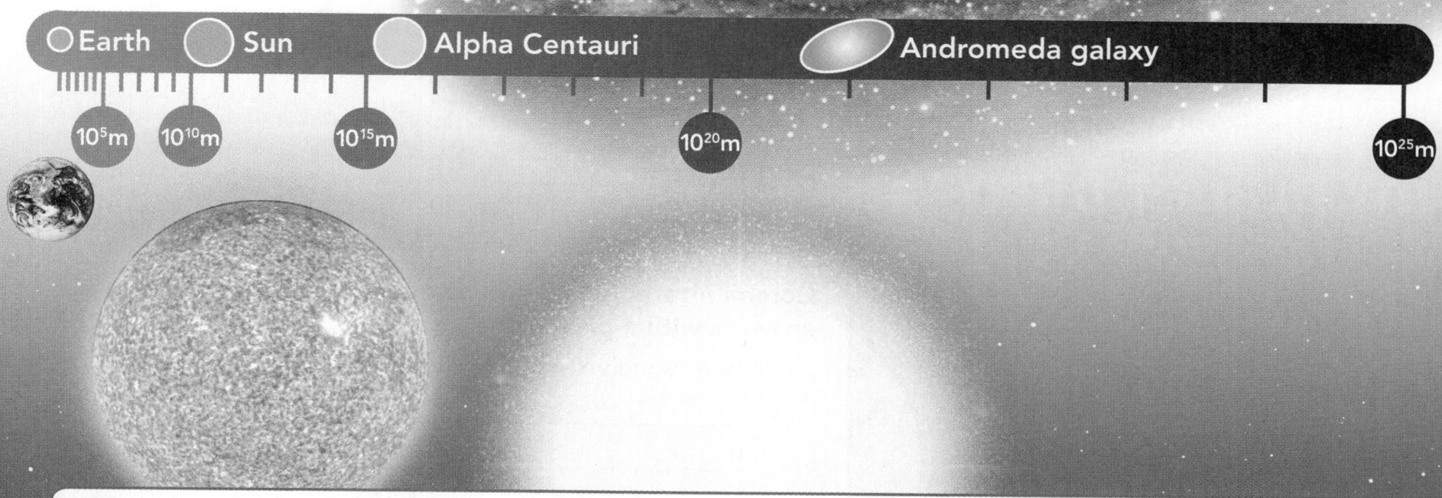

Earth | Sun | Alpha Centauri | Andromeda galaxy

10^5m | 10^{10}m | 10^{15}m | 10^{20}m | 10^{25}m

Calculate Express the distances to the sun and Alpha Centauri in meters by writing out all the zeroes in the number.

Sun: _____

Alpha Centauri: _____

Lab zone® Do the Quick Lab *Measuring the Universe.*

Assess Your Understanding

1a. Review What is scientific notation?

_____

SC.8.E.5.1

b. Explain How is scientific notation useful to astronomers?

_____

SC.8.E.5.1

c. Apply Knowledge The Andromeda galaxy is 2,200,000 light-years away. Write that measurement using scientific notation.

_____

SC.8.E.5.1

got it? ......

○ **I get it!** Now I know that to describe the scale of the universe, astronomers use _____

○ **I need extra help with** _____

Go to MY SCIENCE ⓢ COACH *online for help with this subject.*

SC.8.E.5.1

LESSON

2 Star Systems and Galaxies

UNLOCK THE ESSENTIAL ?

🔑 **What Are the Differences Between the Planets and Stars?**
SC.8.E.5.2, SC.8.E.5.3, LA.8.4.2.2

🔑 **What Are the Major Types of Galaxies?**
SC.8.E.5.2, SC.8.E.5.3

my pLANeT DiaRY for Florida

BLOG

Posted by: Sarah
Location: Interlachen, Florida

Exactly how many stars are there in the universe? This question often puzzles me as I sit in the cool night air gazing at the blanket of stars overhead. Upon glancing through the telescope I can pick out the constellations Ursa Major, Leo, Orion, and a few others. Each time I turn to look at them I always feel closer than I actually am. Even though I must end my night-time star watching, I know they will always be there the next night.

Communicate Answer these questions. Discuss your answers with a partner.

1. Where you live, what can you see in the night sky?

_____

_____

2. Why does Sarah need a telescope to pick out some constellations?

_____

_____

_____

_____

▷ **PLANET DIARY** Go to **Planet Diary** to learn more about galaxies.

Lab® zone Do the Inquiry Warm-Up *Why Does the Milky Way Look Hazy?*

FLORIDA NGSSS

SC.8.E.5.2 Recognize that the universe contains many billions of galaxies and that each galaxy contains many billions of stars.

SC.8.E.5.3 Distinguish the relationships between planets and other astronomical bodies relative to solar system, galaxy, and universe, including distance, size, and composition.

LA.8.4.2.2 The student will record information related to a topic.

What Are the Differences Between Planets and Stars?

Earth seems like a large place, but it is tiny compared to the sun, which is tiny compared to the whole solar system. The solar system is a speck in a much larger galaxy. Our galaxy is small compared to the universe. The universe is all of space and everything in it. It is so large it takes light billions of years to cross only a part of it.

Vocabulary
- star • planet • solar system • binary star • galaxy
- spiral galaxy • elliptical galaxy • irregular galaxy
- quasar

Skills
↻ Reading: Outline
▲ Inquiry: Classify

Stars and Planets Compared A **star** is a giant ball of gas, primarily hydrogen and helium, which undergoes nuclear fusion. Our sun is an example of a star. A **planet** is an object that orbits a star, is large enough to have become rounded by its own gravity, and has cleared the area of its orbit. Earth is an example of a planet.

🔑 **Made mostly of gas as opposed to solids and liquids, most stars are much larger and hotter than planets.** The sun's diameter is 100 times that of Earth. If the sun were hollow, a million Earths would fit inside. But the sun is small compared to the vastness of outer space. The distance from Earth to the sun is about 100 times the diameter of the sun!

A **solar system** contains a star and the planets and other objects that revolve around the star. Solar systems are also called planetary systems. Our solar system contains the sun, Earth, and planets and objects that revolve around the sun. The farthest planet from the sun, Neptune, is 30 times as far away from the sun as Earth.

Not all planets are made up of the same material. Some planets in our solar system are made mostly of rocky and metallic materials, but others are mostly liquid and gas. Furthermore, the outer planets are huge compared to the inner planets. Jupiter's radius is over 11 times as long as Earth's.

✎

↻ **Outline** Use the text on these pages to complete the following outline.
Astronomical Bodies
1. Stars
    a. sun
    b. composed of _____
    c. undergoes nuclear fusion
2. _____
    a. _____
    b. composed of rock or liquid and gas
    c. orbit stars

LA.8.4.2.2

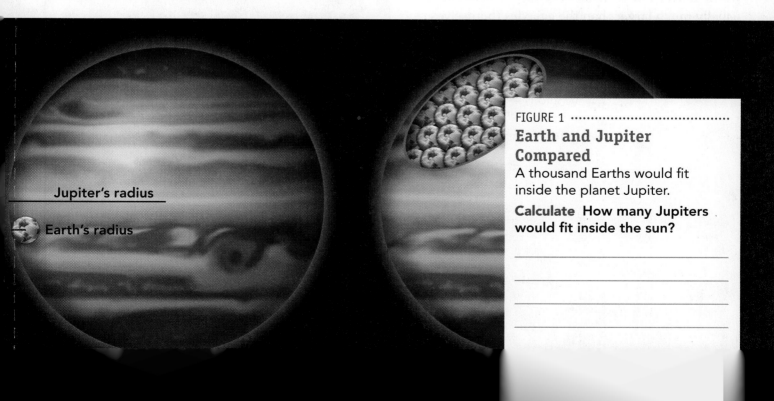

Jupiter's radius

Earth's radius

FIGURE 1
Earth and Jupiter Compared
A thousand Earths would fit inside the planet Jupiter.

Calculate How many Jupiters would fit inside the sun?

_____
_____
_____
_____

Star Systems and Galaxies Our solar system has only one star. But this is not a common situation for stars. Most stars are members of groups of two or more stars, called star systems. If you were on a planet in one of these star systems, you might see two or more suns in the sky!

Star systems that have two stars are called double stars or **binary stars.** (The prefix *bi-* means "two.") Often one star in a binary star system is much brighter and more massive than the other. Astronomers can detect the dim companion by observing the effects of its gravity. The dim star's gravity causes the bright star to wobble. Astronomers use this same method to detect planets around other stars.

Many stars belong to larger groupings of stars called star clusters. All of the stars in a particular cluster formed at around the same time and are about the same distance from Earth.

A **galaxy** is a huge group of single stars, star systems, star clusters, dust, and gas bound together by gravity. Galaxies are much larger than solar systems or star systems. Our galaxy is about 100,000 times as big as our solar system. If you could hold the solar system in your hand, then the galaxy would be about the size of the whole Earth. The distances between galaxies are usually much larger than the galaxies themselves.

Traveling Through Space

What astronomical objects are in the universe?

FIGURE 2 ···

▶ **REAL-WORLD INQUIRY** Imagine you are an astronaut on a spaceship with the mission of classifying all the large objects within the universe. Your spaceship has one top speed, 99 percent the speed of light.

Distinguish In the "Objects" column, write the letter(s) of the object(s) that fit in each category.

Characteristic	Objects
Contains gas	
Contains liquid	
Made of rock	
Consists of multiple objects	
Undergoes nuclear fusion	

Predict Would it be faster for you to travel from planet to planet within a solar system, from star to star within a galaxy, or from galaxy to galaxy within the universe? Explain.

_____

_____

_____

_____

_____

Identify Under each photo, label the object pictured. On the second line, rank the objects from largest to smallest. Use 1 for the largest object.

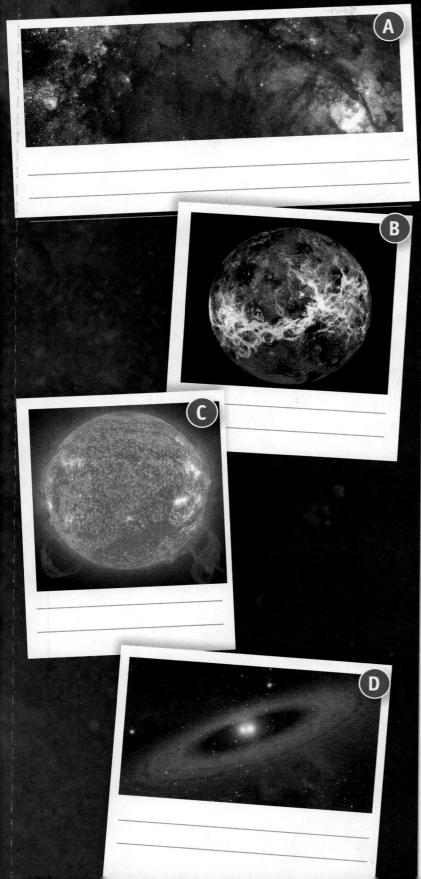

A

B

C

D

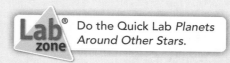
Do the Quick Lab *Planets Around Other Stars.*

Assess Your Understanding

1a. Define What is a star?

_____

_____

SC.8.E.5.3

b. Distinguish What are the main differences between a planet and a star?

_____

_____

_____

_____

_____

_____

SC.8.E.5.3

c. ANSWER THE ESSENTIAL **?** What astronomical objects are in the universe?

_____

_____

_____

_____

_____

_____

_____

SC.8.E.5.2, SC.8.E.5.3

got it? ....

○ **I get it!** Now I know that compared to

planets, stars are _____

_____

_____

○ **I need extra help with** _____

_____

_____

_____

Go to MY SCIENCE ⓢ COACH *online for help with this subject.*

SC.8.E.5.3

FLORIDA NGSSS

SC.8.E.5.2 Recognize that the universe contains many billions of galaxies and that each galaxy contains many billions of stars.

SC.8.E.5.3 Distinguish the relationships between planets and other astronomical bodies relative to solar system, galaxy, and universe, including distance, size, and composition.

What Are the Major Types of Galaxies?

There are billions of galaxies in the universe. The largest galaxies have more than a trillion stars. **Astronomers classify most galaxies into the following types: spiral, elliptical, and irregular.**

1    **2**    **3**   **4**

Spiral Galaxies

Some galaxies appear to have a bulge in the middle and arms that spiral outward, like pinwheels. These galaxies are spiral galaxies. The arms contain gas, dust, and many bright, young stars. Most new stars in spiral galaxies form in these arms. Barred-spiral galaxies have a bar-shaped area of stars and gas that passes through the center.

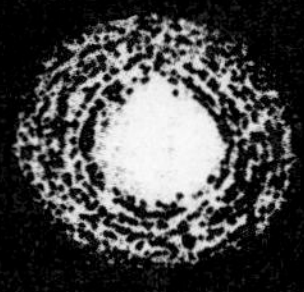

Elliptical Galaxies

Not all galaxies have spiral arms. Elliptical galaxies look like round or flattened balls. These galaxies contain billions of stars but have little gas and dust between the stars. Because there is little gas or dust, stars are no longer forming. Most elliptical galaxies contain only old stars.

Irregular Galaxies

Some galaxies do not have regular shapes. These are known as irregular galaxies. Irregular galaxies are typically smaller than other types of galaxies. They generally have many bright, young stars and lots of gas and dust to form new stars.

Quasars

Astronomers in the 1960s discovered distant, extremely bright objects that looked like stars. Since *quasi* means "as if" in Latin, these objects were called quasi-stellar objects, or quasars. Quasars are active young galaxies with huge black holes at their centers. Gas spins around the black hole, heats up, and glows.

FIGURE 3 ···

Types of Galaxies

Classify **Identify the four galaxies shown on these pages and explain.**

A _____

_____

B _____

_____

C _____

_____

D _____

A

○ Spiral   ○ Elliptical

○ Irregular   ○ Quasar

apply it!

Our solar system is located in a galaxy called the Milky Way. From the side, the Milky Way would look like a narrow disk with a large bulge in the middle. But from the top or bottom, the Milky Way would have a pinwheel shape. You can't see the shape of the Milky Way from Earth because our solar system is inside one of the arms.

When you see the Milky Way at night during the summer, you are looking toward the center of our galaxy. The center of the galaxy is about 25,000 light-years away, but it is hidden from view by large clouds of dust and gas. But astronomers can study the center using X-rays, infrared radiation, and radio waves.

✎ **Draw Conclusions** What kind of galaxy is the Milky Way? Explain why and draw a sketch of what the Milky Way might look like from outside.

_____

_____

_____

_____

B
○ Spiral   ○ Elliptical
○ Irregular   ○ Quasar

C
○ Spiral   ○ Elliptical
○ Irregular   ○ Quasar

D
○ Spiral   ○ Elliptical
○ Irregular   ○ Quasar

Lab zone ® Do the Quick Lab *A Spiral Galaxy*.

🔑 Assess Your Understanding

got it? ....

○ **I get it!** Now I know that astronomers classify most galaxies into one of the following three types: _____

_____

○ **I need extra help with** _____

_____

Go to MY SCIENCE ⓢ COACH *online for help with this subject.*   SC.8.E.5.2, SC.8.E.5.3

Gravity and Motion

UNLOCK THE ESSENTIAL ?

🔑 **What Determines Gravity?**
SC.8.E.5.4

🔑 **What Keeps Objects in Orbit?**
SC.8.E.5.4, MA.6.A.3.6

🔑 **How Does Gravity Help Form Planets, Stars, and Solar Systems?**
SC.8.E.5.4

MY PLANET DIARY

Gravity Assists

You might think that gravity only brings objects down. But gravity can also speed things up and send them flying! If a space probe comes close to a planet, the planet's gravity changes the probe's path. Engineers plan space missions to take advantage of these "gravity assists." A gravity assist can shorten the probe's interplanetary trip by many years. The diagram shows how the probe *Voyager 2* used gravity assists to visit all four outer planets!

TECHNOLOGY

Use what you know about gravity to answer this question.

How does a planet's gravity change the path of a space probe?

_____

_____

_____

> PLANET DIARY Go to **Planet Diary** to learn more about gravity.

Path of spacecraft

Lab zone Do the Inquiry Warm-Up *What Factors Affect Gravity?*

FLORIDA NGSSS

SC.8.E.5.4 Explore the Law of Universal Gravitation by explaining the role that gravity plays in the formation of planets, stars, and solar systems and in determining their motions.

What Determines Gravity?

Earth revolves around the sun in a nearly circular **orbit,** which is the path of an object as it revolves around another object in space. The moon orbits Earth in the same way. But what keeps Earth and the moon in orbit? Why don't they just fly off into space?

Newton realized that there must be a force acting between Earth and the moon that kept the moon in orbit. A **force** is a

Vocabulary

- orbit • force • gravity • law of universal gravitation
- mass • weight • inertia • Newton's first law of motion
- accretion

Skills

↻ Reading: Ask Questions
△ Inquiry: Draw Conclusions

Gravity

Newton hypothesized that the force that pulls an apple to the ground also pulls the moon toward Earth, keeping it in orbit. This force, called **gravity,** attracts all objects toward each other. Newton's **law of universal gravitation** states that every object in the universe attracts every other object. **The strength of the force of gravity between two objects depends on two factors: the masses of the objects and the distance between them.**

Gravity, Mass, and Weight

The strength of gravity depends in part on the masses of each of the objects. **Mass** is the amount of matter in an object. Because Earth is so massive, it exerts a much greater force on you than this book does.

The measure of the force of gravity on an object is called **weight.** Mass doesn't change, but an object's weight can change depending on its location. On the moon, you would weigh about one sixth as much as on Earth. This is because the moon has less mass than Earth, so the pull of the moon's gravity on you would also be less.

Gravity and Distance

Gravity is also affected by the distance between two objects. The force of gravity decreases rapidly as distance increases. If the distance between two objects doubles, the force of gravity decreases to one fourth of its original value.

FIGURE 1 ....

❯VIRTUAL LAB **Gravity, Mass, and Distance**

✎ Compare and Contrast Draw arrows showing the force of gravity in the second and third pictures.

The longer the arrow, the greater the force.

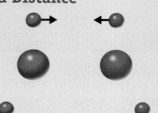

Lab zone® Do the Quick Lab
What's Doing the Pulling?

🔑 Assess Your Understanding

got it? ....

○ I get it! Now I know that the force of gravity depends on _____

_____

○ I need extra help with _____

Go to my science ⓢ coach *online for help with this subject.*

SC.8.E.5.4

FLORIDA NGSSS

SC.8.E.5.4 Explore the Law of Universal Gravitation by explaining the role that gravity plays in the formation of planets, stars, and solar systems and in determining their motions.

MA.6.A.3.6 Construct and analyze tables, graphs, and equations to describe linear functions and other simple relations using both common language and algebraic notation.

Ask Questions Before you read the paragraphs under Inertia, write a question you would like to have answered. Look for the answer as you read.

_____

_____

_____

What Keeps Objects in Orbit?

If the sun and Earth are constantly pulling on one another because of gravity, why doesn't Earth fall into the sun? Similarly, why doesn't the moon crash into Earth? The fact that such collisions have not occurred shows that there must be another factor at work. That factor is called inertia.

Inertia The tendency of an object to resist a change in motion is **inertia.** You feel the effects of inertia every day. When you are riding in a car and it stops suddenly, you keep moving forward. If you didn't have a seat belt on, your inertia could cause you to bump into the car's windshield or the seat in front of you. The more mass an object has, the greater its inertia. An object with greater inertia is more difficult to start or stop.

Isaac Newton stated his ideas about inertia as a scientific law. **Newton's first law of motion** says that an object at rest will stay at rest and an object in motion will stay in motion with a constant speed and direction unless acted on by a force.

Orbital Motion Why do Earth and the moon remain in orbit? **Newton concluded that inertia and gravity combine to keep Earth in orbit around the sun and the moon in orbit around Earth.** You can see how this occurs in **Figure 2.**

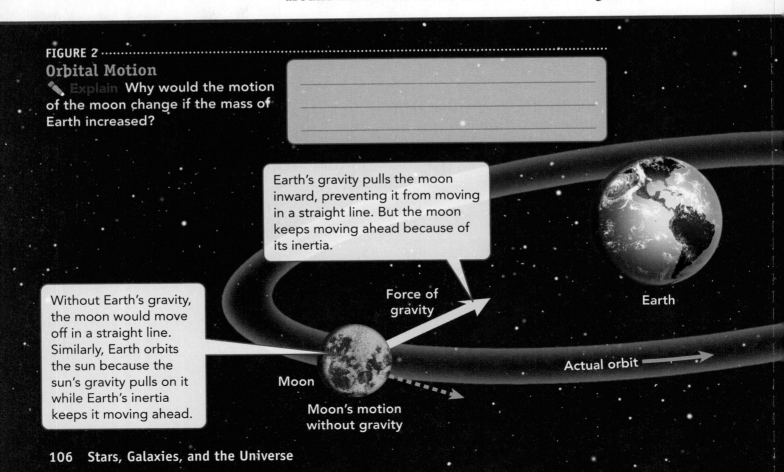

FIGURE 2
Orbital Motion
Explain Why would the motion of the moon change if the mass of Earth increased?

_____

_____

_____

Earth's gravity pulls the moon inward, preventing it from moving in a straight line. But the moon keeps moving ahead because of its inertia.

Without Earth's gravity, the moon would move off in a straight line. Similarly, Earth orbits the sun because the sun's gravity pulls on it while Earth's inertia keeps it moving ahead.

Force of gravity

Earth

Moon

Actual orbit

Moon's motion without gravity

do the math! Analyzing Data

Gravity Versus Distance

As a rocket leaves a planet's surface, the force of gravity between the rocket and the planet changes. Use the graph to answer the questions below.

1 **Read Graphs** The variables being graphed

are _____

and _____

2 **Read Graphs** What is the force of gravity on the rocket at the planet's surface?

_____

3 **Read Graphs** What is the force of gravity on the rocket at two units (twice the planet's radius from its center)?

_____

4 **Draw Conclusions** In general, how does the force of gravity on the rocket change as its distance from the planet increases?

_____

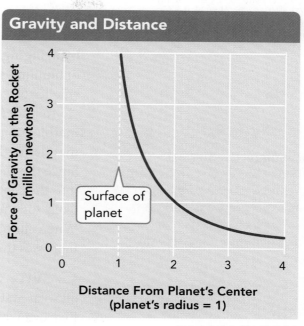

Gravity and Distance

Force of Gravity on the Rocket (million newtons) vs. Distance From Planet's Center (planet's radius = 1)

Surface of planet

MA.6.A.3.6, MA.8.A.1.1

Lab zone Do the Quick Lab *Around and Around We Go.*

🔑 Assess Your Understanding

1a. Identify What two factors keep a planet in orbit around the sun?

_____

SC.8.E.5.4

b. **Draw Conclusions** What keeps Earth from falling into the sun?

_____

SC.8.E.5.4

c. CHALLENGE How would a planet move if the sun suddenly disappeared? Explain.

_____

_____

_____

_____

SC.8.E.5.4

got it? ....

○ **I get it!** Now I know that objects are kept in orbit by _____

○ **I need extra help with** _____

Go to MY SCIENCE ⓢ COACH *online for help with this subject.*

SC.8.E.5.4

FLORIDA NGSSS

SC.8.E.5.4 Explore the Law of Universal Gravitation by explaining the role that gravity plays in the formation of planets, stars, and solar systems and in determining their motions.

How Does Gravity Help Form Planets, Stars, and Solar Systems?

How do astronomical objects, such as galaxies and solar systems, form? **Scientists think that gravity helps form solar systems by bringing material together in a gradual buildup.** The process of building something up gradually by the gathering together of smaller pieces is called **accretion.**

To understand how gravity contributes to accretion, think of marbles on a rubber sheet, as shown in **Figure 3.** A group of marbles in the center of a rubber sheet will cause the sheet to curve. Since the sheet is curved, a rolling marble is more likely to roll into the center. This bends the sheet more, making it even more likely for a marble to roll into the center, and the process continues. When chunks of material get mashed together, their increased mass increases their gravitational pull, attracting more material.

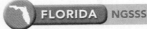

Vocabulary Latin Word Origins *Accretion* comes from the Latin root *crescere*, which means "to grow." Based on the word *crescere* and its meaning, think of another English word that has this root.

Gravity Forms Solar Systems

Scientists think that all solar systems begin as clouds of materials. The clouds include hydrogen, helium, rock, ice, and other materials. The law of universal gravitation states that every object in the universe attracts every other object. So for any solar system to form, gravity must pull the cloud's material together. As the cloud collapses and starts to rotate, it forms a spinning disk.

FIGURE 3

ART IN MOTION **Gravity and Solar Systems**

Marbles on a rubber sheet can be used to model how the gravitational pull of an object increases as it increases in mass. Explain **In each case, draw the path that the marble is likely to take if it is pushed in the direction shown. Then use the space at the right to explain why the path of the marble will change.**

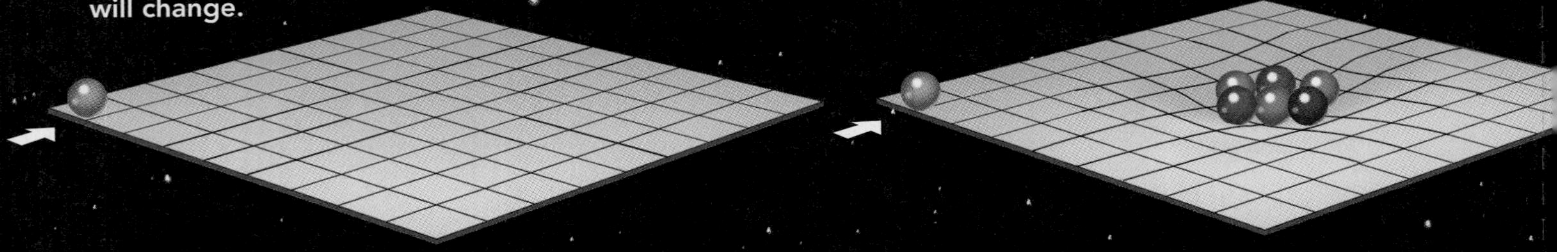

Gravity Forms Stars

Most of the material in the spinning disk is pulled to the center. The material becomes tightly packed as it undergoes accretion. It gets hotter and the pressure on it increases. Eventually, the pressure on it gets so high that hydrogen atoms are fused together to form helium. This process, called nuclear fusion, is what causes a star to release energy once it has formed. Nuclear fusion in a star gives off heat and light.

Gravity Forms Planets

Some of the material in the spinning disk remains outside the star and begins to form into planets. Gravity pulls rock, ices, and gas together. The rock and ice form small bodies as they collide and stick together. Eventually these small bodies combine to form not only planets but all other bodies in a solar system.

Gravity Keeps Solar Systems Together

Why don't the planets of a solar system fly away into space? As you have learned, gravity plays an important role. The star at the center of a solar system exerts a large gravitational force on all the other objects in the solar system. The gravity of the star keeps the other objects from flying away, and so they stay in orbits around the star.

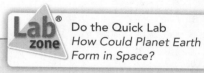

Lab zone® Do the Quick Lab *How Could Planet Earth Form in Space?*

🔑 Assess Your Understanding

2a. Identify What is accretion?

_____

_____

_____

SC.8.E.5.4

b. Draw Conclusions What would happen to a solar system if gravity suddenly stopped working?

_____

_____

_____

SC.8.E.5.4

got it?..........................

O **I get it!** Now I know that gravity helps form planets, stars, and solar systems by _____

_____

O **I need extra help with** _____

_____

Go to **my science** 💬 **coach** online for help with this subject. SC.8.E.5.4

 **LESSON**

4 Characteristics of Stars

 UNLOCK THE ESSENTIAL ?

🔑 **How Are Stars Classified?**
SC.8.N.1.6, SC.8.E.5.5

🔑 **What Is an H-R Diagram and How Do Astronomers Use It?**
SC.8.N.1.5, SC.8.N.1.6, SC.8.N.2.2, SC.8.E.5.5

my planeT DiaRY

CAREERS

Black Holes

If you were an astronomer, you might study some of the strangest objects in the universe. For almost 100 years, scientists believed that some stars became black holes when they died. But a black hole is an object with gravity so strong that not even light can escape. So scientists couldn't prove that black holes existed because they couldn't see them. Eventually, astronomers discovered a way to prove black holes exist. They realized that they could detect the matter being pulled into the black hole. That matter reaches such high temperatures that it releases X-rays. In the 1960s, astronomers launched a rocket to record X-rays from outer space. On this first mission, they found evidence for black holes!

Communicate Answer the questions below. Then discuss your answers with a partner.

1. Why was it so hard to prove that black holes exist?

_____

_____

_____

_____

2. What subjects, other than astronomy, would astronomers have to study in order to discover black holes?

_____

_____

_____

> PLANET DIARY Go to **Planet Diary** to learn more about characteristics of stars.

 Lab zone® Do the Inquiry Warm-Up *How Stars Differ.*

Vocabulary
- spectrograph • apparent brightness
- absolute brightness • Hertzsprung-Russell diagram
- main sequence

Skills
- Reading: Identify the Main Idea
- Inquiry: Infer

How Are Stars Classified?

All stars are huge spheres of glowing gas. Made up mostly of hydrogen, stars produce energy through the process of nuclear fusion. Astronomers classify stars according to their physical characteristics. **Characteristics used to classify stars include color, temperature, size, composition, and brightness.**

Color and Temperature If you look at the night sky, you can see slight differences in the colors of the stars. Some stars look reddish. Others are yellow or blue-white, as shown in **Figure 1.**

A star's color reveals its surface temperature. The coolest stars—with a surface temperature of about 3,200°C—appear red. Our yellow sun has a surface temperature of about 5,500°C. The hottest stars, with surface temperatures of over 20,000°C, appear bluish.

Size When you look at stars in the sky, they all appear to be points of light of the same size. Many stars are actually about the size of the sun. However, some stars are much larger than the sun. Very large stars are called giant stars or supergiant stars.

Most stars are smaller than the sun. White dwarf stars are about the size of Earth. Neutron stars are even smaller, about 20 kilometers in diameter.

FLORIDA NGSSS

SC.8.N.1.6 Understand that scientific investigations involve the collection of relevant empirical evidence, the use of logical reasoning, and the application of imagination in devising hypotheses, predictions, explanations and models to make sense of the collected evidence.

SC.8.E.5.5 Describe and classify specific physical properties of stars: apparent magnitude (brightness), temperature (color), size, and luminosity (absolute brightness).

Identify the Main Idea
Write a sentence that says what the color of a star indicates.

FIGURE 1
Star Color and Temperature
Stars vary in size, color, and temperature.
Draw Conclusions Which of the four stars shown has the highest temperature? Why?

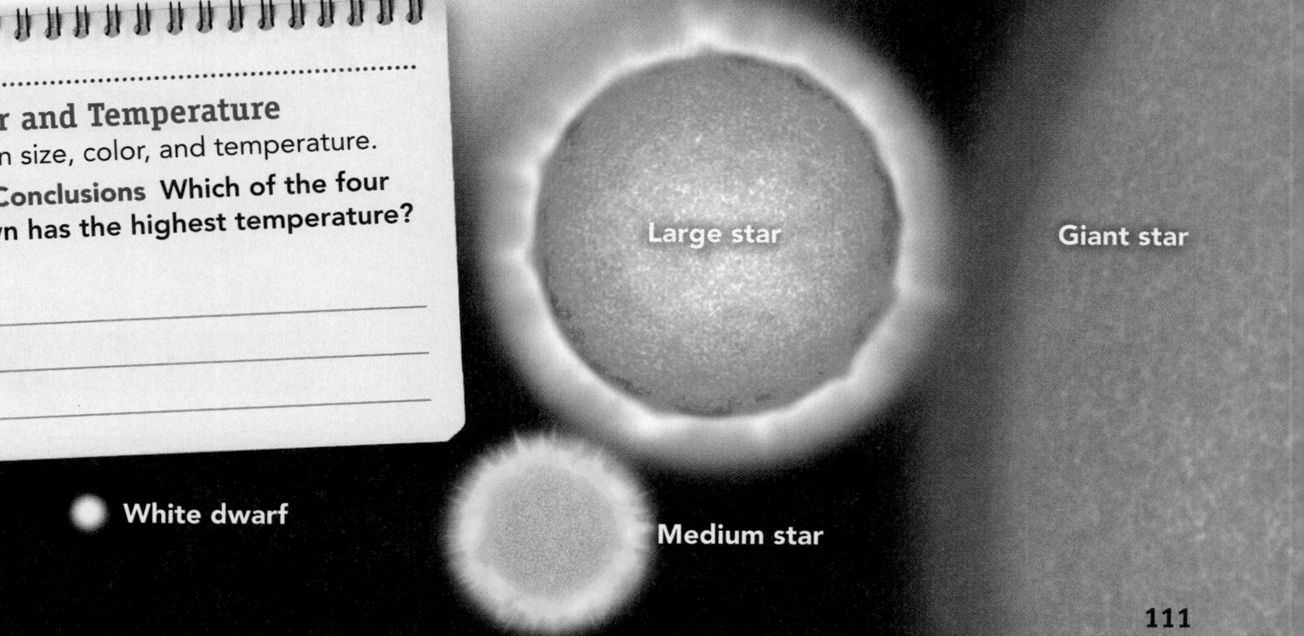

Large star

Giant star

White dwarf

Medium star

111

Chemical Composition Stars vary in their chemical composition. The chemical composition of most stars is about 73 percent hydrogen, 25 percent helium, and 2 percent other elements by mass. This is close to the composition of the sun.

Astronomers use spectrographs to determine the elements found in stars. A **spectrograph** (SPEK truh graf) is a device that breaks light into colors and produces an image of the resulting spectrum. Today, most large telescopes have spectrographs to analyze light.

The gases in a star's atmosphere absorb some wavelengths of light produced within the star. When the star's light is seen through a spectrograph, each absorbed wavelength is shown as a dark line on a spectrum. Each chemical element absorbs light at particular wavelengths. Just as each person has a unique set of fingerprints, each element has a unique set of spectral lines for a given temperature.

Alnitak
approximately
800
light-years away

Alnilam
approximately
1,300
light-years away

apply it!

The lines on the spectrums below are from four different elements. By comparing a star's spectrum with the spectrums of known elements, astronomers can infer each element found in the star. Each star's spectrum is an overlap of the spectrums from the individual elements.

Infer Identify the elements with the strongest lines in Stars A, B, and C.

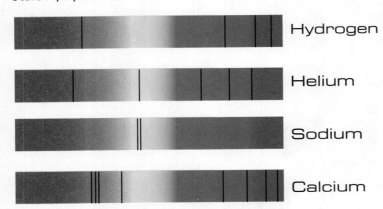

Hydrogen

Helium

Sodium

Calcium

A

_____

_____

B

_____

_____

C

_____

_____

Brightness of Stars

Stars also differ in brightness, the amount of light they give off. 🔑 **The brightness of a star depends on both its size and temperature.** A larger star tends to be brighter than a smaller star. A hotter star tends to be brighter than a cooler star.

How bright a star appears depends on both its distance from Earth and how bright the star truly is. Because of these two factors, the brightness of a star is described in two ways: apparent brightness and absolute brightness.

Apparent Brightness A star's **apparent brightness** or apparent magnitude is its brightness as seen from Earth. Astronomers can measure this fairly easily using electronic devices. However, astronomers can't tell how much light a star gives off just from the star's apparent brightness. Just as a flashlight looks brighter the closer it is to you, a star looks brighter the closer it is to Earth. For example, the sun looks very bright. This does not mean that the sun gives off more light than all other stars. The sun looks so bright simply because it is so close.

Absolute Brightness A star's **absolute brightness** or luminosity is the brightness the star would have if it were at a standard distance from Earth. Finding absolute brightness is more complex than finding its apparent brightness. An astronomer must first find out both the star's apparent brightness and its distance from Earth. The astronomer can then calculate the star's absolute brightness. Astronomers have found that the absolute brightness of stars can vary tremendously. The brightest stars are more than a billion times brighter than the dimmest stars!

FIGURE 2 ....

Apparent and Absolute Brightness

The three stars Alnitak, Alnilam, and Mintaka in the constellation Orion all seem to have the same apparent brightness from Earth. But Alnilam is actually farther away than the other two stars.

✏️ **CHALLENGE** Which star has the greatest absolute brightness? How do you know?

_____

_____

_____

_____

SC.8.N.1.6

Mintaka
approximately
900
light-years away

Lab zone® Do the Lab Investigation *Chemical Composition of the Spectrum.*

🔑 **Assess Your Understanding**

got it? ....

○ **I get it!** Now I know that stars are classified by _____

_____

_____

○ **I need extra help with** _____

_____

Go to MY SCIENCE 🅢 COACH *online for help with this subject.* SC.8.N.1.6, SC.8.E.5.5

What Is an H-R Diagram and How Do Astronomers Use It?

About 100 years ago, two scientists working independently made the same discovery. Both Ejnar Hertzsprung (EYE nahr HURT sprung) in Denmark and Henry Norris Russell in the United States made graphs to find out if the temperature and the absolute brightness of stars are related. They plotted the surface temperatures of stars on the *x*-axis and their absolute brightness on the *y*-axis. The points formed a pattern. The graph they made is still used by astronomers today. It is called the **Hertzsprung-Russell diagram,** or H-R diagram.

SC.8.N.1.5 Analyze the methods used to develop scientific explanations.

SC.8.N.1.6 Understand that scientific investigations involve the collection of relevant empirical evidence, the use of logical reasoning, and the application of imagination in devising hypotheses, predictions, explanations and models to make sense of the collected evidence.

SC.8.N.2.2 Discuss what characterizes science and its methods.

SC.8.E.5.5 Describe and classify specific physical properties of stars: apparent magnitude (brightness), temperature (color), size, and luminosity (absolute brightness).

FIGURE 3 ···

Hertzsprung-Russell Diagram

The H-R diagram shows the relationship between surface temperature and absolute brightness of stars.

✎ **Interpret Diagrams** Place the stars listed in the table on the diagram, and note on the table the classification of each star.　SC.8.N.1.5, SC.8.N.1.6

H-R DIAGRAM

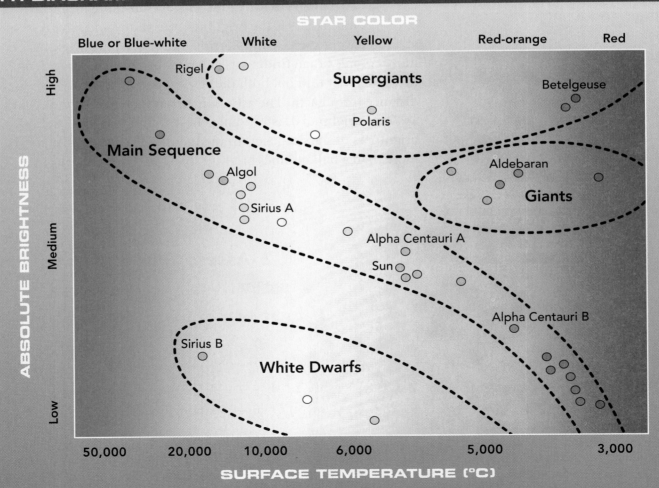

🔑 **Astronomers use H-R diagrams to classify stars and to understand how stars change over time.** As shown in **Figure 3,** most of the stars in the H-R diagram form a diagonal area called the **main sequence.** More than 90 percent of all stars, including the sun, are main-sequence stars. Within the main sequence, the surface temperature increases as absolute brightness increases. Thus, hot bluish stars are located at the left of an H-R diagram and cooler reddish stars are located at the right of the diagram.

The brightest stars are located near the top of an H-R diagram, while the dimmest stars are located at the bottom. Giant and supergiant stars are very bright. They can be found near the top center and right of the diagram. White dwarfs are hot, but not very bright, so they appear at either the bottom left or bottom center of the diagram.

Lab zone ® Do the Quick Lab
Interpreting the H-R Diagram.

🔑 **Assess Your Understanding**

1a. Review What two characteristics of stars are shown in an H-R diagram?

_____

_____

_____

SC.8.N.1.6, SC.8.E.5.5

b. Explain What is the relationship between brightness and temperature shown within the main sequence?

_____

_____

_____

_____

SC.8.E.5.5

c. Classify The star Procyon B has a surface temperature of 7,500°C and a low absolute brightness. What type of star is it?

_____

_____

SC.8.E.5.5

got it? ....

○ **I get it!** Now I know that astronomers use

H-R diagrams to _____

_____

_____

○ **I need extra help with** _____

_____

Go to **my science coach**
online for help with this subject.
SC.8.N.2.2, SC.8.E.5.5

STAR A	
Color	Red-orange
Temperature	5,000°C
Brightness	High
Type	

STAR B	
Color	Yellow
Temperature	6,000°C
Brightness	Medium
Type	

STAR C	
Color	White
Temperature	10,000°C
Brightness	Low
Type	

Lives of Stars

UNLOCK THE ESSENTIAL ?

🔑 **How Does a Star Form and What Determines Its Life Span?**
SC.8.E.5.5, LA.8.2.2.3

🔑 **What Happens to a Star When It Runs Out of Fuel?**
SC.8.E.5.5

MY PLANET DIARY

DISCOVERY

The Supernova of 1054

In the summer of 1054, some Chinese astronomers noticed a "guest star" in the night sky. The star was so bright people could see it during the day! The star remained visible for almost two years. How did these ancient astronomers interpret it? Was it a sign that the emperor would be visited by an important guest? People from around the world recorded and interpreted the event differently. Almost 1,000 years later, scientists realized the "guest star" was the explosion of a giant star 4,000 light-years away. So powerful was the explosion that all life within about 50 light-years would have been wiped out. Now called Supernova 1054, its remains are known as the Crab Nebula.

Communicate Discuss the supernova with a partner and answer the questions below.

1. Why was Supernova 1054 so notable?

_____

_____

_____

_____

2. How do you think ancient astronomers might have interpreted the event differently than astronomers today?

_____

_____

▷ PLANET DIARY Go to **Planet Diary** to learn more about stars.

Lab zone® Do the Inquiry Warm-Up *What Determines How Long Stars Live?*

Vocabulary
- nebula • protostar • white dwarf • supernova
- neutron star • pulsar • black hole

Skills
↻ Reading: Compare and Contrast
△ Inquiry: Predict

How Does a Star Form and What Determines Its Life Span?

FLORIDA NGSSS

SC.8.E.5.5 Describe and classify specific physical properties of stars: apparent magnitude (brightness), temperature (color), size, and luminosity (absolute brightness).

LA.8.2.2.3 The student will organize information to show understanding (e.g., summarizing).

Stars do not last forever. Each star is born, goes through its life cycle, and eventually dies. (Of course, stars are not really alive. The words *born, live,* and *die* are just helpful comparisons.) ⚷ **A star is born when the contracting gas and dust from a nebula become so dense and hot that nuclear fusion starts. How long a star lives depends on its mass.**

A Star Is Born All stars begin their lives as parts of nebulas, such as the one in **Figure 1**. A **nebula** is a large cloud of gas and dust spread out in an immense volume. A star, on the other hand, is made up of a large amount of gas in a relatively small volume.

In the densest part of a nebula, gravity pulls gas and dust together. A contracting cloud of gas and dust with enough mass to form a star is called a **protostar.** *Proto-* means "first" in Greek, so a protostar is the first stage of a star's life.

Recall that nuclear fusion is the process by which atoms combine to form heavier atoms. In the sun, for example, hydrogen atoms combine to form helium. During nuclear fusion, enormous amounts of energy are released. Nuclear fusion begins in a protostar.

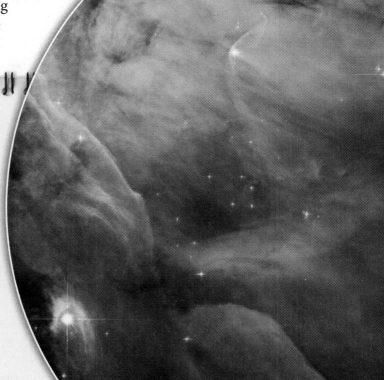

FIGURE 1 ·······································

A Stellar Nursery
New stars are forming in the nebula.

✎ **Describe** Summarize the process of star formation.   LA.8.2.2.3

_____

_____

_____

_____

_____

_____

_____

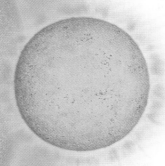

Lifetimes of Stars

How long a star lives depends on the star's mass. You might think that stars with more mass would last longer than stars with less mass. But the reverse is true. You can think of stars as being like cars. A small car has a small gas tank, but it also has a small engine that burns gas slowly. A large car has a larger gas tank, but it also has a larger engine that burns gas rapidly. So the small car can travel farther on a tank of gas than the larger car. Small-mass stars use up their fuel more slowly than large-mass stars, so they have much longer lives.

Generally, stars that have less mass than the sun use their fuel slowly, and can live for up to 200 billion years. A medium-mass star like the sun will live for about 10 billion years. The sun is about 4.6 billion years old, so it is about halfway through its lifetime. In **Figure 2,** the yellow star is similar to the sun.

Stars that have more mass than the sun have shorter lifetimes. A star that is more massive than the sun, such as the blue star shown in **Figure 2,** may live only about 10 million years. That may seem like a very long time, but it is only one tenth of one percent of the lifetime of the sun.

FIGURE 2 ·····························

Life of a Star
A star's lifetime depends on its mass.

✎ **Explain** The yellow star has much less mass than the blue star and so will live longer. Explain why.

_____

_____

_____

_____

_____

Lab zone® Do the Quick Lab
Life Cycle of Stars.

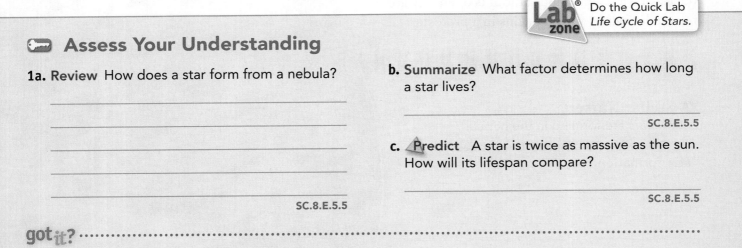

🗝 Assess Your Understanding

1a. Review How does a star form from a nebula?

_____

_____

_____

_____

SC.8.E.5.5

b. Summarize What factor determines how long a star lives?

_____

SC.8.E.5.5

c. Predict A star is twice as massive as the sun. How will its lifespan compare?

_____

SC.8.E.5.5

got it? ··

○ **I get it!** Now I know that stars are born when _____

_____

and how long a star lives depends on _____

○ **I need extra help with** _____

Go to **MY SCIENCE ⓢ COACH** *online for help with this subject.*

SC.8.E.5.5

What Happens to a Star When It Runs Out of Fuel?

FLORIDA NGSSS

SC.8.E.5.5 Describe and classify specific physical properties of stars: apparent magnitude (brightness), temperature (color), size, and luminosity (absolute brightness).

When a star begins to run out of fuel, its core shrinks and its outer portion expands. Depending on its mass, the star becomes either a red giant or a supergiant. Red giants and supergiants evolve in very different ways. 🗝 **After a star runs out of fuel, it becomes a white dwarf, a neutron star, or a black hole.**

White Dwarfs Low-mass stars and medium-mass stars like the sun take billions of years to use up their nuclear fuel. As they start to run out of fuel, their outer layers expand, and they become red giants. Eventually, the outer parts grow larger still and drift out into space, forming a glowing cloud of gas called a planetary nebula. The blue-white core of the star that is left behind cools and becomes a **white dwarf.**

White dwarfs are about the size of Earth, but they have about as much mass as the sun. A white dwarf is about one million times as dense as the sun. White dwarfs have no fuel, but they glow faintly from leftover energy. After billions of years, a white dwarf stops glowing. Then it is called a black dwarf.

Supernovas The life cycle of a high-mass star is quite different. These stars quickly evolve into brilliant supergiants. When a supergiant runs out of fuel, it can explode suddenly. Within hours, the star blazes millions of times brighter. The explosion is called a **supernova.** After a supernova, some of the material from the star expands into space. This material may become part of a nebula. This nebula can then contract to form a new, partly recycled star. Recall that nuclear fusion creates heavy elements. A supernova provides enough energy to create the heaviest elements. Astronomers think that the matter in the sun and the planets around it came from a gigantic supernova. If so, this means that the matter all around you was created in a star, and all matter on Earth is a form of stardust.

🖉 Compare and Contrast
How does the mass and size of a white dwarf compare with the mass and size of the sun?
○ Same mass; greater size
○ Less mass; greater size
○ Same mass; smaller size
○ Less mass; smaller size

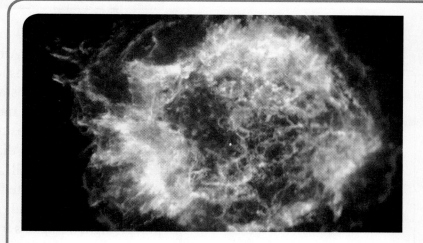

FIGURE 3 ....

Supernova Remnant Cassiopeia A
Cassiopeia A is the remnant of a once-massive star that died in a supernova explosion seen 325 years ago.

🖉 CHALLENGE **Explain the connection between your body and a supernova.**

_____

_____

_____

_____

FIGURE 4 ·······················

INTERACTIVE ART **Lives of Stars**

✎ **Relate Text and Visuals** Fill in the missing stages on the diagram. Now, think about where the sun fits on the diagram. On the lines below, describe what will happen to the sun when it runs out of fuel.

_____

_____

_____

_____

_____

_____

_____

_____

_____

_____

_____

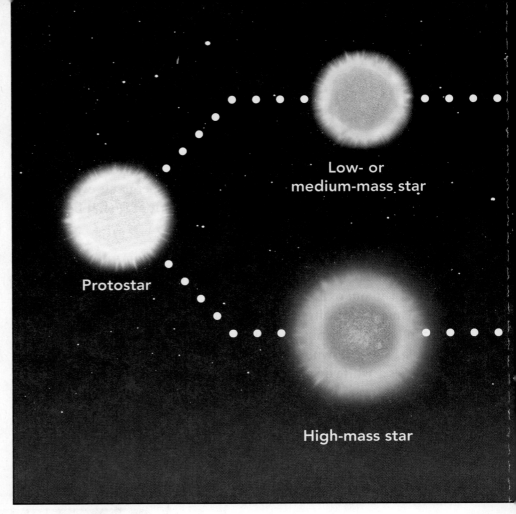

Low- or
medium-mass star

Protostar

High-mass star

apply it!

✎ **Predict** An alien civilization is in orbit around a high-mass supergiant star. Should they stay or should they go elsewhere? Why?

_____

_____

_____

_____

_____

Neutron Stars After a supergiant explodes, some of the material from the star is left behind. This material may form a neutron star. **Neutron stars** are the remains of high-mass stars. They are even smaller and denser than white dwarfs. A neutron star may contain as much as three times the mass of the sun but be only about 25 kilometers in diameter, the size of a city.

In 1967, Jocelyn Bell, a British astronomy student working with Antony Hewish, detected an object in space that appeared to give off regular pulses of radio waves. Some astronomers thought the pulses might be signals from an extraterrestrial civilization. At first, astronomers even named the source LGM, for the "Little Green Men" in early science-fiction stories. Soon, however, astronomers concluded that the source of the radio waves was really a rapidly spinning neutron star. Spinning neutron stars are called **pulsars**, short for pulsating radio sources. Some pulsars spin hundreds of times per second!

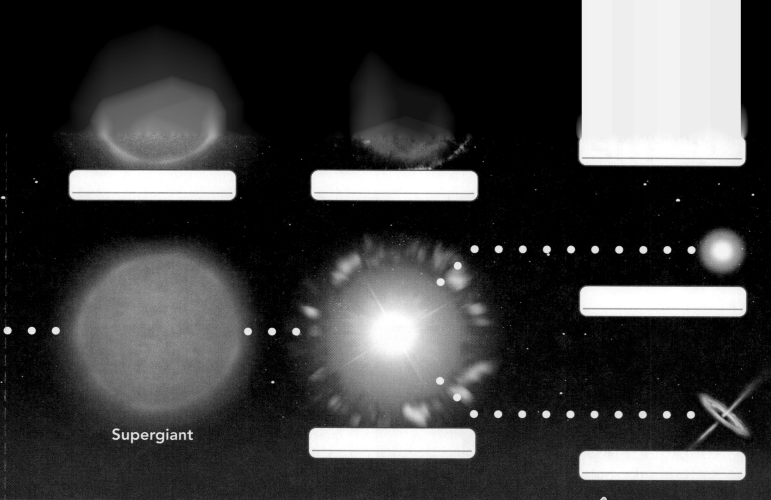

Supergiant

Black Holes

The most massive stars—those that have more than 10 times the mass of the sun—may become black holes when they die. A **black hole** is an object with gravity so strong that nothing, not even light, can escape. After a very massive star dies in a supernova explosion, more than five times the mass of the sun may be left. The gravity of this mass is so strong that the gas is pulled inward, packing the gas into a smaller and smaller space. The star's gas becomes squeezed so hard that it converts into a black hole. Its intense gravity will not allow even light to escape.

No light, radio waves, or any other form of radiation can ever get out of a black hole, so it is not possible to detect directly. But astronomers can detect black holes indirectly. For example, gas near a black hole is pulled so strongly that it revolves faster and faster around the black hole. Friction heats the gas up. Astronomers can detect X-rays coming from the hot gas and infer that a black hole is present.

 Do the Quick Lab
Death of a Star.

🔑 Assess Your Understanding

2a. Review What determines if a star becomes a white dwarf, neutron star, or black hole?

_____

SC.8.E.5.5

b. Predict Will the sun become a white dwarf, neutron star, or a black hole? Why?

_____

_____

SC.8.E.5.5

got it? ·······································

○ **I get it!** Now I know that after a star runs

out of fuel, it becomes _____

_____

_____

○ **I need extra help with** _____

Go to my science 🖥 coach *online for help with this subject.* SC.8.E.5.5

FLORIDA

LESSON

6 The Sun

UNLOCK THE ESSENTIAL ?

🔑 **What Is the Structure of the Sun?**
SC.8.E.5.6

🔑 **What Features Can You See on the Sun?**
SC.8.E.5.6

my planet Diary

DISASTER

Left in the Dark

On March 13, 1989, a flood of electric particles from the sun reached Earth, causing a magnetic storm. Bright streamers of color filled the sky as far south as Jamaica. But in Quebec, Canada, the storm brought problems. At 2:45 A.M., the entire electric power system collapsed. People woke up with no heat or light. Traffic snarled as traffic lights and subways stopped working.

How could particles from the sun take out a power system? The magnetic storm caused an electrical surge through the power lines. Electric stations couldn't handle the extra electricity, and they blew out, taking the power system with them.

✎ **Communicate** Discuss the Quebec blackout with a partner. Then answer the questions below.

1. What caused the Quebec blackout of 1989?

_____

_____

2. How would your life be affected if a magnetic storm shut down electricity in your area?

_____

_____

_____

▶ PLANET DIARY Go to **Planet Diary** to learn more about the sun.

Lab zone Do the Inquiry Warm-Up *How Can You Safely Observe the Sun?*

Vocabulary

- core • nuclear fusion • radiation zone
- convection zone • photosphere • chromosphere
- corona • solar wind • sunspot • prominence
- solar flare

Skills

↻ Reading: Relate Cause and Effect
△ Inquiry: Interpret Data

What Is the Structure of the Sun?

Unlike Earth, the sun has no solid surface. About three fourths of the sun's mass is hydrogen, and about one fourth is helium. There are tiny amounts of other elements. ⌔ **The sun has an interior and an atmosphere. The interior includes the core, the radiation zone, and the convection zone. Figure 1** shows the sun's interior.

FLORIDA   NGSSS

SC.8.E.5.6 Create models of solar properties including: rotation, structure of the Sun, convection, sunspots, solar flares, and prominences.

FIGURE 1 ···

Layers of the Sun

The diagram shows the layers of the sun's interior.

✎ **Create Models** Draw arrows to show energy as it passes from the sun's core through the radiation and convection zones. Underline clues in the text that help you determine the path.

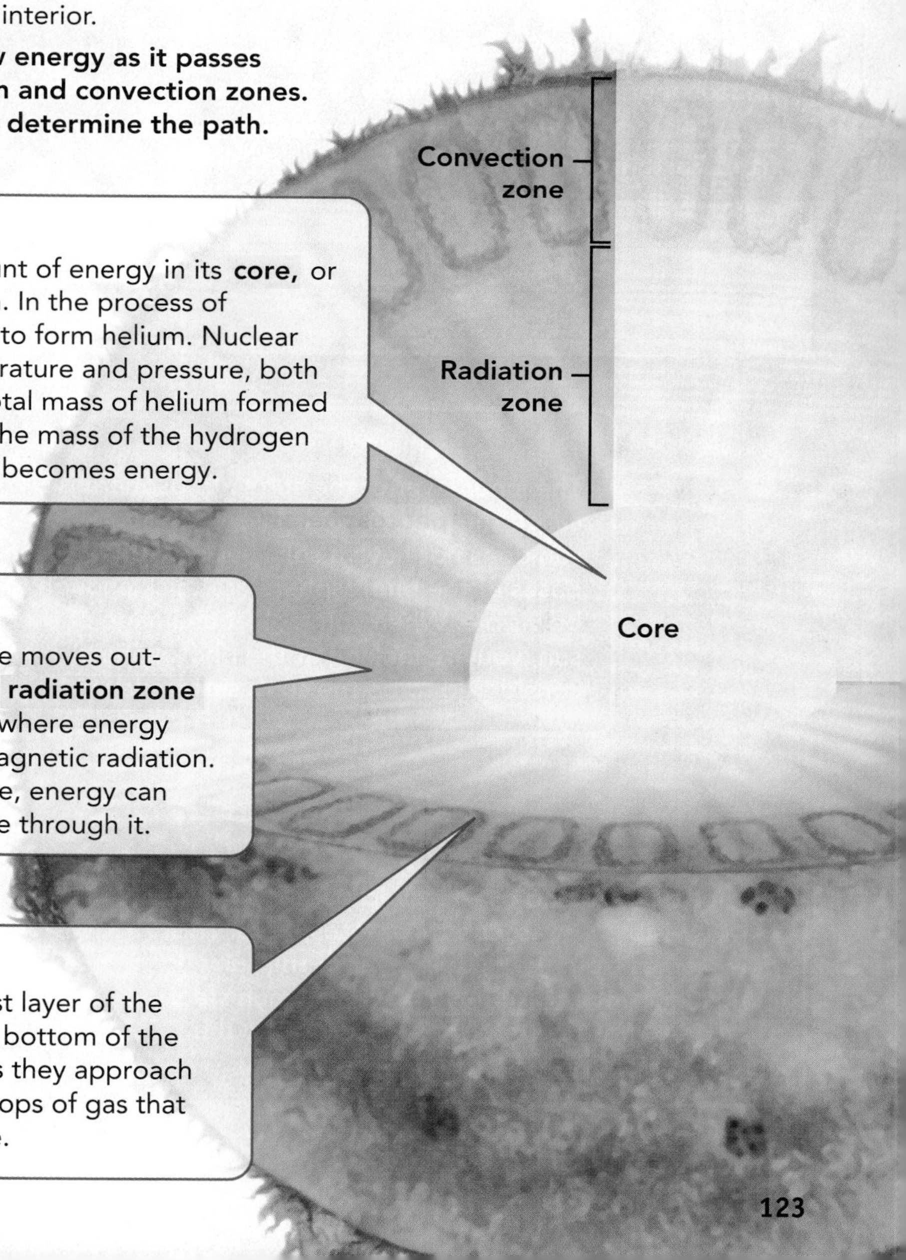

The Core

The sun produces an enormous amount of energy in its **core,** or central region, through nuclear fusion. In the process of **nuclear fusion,** hydrogen atoms join to form helium. Nuclear fusion requires extremely high temperature and pressure, both of which are found in the core. The total mass of helium formed by nuclear fusion is slightly less than the mass of the hydrogen that goes into it. The remaining mass becomes energy.

The Radiation Zone

The energy produced in the sun's core moves outward through the radiation zone. The **radiation zone** is a region of very tightly packed gas where energy moves mainly in the form of electromagnetic radiation. Because the radiation zone is so dense, energy can take more than 100,000 years to move through it.

The Convection Zone

The **convection zone** is the outermost layer of the sun's interior. Hot gases rise from the bottom of the convection zone and gradually cool as they approach the top. Cooler gases sink, forming loops of gas that move energy toward the sun's surface.

Convection zone

Radiation zone

Core

Vocabulary Greek Word Origins
The Greek word *photos* means
"light." What does *photosphere*
mean?

_____

_____

The Sun's Atmosphere

The sun has an atmosphere that stretches far into space, as you can see in Figure 2. The layers of the atmosphere become less dense the farther they are from the radiation zone. Like the sun's interior, the atmosphere is primarily composed of hydrogen and helium. 🔑 The sun's atmosphere includes the photosphere, the chromosphere, and the corona. Each layer has unique properties.

FIGURE 2 ···

▶ INTERACTIVE ART **The Sun's Atmosphere**
This image is a combination of two photographs of the sun. One shows the sun's surface and was taken through a special filter that shows the sun's features. The other shows the corona and was taken during an eclipse.

✎ Relate Text and Visuals On the photograph, label the photosphere and corona. Shade in the area of the chromosphere.

CHALLENGE **Why can the chromosphere and corona only be seen from Earth during an eclipse?**

_____

_____

_____

The Photosphere

The inner layer of the sun's atmosphere is called the photosphere (FOH tuh sfeer). The sun does not have a solid surface, but the gases of the photosphere are thick enough to be visible. When you look at an image of the sun, you are looking at the photosphere. It is considered to be the sun's surface layer.

The Chromosphere

At the start and end of a total eclipse, a reddish glow is visible just around the photosphere. This glow comes from the middle layer of the sun's atmosphere, the chromosphere (KROH muh sfeer). The Greek word *chroma* means "color," so the chromosphere is the "color sphere."

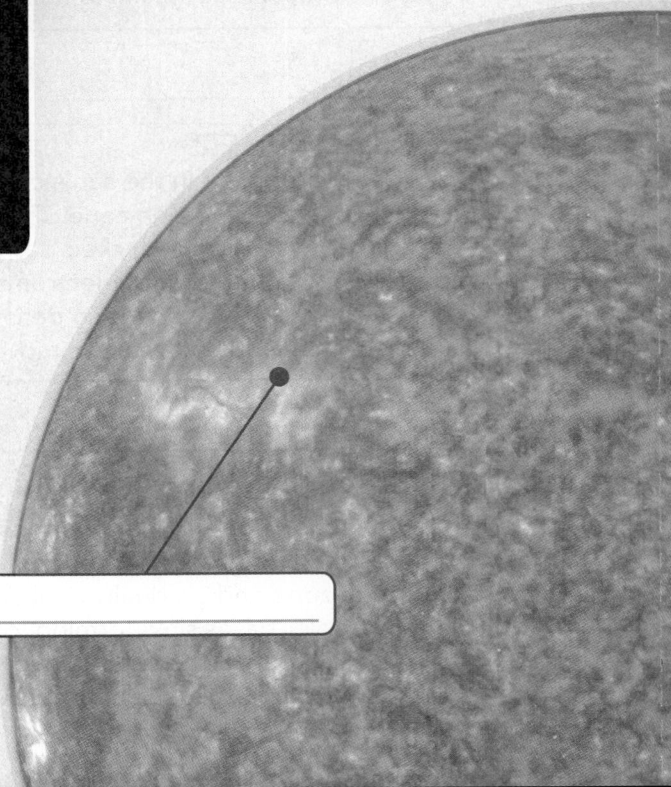

apply it!

Solar Temperature

Use the table to answer the questions.

Layer	Temperature (°C)
Core	About 15,000,000
Radiation and Convection Zones	About 4,000,000
Photosphere	About 6,000
Inner Chromosphere	About 4,300
Outer Chromosphere	About 8,300
Corona	About 1,000,000

1 ⚠ **Interpret Data** Which layer is hottest?

_____

2 **Compare and Contrast** How does the temperature change in the sun's atmosphere differ from the temperature change in the sun's interior?

_____

_____

The Corona

During a total solar eclipse, an even fainter layer of the sun becomes visible, as you can see in **Figure 2.** This outer layer, which looks like a white halo around the sun, is called the **corona,** which means "crown" in Latin. The corona extends into space for millions of kilometers. It gradually thins into streams of electrically charged particles called the **solar wind.**

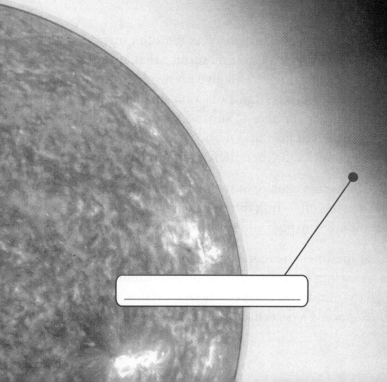

Do the Quick Lab
Layers of the Sun.

🔑 Assess Your Understanding

1a. List List the layers of the sun's interior and atmosphere, starting from the center.

_____

_____

_____

SC.8.E.5.6

b. Compare and Contrast What is one key difference between the radiation and convection zones?

_____

_____

_____

_____

SC.8.E.5.6

got it? ....

○ **I get it!** Now I know that the sun's

structure includes _____

○ **I need extra help with** _____

_____

Go to **my science** 🔊 **coach** *online for help with this subject.*   SC.8.E.5.6

What Features Can You See on the Sun?

For hundreds of years, scientists have used special telescopes to study the sun. They have spotted a variety of features on the sun's surface. 🔑 **Features on or just above the sun's surface include sunspots, prominences, and solar flares.**

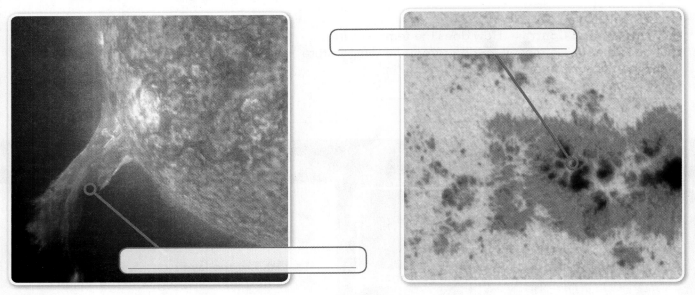

FIGURE 3 ···

Sunspots and Prominences

Sunspots look dark in regular photographs. Some photos of the sun are taken with special filters that show the sun's structure. Sunspots may appear white in these photos. Sunspots are visible in both of the photos above. ✏️ **Classify Label a prominence and a sunspot in the photos.**

Sunspots Photographs show dark areas on the sun's surface. These **sunspots** are areas of gas on the sun's surface that are cooler than the gases around them. Cooler gases give off less light than hotter gases, so sunspots look dark. Sunspots look small, but they can be larger than Earth. The number of sunspots varies in a regular cycle. The most sunspots appear about once every 11 years. The sun emits slightly more radiation when there are more sunspots.

🔄 **Relate Cause and Effect**
When prominences join, they cause (sunspots/solar flares).

Prominences Sunspots usually occur in groups. Huge loops of gas called **prominences** often link different parts of sunspot regions. You can compare sunspots and prominences in **Figure 3**.

Solar Flares Sometimes the loops in sunspot regions suddenly connect, releasing large amounts of magnetic energy. The energy heats gas on the sun to millions of degrees Celsius, causing the gas to erupt into space. These eruptions are called **solar flares.**

Solar Wind

Solar Wind The solar wind is made up of electrical particles from the sun. Solar flares can greatly increase the solar wind, which means that more particles reach Earth's upper atmosphere. Earth's atmosphere and magnetic field normally block these particles. But near the North and South poles, the particles can enter Earth's atmosphere. There, they create powerful electric currents that cause gas molecules in the atmosphere to glow. These particles cause auroras near the poles. They can also cause magnetic storms like the one that caused the blackout in Quebec in 1989. **Figure 4** shows how the solar wind interacts with Earth's magnetic field.

FIGURE 4 ·······································

Solar Wind

Particles from the solar wind spread through the solar system. When they reach Earth, they interact with Earth's magnetic field. (Note: The diagram is not to scale.)

✏ **Make Generalizations** The corona is the least dense layer of the sun's atmosphere. How do you think the density of the solar wind compares to the density of the corona?

_____

_____

_____

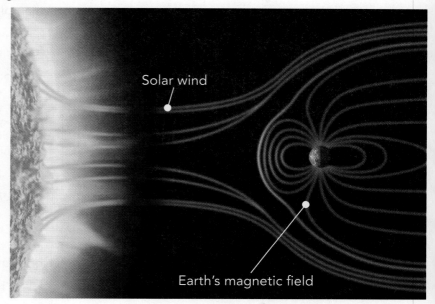

Solar wind

Earth's magnetic field

Do the Quick Lab
Viewing Sunspots.

🔑 Assess Your Understanding

2a. Define (Prominences/sunspots) are loops of gas that extend from the sun's surface.

SC.8.E.5.6

b. Explain Why do sunspots look darker than the rest of the sun's photosphere?

_____

_____

_____

SC.8.E.5.6

c. 🔄 **Relate Cause and Effect** How is the solar wind related to magnetic storms on Earth?

_____

_____

_____

_____

_____

SC.8.E.5.6

got it? ·······································

○ **I get it!** Now I know that features on the sun include _____

_____

○ I need extra help with _____

Go to **my science COACH** *online for help with this subject.*

SC.8.E.5.6

Study Guide

Astronomical objects in the universe include _____

_____

LESSON 1 The Scale of the Universe
SC.8.N.1.6, SC.8.E.5.1

🔑 Astronomers often use parallax to measure distances to nearby stars.

🔑 Since the numbers astronomers use are often very large or very small, they frequently use scientific notation to describe sizes and distances in the universe. They use a unit called the light-year to measure distances between the stars.

Vocabulary
• parallax • universe
• light-year • scientific notation

LESSON 2 Star Systems and Galaxies
SC.8.E.5.2, SC.8.E.5.3

🔑 Made mostly of gas as opposed to solids and liquids, most stars are much larger and hotter than planets.

🔑 Astronomers classify most galaxies into the following types: spiral, elliptical, and irregular.

Vocabulary
• star • planet
• solar system • binary star
• galaxy • spiral galaxy
• elliptical galaxy
• irregular galaxy • quasar

LESSON 3 Gravity and Motion
SC.8.E.5.4

🔑 The strength of the force of gravity between two objects depends on the masses of the objects and the distance between them.

🔑 Inertia and gravity keep Earth in orbit.

🔑 Gravity helps form solar systems by bringing material together in a gradual buildup.

Vocabulary
• orbit • force • gravity
• law of universal gravitation • mass • weight
• inertia • Newton's first law of motion • accretion

LESSON 4 Characteristics of Stars
SC.8.N.1.6, SC.8.N.2.2, SC.8.E.5.5

🔑 Characteristics used to classify stars include color, temperature, size, composition, and brightness.

🔑 The brightness of a star depends on both its size and temperature.

🔑 Scientists use H-R diagrams to classify stars.

Vocabulary
• spectrograph • apparent brightness
• absolute brightness • Hertzsprung-Russell diagram
• main sequence

LESSON 5 Lives of Stars
SC.8.E.5.5

🔑 A star is born when the contracting gas and dust from a nebula becomes so dense and hot that nuclear fusion starts. How long a star lives depends on its mass.

🔑 After a star runs out of fuel, it becomes a white dwarf, a neutron star, or a black hole.

Vocabulary
• nebula • protostar • white dwarf
• supernova • neutron star • pulsar
• black hole

LESSON 6 The Sun
SC.8.E.5.6

🔑 The sun's interior consists of the core, the radiation zone, and the convection zone. The sun's atmosphere includes the photosphere, the chromosphere, and the corona.

🔑 Features on or just above the sun's surface include sunspots, prominences, and solar flares.

Vocabulary
• core • nuclear fusion • radiation zone
• convection zone • photosphere • chromosphere
• corona • solar wind • sunspot • prominence
• solar flare

Review and Assessment

LESSON 1 The Scale of the Universe

1. Which type(s) of numbers does scientific notation best describe?

  a. very small only

  b. very large only

  c. very small and very large

  d. large and small combined

                              SC.8.E.5.1

2. Develop Hypotheses Why can't astronomers measure the parallax of a star that is a million light-years away?

_____

_____

_____

                              SC.8.E.5.1

3. math! The star Antares is about 604 light-years from Earth. Write this distance in scientific notation.

_____

                              SC.8.E.5.1

LESSON 2 Star Systems and Galaxies

4. Which of the following objects is the largest?

  a. star   **b.** solar system

  c. galaxy   **d.** planet

                        SC.8.E.5.3

5. Infer How can scientists use their observations to infer the presence of a binary star when they cannot see the star itself?

_____

_____

_____

_____

                        SC.8.E.5.3

6. Write About It Create a guide for young astronomers to use when classifying galaxies. Focus on the differences among the four types of galaxies that you have studied.

                        SC.8.E.5.2

LESSON 3 Gravity and Motion

7. The tendency of an object to resist a change in motion is called

  a. force.   **b.** gravity.

  c. inertia.   **d.** weight.

                        SC.8.E.5.4

8. An object is kept in orbit by _____

and _____

                        SC.8.E.5.4

9. Predict There are two clouds of material: one with widely spaced objects with small masses and one with closely packed objects with larger masses. Which is more likely to form a solar system, the first or the second? Use gravity to explain your answer.

_____

_____

_____

_____

                        SC.8.E.5.4

LESSON 4 Characteristics of Stars

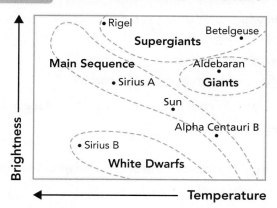

Use the diagram to answer the questions below.

10. Interpret Diagrams On the diagram, circle the star that has a greater absolute brightness: Aldebaran or Sirius B.

                        SC.8.E.5.5

11. Apply Concepts On the diagram, underline the star that is most likely to be red: Rigel, Sirius B, or Betelgeuse.

                        SC.8.E.5.5

LESSON 5 Lives of Stars

12. Relate Cause and Effect How does a star's mass indicate its lifetime?

_____

_____

_____

_____

_____

SC.8.E.5.5

13. Sequence Explain how a black hole forms.

_____

_____

_____

_____

_____

_____

_____

SC.8.E.5.5

LESSON 6 The Sun

14. In which part of the sun does nuclear fusion take place?

a. chromosphere   b. core

c. convection layer   d. corona

SC.8.E.5.6

15. Relatively cool areas on the sun's surface are

called _____

SC.8.E.5.6

16. Explain How can the solar wind affect life on

Earth? _____

_____

_____

SC.8.E.5.6

17. math! The density of the sun's core is about 160 g/cm³. The density of the Earth's core is about 13.0 g/cm³. About how many times denser is the sun's core than Earth's?

_____

SC.8.E.5.6

APPLY THE ESSENTIAL **What astronomical objects are in the universe?**

18. Write a guide for young astronomers that describes the astronomical objects they will be looking for. Be sure to distinguish among different objects and explain the objects' relationships to each other.

_____

_____

_____

_____

_____

_____

_____

_____

_____

_____

_____

_____

_____

_____

_____

_____

_____

_____

_____

_____

_____

_____

SC.8.E.5.2

Florida Benchmarks Review

Circle the letter of the best answer.

1 The table below gives an estimate of star distribution in the Milky Way galaxy. According to the table, what is the most common type of star in the Milky Way?

Type of Star	Percentage of Total
Main sequence	90.75 %
Red giant	0.50 %
Supergiant	< 0.0001 %
White dwarf	8.75 %

- **A** main sequence
- **B** red giant
- **C** supergiant
- **D** white dwarf

SC.8.N.1.6, SC.8.E.5.5

2 What is a prominence?

- **A** a cooler area on the surface of the sun
- **B** a burst of magnetic energy
- **C** a loop of gas that connects different parts of sunspot regions
- **D** electrical particles that enter Earth's atmosphere

SC.8.E.5.6

3 What does a light-year measure?

- **A** time
- **B** volume
- **C** brightness
- **D** distance

SC.8.5.1

4 What are stars primarily composed of?

- **A** rocks and other solids
- **B** hydrogen and helium gases
- **C** oxygen
- **D** liquid

SC.8.E.5.3

5 Suppose the force of gravity between Earth and the moon could be turned off. Which statement best describes the resulting change in the motion of the moon?

- **A** The moon would stop moving.
- **B** The moon would crash into Earth.
- **C** The moon would orbit in the opposite direction.
- **D** The moon would fly off in a straight line.

SC.8.E.5.4

6 Earth is part of the Milky Way galaxy. The sun's relative position in the galaxy is shown in the image below. About how many stars are in the Milky Way galaxy?

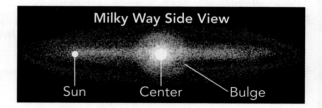

- **A** about 100
- **B** about 100 thousand
- **C** about 100 million
- **D** about 100 billion

SC.8.E.5.2

WHAT MIGHT SATURN'S RINGS BE MADE OF?

Why are objects in the solar system different from each other?

This photograph from the *Cassini* space probe shows Saturn and part of its magnificent system of rings. Space probes such as *Cassini* have helped scientists learn more about the objects in the solar system.

Infer What do you think Saturn's rings are made of? How might they have formed?

_____

_____

_____

_____

_____

_____

_____

> **UNTAMED SCIENCE** Watch the **Untamed Science** video to learn more about the solar system.

The Solar System

FLORIDA | Next Generation Sunshine State Standards

Big Idea 1: SC.8.N.1.6
Big Idea 2: SC.8.N.2.1
Big Idea 5: SC.8.E.5.7, SC.8.E.5.8

Language Arts: LA.8.2.2.3, LA.8.4.2.2
Mathematics: MA.6.A.3.6

4 Getting Started

Check Your Understanding

1. **Background** Read the paragraph below and then answer the question.

> Tyrone is watching a movie. He sees astronauts explore a planet that **revolves** around a star. As the astronauts travel, they notice that the planet **rotates**. Tyrone knows that **gravity** holds the planet in orbit around the star.

- What causes day and night on a planet?

_____

_____

Revolution is the motion of one object around another.

An object **rotates** when it spins around a central axis.

Gravity is the force that attracts all objects toward each other.

▶ MY READING WEB If you had trouble completing the question above, visit **My Reading Web** and type in *The Solar System.*

Vocabulary Skill

Greek Word Origins Many science words come to English from Greek. In this chapter, you will learn the term *geocentric. Geocentric* comes from the Greek word parts *ge*, meaning "Earth," and *kentron*, meaning "center."

$$\begin{array}{ccccc} \textit{ge} & & \textit{kentron} & & \textit{geocentric} \\ \textbf{Earth} & + & \textbf{center} & = & \textbf{having Earth at the center} \end{array}$$

Learn these Greek word parts to help you remember the vocabulary terms.

Greek Word	Meaning	Example
helios	sun	heliocentric, *adj.*
chromas	color	chromosphere, *n.*
sphaira	sphere	photosphere, *n.*

LA.8.1.6.5

2. **Quick Check** Predict the meaning of *heliocentric.*

_____

_____

planet

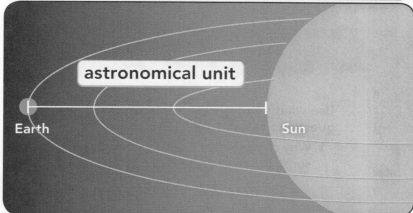

astronomical unit

Earth   Sun

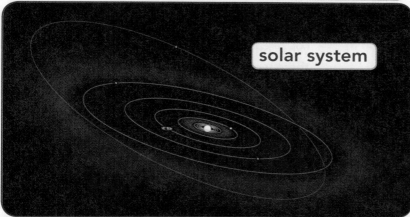

solar system

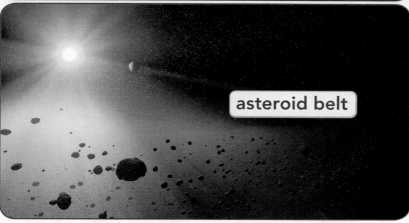

asteroid belt

Chapter Preview

LESSON 1
- solar system • astronomical unit
- planet • dwarf planet
- planetesimal

↻ **Identify Supporting Evidence**
△ **Calculate**

LESSON 2
- maria • crater
- meteoroid

↻ **Compare and Contrast**
△ **Develop Hypotheses**

LESSON 3
- terrestrial planet
- greenhouse effect

↻ **Compare and Contrast**
△ **Communicate**

LESSON 4
- gas giant • ring

↻ **Outline**
△ **Pose Questions**

LESSON 5
- asteroid belt • Kuiper belt
- Oort cloud • comet
- coma • nucleus • asteroid
- meteor • meteorite

↻ **Summarize**
△ **Classify**

LESSON 6
- geocentric • heliocentric
- ellipse

↻ **Sequence**
△ **Make Models**

> **VOCAB FLASH CARDS** For extra help with vocabulary, visit **Vocab Flash Cards** and type in *The Solar System.*

135

1 Introducing the Solar System

UNLOCK THE ESSENTIAL ?

🔑 **What Makes Up the Solar System?**
SC.8.E.5.7, MA.6.A.3.6

🔑 **How Did the Solar System Form?**
SC.8.E.5.7, LA.8.4.2.2

my PLANET DiARY

Extreme Conditions

Imagine a place where the sun shines 11 times brighter than it does on Earth. How could you keep anything cool there? Engineers had to solve just that problem when designing the Mercury *MESSENGER* spacecraft. In 2008, this spacecraft began to visit Mercury, where temperatures can reach up to 370°C. Engineers designed a sunshade to protect *MESSENGER*'s instruments. It's made from ceramic fabric! The fabric, made of elements such as silicon, aluminum, and boron, is resistant to heat. It reflects most of the sun's heat away from the *MESSENGER* spacecraft, keeping all the instruments at a comfortable room temperature (about 20°C).

TECHNOLOGY

Use what you have read to answer the questions below.

1. Why did engineers need to design a sunshade for Mercury *MESSENGER*?

_____

_____

_____

2. What other challenges do you think there would be for engineers designing a spacecraft to travel to Mercury?

_____

_____

_____

▶ PLANET DIARY Go to **Planet Diary** to learn more about the solar system.

 Lab zone

Do the Inquiry Warm-Up
How Big Is Earth?

Vocabulary

- solar system • astronomical unit
- planet • dwarf planet
- planetesimal

Skills

↩ Reading: Identify Supporting Evidence

△ Inquiry: Calculate

What Makes Up the Solar System?

Mercury is just one of many objects that make up the solar system. 🔑 **Our solar system consists of the sun, the planets, their moons, and a variety of smaller objects**. The sun is at the center of the solar system, with other objects orbiting around it. The force of gravity holds the solar system together.

Distances in the Solar System Distances within the solar system are so large that they cannot be easily measured in meters or kilometers. Instead, scientists often use a unit called the astronomical unit. One **astronomical unit** (AU) equals the average distance between Earth and the sun, about 150,000,000 kilometers. The solar system extends more than 100,000 AU from the sun.

FLORIDA NGSSS

SC.8.E.5.7 Compare and contrast the properties of objects in the Solar System including the Sun, planets, and moons to those of Earth, such as gravitational force, distance from the Sun, speed, movement, temperature, and atmospheric conditions.

MA.6.A.3.6 Analyze equations to describe linear functions using common language.

do the math!

Converting Units

To convert from astronomical units (AU) to kilometers (km), you can multiply the number of AU by 150,000,000.

❶ **Calculate** Mars is 1.52 AU from the sun. About how many kilometers is Mars from the sun? _____

❷ **Apply Concepts** If you know an object's distance from the sun in kilometers, how can you find its distance in AU? _____

_____

MA.6.A.3.6, MA.8.A.6.4

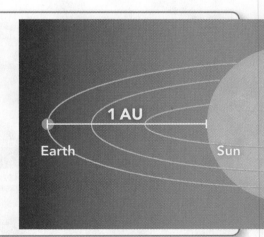

Earth — 1 AU — Sun

The Sun At the center of our solar system is the sun. The sun is much larger than anything else in the solar system. About 99.85 percent of the mass of the solar system is contained within the sun. Despite being more than a million times the volume of Earth, our sun is actually a very ordinary mid-sized star. Using telescopes, we see stars that have volumes a thousand times greater than the sun's! This turns out to be a very good thing for us. Large stars burn out and die quickly, but our sun will last for five billion more years.

✏️
↩ **Identify Supporting Evidence** Underline a sentence that supports the statement, "The sun is much larger than anything else in the solar system."

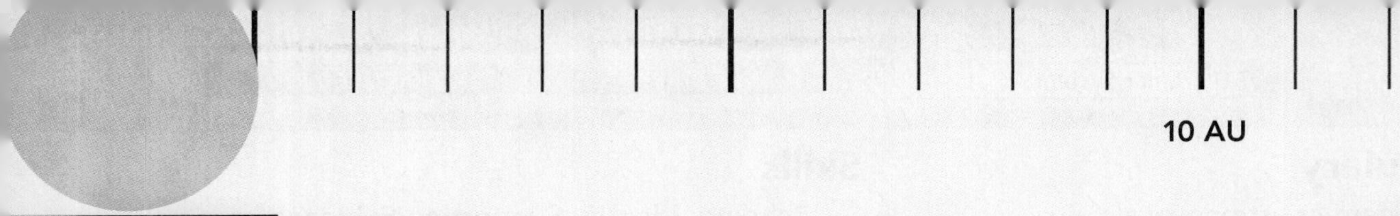

FIGURE 1 ....

> **INTERACTIVE ART** **The Solar System**

The planets' sizes are shown to scale, but their distances from the sun are not.

✎ **Mark the position of each planet on the distance scale above.**

1. **Interpret Data** Where is the largest gap between planets?

_____

2. **CHALLENGE** Could you show the planets' relative sizes and distances from the sun in the same diagram on one page? Why or why not?

_____

_____

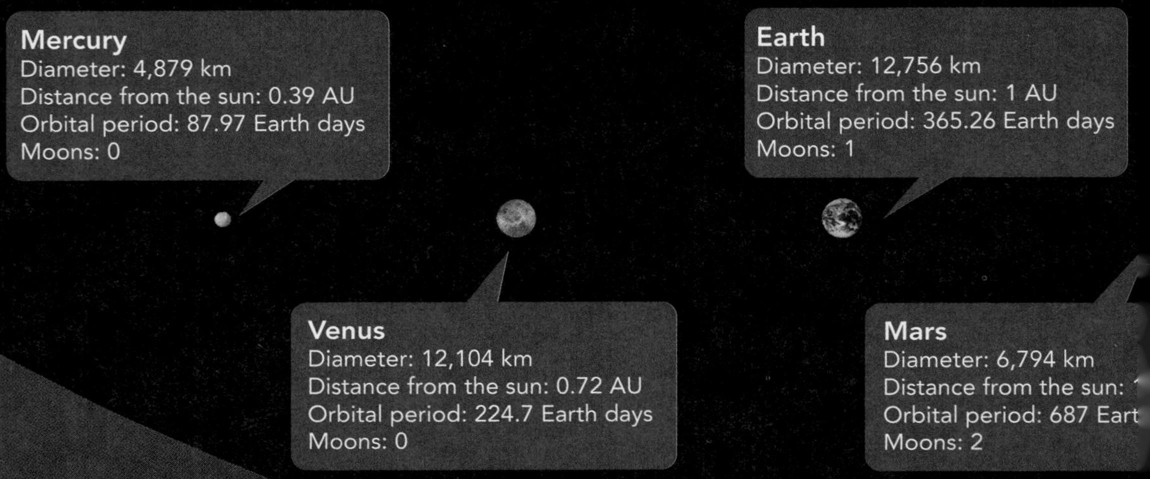

Mercury
Diameter: 4,879 km
Distance from the sun: 0.39 AU
Orbital period: 87.97 Earth days
Moons: 0

Earth
Diameter: 12,756 km
Distance from the sun: 1 AU
Orbital period: 365.26 Earth days
Moons: 1

Venus
Diameter: 12,104 km
Distance from the sun: 0.72 AU
Orbital period: 224.7 Earth days
Moons: 0

Mars
Diameter: 6,794 km
Distance from the sun: 1
Orbital period: 687 Eart
Moons: 2

Planets

There are many different objects in the solar system. How do you decide what is a planet and what isn't? In 2006, astronomers decided that a planet must be round, orbit the sun, and have cleared out the region of the solar system along its orbit. The first four planets are small and are mostly made of rock and metal. The last four planets are very large and are mostly made of gas and liquid. Like Earth, each planet has a "day" and a "year." Its day is the time it takes to rotate on its axis. Its year is the time it takes to orbit the sun. **Figure 1** shows some basic facts about the planets.

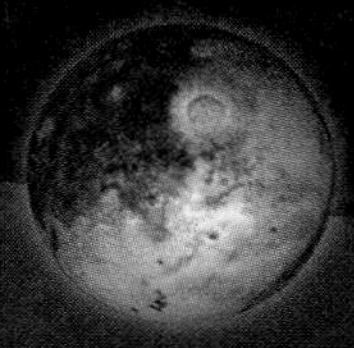

Dwarf Planets

For many years, Pluto was considered the planet in the solar system. But Pluto shares area of its orbit with other objects. Pluto is considered a dwarf planet. A dwarf planet object that orbits the sun and has enough to be spherical, but has not cleared the are orbit. There are five known dwarf planets i solar system: Pluto, Eris, Ceres, Makemake (MAH keh MAH keh), and Haumea (how MAY u scientists observe more distant objects, th

Satellites

Except for Mercury and Venus, every planet in the solar system has at least one natural satellite, or moon. Earth has the fewest moons, with just one. Jupiter and Saturn each have more than 60! Some dwarf planets also have satellites.

Smaller Objects

The solar system also includes many smaller objects that orbit the sun. Some, called asteroids, are small, mostly rocky bodies. Many asteroids are found in an area between the orbits of Mars and Jupiter. Comets are another large group of solar system objects. Comets are loose balls of ice and rock that usually have very long, narrow orbits.

Saturn
Diameter: 120,536 km
Distance from the sun: 9.54 AU
Orbital period: 29.47 Earth years
Moons: 60+

Neptune
Diameter: 49,258 km
Distance from the sun: 30.07 AU
Orbital period: 163.72 Earth years
Moons: 13+

Uranus
Diameter: 51,118 km
Distance from the sun: 19.19 AU
Orbital period: 83.75 Earth years
Moons: 20+

Jupiter
Diameter: 142,984 km
Distance from the sun: 5.20 AU
Orbital period: 11.86 Earth years
Moons: 60+

 Do the Lab Investigation
Speeding Around the Sun.

🔑 Assess Your Understanding

1a. Sequence List the planets in order of increasing distance from the sun.

_____

_____

_____

SC.8.E.5.7

b. Make Generalizations What is the relationship between a planet's distance from the sun and the length of its year?

_____

_____

SC.8.E.5.7

got it?

○ **I get it!** Now I know that the solar system includes _____

_____

_____

○ **I need extra help with** _____

_____

Go to **MY SCIENCE** **COACH** *online for help with this subject.*

SC.8.E.5.7

FLORIDA | NGSSS

SC.8.E.5.7 Compare and contrast the properties of objects in the Solar System including the Sun, planets, and moons to those of Earth, such as gravitational force, distance from the Sun, speed, movement, temperature, and atmospheric conditions.

LA.8.4.2.2 The student will record information (e.g., notes) related to a topic, including visual aids to organize information.

FIGURE 2 ·······································

> ART IN MOTION **Formation of the Solar System**

✎ **Sequence** Write the numbers 1 through 4 in the circles to put the images in order.

How Did the Solar System Form?

Where did the objects in the solar system come from? **Scientists think the solar system formed about 4.6 billion years ago from a cloud of hydrogen, helium, rock, ice, and other materials pulled together by gravity.**

A Spinning Disk The process began as gravity pulled the cloud's material together. The cloud collapsed and started to rotate, forming a disk. Most of the material was pulled to the center. As this material became tightly packed, it got hotter and the pressure on it increased.

Eventually, the temperature and pressure became so high that hydrogen atoms were pressed together to form helium. This process, called nuclear fusion, releases large amounts of energy. Once nuclear fusion began, the sun gave off light and became a stable star. Sunlight is one form of the energy produced by fusion.

The Planets Form Away from the sun, planets began to form as gravity pulled rock, ice, and gas together. The rock and ice formed small bodies called **planetesimals** (pla nuh TE suh muhlz). Over time, planetesimals collided and stuck together, eventually combining to form all the other objects in the solar system.

Inner Planets Close to the sun, the solar system was very hot. Most water evaporated, preventing ice from forming. The bodies that formed in this region were comparatively low in mass. Their gravity was too weak to hold on to light gases such as hydrogen and helium. This is why the inner planets are small and rocky.

Outer Planets At greater distances from the sun, temperatures were cooler. Ice formed, adding mass to the planets that formed at these distances. As the planets grew, their gravity was strong enough to hold hydrogen and helium, forming the gas giant planets. Beyond the gas giants, temperatures were even lower. Ice and other materials produced comets and dwarf planets.

Solve THE SOLAR SYSTEM

EXPLORE THE ESSENTIAL **?**

Why are objects in the solar system different from each other?

FIGURE 3 ·····················
Use the clues to complete the puzzle.
Then answer the question.

ACROSS

3 The planet farthest from the sun
4 A loose, icy body with a long, narrow orbit
6 A gas giant planet that is smaller than Jupiter but larger than Neptune
7 The smallest planet in the solar system
8 An object that orbits a planet

DOWN

1 The largest planet in the solar system
2 A planet that formed closer to the sun than Earth but not closest to the sun
5 A small rocky body that orbits the sun

✏️ **Compare and Contrast** Why are the objects in clues 2 and 6 so different from each other?   LA.8.4.2.2

_____

_____

_____

 Lab zone® Do the Quick Lab *Clumping Planets.*

🔑 Assess Your Understanding

2a. Explain What force formed the solar system?

_____
SC.8.E.5.7

b. ANSWER THE ESSENTIAL **?** Why are objects in the solar system different from each other?

_____

_____

_____

_____
SC.8.E.5.7

got it?

○ **I get it!** Now I know that the solar system formed when _____

_____

_____

○ **I need extra help with** _____

Go to **MY SCIENCE ⓢ COACH** online for help with this subject.
SC.8.E.5.7

Earth's Moon

UNLOCK THE ESSENTIAL ?

🔑 **What Is the Moon Like?**
SC.8.E.5.7, LA.8.2.2.3

MY PLANET DIARY

VOICES FROM HISTORY

Galileo Galilei

In 1609, the Italian astronomer Galileo Galilei turned a new tool—the telescope—toward the moon. What he saw amazed him: wide dark areas and strange spots and ridges.

I have been led to that opinion ... that I feel sure that the surface of the Moon is not perfectly smooth ...but that, on the contrary, it is ... just like the surface of the Earth itself, which is varied everywhere by high mountains and deep valleys.

Today, scientists know that Galileo was right. Powerful telescopes have shown the mountains and craters on the moon, and astronauts have walked and driven over the moon's surface.

✏️ **Communicate** Discuss Galileo's observations with a partner. Then answer the questions below.

1. What conclusions did Galileo draw about the moon?

_____

_____

2. How do you think it would feel to make an observation that no one had made before?

_____

_____

_____

▶ PLANET DIARY Go to **Planet Diary** to learn more about Earth's moon.

Lab zone® Do the Inquiry Warm-Up *Why Do Craters Look Different From Each Other?*

Vocabulary
- maria • crater
- meteoroid

Skills
- Reading: Compare and Contrast
- Inquiry: Develop Hypotheses

What Is the Moon Like?

For thousands of years, people could see the moon, but didn't know much about it. Galileo's observations were some of the first to show details on the moon's surface. Scientists have since learned more about the moon's features. **The moon is dry and airless and has an irregular surface. Compared to Earth, the moon is small and has large variations in its surface temperature.**

Surface Features As **Figure 1** shows, the moon has many unusual structures, including maria, craters, and highlands.

Maria Dark, flat areas, called **maria** (MAH ree uh), are hardened rock formed from huge lava flows that occurred 3–4 billion years ago. The singular form of *maria* is *mare* (MAH ray).

Craters Large round pits called **craters** can be hundreds of kilometers across. These craters were caused by the impacts of **meteoroids,** chunks of rock or dust from space. Maria have relatively few craters. This means that most of the moon's craters formed from impacts early in its history, before maria formed.

Highlands Some of the light-colored features you can see on the moon's surface are highlands, or mountains. The peaks of the lunar highlands and the rims of the craters cast dark shadows. The highlands cover most of the moon's surface.

FLORIDA NGSSS

SC.8.E.5.7 Compare and contrast the properties of objects in the Solar System including the Sun, planets, and moons to those of Earth, such as gravitational force, distance from the Sun, speed, movement, temperature, and atmospheric conditions.

LA.8.2.2.3 The student will organize information to show understanding or relationships among facts (e.g., representing key points within text through charting or comparing/contrasting).

FIGURE 1 ·····························
Moon Features
This photograph shows the features of the northern part of the side of the moon that you can see from Earth.

✎ **Relate Diagrams and Photos** How is the photograph different from Galileo's drawing on the previous page?

_____

_____

_____

_____

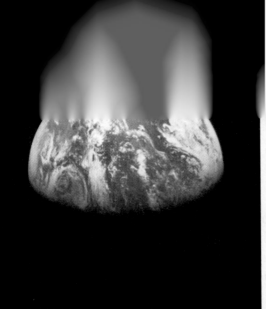

FIGURE 2 ·······························

Different Worlds
This photo of Earth, taken from orbit around the moon, clearly shows the contrast between the barren moon and water-covered Earth.

Size and Density The moon is 3,476 kilometers across, a little less than the distance across the United States. This is about one fourth of Earth's diameter. However, the moon has only one eightieth as much mass as Earth. Though Earth has a very dense core, its outer layers are less dense. The moon's average density is similar to the density of Earth's outer layers. Its gravity is about one sixth of Earth's.

Temperature At the moon's equator, temperatures range from a torrid 130°C in direct sunlight to a frigid −170°C at night. Temperatures at the poles are even colder. Temperatures vary so much because the moon does not have an atmosphere. The moon's surface gravity is so weak that gases can easily escape into space.

Water For many years, people thought the moon had no water, except for small amounts of ice. In 2009, scientists using data from several space probes determined that a thin layer of water exists in the moon's soil. The total amount of water is very small, but it is found in many places on the moon's surface.

Origins of the Moon Scientists have suggested many possible theories for how the moon formed. The theory that seems to best fit the evidence is called the collision-ring theory. About 4.5 billion years ago, when Earth was very young, the solar system was full of rocky debris. Scientists theorize that a planet-sized object collided with Earth. Material from the object and Earth's outer layers was ejected into orbit around Earth, where it formed a ring. Gravity caused this material to clump together to form the moon.

↩ Compare and Contrast
Complete the table below to compare and contrast Earth and the moon.   LA.8.2.2.3

	Density	Temperatures	Atmosphere	Water
Earth				
Moon				

apply it!

Within your lifetime, tourists may be able to travel to the moon. If you were taking a trip to the moon, what would you pack? Remember that the moon is dry, has almost no liquid water, and has no atmosphere.

1 **Solve Problems** On the packing list to the right, list five items you would need on the moon.

2 [CHALLENGE] List two items that you could not use on the moon. Why would they not work?

_____

_____

_____

_____

_____

_____

_____

Things to Pack

1. _____
2. _____
3. _____
4. _____
5. _____

 Do the Quick Lab
Moonwatching.

🔑 Assess Your Understanding

1a. List What are the three main surface features on the moon?

_____

SC.8.E.5.7

b. 🔄 **Compare and Contrast** How does the moon's gravity compare with Earth's?

_____

SC.8.E.5.7

c. △ **Develop Hypotheses** Write a hypothesis explaining why the moon has very little liquid water.

_____

_____

_____

SC.8.E.5.7

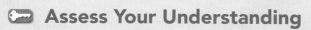

got it? ....

○ **I get it!** Now I know that the characteristics of Earth's moon are _____

_____

_____

○ **I need extra help with** _____

Go to **MY SCIENCE** 🔵 **COACH** *online for help with this subject.*

SC.8.E.5.7

145

The Inner Planets

What Do the Inner Planets Have in Common?
SC.8.E.5.7

What Are the Characteristics of the Inner Planets?
SC.8.N.2.1, LA.8.2.2.3

my planet Diary

What's in a Name?

Where in the solar system could you find Lewis and Clark's guide Sacagawea, artist Frida Kahlo, writer Helen Keller, and abolitionist Sojourner Truth all in the same place? On Venus! In fact, almost every feature on Venus is named for a real, fictional, or mythological woman.

In general, the person or people who discover an object or feature in the solar system get to choose its name. But scientists have agreed on some guidelines. Features on Mercury are named for authors, artists, and musicians. Many craters on Mars are named for towns on Earth. And most of the craters on Earth's moon are named for astronomers, physicists, and mathematicians.

FUN FACT

After you read the information to the left, answer the questions below.

1. Who decides what to name a newly discovered feature in the solar system?

_____

_____

2. If you discovered a new planet, how would you decide what to name its features?

_____

_____

> PLANET DIARY Go to **Planet Diary** to learn more about the inner planets.

Lab zone Do the Inquiry Warm-Up *Ring Around the Sun.*

Vocabulary
- terrestrial planet
- greenhouse effect

Skills
- Reading: Compare and Contrast
- Inquiry: Communicate

What Do the Inner Planets Have in Common?

Earth, Mercury, Venus, and Mars are more like each other than they are like the outer planets. **The inner planets are small and dense and have rocky surfaces.** The inner planets are often called the **terrestrial planets,** from the Latin word *terra*, which means "Earth." **Figure 1** summarizes data about the inner planets.

The terrestrial planets all have relatively high densities. They are rich in rocky and metallic materials, including iron and silicon. Each has a solid surface. All except Mercury have atmospheres.

> **FLORIDA** NGSSS
>
> **SC.8.E.5.7** Compare and contrast the properties of objects in the Solar System including the Sun, planets, and moons to those of Earth, such as gravitational force, distance from the Sun, speed, movement, temperature, and atmospheric conditions.

FIGURE 1 ···

> INTERACTIVE ART

The Inner Planets
Interpret Data Use the table to answer the questions below.

1. Which planet is largest?

_____

2. Which planet has the most moons?

_____

3. Which planet is most similar to Earth in size?

_____

Planet	 Mercury	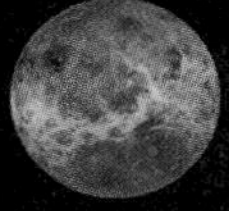 Venus	 Earth	 Mars
Diameter (km)	4,879	12,104	12,756	6,794
Period of rotation (Earth days)	58.9	244	1.0	1.03
Average distance from sun (AU)	0.39	0.72	1.0	1.52
Period of revolution (Earth days)	88	224.7	365.2	687
Number of moons	0	0	1	2

Note: Planets are not shown to scale.

 Lab zone Do the Quick Lab *Characteristics of the Inner Planets.*

Assess Your Understanding

got it? ···

O I get it! Now I know that the inner planets are _____

_____

O I need extra help with _____

Go to MY SCIENCE COACH online for help with this subject.

FLORIDA NGSSS

SC.8.N.2.1 Distinguis between scientific and pseudoscientific ideas.

SC.8.E.5.7 Compare and contrast the properties of objects in the Solar System including the Sun, planets, and moons to those of Earth.

LA.8.2.2.3 The student will organize information to show understanding among facts (e.g., comparing/contrasting).

Size of Mercury
compared to Earth

I'm visiting the planets! As you read this lesson and the next one, keep track of how far I've traveled.

TOTAL AU:

SOL TOURS

INTERPLANETARY FREQUENT TRAVELER REWARDS PROGRAM

SPF 1000000

What Are the Characteristics of the Inner Planets?

Though the four inner planets have many features in common, they differ in size and composition as well as distance from the sun.

Mercury Would you like to visit a place where the temperature can range from 430°C to below −170°C? 🔑 **Mercury is the smallest terrestrial planet and the planet closest to the sun.** Mercury is not much larger than Earth's moon. The interior of Mercury is probably made up mainly of the dense metal iron.

Mercury's Surface As you can see in **Figure 2,** Mercury has flat plains and craters on its surface. Most of these craters formed early in the history of the solar system. Since Mercury has no water and not much atmosphere, the craters have not worn away over time.

Mercury's Atmosphere Mercury has virtually no atmosphere. Because Mercury's mass is small, its gravity is weak. Gas particles can easily escape into space. However, astronomers have detected small amounts of sodium and other gases around Mercury.

During the day, the side of Mercury facing the sun can reach temperatures of 430°C. Because there is so little atmosphere, the planet's heat escapes at night. Then the temperature drops below −170°C.

Exploring Mercury Much of what astronomers know about Mercury has come from space probes. *Mariner 10* flew by Mercury three times in 1974 and 1975. *Mercury MESSENGER* has passed Mercury several times, and will begin orbiting Mercury in 2011.

FIGURE 2 ···
Mercury
The photo shows Mercury's cratered surface.

✏️ **Answer the questions below.**

1. **Solve Problems** List three things a visitor to Mercury would need to bring.

_____

_____

_____

2. CHALLENGE Refer to **Figure 1.** How many Mercury days are there in a Mercury year?

_____

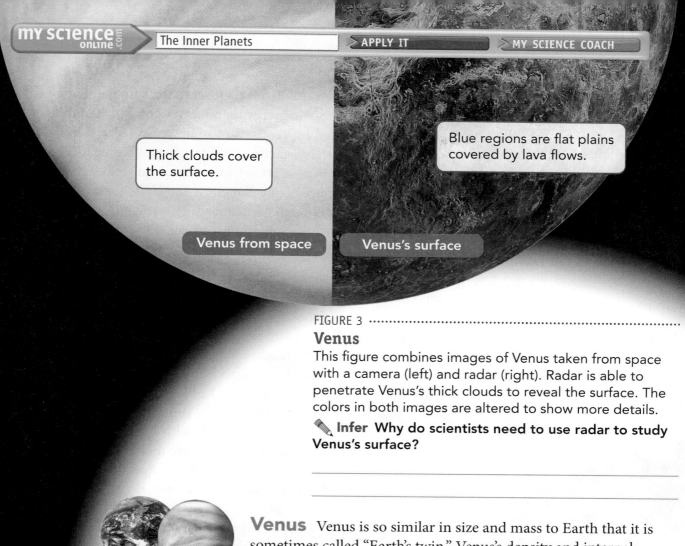

Thick clouds cover the surface.

Blue regions are flat plains covered by lava flows.

Venus from space

Venus's surface

FIGURE 3 ·······································

Venus

This figure combines images of Venus taken from space with a camera (left) and radar (right). Radar is able to penetrate Venus's thick clouds to reveal the surface. The colors in both images are altered to show more details.

✎ **Infer** Why do scientists need to use radar to study Venus's surface?

_____

_____

Size of Venus compared to Earth

Venus Venus is so similar in size and mass to Earth that it is sometimes called "Earth's twin." Venus's density and internal structure are similar to Earth's. But in other ways Venus and Earth are very different. ⚷ **Venus has a thick atmosphere, an unusual pattern of rotation, and the hottest surface of any planet.**

Venus's Atmosphere Venus's atmosphere is so thick that it is always cloudy. As you can see in **Figure 3,** astronomers can see only a smooth cloud cover over Venus. The thick clouds are made mostly of droplets of sulfuric acid.

At Venus's surface, you would quickly be crushed by the weight of its atmosphere. The pressure of Venus's atmosphere is 90 times greater than the pressure of Earth's atmosphere. You couldn't breathe on Venus because its atmosphere is mostly carbon dioxide.

Venus's Rotation Venus takes about 7.5 Earth months to revolve around the sun. It takes about 8 months for Venus to rotate once on its axis. Thus, Venus rotates so slowly that its day is longer than its year! Oddly, Venus rotates from east to west, the opposite direction from most other planets and moons. Astronomers hypothesize that this unusual rotation was caused by a very large object that struck Venus billions of years ago. Such a collision could have caused the planet to change its direction of rotation. Another hypothesis is that Venus's thick atmosphere could have somehow altered its rotation.

Compare and Contrast

List one feature Venus has in common with Earth and one feature that is different. **LA.8.2.2.3**

In common: _____

_____

Different: _____

_____

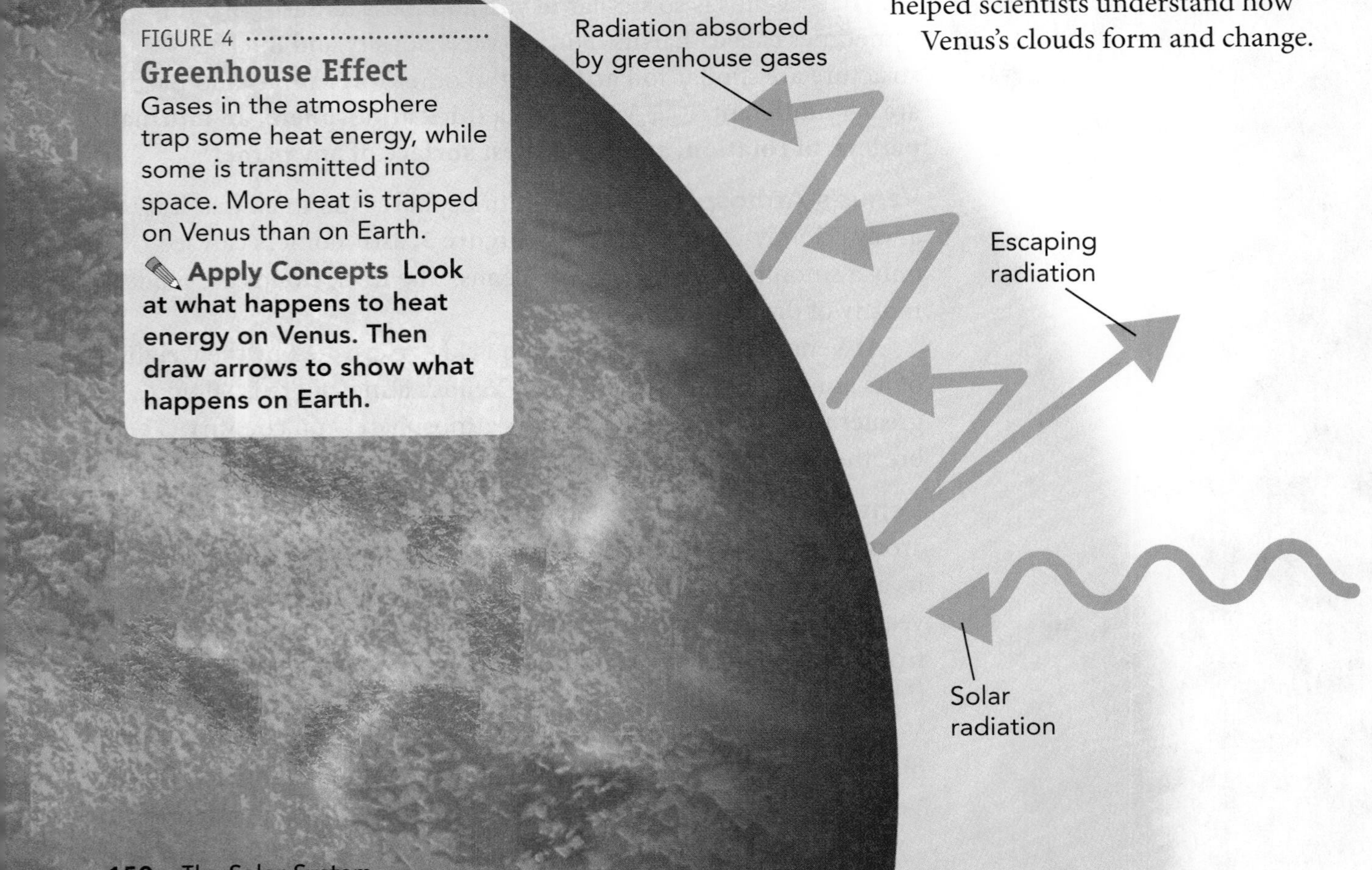

A Hot Planet Because Venus is closer to the sun than Earth is, it receives more solar energy than Earth does. Much of this radiation is reflected by Venus's atmosphere. However, some radiation reaches the surface and is later given off as heat. The carbon dioxide in Venus's atmosphere traps heat so well that Venus has the hottest surface of any planet. At 460°C, its average surface temperature is hot enough to melt lead. This trapping of heat by the atmosphere is called the **greenhouse effect. Figure 4** shows how the greenhouse effect occurs.

Exploring Venus The first probe to land on Venus's surface and send back data, *Venera 7*, landed in 1970. It survived for only a few minutes because of the high temperature and pressure. Later probes were more durable and sent images and data back to Earth.

The *Magellan* probe reached Venus in 1990, carrying radar instruments. Radar works through clouds, so *Magellan* was able to map nearly the entire surface. The *Magellan* data confirmed that Venus is covered with rock. Venus's surface has more than 10,000 volcanoes and plains formed by lava flows. More recent probes have included *Venus Express,* from the European Space Agency, as well as brief visits by space probes headed for other planets. Images from *Venus Express* have helped scientists understand how Venus's clouds form and change.

FIGURE 4
Greenhouse Effect
Gases in the atmosphere trap some heat energy, while some is transmitted into space. More heat is trapped on Venus than on Earth.

Apply Concepts Look at what happens to heat energy on Venus. Then draw arrows to show what happens on Earth.

Radiation absorbed by greenhouse gases

Escaping radiation

Solar radiation

Earth There's only one planet in the solar system where you could live easily: Earth. **Earth has liquid water and a suitable temperature range and atmosphere for living things to survive.**

The Water Planet Earth is unique in our solar system in having liquid water on its surface. In fact, most of Earth's surface, about 70 percent, is covered with water.

Earth's Temperature Scientists sometimes speak of Earth as having "Goldilocks" conditions—in other words, Earth is "just right" for life as we know it. Earth is not too hot and not too cold. If Earth were a little closer to the sun, it would be so hot that liquid water would evaporate. If it were a little farther away and colder, water would always be solid ice.

Earth's Atmosphere Earth has enough gravity to hold on to most gases. These gases make up Earth's atmosphere. Earth is the only planet with an atmosphere that is rich in oxygen. Oxygen makes up about 20 percent of Earth's atmosphere. Nearly all the rest is nitrogen, with small amounts of other gases such as argon, carbon dioxide, and water vapor.

Like Venus, Earth experiences a greenhouse effect. Earth's atmosphere traps heat, though less heat than Venus's atmosphere does. Without the atmosphere, Earth would be much colder.

FIGURE 5 ···

Earth's Structure

Earth has three main layers—a crust, a mantle, and a core. The crust includes the solid, rocky surface. Under the crust is the mantle, a layer of hot rock. Earth has a dense core made mainly of iron and nickel.

✎ **Relate Text and Visuals** Label the layer of Earth with the highest density.

Solar radiation

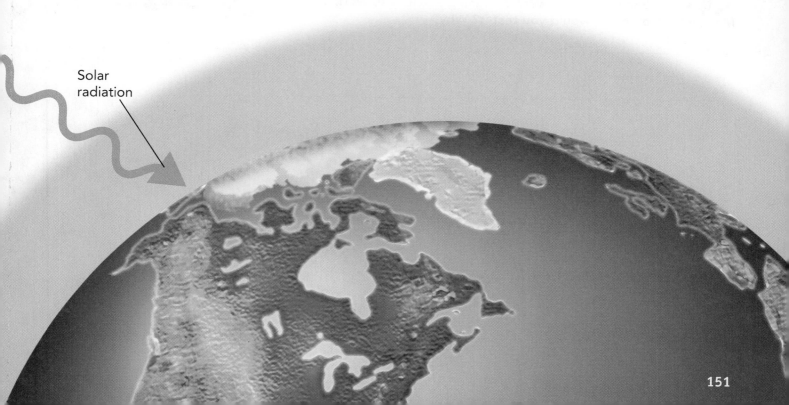

Size of Mars
compared to Earth

Mars Mars is called the "red planet." **Figure 6** shows why. This reddish color is due to the breakdown of iron-rich rocks, leaving a rusty dust behind. **Though Mars is too cold for liquid water, it does have water ice now and had liquid water in the past.**

Mars's Atmosphere The atmosphere of Mars is more than 95 percent carbon dioxide. You could walk around on Mars, but you would have to wear an airtight suit and carry your own oxygen. Mars has few clouds, and they are very thin compared to clouds on Earth. Temperatures on the surface range from −140°C to 20°C.

Water and Ice Images of Mars taken from space show a variety of features that look as if they were made by ancient streams, lakes, or floods. Scientists think that liquid water flowed on Mars's surface in the distant past. Scientists infer that Mars must have been much warmer and had a thicker atmosphere at that time.

Today, Mars's atmosphere is so thin that any liquid water would quickly turn into a gas. So where is Mars's water now? Some is located in the planet's two polar ice caps. Scientists thought the ice caps contained frozen carbon dioxide, but recent data show that the caps are almost entirely made of frozen water. Observations from the space probes *Mars Global Surveyor* and *Mars Reconnaissance Orbiter* have found large ice deposits just under the surface.

FIGURE 6

The Red Planet
Remote-controlled landers such as *Phoenix*, *Spirit*, and *Opportunity* have sent back pictures of the surface of Mars.

✎ **Design a Solution** If you were designing a lander to work on Mars, where on Earth would you test it? Why?

apply it!

Communicate Choose one of the inner planets other than Earth. Describe an alien that could live there. Include at least three features of your alien that make it well suited for the planet you chose. Draw your alien to the right.

_____
_____
_____
_____
_____

FIGURE 7 ··

Olympus Mons

This computer-generated image is based on data from the _Mars Global Surveyor_ mission.

Volcanoes Some regions of Mars have giant volcanoes. There are signs that lava flowed from the volcanoes in the past, but the volcanoes are rarely active today. Olympus Mons, shown in **Figure 7,** is the largest volcano in the solar system. It is as large as Missouri and is nearly three times as tall as Mount Everest!

Mars's Moons Mars has two very small moons. Phobos, the larger moon, is about 22 kilometers across. Deimos is even smaller, about 13 kilometers across. Like Earth's moon, Phobos and Deimos are covered with craters.

Exploring Mars Many space probes have visited Mars. Recent missions have focused on finding signs of water and possible life on Mars. Rovers called _Spirit_ and _Opportunity_ found traces of salts and minerals that form in the presence of water. The _Phoenix_ mission took samples of soil and found frozen water near the north polar cap. Orbiting spacecraft such as _Mars Express_ have detected methane gas in Mars's atmosphere. This gas might be a clue that microscopic life forms exist on Mars, even today!

 Do the Quick Lab _Greenhouse Effect._

🔑 Assess Your Understanding

1a. Name Which inner planet has the thickest

atmosphere? _____

SC.8.E.5.7

b. Relate Cause and Effect Why is Venus hotter than Mercury? _____

_____
_____

SC.8.E.5.7

got it?

○ **I get it!** Now I know that the inner planets

differ in _____

_____

○ **I need extra help with** _____

Go to **MY SCIENCE COACH** _online for help with this subject._

SC.8.E.5.7

The Outer Planets

🔑 **What Do the Outer Planets Have in Common?**
SC.8.E.5.7

🔑 **What Are the Characteristics of Each Outer Planet?**
SC.8.E.5.7

my planet diary

Predicting a Planet

In the 1840s, astronomers were puzzled. Uranus didn't move as expected, based on the theory of gravity. Astronomers John Couch Adams and Urbain Leverrier independently hypothesized that Uranus was being affected by another planet's gravity. They calculated where this planet should be. Another astronomer, Johann Galle, aimed his telescope at the place Leverrier predicted. On September 23, 1846, he discovered the new planet—Neptune.

DISCOVERY

✏️ **Communicate** **Work with a partner to answer the question.**

What science skills did the astronomers use when they discovered Neptune?

_____

_____

_____

_____

▷ PLANET DIARY **Go to Planet Diary to learn more about the outer planets.**

Lab zone Do the Inquiry Warm-Up
How Big Are the Planets?

FLORIDA NGSSS

SC.8.E.5.7 Compare and contrast the properties of objects in the Solar System including the Sun, planets, and moons to those of Earth, such as gravitational force, distance from the Sun, speed, movement, temperature, and atmospheric conditions.

What Do the Outer Planets Have in Common?

If you could visit the outer planets, you wouldn't have a solid place to stand! 🔑 **The four outer planets are much larger and more massive than Earth, and they do not have solid surfaces.** Because these four planets are so large, they are often called gas giants. **Figure 1** summarizes some basic facts about the gas giants.

Composition Jupiter and Saturn are composed mainly of hydrogen and helium. Uranus and Neptune contain some of these gases, but also ices of ammonia and methane. Because they are so massive, the gas giants exert a very strong gravitational force. This gravity keeps gases from escaping, forming thick atmospheres.

Vocabulary
- gas giant
- ring

Skills
- ➲ Reading: Outline
- △ Inquiry: Pose Questions

Despite the name "gas giant," much of the material in these planets is actually liquid because the pressure inside the planets is so high. The outer layers are extremely cold because they are far from the sun. Temperatures increase greatly within the planets.

Moons and Rings
All the gas giants have many moons, ranging from 13 around Neptune to more than 60 around Jupiter! These moons vary from tiny balls of rock and ice barely a kilometer across to moons larger than Mercury. Some of these moons even have their own atmospheres!

In addition, each of the gas giants is surrounded by a set of rings. A **ring** is a thin disk of small particles of ice and rock. Saturn's rings are the largest and most complex.

As you visit each planet, don't forget to keep track of how many AU you've collected!

Planet	Jupiter	Saturn	Uranus	Neptune
Diameter (km)	142,984	120,536	51,118	49,528
Period of rotation (Earth hours)	9.9	10.7	17.2	16.1
Average distance from sun (AU)	5.20	9.54	19.2	30.07
Period of revolution (Earth years)	11.9	29.5	83.8	163.8
Number of moons	at least 63	at least 61	at least 27	at least 13

Note: Planets are not shown to scale.

FIGURE 1 ··································
▶ INTERACTIVE ART
The Outer Planets
The table summarizes data about the outer planets.

✎ **Estimate** Earth's diameter is about 12,750 km. About how many times larger is Jupiter's diameter than Earth's?

Lab ® Do the Quick Lab
zone *Density Mystery.*

🗝 Assess Your Understanding

got it? ···

○ **I get it!** Now I know that the gas giants all _____

_____

○ **I need extra help with** _____

Go to **my science** s **coach** *online for help with this subject.*

SC.8.E.5.7

155

FLORIDA NGSSS

SC.8.E.5.7 Compare and contrast the properties of objects in the Solar System including the Sun, planets, and moons to those of Earth, such as gravitational force, distance from the Sun, speed, movement, temperature, and atmospheric conditions.

What Are the Characteristics of Each Outer Planet?

Since telescopes were first invented, scientists have studied the features of the outer planets and their moons. Today, space-based telescopes and space probes including the *Voyager, Galileo,* and *Cassini* missions have revealed many details of these planets that are not visible from Earth. Scientists are constantly discovering new information about these planets and their moons.

Jupiter 🔑 **Jupiter is the largest and most massive planet.** Jupiter's enormous mass dwarfs the other planets. In fact, its mass is about $2\frac{1}{2}$ times that of all the other planets combined!

Jupiter's Atmosphere Like all of the gas giants, Jupiter has a thick atmosphere made up mainly of hydrogen and helium. One notable feature of Jupiter's atmosphere is its Great Red Spot, a storm that is larger than Earth! The storm's swirling winds are similar to a hurricane, as you can see in **Figure 2.** Unlike hurricanes on Earth, however, the Great Red Spot shows no signs of going away.

Jupiter's Structure Astronomers think that Jupiter probably has a dense core of rock and iron at its center. A thick mantle of liquid hydrogen and helium surrounds this core. Because of the weight of Jupiter's atmosphere, the pressure at Jupiter's core is estimated to be about 30 million times greater than the pressure at Earth's surface.

Size of Jupiter compared to Earth

Outline As you read, make an outline about Jupiter.

I. Atmosphere

    A. _____

    _____

    B. _____

II. Structure

    A. _____

    _____

    B. _____

    _____

    C. _____

    _____

FIGURE 2

The Great Red Spot
This storm is about 20,000 km long and 12,000 km wide. The largest tropical storm on Earth was 2,200 km across.

✎ **Calculate** Think of the storm on Earth as a square and the Great Red Spot as a rectangle. About how many Earth storms would fit inside the Great Red Spot?

Jupiter's Moons The Italian astronomer Galileo Galilei discovered Jupiter's largest moons in 1610. These moons, shown in **Figure 3,** are named Io, Europa, Ganymede, and Callisto. Since Galileo's time, astronomers have discovered dozens of additional moons orbiting Jupiter. Many of these are small moons that have been found in the last few years thanks to improved technology.

FIGURE 3 ···

The Moons of Jupiter

Jupiter's four largest moons are larger than Earth's moon. Each has characteristics that set it apart from the others.

✎ **Relate Text and Visuals** Based on the photograph, match each description below to its moon.

❶ Ganymede is Jupiter's largest moon. It is larger than Mercury! Its surface is divided into dark and bright areas.

❷ Callisto is second to Ganymede in size, but has less ice. It has the most craters of any of Jupiter's moons.

❸ Io is not icy, unlike most of Jupiter's moons. It may have as many as 300 active volcanoes. The eruptions from those volcanoes constantly change the moon's surface.

❹ Europa is covered with ice. There may be liquid water below the ice—and if there's water, there might be life!

TOTAL AU:

SOL ☿ TOURS
INTERPLANETARY
FREQUENT TRAVELER
REWARDS PROGRAM

Titan This giant moon has a thick atmosphere.

TOTAL AU:

SOL 8 TOURS

INTERPLANETARY FREQUENT TRAVELER REWARDS PROGRAM

FIGURE 4 ·····················

The Saturn System

Recent space probes have shown details of Saturn and its moons.

✎ **Answer the questions below.**

1. **Make Judgments** Would it be easier to build a space colony on Saturn or on one of its moons? Why?

_____

_____

2. CHALLENGE Look at the photographs of Mimas and Tethys. What can you infer about the history of these moons?

_____

_____

Mimas A giant impact nearly broke Mimas apart, leaving the enormous crater shown here.

Iapetus This moon has light and dark areas.

✎ **Develop Hypotheses** What might the light areas be?

_____

Saturn

The second-largest planet in the solar system is Saturn. Saturn, like Jupiter, has a thick atmosphere made up mainly of hydrogen and helium. Saturn's atmosphere also contains clouds and storms, but they are less dramatic than those on Jupiter. The *Cassini* space probe found unusual six-sided cloud patterns around Saturn's north pole. Scientists aren't sure what causes these patterns.

Saturn's Rings 🔑 **Saturn has the most spectacular rings of any planet.** These rings are made of chunks of ice and rock, each traveling in its own orbit around Saturn. From Earth, it looks as though Saturn has only a few rings and that they are divided from each other by narrow, dark regions. Space probes have shown that each of these obvious rings is divided into many thinner rings. Saturn's rings are broad and thin, like a compact disc. Some rings are kept in place by gravity from tiny moons that orbit on either side of the ring.

Saturn's Moons Saturn's largest moon, Titan, is larger than the planet Mercury. It is also the only moon in the solar system that has a thick atmosphere. The atmosphere is composed mostly of nitrogen and methane. Some of these gases break down high in the atmosphere, forming a haze that is somewhat like smog on Earth. In 2005, the *Huygens* probe landed on Titan's surface. Photos from *Huygens* show features that may have been formed by flowing liquid. A few scientists think that Titan might support life.

Scientists have learned a great deal about Saturn's moons from the *Cassini* space probe. Giant craters and trenches cut cross Mimas (MY mus) and Tethys (TEE this). Ice and water erupt in geysers from the surface of Enceladus (en SEL uh dus). In 2009, scientists discovered a ring of material that may come from the outermost moon, Phoebe (FEE BEE). **Figure 4** shows some of the members of the Saturn system.

Size of Saturn compared to Earth

did you know?

Saturn has the lowest density of any planet. If you could build a bathtub big enough, Saturn would float!

Tethys In this photo, you can just see a group of canyons that circle this moon.

Enceladus This photo shows faint bluish plumes erupting from the surface of Enceladus.

✏️ **Make Generalizations** Eruptions from Enceladus form one of Saturn's rings. What is that ring most likely made of?

Size of Uranus
compared to Earth

Uranus Although the gas giant Uranus (YOOR uh nus) is about four times the diameter of Earth, it is still much smaller than Jupiter and Saturn. Uranus is twice as far from the sun as Saturn, so it is much colder. Uranus looks blue-green because of traces of methane in its atmosphere. Like the other gas giants, Uranus is surrounded by a group of thin, flat rings, although they are much darker than Saturn's rings.

Uranus's Moons Photographs from *Voyager 2* show that Uranus's five largest moons have icy, cratered surfaces. The craters show that rocks from space have hit the moons. Uranus's moons also have lava flows on their surfaces, suggesting that material has erupted from inside each moon. *Voyager 2* images revealed 10 moons that had never been seen before. Recently, astronomers discovered several more moons, for a total of at least 27.

A Tilted Planet 🔑 **Uranus's axis of rotation is tilted at an angle of about 90 degrees from the vertical.** Viewed from Earth, Uranus rotates from top to bottom instead of from side to side, as other planets do. You can see the tilt in **Figure 5.** Uranus's rings and moons rotate around this tilted axis. Astronomers think that billions of years ago, an object hit Uranus and knocked it on its side. Images from the *Voyager 2* space probe allowed scientists to determine that Uranus rotates in about 17 hours.

FIGURE 5 ·····························
A Sideways Planet
✎ **Compare and Contrast** How do day and night at Uranus's equator change as Uranus revolves around the sun?

_____
_____
_____
_____
_____
_____
_____
_____

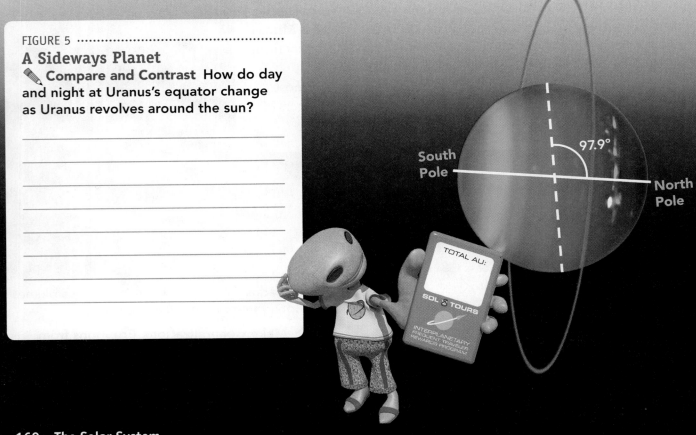

South Pole

97.9°

North Pole

TOTAL AU:

SOL TOURS

INTERPLANETARY FREQUENT TRAVELER REWARDS PROGRAM

Neptune Neptune is similar in size and color to Uranus. **Neptune is a cold, blue planet. Its atmosphere contains visible clouds.** The color comes from methane in the atmosphere. Neptune's interior is hot due to energy left over from its formation. As this energy rises, it produces clouds and storms in the atmosphere.

Size of Neptune compared to Earth

Neptune's Atmosphere In 1989, *Voyager 2* flew by Neptune and photographed a Great Dark Spot about the size of Earth. Like the Great Red Spot on Jupiter, the Great Dark Spot was probably a giant storm. But it didn't last long. Images taken five years later showed that the spot was gone.

Neptune's Moons Astronomers have discovered at least 13 moons orbiting Neptune. The largest moon is Triton, which has a thin atmosphere. *Voyager 2* images show that the area of Triton's south pole is covered by nitrogen ice.

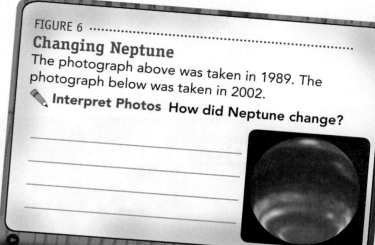

FIGURE 6 ....

Changing Neptune
The photograph above was taken in 1989. The photograph below was taken in 2002.

✏ **Interpret Photos** How did Neptune change?

_____

_____

_____

_____

apply it!

Congratulations! You've earned enough AU in your travels to qualify for a free mission to one planet or moon of your choice!

❶ **Make Judgments** Which planet or moon do you choose? List three reasons for your choice.

_____

_____

❷ **Pose Questions** What is one question you would want your mission to answer?

_____

Lab zone Do the Quick Lab
Make a Model of Saturn.

☞ Assess Your Understanding

1. **Compare and Contrast** List one distinguishing feature for each outer planet.

_____

_____

_____

_____

SC.8.E.5.7

got it?

○ **I get it!** Now I know that the outer planets differ in _____

_____

○ **I need extra help with** _____

Go to MY SCIENCE ⓢ COACH *online for help with this subject.*

SC.8.E.5.7

5 Small Solar System Objects

UNLOCK THE ESSENTIAL

How Do Scientists Classify Small Objects in the Solar System?
SC.8.E.5.7, LA.8.2.2.3

my PLANET DiARY

Posted by: Haley

Location: Constantia, New York

During the summer my dad and I go outside when it gets dark. We like to go stargazing. I have even seen shooting stars! Shooting stars are very hard to spot. You have to stare at the sky and sometimes you will see one shoot by. They only stick around for one split second, but it is really amazing to see one. This is my favorite thing to do when it gets dark during the summer!

✎ **Communicate** **Discuss your answers to these questions with a partner.**

1. What do you think shooting stars are?

_____

_____

_____

_____

2. What do you like to observe in the night sky?

_____

_____

_____

> PLANET DIARY Go to **Planet Diary** to learn more about small solar system objects.

Lab® zone Do the Inquiry Warm-Up
Collecting Micrometeorites.

Vocabulary
- asteroid belt • Kuiper belt • Oort cloud
- comet • coma • nucleus • asteroid
- meteor • meteorite

Skills
↻ Reading: Summarize
▲ Inquiry: Classify

How Do Scientists Classify Small Objects in the Solar System?

The solar system contains many small objects that, like the planets, orbit the sun.  **Scientists classify these objects based on their sizes, shapes, compositions, and orbits. The major categories include dwarf planets, comets, asteroids, and meteoroids.**

Areas of the Solar System Most of the small objects in the solar system are found in three areas: the asteroid belt, the Kuiper belt, and the Oort cloud. The **asteroid belt** is a region of the solar system between Mars and Jupiter. Beyond Neptune's orbit is a region called the **Kuiper belt** (KY per) which extends to about 100 times Earth's distance from the sun. Beyond the Kuiper belt, the **Oort cloud** (ort) stretches out more than 1,000 times the distance between the sun and Neptune. **Figure 1** shows these areas.

🌴 **FLORIDA** NGSSS

SC.8.E.5.7 Compare and contrast the properties of objects in the Solar System including the Sun, planets, and moons to those of Earth, such as gravitational force, distance from the Sun, speed, movement, temperature, and atmospheric conditions.

LA.8.2.2.3 The student will organize information to show understanding (e.g., summarizing).

FIGURE 1 ···

Areas of the Solar System
The diagram below shows the relative positions of the asteroid belt, the Kuiper belt, and the Oort cloud.

✏️ **Relate Text and Visuals** As you read this lesson, write a C to show where a comet would most likely come from. Write a P to show where you would expect to find a plutoid. Write an A to show where you would expect to find an asteroid.

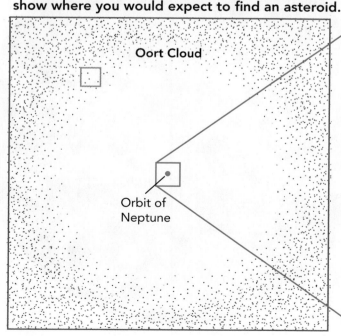

Oort Cloud

Orbit of Neptune

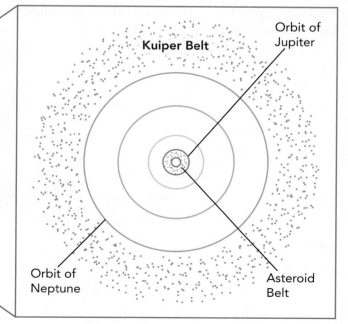

Kuiper Belt

Orbit of Jupiter

Orbit of Neptune

Asteroid Belt

163

Dwarf Planets

"What happened to Pluto?" You may have found yourself asking this question as you have learned about the solar system. For many years, Pluto was considered a planet. But then scientists discovered other objects that were at least Pluto's size. Some were even farther away than Pluto. Scientists began debating how to define a planet.

Defining Dwarf Planets In 2006, astronomers developed a new category of objects, called dwarf planets. These objects orbit the sun and have enough gravity to pull themselves into spheres, but they have other objects in the area of their orbits. As of 2009, scientists had identified five dwarf planets: Pluto, Eris, Makemake, Haumea, and Ceres. Eris is believed to be the largest dwarf planet so far. There are at least a dozen more objects that may turn out to be dwarf planets, once scientists are able to study them.

Like planets, dwarf planets can have moons. Pluto has three moons: Charon, Nix, and Hydra. Haumea has two and Eris has one.

Kuiper Belt Objects All the known dwarf planets except Ceres orbit beyond Neptune. (Ceres orbits in the asteroid belt.) A dwarf planet that orbits beyond Neptune is also called a plutoid. Most plutoids orbit the sun in the Kuiper belt, though Eris may be beyond it. The Kuiper belt also includes many other objects that are too small to be considered dwarf planets.

FIGURE 2 ································

▶VIRTUAL LAB Planet or Not?

This figure shows one artist's idea of what the surface of Pluto looks like.

✎ **Make Judgments** Do you think Pluto should be considered a planet? Why or why not?

_____

_____

_____

_____

_____

_____

_____

Comets A comet is one of the most dramatic objects you can see in the night sky. On a dark night, you can see its fuzzy white head and long, streaming tails. **Comets** are loose collections of ice, dust, and small rocky particles whose orbits can be very long, narrow ellipses. Some comets have smaller orbits that bring them near Earth regularly. Most comets originate in the Oort cloud.

A Comet's Head When a comet gets close to the sun, the energy in sunlight turns the ice into gas, releasing gas and dust. Clouds of gas and dust form a fuzzy outer layer called a **coma. Figure 3** shows the coma and the **nucleus,** the solid inner core of a comet. The nucleus is usually only a few kilometers across.

A Comet's Tail As a comet approaches the sun, it heats up and starts to glow. Some of its gas and dust stream outward, forming a tail. Most comets have two tails—a gas tail and a dust tail. The gas tail points away from the sun and the dust tail points along the path the comet has taken. A comet's tail can be more than 100 million kilometers long and from Earth, appears to stretch across most of the sky. The material is stretched out very thinly, however.

Summarize Write a few sentences to summarize the structure of a comet. **LA.8.2.2.3**

_____

_____

_____

_____

_____

_____

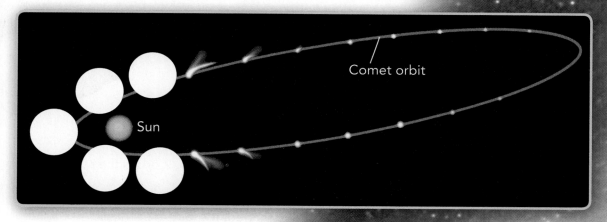

Comet orbit

Sun

FIGURE 3

A Comet's Orbit

Comets, as shown here, have long, narrow orbits. Their tails tend to grow longer as they approach the sun.

Apply Concepts Complete the diagram above by adding the comet's tails.

Gas tail

Dust tail

Nucleus

Coma

Asteroids Hundreds of small, irregular, rocky objects orbit the sun. These **asteroids** are rocky objects, most of which are too small and too numerous to be considered planets or dwarf planets. Astronomers have discovered more than 100,000 asteroids, and they are constantly finding more.

Small Bodies Most asteroids are small—less than a kilometer in diameter. Only Ceres, Pallas, Vesta, and Hygiea are more than 300 kilometers across. (Ceres is both a dwarf planet and the largest asteroid.) Most asteroids are not spherical. Scientists hypothesize that asteroids are leftover pieces of the early solar system that never came together to form a planet.

Asteroid Orbits Most asteroids orbit the sun in the asteroid belt. Some, however, have very elliptical orbits that bring them closer to the sun than to Earth's orbit. Someday, an asteroid will hit Earth. One or more large asteroids did hit Earth about 65 million years ago, filling the atmosphere with dust and smoke and blocking out sunlight around the world. Scientists hypothesize that many species of organisms, including the dinosaurs, became extinct as a result.

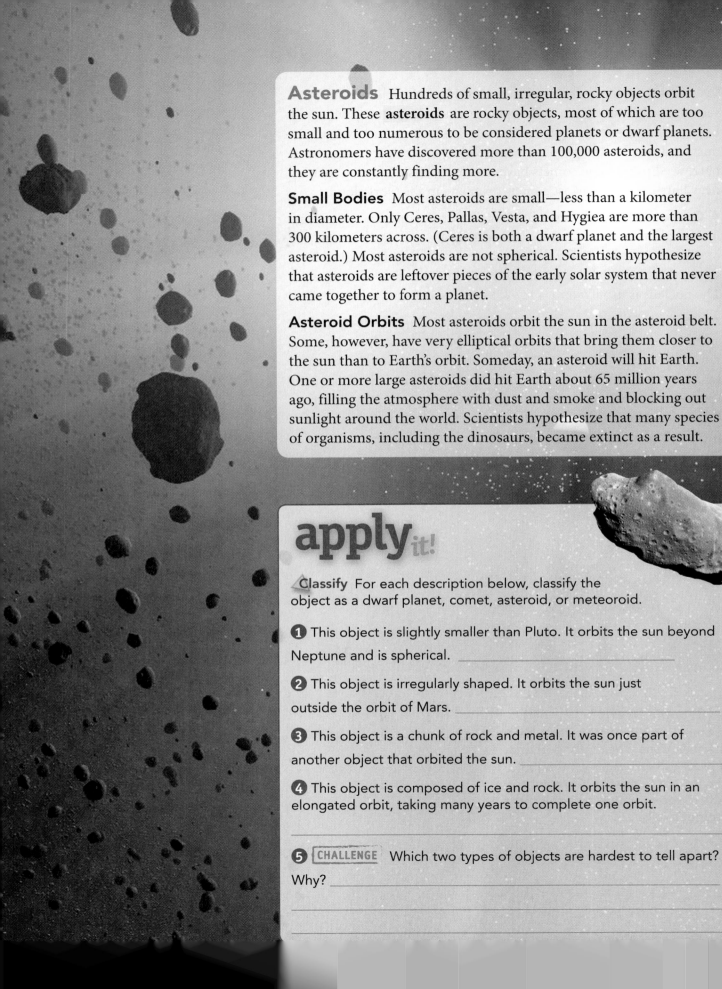

apply it!

Classify For each description below, classify the object as a dwarf planet, comet, asteroid, or meteoroid.

1 This object is slightly smaller than Pluto. It orbits the sun beyond Neptune and is spherical. _____

2 This object is irregularly shaped. It orbits the sun just outside the orbit of Mars. _____

3 This object is a chunk of rock and metal. It was once part of another object that orbited the sun. _____

4 This object is composed of ice and rock. It orbits the sun in an elongated orbit, taking many years to complete one orbit.

_____

5 CHALLENGE Which two types of objects are hardest to tell apart? Why? _____

_____

_____

Meteoroids Chunks of rock or dust smaller than asteroids are called meteoroids. Meteoroids are generally less than 10 meters across. Some meteoroids form when asteroids collide. Others form when comets break up, creating dust clouds.

Meteors and Meteorites When a meteoroid enters Earth's atmosphere, friction with the air creates heat and produces a streak of light. This streak is a **meteor.** (People often call meteors shooting stars, but they are not stars.) Most meteors come from tiny bits of rock or dust that burn up completely. But some larger meteoroids do not burn up. Meteoroids that pass through the atmosphere and are found on Earth's surface are called **meteorites.** Meteorite impacts can leave craters, such as the one shown in **Figure 4.**

Meteor Showers Meteor showers occur when Earth passes through an area with many meteoroids. Some of these groups of meteoroids are bits of comets that broke up. These meteor showers occur every year as Earth passes through the same areas. Meteor showers are often named for the constellation from which they appear to come. The Perseids, Geminids, and Orionids are examples of meteor showers.

FIGURE 4 ·······································
Meteor Crater
Meteor Crater in Arizona formed about 50,000 years ago from the impact of a meteorite 50–100 meters wide. ✎ **Predict How would a large meteorite impact affect Earth today?**

_____

_____

_____

○ Approximate size of meteorite relative to crater

Do the Quick Lab
Changing Orbits.

🔑 Assess Your Understanding

1a. Review (Comets/Asteroids) are rocky, while (comets/asteroids) are made of ice and dust.

b. Compare and Contrast What is the difference between a dwarf planet and an asteroid?

_____

_____

SC.8.E.5.7

c. Relate Cause and Effect How and why does a comet change as it approaches the sun?

_____

_____

_____

SC.8.E.5.7

got it? ··

○ **I get it!** Now I know that small solar system objects include _____

_____

_____

○ I need extra help with _____

Go to MY SCIENCE Ⓢ COACH *online for help with this subject.*

SC.8.E.5.7

LESSON 6 Models of the Solar System

UNLOCK THE ESSENTIAL ?

What Was the Geocentric Model?
SC.8.N.1.6, SC.8.E.5.8

How Did the Heliocentric Model Develop?
SC.8.N.1.6, SC.8.E.5.8, MA.6.A.3.6

my planet Diary

CAREER

Picturing the Solar System

When Walter Myers was seven years old, he found a book with drawings of astronauts walking on the moons of Saturn. Ever since, he's been making space pictures himself. At first, he used pencil. Today, he works on computers. He likes using computers because he can create images that are more like photographs, such as the ones below.

As an artist, Mr. Myers can show scenes that haven't been photographed, such as ideas for future spacecraft and the views from another planet's moons. Mr. Myers especially likes creating views of what human visitors to other planets might see. His work has appeared in books, magazines, Web sites, and even on television!

Use what you have read to answer these questions.

1. What tool does Walter Myers use?

_____

2. Why do people use art or other models to show objects in the solar system?

_____

_____

_____

_____

> PLANET DIARY Go to **Planet Diary** to learn more about models of the solar system.

Lab zone
Do the Inquiry Warm-Up
What Is at the Center?

Vocabulary
- geocentric
- heliocentric
- ellipse

Skills
↩ Reading: Sequence
△ Inquiry: Make Models

What Was the Geocentric Model?

From here on Earth, it seems as if our planet is stationary and that the sun, moon, and stars are moving around Earth. But is the sky really moving above you? Centuries ago, before there were space shuttles or even telescopes, people had no easy way to find out.

Ancient Observations Ancient observers, including the Greeks, Chinese, and Mayans, noticed that the patterns of the stars didn't change over time. Although the stars seemed to move, they stayed in the same position relative to one another. These people also observed planets, which moved among the stars.

Many early observers thought Earth was at the center of the universe. Some Chinese observers thought Earth was under a dome of stars. Many Greek astronomers thought that Earth was inside rotating spheres nested inside each other. These spheres contained the stars and planets. Since *ge* is the Greek word for "Earth," an Earth-centered model is known as a **geocentric** (jee oh SEN trik) model. ⚷ **In a geocentric model, Earth is at the center of the revolving planets and stars.**

Ptolemy's Model About A.D. 140, the Greek astronomer Ptolemy (TAHL uh mee) further developed the geocentric model. Like the earlier Greeks, Ptolemy thought that Earth was at the center of the universe. In Ptolemy's model, however, the planets moved in small circles carried along in bigger circles.

Ptolemy's geocentric model explained the motions observed in the sky fairly accurately. As a result, the geocentric model of the universe was widely accepted for nearly 1,500 years after Ptolemy.

FLORIDA NGSSS

SC.8.N.1.6 Understand that scientific investigations involve the collection of empirical evidence, the use of logical reasoning, and the application of imagination in devising models to make sense of the collected evidence.

SC.8.E.5.8 Compare various historical models of the Solar System, including geocentric and heliocentric.

apply it!

Critique Scientific Explanations and Models Describe an experience from everyday life that appears to support the geocentric model.

_____

_____

_____

_____

_____

_____

_____

Lab zone ® Do the Quick Lab *Going Around in Circles.*

⚷ Assess Your Understanding

got it? ....

○ **I get it!** Now I know that the geocentric model is _____

_____

○ **I need extra help with** _____

Go to **my science** ⓢ **COACH** *online for help with this subject.*

SC.8.N.1.6, SC.8.E.5.8

FLORIDA NGSSS

SC.8.N.1.6 Understand that scientific investigations involve the collection of empirical evidence, the use of logical reasoning, and the application of imagination in devising models.

SC.8.E.5.8 Compare various historical models of the Solar System, including geocentric and heliocentric.

MA.6.A.3.6 Construct equations to describe simple relations using algebraic notation.

How Did the Heliocentric Model Develop?

Not everybody believed in the geocentric system. An ancient Greek scientist named Aristarchus developed a sun-centered model called a heliocentric (hee lee oh SEN trik) system. *Helios* is Greek for "sun." In a **heliocentric** system, Earth and the other planets revolve around the sun. This model was not well received in ancient times, however, because people could not accept that Earth was not at the center of the universe.

FIGURE 1 ··

▶VIRTUAL LAB **Changing Models**
Make Models Draw each model of the solar system. Include the sun, Earth, the moon, and Jupiter. Include Jupiter's moons in Galileo's model.

CHALLENGE Why might people not have believed Galileo's discoveries?

_____

_____

A.D. ——————————— **1500** ——————————————— **1550**

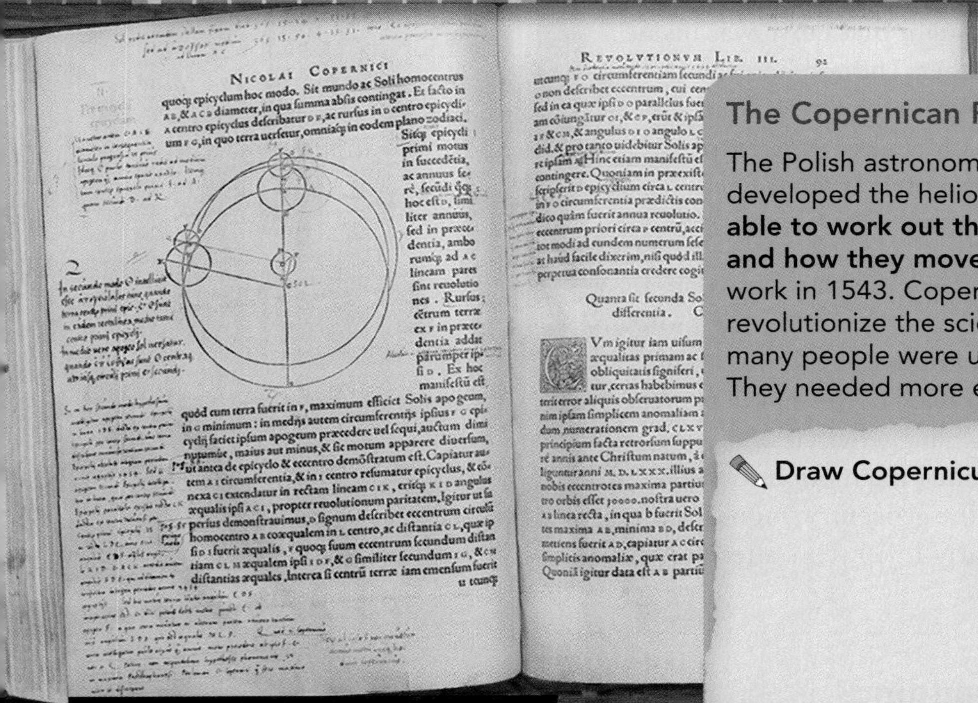

The Copernican Revolution

The Polish astronomer Nicolaus Copernicus further developed the heliocentric model. 🔑 **Copernicus was able to work out the arrangement of the known planets and how they move around the sun.** He published his work in 1543. Copernicus's theory would eventually revolutionize the science of astronomy. But at first many people were unwilling to accept his theory. They needed more evidence to be convinced.

✏️ **Draw Copernicus's model.**

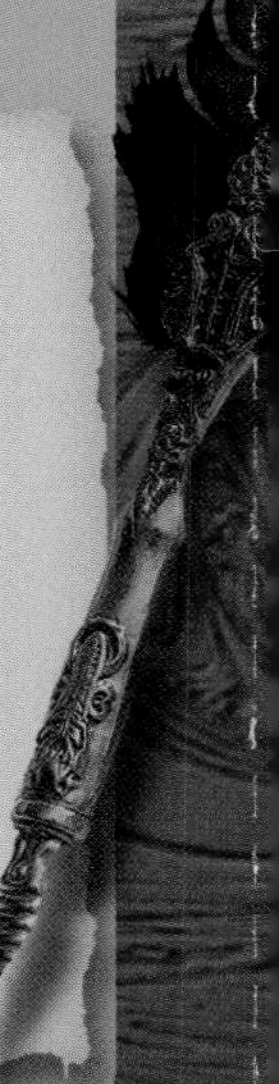

🔁 **Sequence** Which astronomer did his work first?
- Tycho Brahe
- Nicolaus Copernicus
- Galileo Galilei
- Johannes Kepler

Brahe and Kepler

Ptolemy and Copernicus both assumed that planets moved in perfect circles. Their models fit existing observations fairly well. But in the late 1500s, the Dutch astronomer Tycho Brahe (TEE koh BRAH uh) made much more accurate observations. Brahe's assistant, Johannes Kepler, used the observations to figure out the shape of the planets' orbits. When he used circular orbits, his calculations did not fit the observations. ⌐ **After years of detailed calculations, Kepler found that the orbit of each planet is an ellipse.** An **ellipse** is an oval shape.

Tycho Brahe's Observatory

✏ **Draw Kepler's model.**

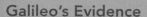 **1600**

1650

Galileo's Evidence

In the 1500s and early 1600s, most people still believed in the geocentric model. ⌐ **However, evidence collected by the Italian scientist Galileo Galilei gradually convinced others that the heliocentric model was correct.** In 1610, Galileo used a telescope to discover four moons around Jupiter. These moons proved that not everything in the sky revolves around Earth. Galileo also discovered that Venus goes through a series of phases similar to the moon's. But Venus would not have a full set of phases if both it and the sun circled around Earth. Therefore, Galileo reasoned, the geocentric model must be incorrect.

✏ **Draw Galileo's model.**

The work of Copernicus, Brahe, Kepler, and Galileo established the truth of the heliocentric model, but did not explain why this model was correct. It required the work of one more scientist, Isaac Newton, to explain the motion of objects in the solar system.

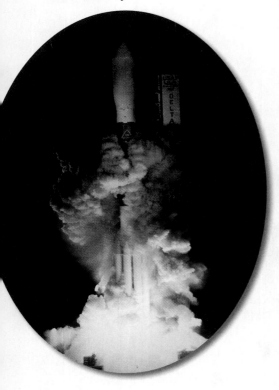

Newton's Gravity

Newton's Gravity The English scientist Isaac Newton was born in 1643, the year after Galileo died. Recall that Newton studied motion and developed three laws of motion. His first law of motion says that an object at rest will stay at rest and that an object in motion will stay in motion with a constant speed and direction unless acted on by a force. This tendency to resist a change of motion is called inertia.

Newton also developed the law of universal gravitation, which says that the strength of the force of gravity between two objects depends on the masses of the objects and the distance between them.

Newton used these laws to analyze the motion of the moon around Earth. Applying the first law of motion, Newton noted that the moon should move off in a straight line. But Earth's gravity pulls the moon inward, preventing the moon from moving in a straight line. Instead, the moon orbits Earth.

Newton saw that the same combination of gravity and inertia would keep the planets moving in orbits around the more massive body of the sun. He performed calculations based on the laws of motion and universal gravitation. His calculations supported Kepler and Galileo's models of the solar system.

🔑 **Newton proved that gravity and inertia working together explained the motions of the planets and their moons, which confirmed the heliocentric model.** It had taken Kepler years of calculations to show that planets moved in ellipses. Using the laws of gravity and motion, Newton was able to prove this same fact in an afternoon.

FIGURE 2 ·······································

Newton and the Apple

Newton realized that the moon is falling toward Earth, just like an apple falls from the tree.

✏️ **Interpret Diagrams** Draw the path of the apple and the path of the moon. Why doesn't the moon hit Earth?

_____

_____

_____

do the math!

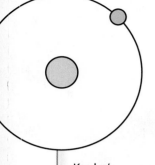

Kepler's First Law

Kepler's Third Law

Kepler discovered two laws of planetary motion besides the fact that planets move in ellipses. His second law states that planets sweep out equal areas of the ellipse in equal times, so planets move faster when they are closer to the sun. His third law states that the period *P* of a planet's orbit squared is proportional to the average distance *a* from the sun cubed. If the period is given in years and the distance in AU, then this becomes an equation.

Kepler's Second Law: Equal areas in equal time

$$P^2 = a^3$$

✏️ **CHALLENGE** Calculate the periods of the orbits according to Kepler's third law and write them in the table below.

Planet	Mercury	Venus	Earth	Mars	Jupiter	Saturn	Uranus	Neptune
Average Distance from sun (AU)	0.39	0.72	1.0	1.52	5.2	9.54	19.2	30.05
Period of orbit (years)								

MA.6.A.3.6, MA.8.A.4.1

Lab zone® Do the Quick Lab *A Loopy Ellipse.*

🔑 Assess Your Understanding

1a. Review (Kepler/Copernicus) discovered that planets move in ellipses.

SC.8.N.1.6, SC.8.E.5.8

b. Relate Evidence and Explanation What discoveries by Galileo support the heliocentric model?

_____

_____

SC.8.N.1.6, SC.8.E.5.8

c. Make Judgments Why does Newton's work finally confirm the heliocentric model?

_____

_____

_____

_____

_____

_____

SC.8.N.1.6, SC.8.E.5.8

got it? ....

○ **I get it!** Now I know that the heliocentric model was developed _____

○ **I need extra help with** _____

Go to **MY SCIENCE** COACH online for help with this subject.

SC.8.N.1.6, SC.8.E.5.8

Study Guide

Objects in the solar system are different because they formed _____

_____

LESSON 1 Introducing the Solar System
SC.8.E.5.7

🔑 Our solar system consists of the sun, the planets, their moons, and smaller objects.

🔑 The solar system formed about 4.6 billion years ago from a cloud of hydrogen, helium, rock, ice, and other materials pulled together by gravity.

Vocabulary
• solar system • astronomical unit • planet
• dwarf planet • planetesimal

LESSON 2 Earth's Moon
SC.8.E.5.7

🔑 The moon is dry and airless and has an irregular surface. Compared to Earth, the moon is small and has large variations in its surface temperature.

Vocabulary
• maria • crater
• meteoroid

LESSON 3 The Inner Planets
SC.8.N.2.1, SC.8.E.5.7

🔑 The inner planets are small and dense and have rocky surfaces.

🔑 Mercury is the smallest terrestrial planet and the planet closest to the sun. Venus has a thick atmosphere and the hottest surface of any planet. Earth has a suitable temperature range and atmosphere for living things to survive. Mars has ice and may have had liquid water in the past.

Vocabulary
• terrestrial planet • greenhouse effect

LESSON 4 The Outer Planets
SC.8.E.5.7

🔑 The outer planets are much larger than Earth and do not have solid surfaces.

🔑 Jupiter is the largest and most massive planet. Saturn has the most spectacular rings of any planet. Uranus's axis of rotation is tilted at an angle of about 90 degrees from the vertical. Neptune is a cold, blue planet with visible clouds.

Vocabulary
• gas giant • ring

LESSON 5 Small Solar System Objects
SC.8.E.5.7

🔑 Scientists classify small objects based on their sizes, shapes, compositions, and orbits. The major categories include dwarf planets, comets, asteroids, and meteoroids.

Vocabulary
• asteroid belt • Kuiper belt • Oort cloud
• comet • coma • nucleus • asteroid
• meteor • meteorite

LESSON 6 Models of the Solar System
SC.8.N.1.6, SC.8.E.5.8

🔑 In a geocentric model, Earth is at the center.

🔑 Copernicus worked out the arrangement of the known planets and how they orbit the sun.

🔑 Kepler found that planets' orbits are ellipses.

🔑 Evidence from Galileo and Newton confirmed that the heliocentric model was correct.

Vocabulary
• geocentric • heliocentric • ellipse

Review and Assessment

LESSON 1 Introducing the Solar System

1. Pluto is an example of a(n)

    a. dwarf planet.   **b.** inner planet.

    c. outer planet.   **d.** planetesimal.

SC.8.E.5.7

2. An astronomical unit is equal to _____

_____

SC.8.E.5.7

3. Compare and Contrast Compare the conditions that led to the formation of the inner planets with those that led to the formation of the outer planets.

_____

_____

_____

_____

SC.8.E.5.7

LESSON 2 Earth's Moon

4. What caused the moon's craters?

    a. maria   **b.** meteoroids

    c. tides   **d.** volcanoes

SC.8.E.5.7

5. The moon's light-colored highlands are

_____

SC.8.E.5.7

6. Explain Why do temperatures vary so much on the moon? _____

_____

_____

SC.8.E.5.7

7. **Write About It** Suppose you were hired to design a spacesuit for use on the moon. What characteristics of the moon would be important for you to consider? Explain.

SC.8.E.5.7

LESSON 3 The Inner Planets

8. What feature is shared by all the inner planets?

    a. thick atmosphere   **b.** rocky surface

    c. ring system   **d.** liquid water

SC.8.E.5.7

9. The inner planets are also called _____

_____

SC.8.E.5.7

10. Apply Concepts Explain why Venus has the hottest surface of any planet.

_____

_____

_____

_____

SC.8.E.5.7

11. **Write About It** Choose one inner planet. Write a news article describing a visit to that planet's surface. Include descriptive details.

SC.8.E.5.7

LESSON 4 The Outer Planets

Use the illustration to answer Question 12.

12. Interpret Diagrams What planet is shown above? What is unusual about it? What do scientists think caused that unusual feature?

_____

_____

_____

_____

SC.8.E.5.7

CHAPTER

LESSON 5 Small Solar System Objects

13. Where are most dwarf planets found?

   a. asteroid belt   **b.** Kuiper belt

   c. Oort cloud   **d.** plutoid belt

   SC.8.E.5.7

14. A _____ is a meteoroid that reaches Earth's surface.

   SC.8.E.5.7

15. **Compare and Contrast** Compare and contrast asteroids, comets, and meteoroids.

   _____

   _____

   _____

   _____

   _____

   _____

   SC.8.E.5.7

16. **Distinguish** What is the difference between an asteroid and a dwarf planet?

   _____

   _____

   _____

   _____

   SC.8.E.5.7

17. **Write About It** Suppose you could witness a large meteorite or asteroid striking Earth. Write a news report explaining the event.

   SC.8.E.5.7

18. **Predict** Do you think astronomers have found all solar system objects? Explain.

   _____

   _____

   _____

   _____

   _____

   _____

   SC.8.E.5.7

LESSON 6 Models of the Solar System

19. What object is at the center of a geocentric system?

   a. Earth   **b.** the moon

   c. a star   **d.** the sun

   SC.8.E.5.8

20. Kepler discovered that planets move in

   _____

   SC.8.E.5.8

21. **Relate Cause and Effect** How did Tycho Brahe's work contribute to the development of the heliocentric model?

   _____

   _____

   _____

   SC.8.E.5.8

22. **Write About It** Suppose you lived at the time of Copernicus. Write a letter to a scientific journal supporting the heliocentric model.

   SC.8.N.1.6, SC.8.E.5.8

APPLY THE ESSENTIAL ?

Why are objects in the solar system different from each other?

Gaseous hydrogen and helium

Liquid hydrogen and helium

Liquid "ices"

Rocky core

23. What type of planet is shown? Under what conditions would it most likely have formed?

   _____

   _____

   _____

   _____

   SC.8.E.5.7

Florida Benchmarks Review

Circle the letter of the best answer.

1 The table below shows data for five planets.

Planet	Period of Rotation (Earth days)	Period of Revolution (Earth years)	Average Distance from the Sun (million km)
Mars	1.03	1.9	228
Jupiter	0.41	12	779
Saturn	0.45	29	1,434
Uranus	0.72	84	2,873
Neptune	0.67	164	4,495

According to the table, which planet has a "day" that is most similar in length to a day on Earth?

A Mars   **B** Jupiter
C Neptune   **D** Uranus

SC.8.E.5.7

2 What characteristic do all of the outer planets share?

A They have rocky surfaces.
B They are larger than the sun.
C They have many moons.
D They have thin atmospheres.

SC.8.E.5.7

3 The dark, flat areas on the moon are called

A maria.
B highlands.
C craters.
D meteoroids.

SC.8.E.5.7

4 Mercury has a daytime temperature of about 430°C and a nighttime temperature below −170°C. What is the **best** explanation for this?

A Mercury has a greenhouse effect.
B Mercury is the closest planet to the sun.
C Mercury has little to no atmosphere.
D Mercury has no liquid water.

SC.8.E.5.7

5 From what region do **most** comets come?

A asteroid belt
B inner solar system
C Kuiper belt
D Oort cloud

SC.8.E.5.7

6 What model of the solar system is shown?

A geocentric   **B** heliocentric
C universal   **D** Ptolemy's

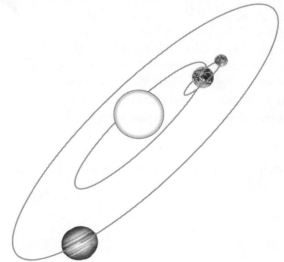

SC.8.N.1.6, SC.8.E.5.8

WHAT'S HAPPENING TO THE MOON?

 How do Earth, the moon, and the sun interact?

This photograph shows a series of images of the moon taken over the course of an evening. Why do you think the moon looks different in each image? Develop Hypotheses Explain what you think happened during the period of time shown in the photograph.

> **UNTAMED SCIENCE** Watch the **Untamed Science** video to learn more about the moon.

_____

_____

_____

_____

_____

_____

_____

Earth, Moon, and Sun

CHAPTER 5

FLORIDA Next Generation Sunshine State Standards

Big Idea 1: SC.8.N.1.6
Big Idea 5: SC.8.E.5.9

Language Arts: LA.8.2.2.3, LA.8.4.2.2
Mathematics: MA.6.A.3.6, MA.6.A.5.6.3

5 Getting Started

Check Your Understanding

1. Background Read the paragraph below and then answer the question.

Santiago is studying a globe. He sees that Earth has North and South poles. The globe **rotates** around a line through its center between the two poles. Another line called the **equator** divides Earth into two halves, the **Northern Hemisphere** and the **Southern Hemisphere.**

To **rotate** is to spin in place around a central line, or axis.

The **equator** is the imaginary line that divides Earth into two halves, the **Northern Hemisphere** and the **Southern Hemisphere.**

• Where is the equator found?

_____

_____

> MY READING WEB If you had trouble answering the question above, visit **My Reading Web** and type in *Earth, Moon, and Sun.*

Vocabulary Skill

Identify Multiple Meanings Words you use every day may have different meanings in science. Look at the different meanings of the words below.

Word	Everyday Meaning	Scientific Meaning
weight	*n.* a heavy object used for exercise **Example:** The athlete lifted *weights* to build strength.	*n.* a measure of the force of gravity on an object **Example:** The object's *weight* was 10 newtons.
force	*v.* to use power to make someone do something **Example:** She had to *force* herself to get up early.	*n.* a push or pull exerted on an object **Example:** You exert *force* when you open and close a door.

LA.8.1.6.9

2. Quick Check Circle the sentence below that uses the scientific meaning of *force.*

• The *force* of gravity holds objects in their orbits.

• Her parents are trying to *force* her to get a job.

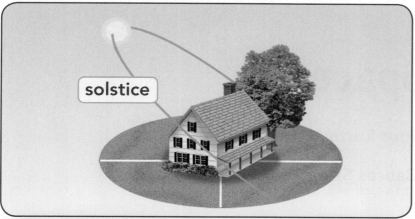

solstice

phase

solar eclipse

spring tide

Chapter Preview

LESSON 1
- axis
- rotation
- revolution
- calendar
- solstice
- equinox
- ↻ **Sequence**
- △ **Infer**

LESSON 2
- phase
- eclipse
- solar eclipse
- umbra
- penumbra
- lunar eclipse
- ↻ **Relate Text and Visuals**
- △ **Make Models**

LESSON 3
- tide
- spring tide
- neap tide
- ↻ **Relate Cause and Effect**
- △ **Observe**

> VOCAB FLASH CARDS For extra help with vocabulary, visit **Vocab Flash Cards** and type in *Earth, Moon, and Sun.*

UNLOCK THE ESSENTIAL ?

🔑 **How Does Earth Move?**
SC.8.E.5.9

🔑 **What Causes Seasons?**
SC.8.E.5.9, LA.8.2.2.3, MA.6.A.3.6

my planeт diary

The Seasons

Misconception: The seasons change because Earth's distance from the sun changes.

Fact: Seasons are the result of Earth's tilted axis.

Evidence: Earth's distance from the sun does change, but that's not why Earth has seasons. If that were the cause, people in the Northern and Southern hemispheres would have the same seasons at the same time. Instead, seasons in the Northern and Southern hemispheres are reversed. As Earth moves around the sun, sometimes the Northern Hemisphere is tilted toward the sun. At other times the Southern Hemisphere is tilted toward the sun.

MISCONCEPTION

Before you read the rest of this lesson, answer the questions below.

1. Why are summers generally warmer than winters?

_____

_____

_____

_____

2. Why are the winters wamer in Florida than in Massachusetts?

_____

_____

_____

_____

_____

> PLANET DIARY Go to **Planet Diary** to learn more about Earth's motions.

January 21 *where are you and what are you doing today?*

Lab zone® Do the Inquiry Warm-Up *What Causes Day and Night?*

Vocabulary
- axis • rotation • revolution
- calendar • solstice • equinox

Skills
- Reading: Sequence
- Inquiry: Infer

How Does Earth Move?

Until a few hundred years ago, most people thought that Earth stood still and the sun, moon, and stars moved around it. But today, scientists know that Earth itself moves and that objects seem to move across the sky because of Earth's motion. **Earth moves in space in two major ways: rotation and revolution.**

Rotation The imaginary line that passes through Earth's center and the North and South poles is Earth's **axis.** The spinning of Earth on its axis is called **rotation.**

Earth's rotation causes day and night, as you can see in **Figure 1.** As Earth rotates eastward, the sun appears to move west across the sky. As Earth continues to turn to the east, the sun appears to set in the west. Sunlight can't reach the side of Earth facing away from the sun, so it is night there. It takes Earth about 24 hours to rotate once. As you know, each 24-hour cycle of day and night is called a day.

FLORIDA NGSSS

SC.8.E.5.9 Explain the impact of objects in space on each other including:
1. the Sun on the Earth including seasons and gravitational attraction.
2. the Moon on the Earth, including the phases, tides, and eclipses, and the relative position of each body.

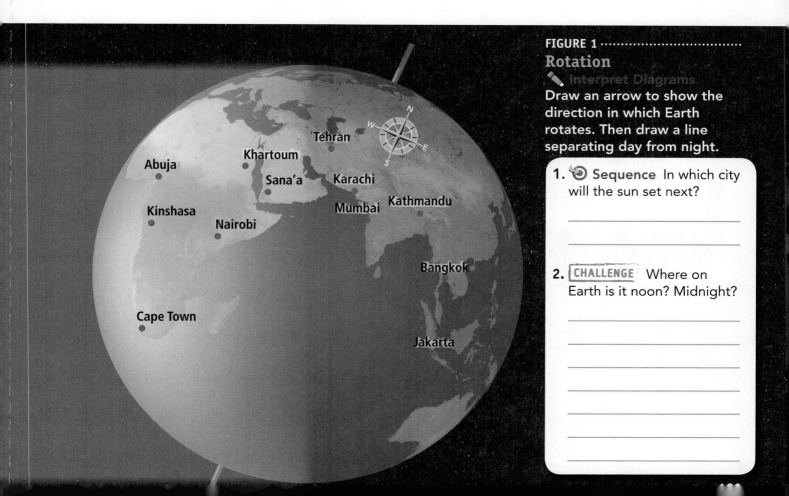

FIGURE 1
Rotation
Interpret Diagrams
Draw an arrow to show the direction in which Earth rotates. Then draw a line separating day from night.

1. **Sequence** In which city will the sun set next?

_____

_____

2. **CHALLENGE** Where on Earth is it noon? Midnight?

_____

_____

_____

_____

_____

Revolution Recall that Earth revolves around the sun because the sun's gravity pulls on it while Earth's inertia keeps it moving ahead. **Revolution** is the movement of one object around another. One revolution of Earth around the sun is called a year. Earth's path, or orbit, is a slightly elongated circle, or ellipse. Earth's orbit brings the planet closest to the sun in January.

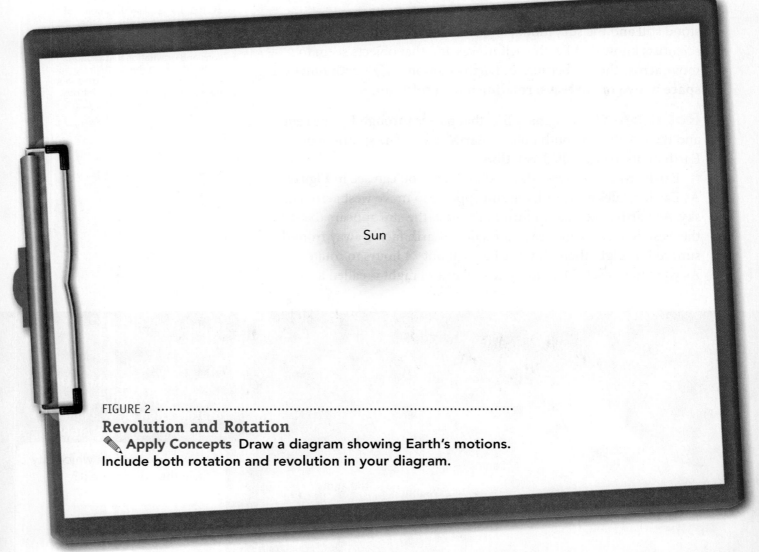

Sun

FIGURE 2 ···
Revolution and Rotation
✎ **Apply Concepts** Draw a diagram showing Earth's motions. Include both rotation and revolution in your diagram.

···✎·······················
⟳ **Sequence** Which calendar discussed in this section was developed most recently?

Calendars People of many cultures have divided time based on the motions of Earth and the moon. They have used the motions to establish calendars. A **calendar** is a system of organizing time that defines the beginning, length, and divisions of a year.

The most common calendar today is divided into years, months, and days. One year equals the time it takes Earth to complete one orbit. One day equals the time it takes Earth to turn once on its axis. People also divide the year into months based on the moon's cycle. The time from one full moon to another is about 29 days, though modern months do not match the moon's cycle exactly.

The History of the Calendar

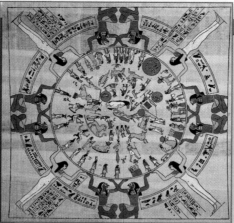

Egyptian

The ancient Egyptians created one of the first calendars. Based on star motions, they calculated that the year was about 365 days long. They divided the year into 12 months of 30 days each, with an extra 5 days at the end.

Roman

The Romans borrowed the Egyptian calendar. But Earth's orbit actually takes about 365¼ days. The Romans adjusted the Egyptian calendar by adding one day every four years. You know this fourth year as "leap year," when February is given 29 days instead of its usual 28. Using leap years helps to ensure that annual events, such as the beginning of summer, occur on the same date each year.

Gregorian

The Roman calendar was off by a little more than 11 minutes a year. Over the centuries, these minutes added up. By the 1500s, the beginning of spring was about ten days too early. To straighten things out, Pope Gregory XIII dropped ten days from the year 1582. He also made some other minor changes to the Roman system to form the calendar that we use today.

Lab zone® Do the Quick Lab *Sun Shadows.*

🔑 Assess Your Understanding

1a. Identify Earth's _____ causes day and night.   SC.8.E.5.9

b. Explain How does the sun's gravitational attraction impact Earth's motion?

_____

_____

SC.8.E.5.9

c. Infer Why do people use Earth's motions to determine units of time?

_____

_____

_____

SC.8.E.5.9

got it?

○ **I get it!** Now I know that Earth moves by _____

_____

○ **I need extra help with** _____

Go to **my science ⑤ coach** online for help with this subject.   SC.8.E.5.9

FLORIDA NGSSS

SC.8.E.5.9 Explain the impact of the Sun on the Earth including seasons and gravitational attraction.

LA.8.2.2.3 The student will organize information to show understanding or relationships among facts, ideas, and events (e.g., representing key points within text through comparing/contrasting).

MA.6.A.3.6 Construct and analyze tables and equations to describe simple relations using both common language and algebraic notation.

What Causes Seasons?

Many places that are far from Earth's equator and its poles have four distinct seasons: winter, spring, summer, and autumn. But there are differences in temperature from place to place. For instance, it is generally warmer near the equator than near the poles. Why?

How Sunlight Hits Earth

Figure 3 shows how sunlight strikes Earth's surface. Notice that, near the equator, sunlight hits Earth's surface from almost overhead. Near the poles, sunlight arrives at a steep angle. As a result, it is spread out over a greater area. That's why it is warmer near the equator than near the poles.

Earth's Tilted Axis

If Earth's axis were straight up and down relative to its orbit, temperatures in an area would remain fairly constant year-round. There would be no seasons. **Earth has seasons because its axis is tilted as it revolves around the sun.**

Notice in **Figure 4** that Earth's axis is always tilted at an angle of 23.5° from the vertical. The North Pole always points in the same direction. As Earth revolves around the sun, the north end of its axis is tilted away from the sun for part of the year and toward the sun for part of the year. Summer and winter are caused by Earth's tilt as it revolves around the sun.

FIGURE 3 ·······························

Sunlight on Earth

The diagram shows how Earth's tilted axis affects the strength of sunlight in different places.

⚠Infer **Draw a circle around the area where sunlight is most direct. Mark an X on the places that sunlight reaches, but where it is less direct.**

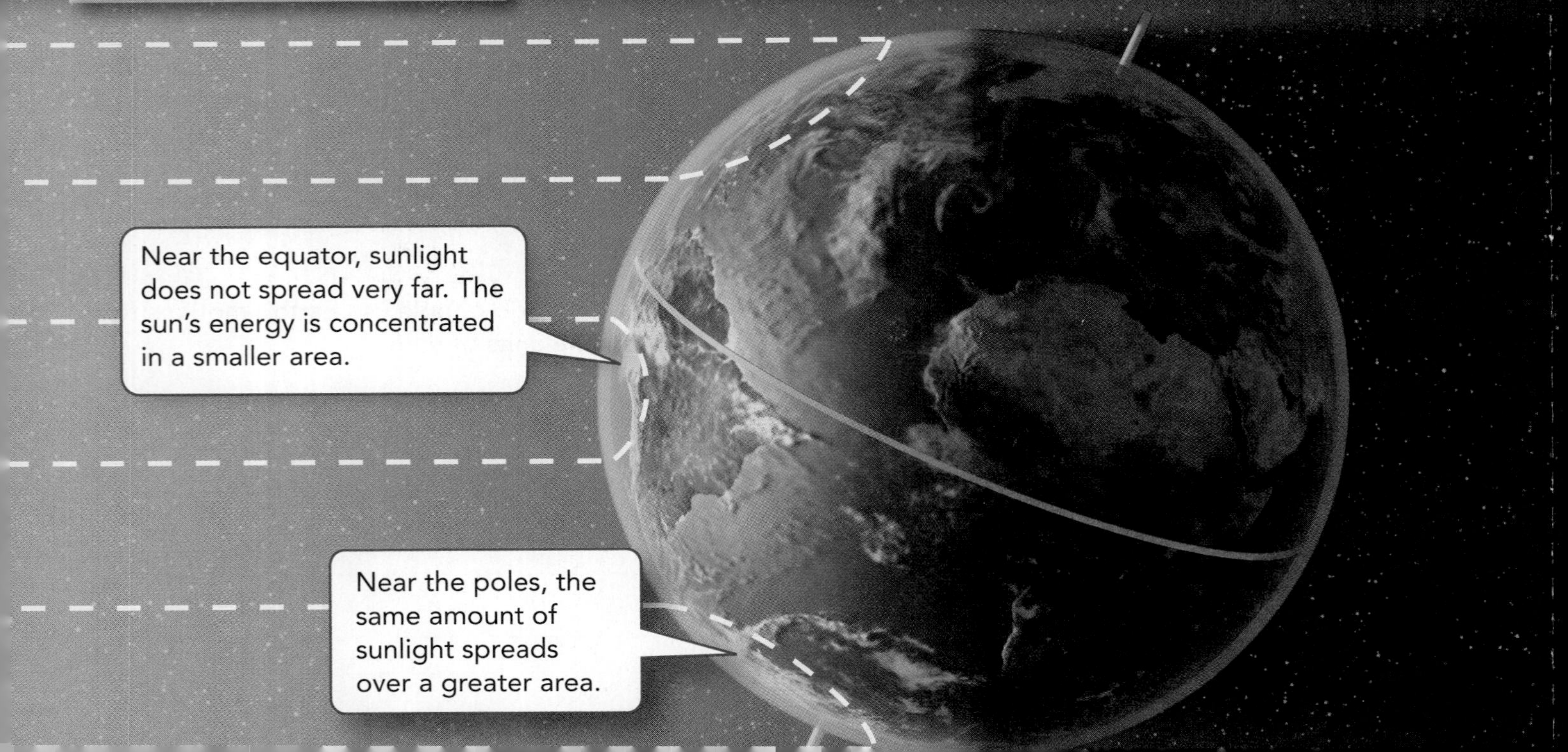

Near the equator, sunlight does not spread very far. The sun's energy is concentrated in a smaller area.

Near the poles, the same amount of sunlight spreads over a greater area.

June In June, the north end of Earth's axis is tilted toward the sun. In the Northern Hemisphere, the noon sun is high in the sky and there are more hours of daylight than darkness. The sun's rays are concentrated. It is summer in the Northern Hemisphere.

At the same time south of the equator, the sun's energy is spread over a larger area. The sun is low in the sky and days are shorter than nights. It is winter in the Southern Hemisphere.

December In December, people in the Southern Hemisphere receive the most direct sunlight, so it is summer. At the same time, the sun's rays in the Northern Hemisphere are more slanted and there are fewer hours of daylight. So it is winter in the Northern Hemisphere.

March

June

December

September

FIGURE 4 ·······················
> INTERACTIVE ART **Seasons**
The diagram shows how
Earth moves during the year.
It is not drawn to scale.

✎ **Compare and Contrast**
Compare the weather and
sunlight in the Northern
and Southern hemispheres
in March and September.
LA.8.2.2.3

Florida has many trees that stay green year-round, such as live oaks, gumbo-limbo, mahogany, pines, and palms. But parts of Florida also have deciduous trees, or trees that shed their leaves in the fall. Sumac, birch, and ash are deciduous trees found in Florida.

Solstices

The sun appears farthest north of the equator once each year and farthest south once each year. Each of these days is known as a **solstice** (SOHL stis). The day when the sun appears farthest north is the summer solstice in the Northern Hemisphere and the winter solstice in the Southern Hemisphere. This solstice occurs around June 21 each year. It is the longest day of the year in the Northern Hemisphere and the shortest day in the Southern Hemisphere. As you can see in **Figure 5,** the sun rises to the northeast and sets to the northwest.

Similarly, around December 21, the sun appears farthest south. This is the winter solstice in the Northern Hemisphere and the summer solstice in the Southern Hemisphere. The sun rises to the southeast and sets to the southwest.

Equinoxes

Halfway between the solstices, neither hemisphere is tilted toward the sun. The noon sun is directly overhead at the equator, rises due east, and sets due west. Each of these days is known as an **equinox,** which means "equal night." During an equinox, day and night are each about 12 hours long everywhere. The vernal (spring) equinox occurs around March 21 and marks the beginning of spring in the Northern Hemisphere. The fall, or autumnal, equinox occurs around September 22. It marks the beginning of fall in the Northern Hemisphere.

FIGURE 5 ....

Solstices and Equinoxes
The diagrams show the apparent path of the sun at the solstices and equinoxes in the Northern Hemisphere. The sun rises and sets farthest north at the June solstice and farthest south at the December solstice.

✎ **Apply Concepts** Draw the sun's path at the equinoxes and the December solstice for the Southern Hemisphere.

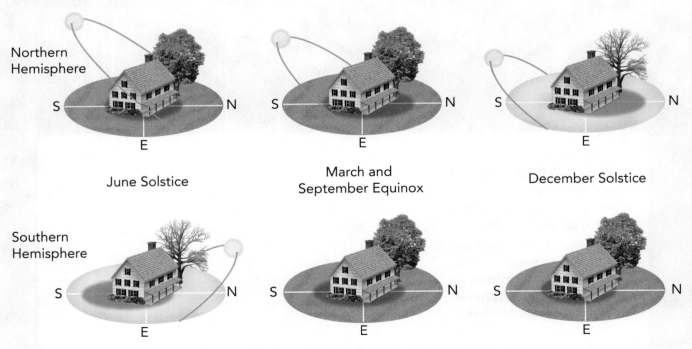

Northern Hemisphere

June Solstice

March and September Equinox

December Solstice

Southern Hemisphere

do the math! Sample Problem

Calculating Percents

The table shows the number of hours of sunlight in three cities at different times of year. What percentage of a 24-hour day has sunlight in Miami on January 1?

STEP 1 Divide the number of hours of sunlight by the total number of hours.

$$\frac{\text{Hours of sunlight}}{\text{Total hours}} = \frac{10.57 \text{ hours}}{24 \text{ hours}} = 0.44$$

STEP 2 Multiply by 100 to find the percent.

$$0.44 \times 100 = 44\%$$

In Miami, 44% of a 24-hour day has sunlight on January 1.

City	Approximate Latitude	Hours of Daylight			
		January 1	April 1	July 1	October 1
Helsinki, Finland	60°N	5.98	13.33	18.80	11.45
Toronto, Canada	43°N	9.00	12.75	15.38	11.70
Miami, Florida	25°N	10.57	12.42	13.72	11.90

MA.6.A.3.6, MA.8.A.6.4

① Calculate What percentage of a day has sunlight in Helsinki on July 1?

_____

② Calculate What is the difference in the percentage of the day that has sunlight in Helsinki and in Toronto on January 1?

_____

③ Infer What percentage of the day would you expect to have sunlight at the equator in January? In June?

_____

_____

Lab zone ® Do the Lab Investigation
Reasons for the Seasons.

🔑 Assess Your Understanding

2a. Define The noon sun is directly overhead at the equator during (a solstice/an equinox).

SC.8.E.5.9

b. Relate Cause and Effect What causes the seasons? _____

_____

_____

SC.8.E.5.9

c. Predict How would the seasons be different if Earth were not tilted on its axis? Explain.

_____

_____

_____

_____

_____

SC.8.E.5.9

got it? ....

O **I get it!** Now I know that Earth's seasons are caused by _____

_____

O **I need extra help with** _____

Go to **MY SCIENCE COACH** *online for help with this subject.*

SC.8.E.5.9

Phases and Eclipses

🔑 **What Causes the Moon's Phases?**
SC.8.E.5.9, SC.8.N.1.6

🔑 **What Are Eclipses?**
SC.8.E.5.9, LA.8.4.2.2

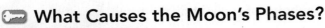

my PLaNeT DiaRY

BLOG

Posted by: Nicole

Location: Bernhard's Bay, New York

One night, my mom, dad, and I were coming home from eating dinner. When we got out of the car, we saw that the moon was turning red. We looked at the moon for a while. Then our neighbor called and said that it was a lunar eclipse. It was an amazing sight.

Think about your own experiences as you answer the question below.

What is the most interesting or unusual event you have ever seen in the sky?

_____

_____

_____

_____

> PLANET DIARY Go to **Planet Diary** to learn more about eclipses.

Lab zone Do the Inquiry Warm-Up *How Does the Moon Move?*

FLORIDA NGSSS

SC.8.E.5.9 Explain the impact of the Moon on the Earth, including phases, tides, and eclipses, and the relative position of each body.

SC.8.N.1.6 Understand that scientific investigations involve the collection of relevant empirical evidence and the use of models to make sense of the collected evidence.

What Causes the Moon's Phases?

Have you ever been kept awake by bright moonlight? The light streaming through your window actually comes from the sun! The moon does not shine with its own light. Instead, it reflects light from the sun. When the moon is full, this light may be bright enough to read by! But at other times, the moon is just a thin crescent in the sky. The different shapes of the moon you see from Earth are called **phases.** Phases are caused by the motions of the moon around Earth.

Vocabulary
- phase   • eclipse   • solar eclipse
- umbra   • penumbra   • lunar eclipse

Skills
Reading: Relate Text and Visuals
Inquiry: Make Models

Motions of the Moon When you look up at the moon, you may see what looks like a face. What you are really seeing is a pattern of light-colored and dark-colored areas on the moon's surface that just happens to look like a face. Oddly, this pattern never seems to move. The same side of the moon, the "near side," always faces Earth. The "far side" of the moon always faces away from Earth. Why? The answer has to do with the moon's motions.

Like Earth, the moon moves through space in two ways. The moon revolves around Earth and also rotates on its own axis. The moon rotates once on its axis in the same time that it takes to revolve once around Earth. Thus, a "day" on the moon is the same length as a month on Earth. For this reason, the same side of the moon always faces Earth, as you can see in **Figure 1**.

As the moon orbits Earth, the relative positions of the moon, Earth, and sun change. **The changing relative positions of the moon, Earth, and sun cause the phases of the moon.**

Vocabulary Identify Multiple Meanings Which sentence uses the scientific meaning of *phase*?

○ The doctor told the parent that the child was just going through a phase.

○ The moon goes through a cycle of phases every month.

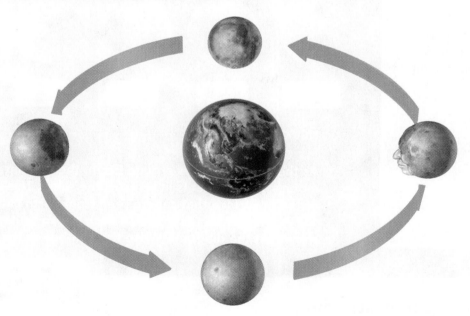

FIGURE 1 ·······

The Moon's Motion
The diagram shows the moon's rotation and revolution. **Infer** Find the face on the rightmost view of the moon. Draw the face as it would appear on each view.

CHALLENGE How would the moon appear from Earth if the moon did not rotate?

_____

_____

Phases of the Moon

Half the moon is almost always in sunlight. But since the moon orbits Earth, you see the moon from different angles. The phase of the moon you see depends on how much of the sunlit side of the moon faces Earth.

During the new moon phase, the side of the moon facing Earth is not lit. As the moon revolves around Earth, you see more of the lit side of the moon, until you see all of the lit side. As the month continues, you see less of the lit side. You can see these changes in Figure 2. About 29.5 days after the last new moon, a new moon occurs again.

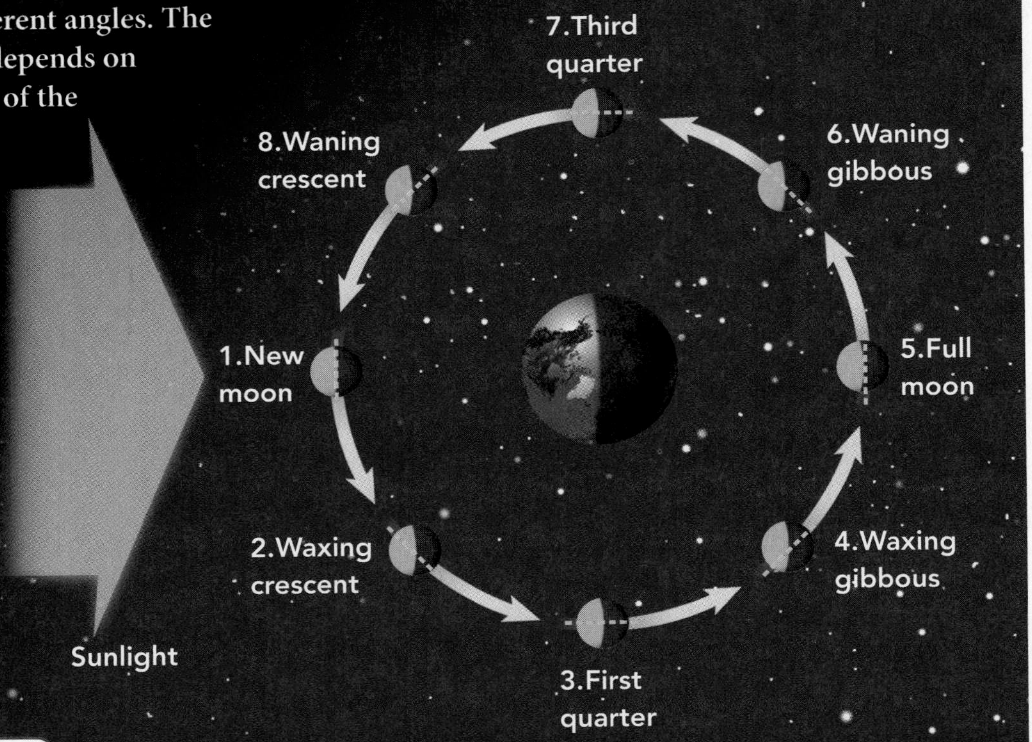

Sunlight

7. Third quarter

8. Waning crescent

6. Waning gibbous

1. New moon

5. Full moon

2. Waxing crescent

4. Waxing gibbous

3. First quarter

apply it!

Make Models Describe a way to model the moon's phases using items you might have at home.

_____

_____

_____

_____

_____

SC.8.N.1.6

FIGURE 2

Moon Phases

As the moon revolves around Earth, the amount of the moon's surface that is lit remains the same. The part of the lit surface that can be seen from Earth changes.

✏ **Interpret Diagrams** **Match each photo to its phase shown on the diagram. Write the number of the phase.**

Lab zone ® Do the Quick Lab Moon Phases.

🗝 Assess Your Understanding

got it? ....

O **I get it!** Now I know that moon phases are caused by _____

_____

O **I need extra help with** _____

Go to MY SCIENCE ⬛ COACH online for help with this subject.

SC.8.E.5.9

What Are Eclipses?

The moon's orbit around Earth is slightly tilted with respect to Earth's orbit around the sun. As a result, the moon travels above and below Earth's orbit. But on rare occasions, Earth, the moon, and the sun line up.

When an object in space comes between the sun and a third object, it casts a shadow on that object, causing an **eclipse** (ih KLIPS) to take place. There are two types of eclipses: solar eclipses and lunar eclipses. (The words *solar* and *lunar* come from the Latin words for "sun" and "moon.")

FLORIDA NGSSS

SC.8.E.5.9 Explain the impact of objects in space on each other including the Moon on the Earth, the phases, tides, and eclipses, and the relative position of each body.

LA.8.4.2.2 The student will record information (e.g., observations and notes) related to a topic, including visual aids to organize and record information.

Solar Eclipses During a new moon, the moon lies between Earth and the sun. 🔑 A **solar eclipse** occurs when the moon passes directly between Earth and the sun, blocking sunlight from Earth. The moon's shadow then hits Earth.

Total Solar Eclipses The very darkest part of the moon's shadow is the **umbra** (UM bruh). You can see how the umbra strikes Earth in **Figure 3**. Within the umbra, the sun's light is completely blocked. Only people within the umbra experience a total solar eclipse. During a total solar eclipse, the sky grows as dark as night. The air gets cool and the sky becomes an eerie color. You can see the stars and the solar corona, which is the faint outer atmosphere of the sun.

Partial Solar Eclipses The moon casts another part of its shadow that is less dark than the umbra. This larger part of the shadow is called the **penumbra** (peh NUM bruh). In the penumbra, part of the sun is visible from Earth. During a solar eclipse, people in the penumbra see only a partial eclipse.

FIGURE 3 ······························
Solar Eclipse
The diagram shows the moon's penumbra and umbra during an eclipse. It is not drawn to scale.
↻ Relate Text and Visuals
Mark an X to show where a total solar eclipse would be visible. Circle the area in which a partial solar eclipse would be visible.

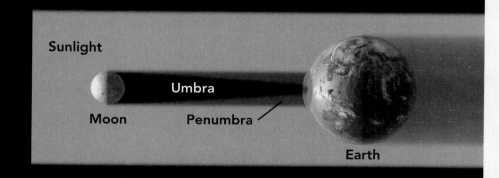

Sunlight
Moon
Umbra
Penumbra
Earth

Lunar Eclipses

During most months, the moon moves near Earth's shadow but not quite into it. A lunar eclipse occurs at a full moon when Earth is directly between the moon and the sun. You can see a lunar eclipse in Figure 4. 🔑 During a lunar eclipse, Earth blocks sunlight from reaching the moon. Lunar eclipses occur only when there is a full moon because the moon is closest to Earth's shadow at that time.

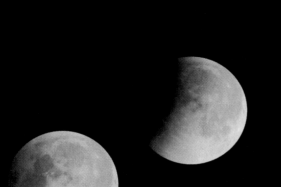

🔄 Relate Text and Visuals
Mark an X on the photograph above that shows a total eclipse.

Total Lunar Eclipses

Like the moon's shadow in a solar eclipse, Earth's shadow has an umbra and a penumbra. When the moon is in Earth's umbra, you see a total lunar eclipse. Unlike a total solar eclipse, a total lunar eclipse can be seen anywhere on Earth that the moon is visible. So you are more likely to see a total lunar eclipse than a total solar eclipse.

Partial Lunar Eclipses

For most lunar eclipses, Earth, the moon, and the sun are not quite in line, and only a partial lunar eclipse results. A partial lunar eclipse occurs when the moon passes partly into the umbra of Earth's shadow. The edge of the umbra appears blurry, and you can watch it pass across the moon for two or three hours.

FIGURE 4 ·······························

Lunar Eclipse

As the moon moves through Earth's shadow, total and partial eclipses occur. This diagram is not to scale.

✏️ Infer Draw a circle labeled *T* to show where the moon would be during a total eclipse. Draw two circles labeled *P* to show two places the moon could be during a partial eclipse.

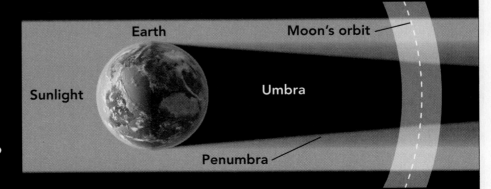

Earth · Moon's orbit · Sunlight · Umbra · Penumbra

Seasons and Shadows

How do Earth, the moon, and the sun interact?

FIGURE 5 ··

▶ **INTERACTIVE ART** Look at the diagram below. (The diagram is not to scale.) Identify what season it is in the Northern Hemisphere, what the phase of the moon is, and what kind of eclipse, if any, could occur.

LA.8.4.2.2

Season

_____

Moon Phase

_____

Eclipse

_____

Use the above diagram as a model. Draw the arrangement of Earth, the moon, and the sun during a total lunar eclipse in December.

 Lab zone® Do the Quick Lab *Eclipses.*

🔑 Assess Your Understanding

1a. Explain A (solar/lunar) eclipse occurs when the moon passes into Earth's shadow. A (solar/lunar) eclipse occurs when Earth passes into the moon's shadow.

SC.8.E.5.9

b. ANSWER THE ESSENTIAL ? How do Earth, the moon, and the sun interact? _____

_____

_____

SC.8.E.5.9

got it? ··

○ **I get it!** Now I know that eclipses occur when _____

_____

○ **I need extra help with** _____

Go to **MY SCIENCE** Ⓢ **COACH** *online for help with this subject.*

SC.8.E.5.9

UNLOCK THE ESSENTIAL ?

🔑 **What Causes Tides?**
SC.8.E.5.9, MA.6.S.6.2

my planeT DiaRY

A River in Reverse

If you were visiting New Brunswick in Canada, you might see the Saint John River flowing into the ocean. But six hours later, you might find that the river changed direction while you were gone! How could this happen? The Saint John River really does reverse course twice a day. At low tide, it empties into the Bay of Fundy, shown below. At high tide, the Bay of Fundy's tide pushes into the river, forcing the river to run in the opposite direction. The Bay of Fundy's tides are among the highest in the world.

FUN FACT

Answer the following questions.

1. Why does the Saint John River change direction?

_____

_____

_____

2. Have you ever seen a natural event that surprised you? Why was it surprising?

_____

_____

_____

> PLANET DIARY   Go to **Planet Diary** to learn more about tides.

Lab zone® Do the Inquiry Warm-Up *When Is High Tide?*

High tide

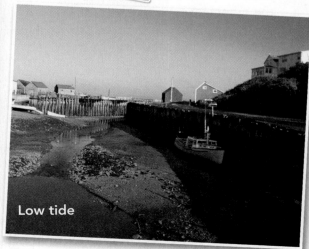
Low tide

Vocabulary
- tide
- spring tide
- neap tide

Skills
- Reading: Relate Cause and Effect
- Inquiry: Observe

What Causes Tides?

The reversing Saint John River is caused by ocean **tides,** the rise and fall of ocean water that occurs every 12.5 hours or so. The water rises for about six hours, then falls for about six hours.

The Tide Cycle   The force of gravity pulls the moon and Earth (including the water on Earth's surface) toward each other. 🔑 **Tides are caused mainly by differences in how much gravity from the moon and the sun pulls on different parts of Earth.**

At any one time on Earth, there are two places with high tides and two places with low tides. As Earth rotates, one high tide occurs on the side of Earth that faces the moon. The second high tide occurs on the opposite side of Earth. **Figure 1** explains why.

FLORIDA   NGSSS

SC.8.E.5.9 Explain the impact of the Moon on the Earth, including tides, and the relative position of each body.

MA.6.S.6.2 Select and analyze the measures of central tendency or variability to represent, describe, analyze, and/or summarize a data set for the purposes of answering questions appropriately.

🖉 **Relate Cause and Effect**
As you read **Figure 1,** underline the causes of high and low tides.

FIGURE 1 ···

> ART IN MOTION   **Tides**

You can think of Earth as a ball surrounded by a layer of water, as shown here. The layer is really much thinner than this, but is drawn thicker so it is easier to see.

North Pole

The Near Side   The moon's gravity pulls a little more strongly on the water on the side closest to the moon than on Earth as a whole. This difference causes a bulge of water on the side of Earth closest to the moon. This bulge causes high tide.

The Far Side   The moon's gravity pulls more weakly on the water on the far side of Earth than on Earth as a whole. Since Earth is pulled more strongly, the water is "left behind." Water flows toward the far side, causing high tide. Halfway between the high tides, water flows toward the high tides, causing low tide.

🖉 **Interpret Diagrams**
Write an *H* where high tides occur and an *L* where low tides occur.

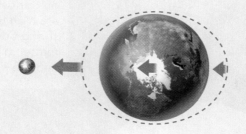
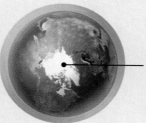

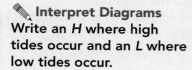

The Sun's Role Even though the sun is about 150 million kilometers from Earth, it is so massive that its gravity affects the tides. The sun pulls the water on Earth's surface toward it. Changes in the positions of Earth, the moon, and the sun affect the heights of the tides during a month.

New Moon

The sun, the moon, and Earth are nearly in a line during a new moon. The gravity of the sun and the moon pull in the same direction. Their combined forces produce a tide with the greatest difference between consecutive low and high tides, called a **spring tide.** The term "spring tide" comes from an Old English word, *springen,* meaning "to jump."

First Quarter

During the moon's first-quarter phase, the line between Earth and the sun is at right angles to the line between Earth and the moon. The sun's pull is at right angles to the moon's pull. This arrangement produces a **neap tide**, a tide with the least difference between consecutive low and high tides. Neap tides occur twice a month.

Full Moon

At full moon, the moon and the sun are on opposite sides of Earth. Since there are high tides on both sides of Earth, a spring tide is also produced. It doesn't matter in which order the sun, Earth, and the moon line up.

Third Quarter

✎ **Infer** Draw the position of the moon and the tide bulges at third quarter. What kind of tide occurs?

_____

The table shows high and low tides at four times in May 2008, in St. John, New Brunswick. St. John is on the Bay of Fundy.

High and Low Tides at St. John, New Brunswick

Date	High Tide (meters)	Low Tide (meters)
May 6–7	8.7	0.0
May 13–14	7.1	1.7
May 21	7.5	1.2
May 26	6.9	2.0

1 Interpret Data Spring tides occurred at two of the times shown. Which two? How do you know?

_____

_____

_____

2 Identify Which measure of central tendency—mean, median, or mode—represents the average high tide?

_____

3 Calculate Solve for the average high tide and low tide.

_____

_____

4 Summarize On which date are the high and low tides closest to the average high and low tides?

_____

MA.6.S.6.2

Vocabulary Identify Multiple Meanings Does a spring tide always happen in the season of spring? Explain your answer.

_____

_____

_____

_____

_____

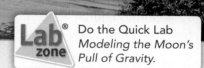

Do the Quick Lab
Modeling the Moon's Pull of Gravity.

🔑 Assess Your Understanding

1a. Review Most coastal areas have _____ high tides and _____ low tides each day.

SC.8.E.5.9

b. Explain How do the relative positions of the moon and Earth impact tides?

_____

_____

_____

SC.8.E.5.9

c. Observe Look at the diagrams on the previous page. What is the angle formed by the sun, Earth, and the moon during a neap tide? A spring tide?

_____

_____

_____

SC.8.E.5.9

got it? ....

○ **I get it!** Now I know that tides are caused by _____

_____

○ **I need extra help with** _____

Go to MY SCIENCE COACH online for help with this subject.

SC.8.E.5.9

5 Study Guide

Interactions between Earth, the moon, and the sun cause _____,
_____, _____, and _____.

LESSON 1 Earth in Space

SC.8.E.5.9

🔑 Earth moves in space in two major ways: rotation and revolution.

🔑 Earth has seasons because its axis is tilted as it revolves around the sun.

Vocabulary
- axis
- rotation
- revolution
- calendar
- solstice
- equinox

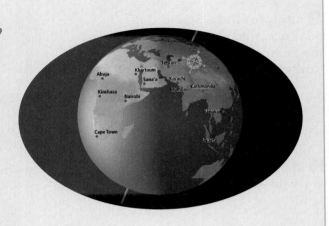

LESSON 2 Phases and Eclipses

SC.8.E.5.9, SC.8.N.1.6

🔑 The changing relative positions of the moon, Earth, and sun cause the phases of the moon.

🔑 A solar eclipse occurs when the moon passes directly between Earth and the sun, blocking sunlight from Earth. The moon's shadow then reaches Earth.

🔑 During a lunar eclipse, Earth blocks sunlight from reaching the moon.

Vocabulary
- phase • eclipse • solar eclipse • umbra
- penumbra • lunar eclipse

LESSON 3 Tides

SC.8.E.5.9

🔑 Tides are caused by differences in how much gravity from the moon and the sun pulls on different parts of Earth.

Vocabulary
- tide
- spring tide
- neap tide

Review and Assessment

LESSON 1 Earth in Space

1. What is Earth's annual motion around the sun called?

a. month

b. revolution

c. rotation

d. seasons

SC.8.E.5.9

2. The _____ occurs when the sun is farthest north of the equator.

SC.8.E.5.9

3. Infer Why might ancient astronomers have been convinced that the sun and moon revolved around Earth?

_____

_____

_____

_____

SC.8.E.5.9

4. Apply Concepts Mars's axis is tilted at about the same angle as Earth's axis. Do you think Mars has seasons? Explain your answer.

_____

_____

_____

_____

SC.8.E.5.9

5. Compare and Contrast How does the position of Earth's axis at the March and September equinoxes compare to its position at the summer solstice?

_____

_____

_____

_____

_____

_____

SC.8.E.5.9

 6. **Write About It** Write a guide for younger children explaining how Earth's motions are related to the lengths of days and years.

SC.8.E.5.9

LESSON 2 Phases and Eclipses

7. The moon's shadow falling on Earth causes a

a. full moon.

b. lunar eclipse.

c. phase.

d. solar eclipse.

SC.8.E.5.9

8. The darkest part of the moon's shadow is the

_____

SC.8.E.5.9

9. Relate Cause and Effect Why does the moon have phases? _____

_____

_____

SC.8.E.5.9

The photos below show two phases of the moon. Use the photos to answer Questions 10 and 11.

_____   _____

_____   _____

SC.8.E.5.9

10. Interpret Photos Label each photo with the correct phase.

11. Compare and Contrast Why do you see different amounts of the moon's surface during each of these phases?

_____

_____

_____

_____

SC.8.E.5.9

12. Make Generalizations Which occurs more often, a partial or a total lunar eclipse? Why?

_____

_____

_____

SC.8.E.5.9

201

LESSON 3 **Tides**

13. About how long passes between high tides?

   a. 6 hours   **b.** 12 hours

   c. 24 hours   **d.** 48 hours

                                  SC.8.E.5.9

14. The least difference between high and low

tides occurs during a _____

                                  SC.8.E.5.9

Use the diagram to answer Questions 15 and 16.

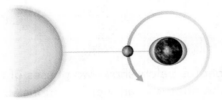

15. Interpret Diagrams Does the diagram show a spring or a neap tide? How do you know?

_____

_____

                                  SC.8.E.5.9

16. Relate Cause and Effect Why is there a high tide on the far side of Earth?

_____

_____

_____

_____

_____

                                  SC.8.E.5.9

17. Compare and Contrast Compare the size of high and low tides in spring and neap tides.

_____

_____

_____

_____

_____

_____

                                  SC.8.E.5.9

 APPLY THE ESSENTIAL **How do Earth, the moon, and the sun interact?**

18. Is a total solar eclipse or a total lunar eclipse visible to more people on Earth? Explain your answer.

_____

_____

_____

_____

_____

_____

_____

_____

_____

_____

_____

_____

_____

_____

_____

_____

_____

_____

_____

_____

_____

                                  SC.8.E.5.9

Florida Benchmarks Review

Circle the letter of the best answer.

1 Which of the following can occur when the moon is at location 1?

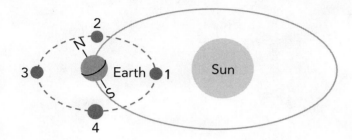

A only a lunar eclipse

B only a solar eclipse

C both a solar and a lunar eclipse

D neither a solar nor a lunar eclipse

SC.8.E.5.9

2 Why is only one side of the moon visible from Earth?

A The moon does not rotate on its axis.

B The moon does not revolve around Earth.

C The moon rotates faster than it revolves.

D The moon rotates once on its axis in the same period of time that it takes to revolve once around Earth.

SC.8.E.5.9

3 What happens at a spring tide?

A There is only one high tide each day.

B There is only one low tide each day.

C There is the most difference between consecutive high and low tides.

D There is the least difference between consecutive high and low tides.

SC.8.E.5.9

4 What term describes the movement of Earth around the sun once a year?

A inertia

B revolution

C rotation

D axis

SC.8.E.5.9

5 What type of day occurs when the sun reaches its greatest distance north or south of the equator?

A solstice

B penumbra

C umbra

D equinox

SC.8.E.5.9

6 In the diagram below, what type of day is occurring in the Northern Hemisphere?

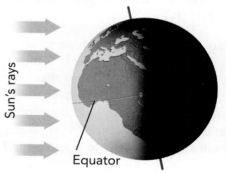

A summer solstice

B winter solstice

C September equinox

D March equinox

SC.8.E.5.9

203

HOW IS THIS SWIMSUIT LIKE A SPACESUIT?

How does exploring space benefit people on Earth?

This high-tech swimsuit is made of a specially developed lightweight fabric with ultrasonically fused seams that make the suit very sleek. The swimsuit compresses the body to help the athletes go faster. ⬠Draw Conclusions **How might this swimsuit be similar to a spacesuit?**

_____

_____

_____

_____

_____

_____

▷ UNTAMED SCIENCE   Watch the **Untamed Science** video to learn more about exploring space.

Exploring Space

FLORIDA | Next Generation Sunshine State Standards

Big Idea 4: SC.8.N.4.1, SC.8.N.4.2
Big Idea 5: SC.8.E.5.10, SC.8.E.5.11, SC.8.E.5.12

Language Arts: LA.8.4.2.2
Mathematics: MA.6.A.3.6

my science online.com | Exploring Space > UNTAMED SCIENCE > ESSENTIAL QUESTION

Check Your Understanding

1. **Background** Read the paragraph below and then answer the question.

Bill wonders how a rocket gets off the ground. His sister Jan explains that the rocket's engines create a lot of **force.** The force causes the rocket to travel upward with great **speed.** The force helps the rocket push against **gravity** and have enough speed to rise into space.

A **force** is a push or pull.

Speed is the distance an object moves per unit of time.

Gravity is the force that pulls objects toward each other.

- What force is pulling down on the rocket as it pushes off the ground?

_____

> **MY READING WEB** If you had trouble completing the question above, visit **My Reading Web** and type in *Exploring Space.*

Vocabulary Skill

Identify Related Word Forms You can expand your vocabulary by learning the related forms of a word. If you know that the verb *collect* means "to gather together," then you can figure out the meaning of the noun *collection* and the adjective *collective.*

Verb	Noun	Adjective
probe to examine something carefully	**probe** an unmanned space vehicle	**probing** serving to test or try
orbit to revolve around an object	**orbit** the path of an object as it revolves around another	**orbital** of or relating to a path in space

LA.8.1.6.9

2. **Quick Check** Circle the sentence below that uses the noun form of the word *probe.*
   - The satellite *probes* Earth's surface thoroughly.
   - The *probe* collected photographs and data for the scientists to analyze.

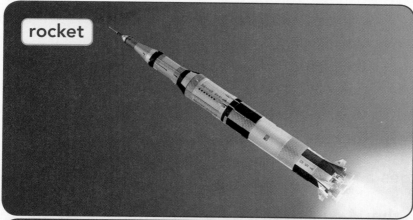

rocket

satellite

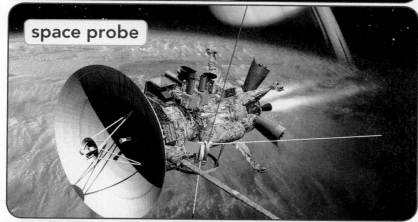

space probe

space spinoff

Chapter Preview

LESSON 1
- rocket • thrust • velocity
- orbital velocity • escape velocity

⟲ Relate Text and Visuals

△ Interpret Data

LESSON 2
- satellite • space shuttle
- space station • space probe
- remote sensing • rover

⟲ Ask Questions

△ Make Models

LESSON 3
- vacuum • microgravity
- space spinoff
- geostationary orbit

⟲ Identify the Main Idea

△ Draw Conclusions

LESSON 4
- electromagnetic radiation
- visible light • wavelength
- frequency • spectrum
- refracting telescope
- reflecting telescope
- satellite photograph • pixel
- planetary image

⟲ Ask Questions

△ Infer

LESSON 5
- spaceport • Space Coast

⟲ Relate Cause and Effect

△ Draw Conclusions

> VOCAB FLASH CARDS For extra help with vocabulary, visit **Vocab Flash Cards** and type in *Exploring Space.*

1 The Science of Rockets

UNLOCK THE ESSENTIAL **?**

🗝 **How Were Rockets Developed?**
SC.8.N.4.2, SC.8.E.5.10, LA.8.4.2.2

🗝 **How Does a Rocket Work?**
SC.8.E.5.10, MA.6.A.3.6

🗝 **What Is the Main Advantage of a Multistage Rocket?**
SC.8.E.5.10, LA.8.4.2.2

MY PLANET DIARY

Jet Packs

It's been snowing all day and the roads haven't been plowed yet. No problem. Just strap on a jet pack and fly over the snow.

Does this sound like something out of a science fiction movie? Actually, manufacturers have already started making one-person jet packs. The jet packs are very expensive. They also use a lot of heavy fuel—about 10 gallons of gasoline per hour. And jet packs can carry a person for only about 30 minutes before they have to be refueled. However, 30 minutes is long enough to get many people to work—if they can find a place to land and park the jet pack once they get there.

FUN FACT

Study the picture of the person using a jet pack. Use your knowledge of science to answer the question.

Assess What would be the advantages and disadvantages of using a jet pack for transportation?

_____

_____

_____

_____

_____

_____

▶ PLANET DIARY Go to **Planet Diary** to learn more about rockets.

 Lab zone® Do the Inquiry Warm-Up
What Force Moves a Balloon?

 FLORIDA NGSSS

SC.8.N.4.2 Explain how political, social, and economic concerns can affect science, and vice versa.

SC.8.E.5.10 Assess how technology is essential to science for such purposes as access to outer space.

LA.8.4.2.2 The student will record information (e.g., lists) related to a topic, including visual aids to organize and record information.

How Were Rockets Developed?

You've probably seen rockets at fireworks displays. As the rockets moved skyward, you may have noticed a fiery gas rushing out of the back. A **rocket** is a device that expels gas in one direction to move the rocket in the opposite direction. 🗝 **Rocket technology originated in China hundreds of years ago and then gradually spread to other parts of the world.** Rockets were developed for military use as well as for fireworks.

Vocabulary
- rocket • thrust • velocity
- orbital velocity • escape velocity

Skills
↻ Reading: Relate Text and Visuals
△ Inquiry: Interpret Data

Origins of Rockets
The first rockets were made in China in the 1100s. These early "rockets" weren't rockets, but simply arrows coated with a flammable powder that were lighted and shot with bows. By about 1200, the Chinese were using gunpowder inside their rockets.

The British greatly improved rocketry in the early 1800s. British ships used rockets against American troops in the War of 1812. "The Star-Spangled Banner" contains the words "the rockets' red glare, the bombs bursting in air." These words describe a British rocket attack on Fort McHenry in Baltimore, Maryland.

Development of Modern Rockets
Modern rockets were first developed by scientists in the early 1900s. One such scientist was the Russian physicist Konstantin Tsiolkovsky. He described in scientific terms how rockets work and proposed designs for advanced rockets. The American physicist Robert Goddard also designed rockets. Beginning around 1915, he built rockets to test his designs.

Scientists made major advances in rocket design during World War II. The Germans used a rocket called the V-2 to destroy both military and civilian targets. The V-2 was a large rocket that could travel about 300 kilometers. The designer of the V-2, Wernher von Braun, was brought to the United States after the war ended. Von Braun used his experience to direct the development of many rockets used in the United States space program.

FIGURE 1 ·······························

Rocket Timeline
A legend claims the Chinese official Wan-Hoo tried to fly to the moon around the year 1500 by tying rockets to his chair.

✎ **On the cards below, write a brief entry for the events that took place in the development of rockets.**   LA.8.4.2.2

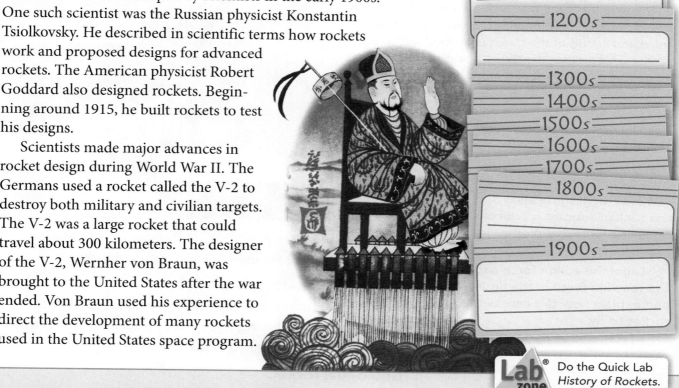

1100s

1200s

1300s
1400s
1500s
1600s
1700s
1800s

1900s

Lab® Do the Quick Lab
zone *History of Rockets.*

🔑 Assess Your Understanding

got it? ···

○ **I get it!** Now I know that rocket technology originated _____
and gradually spread to _____

○ **I need extra help with** _____

Go to my science *S* coach *online for help with this subject.*   SC.8.N.4.2, SC.8.E.5.10

How Does a Rocket Work?

A rocket can be as small as your finger or as large as a skyscraper. An essential feature of any rocket, though, is that it expels gas in one direction. 🔑 **A rocket moves forward when gases shooting out the back of the rocket push it in the opposite direction.**

A rocket works like a balloon that is propelled through the air by releasing gas. In most rockets, fuel is burned to make hot gas. The gas pushes in every direction, but it can leave the rocket only through openings at the back. This moves the rocket forward.

Action and Reaction Forces

A rocket demonstrates a basic law of physics: For every force, or action, there is an equal and opposite force, or reaction. Look at **Figure 2.** The force of the gas shooting out of the rocket is an action force. An equal force—the reaction force—pushes the rocket forward.

The reaction force that propels a rocket forward is called **thrust.** The amount of thrust depends on the mass and speed of the gases propelled out of the rocket. The greater the thrust, the greater a rocket's velocity. **Velocity** is speed in a given direction.

FIGURE 2 ·······························

▶ **VIRTUAL LAB** **Rocket Action and Reaction**

The force of gas propelled out the back of a rocket produces an opposing force that propels the rocket forward.

✎ **Label the action force and the reaction force in the figure, and explain how this causes the rocket to fly.**

_____

_____

_____

_____

_____

_____

_____

_____

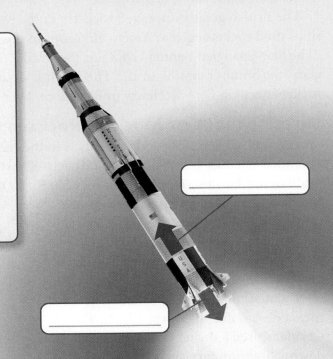

Rocket Fuels

Three types of fuel are used to power modern rockets.

Solid-fuel rocket:
- Oxygen is mixed with the fuel (a dry explosive chemical).
- The rocket can be triggered from a distance by an igniter.
- Once the fuel is ignited, it burns until all of it is gone.

Liquid-fuel rocket:
- Oxygen and the fuel are in liquid form, stored separately.
- When the rocket fires, the fuel and oxygen are pumped into the same chamber and ignited.
- The burning of fuel can be controlled.

Ion rocket:
- This type expels charged gas particles out of the engine.
- Ion rockets are very fuel-efficient.

Orbital and Escape Velocity

In order to lift off the ground, a rocket must have more upward thrust than the downward force of gravity. Once a rocket is off the ground, it must reach a certain velocity in order to go into orbit. **Orbital velocity** is the velocity a rocket must achieve to establish an orbit around Earth. If the rocket has an even greater velocity, it can fly off into space. **Escape velocity** is the velocity a rocket must reach to fly beyond a planet's gravitational pull. The escape velocity a rocket needs to leave Earth is about 40,200 km per hour. That's more than 11 kilometers every second!

do the math!

Rocket Altitude

A rocket's altitude is how high it rises above the ground. Use the graph to answer the questions about a model rocket with a parachute packed inside.

❶ **Interpret Data** What was the altitude after 2 seconds?

_____

❷ **CHALLENGE** Did the rocket rise or fall faster? How do you know?

_____

MA.6.A.3.6, MA.8.A.1.3

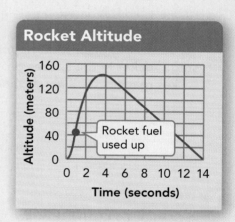

Rocket Altitude

Rocket fuel used up

Altitude (meters) vs Time (seconds)

Lab zone ® Do the Quick Lab
Be a Rocket Scientist.

🔑 Assess Your Understanding

1a. Explain What is thrust?

_____

_____

SC.8.E.5.10

b. Interpret Diagrams Use **Figure 2** to explain how a rocket moves forward.

_____

_____

_____

_____

_____

SC.8.E.5.10

got it?

○ **I get it!** Now I know that a rocket moves forward when _____

_____

_____

○ **I need extra help with** _____

_____

Go to **MY SCIENCE** s **COACH** *online for help with this subject.*

SC.8.E.5.10

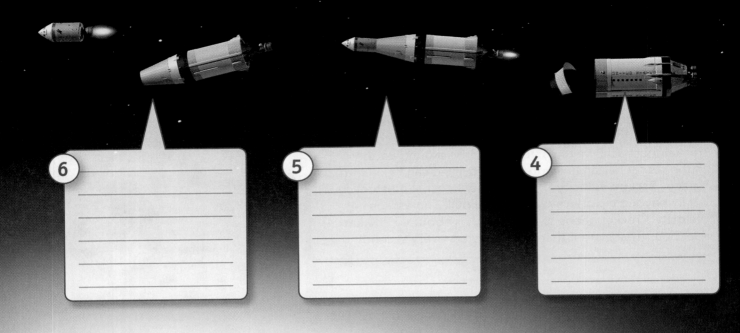

6 _____

5 _____

4 _____

FIGURE 3 ··

A Multistage Rocket

✎ **Assess** Explain what happens in the steps of the multi-stage rocket in the spaces provided. Which part of the rocket reaches the final destination? Why is this useful?

_____

_____

_____

LA.8.4.2.2

FLORIDA NGSSS

SC.8.E.5.10 Assess how technology is essential to science for such purposes as access to outer space and other remote locations, sample collection, measurement, data collection and storage, computation, and communication of information.

LA.8.4.2.2 The student will organize information (e.g., notes) related to a topic, including visual aids to organize and record information.

What Is the Main Advantage of a Multistage Rocket?

A rocket can carry only so much fuel. As the fuel in a rocket burns, its fuel chambers begin to empty. Even though much of the rocket is empty, the whole rocket must still be pushed upward by the remaining fuel. But what if the empty part of the rocket could be thrown off? Then the remaining fuel wouldn't have to push a partially empty rocket. This is the idea behind multistage rockets.

Konstantin Tsiolkovsky proposed multistage rockets in 1924. ⚷ **The main advantage of a multistage rocket is that the total weight of the rocket is greatly reduced as the rocket rises.**

In a multistage rocket, smaller rockets, or stages, are placed one on top of the other and then fired in succession. **Figure 3** shows how a multistage rocket works. As each stage of the rocket uses up its fuel, the empty fuel container falls away. The next stage then ignites and continues powering the rocket toward its destination. At the end, there is just a single stage left, the very top of the rocket.

Multistage rockets were used in the 1960s to send astronauts to the moon. Today, they are used to launch a variety of satellites and space probes.

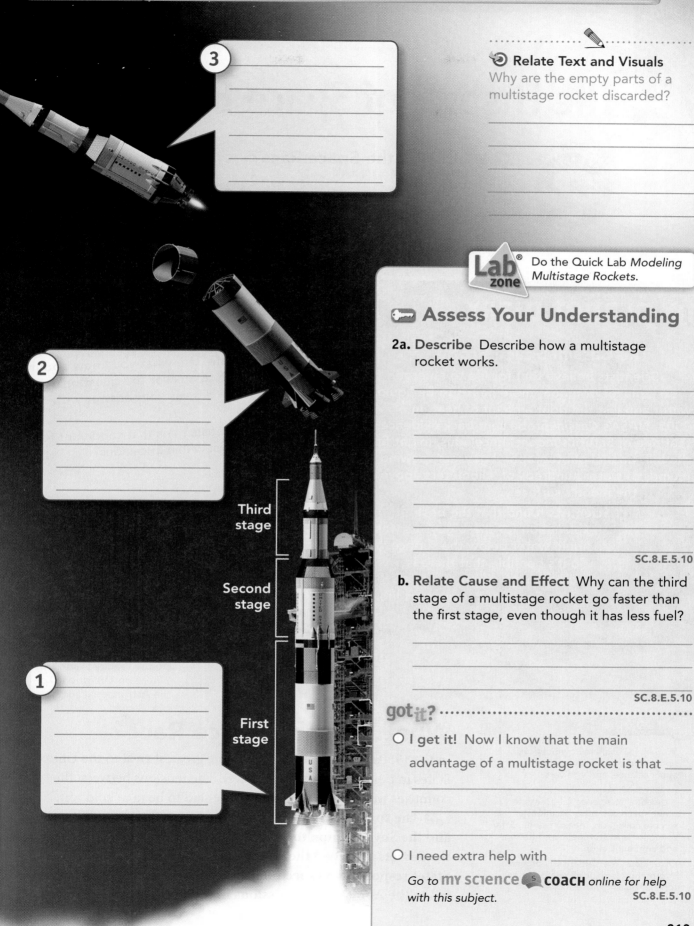

3

2

1

Third stage

Second stage

First stage

USA

Lab zone | Do the Quick Lab *Modeling Multistage Rockets*.

Relate Text and Visuals

Why are the empty parts of a multistage rocket discarded?

Assess Your Understanding

2a. Describe Describe how a multistage rocket works.

SC.8.E.5.10

b. Relate Cause and Effect Why can the third stage of a multistage rocket go faster than the first stage, even though it has less fuel?

SC.8.E.5.10

got it?

○ **I get it!** Now I know that the main advantage of a multistage rocket is that ____

○ **I need extra help with** _____

Go to **my science** **coach** *online for help with this subject.* SC.8.E.5.10

The History of Space Exploration

UNLOCK THE ESSENTIAL ?

🔑 **What Was the Space Race?**
SC.8.N.4.2, SC.8.E.5.10, LA.8.4.2.2

🔑 **How Are Space Shuttles and Space Stations Used?**
SC.8.N.4.2, SC.8.E.5.10, LA.8.1.6.9

🔑 **How Are Space Probes Used?**
SC.8.E.5.10

my pLaneT DiaRY

The *Cassini* Space Probe

Scientists believe that for life to emerge on a planet or moon, there needs to be liquid water and just the right amount of heat. In 2005, NASA's *Cassini* probe sent back evidence that one of Saturn's moons, Enceladus, might fit the bill. *Cassini* photographed geysers spewing plumes of water hundreds of kilometers above the moon's surface.

Scientists found that the best explanation for these geysers was liquid water below the surface. So it's possible that there is both enough water and heat within Enceladus to support life.

DISCOVERY

Communicate Use what you know about life on Earth to answer the question below. Then discuss your answer with a partner.

Why do scientists think that conditions for life might exist within Enceladus?

_____

_____

_____

> PLANET DIARY Go to **Planet Diary** to learn more about space probes.

Lab zone® Do the Inquiry Warm-Up *Where on the Moon Did the Astronauts Land?*

FLORIDA NGSSS

SC.8.N.4.2 Explain how political, social, and economic concerns can affect science, and vice versa.

SC.8.E.5.10 Assess how technology is essential to science for access to outer space and other locations, sample collection, measurement, data collection and storage, computation, and communication.

LA.8.4.2.2 The student will organize information (e.g., lists) related to a topic, including visual aids.

What Was the Space Race?

In the 1950s, the Soviet Union was the greatest rival to the United States in politics and military power. The tensions between the two countries were so high that they were said to be in a "cold war." 🔑 The space race was the rivalry between the United States and the Soviet Union to explore space. It began in 1957, when the Soviets launched the satellite *Sputnik I* into orbit. The United States responded by speeding up its own space program, which led to the Apollo moon missions in the 1960s and early 1970s.

Vocabulary
- satellite • space shuttle
- space station • space probe
- remote sensing • rover

Skills
- Reading: Ask Questions
- Inquiry: Make Models

The First Artificial Satellites

A **satellite** is an object that revolves around another object in space. The moon is a natural satellite of Earth. A spacecraft orbiting Earth is an artificial satellite. *Sputnik I* was the first artificial satellite. This success by the Soviets caused great alarm in the United States.

The United States responded in early 1958 by launching its own satellite, *Explorer 1,* into orbit. Over the next few years, the United States and the Soviet Union launched many more satellites.

Later in 1958, the United States created a government agency in charge of its space program called the National Aeronautics and Space Administration (NASA). NASA brought together the talents of many scientists and engineers. They solved the difficult technical problems of space flight.

Humans in Space

In 1961, the Soviets launched the first human into space. Yuri Gagarin flew one orbit around Earth aboard *Vostok 1.* Less than a month later, Alan Shepard became the first American in space, but did not orbit Earth. His spacecraft, *Freedom 7,* was part of the Mercury space program.

The first American to orbit Earth was John Glenn. He was launched into space from Florida aboard the space capsule *Friendship 7* in 1962. The capsule orbited Earth three times.

FIGURE 1 ··

Space Race Timeline

✎ **Relate Text and Visuals** Write the name and historic first of each spacecraft with its picture.

LA.8.4.2.2

Name: _____
First: _____
_____

1962

Name: _____
First: _____
_____

1961

1961

Name: _____
First: _____
_____

1957

1958

Name: _____
First: _____
_____

Name: _____
First: _____
_____

The Apollo Program "I believe that this nation should commit itself to achieving the goal, before the decade is out, of landing a man on the moon and returning him safely to Earth." With these words from a May 1961 speech, President John F. Kennedy launched a program of space exploration and scientific research. 🔑 **The American effort to land astronauts on the moon and return them to Earth was named the Apollo program. Figure 2** shows some major events of Apollo.

FIGURE 2 ··

Major Events in Moon Exploration

Apollo astronaut Buzz Aldrin described the landscape of the moon as "magnificent desolation."

✏️ **Make Generalizations** Look at the pictures of the moon's surface. Why is Aldrin's phrase appropriate?

_____

_____

_____

_____

_____

❶ Exploring the Moon

Between 1959 and 1972, the United States and the Soviet Union sent many unpiloted spacecraft to explore the moon. When a U.S. spacecraft called *Surveyor* landed on the moon, it didn't sink into the surface. This proved that the moon had a solid, rocky surface. Next, scientists searched for a suitable place to land humans on the moon.

❷ The Moon Landings

In July 1969, three American astronauts circled the moon aboard *Apollo 11*. Once in orbit, Neil Armstrong and Buzz Aldrin entered a tiny spacecraft called *Eagle*. On July 20, the *Eagle* descended toward a flat area on the moon's surface called the Sea of Tranquility. When Armstrong radioed that the *Eagle* had landed, cheers rang out at the NASA Space Center in Houston, Texas. A few hours later, Armstrong and Aldrin left the *Eagle* to walk on the surface of the moon.

❸ Moon Rocks and Moonquakes

The astronauts collected 382 kilograms of lunar samples, commonly called "moon rocks," for analysis. Scientists such as Andrea Mosie, shown in the photograph with astronaut Jack Schmitt, studied these rocks. They learned that the minerals that make up moon rocks are among the same minerals that are found on Earth. However, in some moon rocks these minerals combine to form kinds of rocks that are not found on Earth.

One way Apollo astronauts explored the structure of the moon was to study the many moonquakes that occur there. Instruments they left behind, called seismometers, identified more than 7000 moonquakes. By measuring these waves, scientists found that the moon may have a small core of molten rock or metal at its center.

❹ On the Moon's Surface

Everything that the *Apollo 11* astronauts found was new and exciting. For about two hours, Armstrong and Aldrin explored the moon's surface, collecting samples to take back to Earth. They also planted an American flag.

Over the next three years, five more Apollo missions landed on the moon. In these later missions, astronauts were able to stay on the moon for days instead of hours. Some astronauts even used a lunar rover, or buggy, to explore larger areas of the moon.

Summarize After reading through the story of the Apollo program, list three discoveries that scientists made about the moon.

_____

_____

_____

_____

_____

_____

_____

_____

_____

New Missions to the Moon

New Missions to the Moon The Apollo missions were a tremendous achievement. They yielded fascinating information and memorable images. Yet the cost of those missions was high. There were few immediate benefits beyond the knowledge gained about the moon and Earth's formation. NASA moved on to other projects. For many years after, the moon was largely ignored.

Recently, interest in the moon has revived. In 2003, the European Space Agency launched an unpiloted spacecraft to orbit the moon. Its main purpose was to collect data for a lunar map.

Soon, humans may walk on the moon again. In 2004, the United States announced a plan to establish a permanent colony of people on the moon. People arriving on the moon first would need to bring food, water, and other supplies from Earth to set up their base. **Figure 3** shows what a lunar base might look like. Living on the moon could teach people how to live on Mars.

FIGURE 3 ·······························

Lunar Base

A possible future base on the moon is shown in this artist's conception.

✏️ **Describe** Explain how living on the moon would be similar to going camping.

_____

_____

_____

_____

_____

Lab zone® Do the Quick Lab *Humans in Space.*

🔑 Assess Your Understanding

1a. Identify What was the Apollo program?

_____

_____

SC.8.N.4.2, SC.8.E.5.10

b. Assess Was the Apollo program successful in meeting President Kennedy's challenge?

_____

_____

_____

SC.8.N.4.2, SC.8.E.5.10

got it?

○ **I get it!** Now I know that the space race began when the Soviets launched _____ _____ and it continued with the American program called _____

○ **I need extra help with** _____

_____

Go to **MY SCIENCE** 🅢 **COACH** *online for help with this subject.* SC.8.N.4.2, SC.8.E.5.10

How Are Space Shuttles and Space Stations Used?

After the great success of the moon landings, the question for space exploration was, "What comes next?" Scientists and public officials decided that one goal should be to build space shuttles and space stations where astronauts could live and work.

Space Shuttles Before 1981, spacecraft could be used only once. In contrast, a space shuttle is like an airplane—it can fly, land, and then fly again. A **space shuttle** is a spacecraft that can carry a crew into space, return to Earth, and then be reused for the same purpose. Because it can be reused, NASA doesn't have to build a new spacecraft for each mission. ⚷ **NASA has used space shuttles to perform many important tasks. These include taking satellites into orbit, repairing damaged satellites, and carrying astronauts and equipment to and from space stations.**

During a shuttle mission, astronauts live in a pressurized crew cabin at the front of the shuttle. There, they can wear regular clothes and breathe without an oxygen tank. Behind the crew cabin is a large, open area called the payload bay. A shuttle payload bay might carry a satellite to be released into orbit. It could also carry a laboratory in which astronauts can perform experiments. **Figure 4** shows the main parts of the space shuttle.

FLORIDA NGSSS

SC.8.N.4.2 Explain how political, social, and economic concerns can affect science, and vice versa.

SC.8.E.5.10 Assess how technology is essential to science for such purposes as access to outer space and other remote locations, sample collection, measurement, data collection and storage, computation, and communication of information.

Vocabulary Identify Related Word Forms In science, the word *pressure* means "force per a given area." What does the word *pressurized* mean about the air in the crew cabin?

_____

_____

_____

_____

FIGURE 4 ···

A Space Shuttle

A space shuttle has a crew cabin, a payload bay, and rockets.

✎ **Interpret Diagrams On the diagram, label the main parts of the space shuttle and explain their use.**

_____

_____

_____

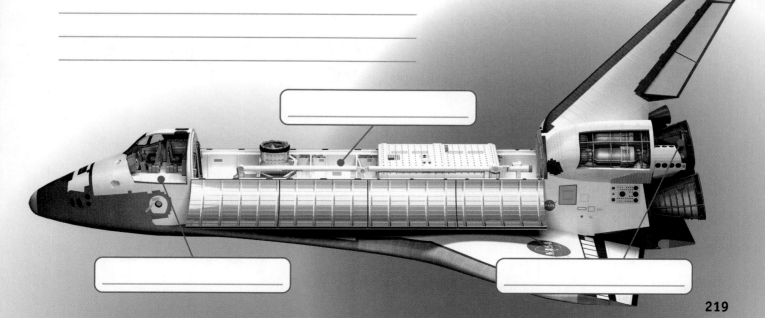

FIGURE 5 ·····················

International Space Station

🖊 CHALLENGE State one advantage of building a space station in orbit instead of sending it up all in one piece.

_____

_____

_____

_____

_____

Space Stations Have you ever wondered what it would be like to live in space? A **space station** is a large artificial satellite on which people can live and work for long periods. 🗝 **A space station provides a place where long-term observations and experiments can be carried out in space.** In the 1970s and 1980s, both the United States and the Soviet Union placed space stations in orbit. The Soviet space station *Mir* stayed in orbit for 15 years before it fell to Earth in 2001. Astronauts from many countries spent time aboard *Mir.*

In the 1990s, the United States and 15 other countries began constructing the International Space Station (ISS). The first module, or section, of the station was placed into orbit in 1998. Since then, many other modules have been added. On board, astronauts from many countries are carrying out experiments in various fields of science. They are also learning more about how humans adapt to space.

The main source of power for the International Space Station is its eight large arrays of solar panels, as shown in **Figure 5.** Together, the solar panels contain more than 250,000 solar cells, each capable of converting sunlight into electricity. At full power, the solar panels produce enough electricity to power about 55 houses on Earth. The ISS carries large batteries to provide power when it is in Earth's shadow.

Lab® **zone** Do the Quick Lab *Which Tool Would You Use in Space?*

🗝 Assess Your Understanding

2a. Describe What is a space shuttle? What is a space station?

_____

_____

_____

_____

SC.8.E.5.10

b. Compare and Contrast What is the main difference between space shuttles and space stations?

_____

_____

SC.8.E.5.10

got it?

○ I get it! Now I know that space shuttles are

used to _____

_____

and a space station is used to _____

_____

_____

_____

○ I need extra help with _____

Go to MY SCIENCE 🇸 COACH *online for help with this subject.* SC.8.N.4.2, SC.8.E.5.10

How Are Space Probes Used?

Since space exploration began, no one has traveled farther than the moon. Yet, during this period, space scientists have gathered information about other parts of the solar system. These data were collected by space probes. A **space probe** is a spacecraft that carries scientific instruments that can collect data, but has no human crew.

Each space probe is designed for a specific mission. Some are designed to land on a certain planet, as shown in **Figure 6.** Others are designed to fly by and collect data about more than one planet. 🔑 **A space probe collects data about the solar system and sends the information back to Earth.**

Each space probe has a power system to produce electricity and a communication system to send and receive signals. Probes also carry scientific instruments to collect data and perform experiments. Some probes, called orbiters, are equipped to photograph and analyze the atmosphere of a planet. They do this through **remote sensing,** which is the collection of information about Earth and the other objects in space without being in direct contact. Other probes, called landers, are equipped to land on a planet and analyze the materials on its surface. Some have small robots called **rovers** that move around on the surface. Rovers often have instruments that collect and analyze soil and rock samples.

FLORIDA NGSSS

SC.8.E.5.10 Assess how technology is essential to science for such purposes as access to outer space and other remote locations, sample collection, measurement, data collection and storage, computation, and communication of information.

✏️

⟳ **Ask Questions** What is one question about another planet you would want information from a space probe to answer?

_____

_____

_____

FIGURE 6 ·····················

▶ INTERACTIVE ART **Space Probe Mission**
The postcards show the steps of a space probe mission.

✏️ **Write captions to tell the story of the space probe.**

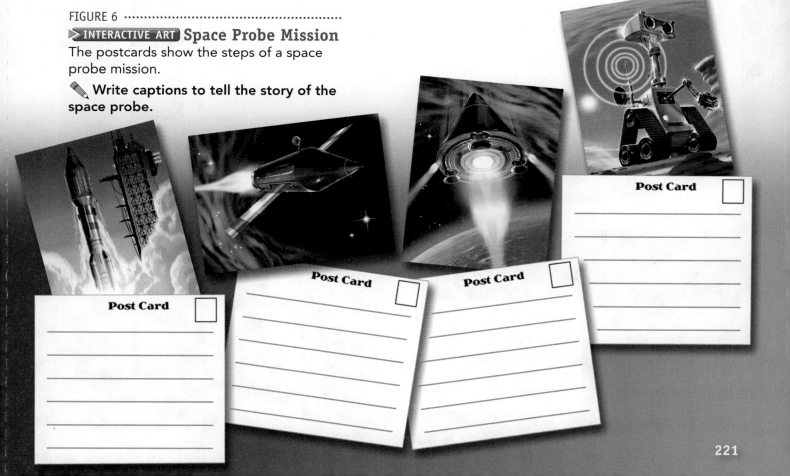

Post Card

Post Card

Post Card

Post Card

apply it!

Space probes such as the ones pictured here have now visited or passed near all of the planets. They have also explored many moons, asteroids, and comets.

1 **Make Models** Choose a type of probe, either an orbiter or lander, and draw your probe in the space provided below. List by number the tools required by each type of probe.

Lander: _____

Orbiter: _____

2 **CHALLENGE** On the note paper, explain why you chose each item.

Design Your Own Space Probe

1 Solar panel

2 Wheels

3 Parachute

4 Camera

5 Antenna

6 Robotic arm

7 Landing pad

8 Mini lab

Lunar Prospector, 1998
Lunar Prospector found evidence of water ice and identified other minerals on the moon's surface.

New Horizons, 2006–2015
New Horizons is the first mission to the dwarf planet Pluto. It will reach Pluto in July 2015.

Cassini, 2004
Cassini explored Saturn's moons. It launched a smaller probe, *Huygens*, which explored Titan, Saturn's largest moon.

Mars Exploration Rovers, 2004
Two rovers, *Opportunity* and *Spirit*, explored Mars's surface and found evidence of ancient water.

Lab zone® Do the Quick Lab *Remote Control.*

🔑 Assess Your Understanding

3a. Summarize What is a space probe?

_____

_____

SC.8.E.5.10

b. Assess What are the advantages and disadvantages of a space probe compared to a piloted spacecraft?

_____

_____

_____

_____

SC.8.E.5.10

got it? ···

○ **I get it!** Now I know that a space probe ____

_____

_____

○ **I need extra help with** _____

Go to **MY SCIENCE** s **COACH** online for help with this subject. SC.8.E.5.10

Space and Technology

🔑 **How Does Technology Help People Live in Space?**
SC.8.E.5.10

🔑 **How Has Space Technology Benefited People?**
SC.8.N.4.2, SC.8.E.5.10

🔑 **What Are Some Uses of Satellites Orbiting Earth?**
SC.8.N.4.2, SC.8.E.5.10

MY PLANET DIARY

Ellen Ochoa

A couple of years after Sally Ride became the first American woman astronaut, Ellen Ochoa applied to NASA. She eventually went on missions aboard the space shuttle. Before she flew in space, however, Ochoa worked for NASA and other research organizations as an engineer. She invented three systems that use optical devices like lasers and holograms to get information from images. Her research can be applied to many different applications. They include inspecting equipment in a manufacturing plant and helping a spacecraft make a safe landing on Mars.

CAREERS

Communicate Discuss Ochoa's career with a partner. Then answer the question below.

How do you think Ochoa's inventions could be useful on Earth?

_____

_____

_____

_____

_____

_____

▶ **PLANET DIARY** Go to **Planet Diary** to learn more about space technology.

Lab zone® Do the Inquiry Warm-Up *Using Space Science.*

FLORIDA NGSSS

SC.8.E.5.10 Assess how technology is essential to science for such purposes as access to outer space and other remote locations, sample collection, measurement, data collection and storage, computation, and communication of information.

How Does Technology Help People Live in Space?

Astronauts who travel into space face conditions that are extremely different from those on Earth. Conditions in space that differ from those on Earth include near vacuum, extreme temperatures, and microgravity. 🔑 **To help people live in space, engineers have created technology that provides air and insulation as well as the ability to work in microgravity.**

Vocabulary

- vacuum
- microgravity
- space spinoff
- geostationary orbit

Skills

- Reading: Identify the Main Idea
- Inquiry: Draw Conclusions

Vacuum Even though you can't see the air, it fills every room in your house. But space has no air and is nearly a vacuum. A **vacuum** is a place that is empty of all matter. Except for a few stray atoms and molecules, space is mostly empty. Since there is no air in space, there is no oxygen for astronauts to breathe. To protect astronauts, spacecraft must be airtight.

Because there is no air, there is nothing to hold the sun's heat. In direct sunlight, the surface of a spacecraft heats up to high temperatures. But in shadow, temperatures fall to very low levels. Spacecraft must be well insulated to protect astronauts against the extreme temperatures outside.

Microgravity Have you ever floated in a swimming pool? Astronauts in orbit experience a similar feeling of weightlessness, or **microgravity.** Their mass is the same as it was on Earth, but on a scale their weight would register as zero. Although they are in microgravity, they are still under the influence of Earth's gravity. In fact, Earth's gravity is holding them in orbit. Astronauts in orbit feel weightless because they are falling through space with their spacecraft. They don't fall to Earth because their inertia keeps them moving forward. Recall that inertia is the tendency of an object to resist a change in motion.

Figure 1 shows astronaut Jan Davis experiencing microgravity. Engineers must create devices that are capable of working in microgravity. Drink containers must be designed so that their contents do not float off. Long periods spent in microgravity can cause health problems. Scientists are trying to discover how to reduce the effects of microgravity on people.

FIGURE 1 ·······················

Eating in Space

Astronaut Jan Davis eats Girl Scout cookies in orbit.

✎ Draw Conclusions
How is eating in space different from eating on Earth?

_____

_____

_____

Lab zone® Do the Quick Lab *What Do You Need to Survive in Space?*

Assess Your Understanding

got it? ··

○ **I get it!** Now I know to help people live in space, engineers have created technology that _____

_____

○ **I need extra help with** _____

Go to **MY SCIENCE** ⓢ **COACH** *online for help with this subject.*

SC.8.E.5.10

225

FLORIDA NGSSS

SC.8.N.4.2 Explain how political, social, and economic concerns can affect science, and vice versa.

SC.8.E.5.10 Assess how technology is essential to science for such purposes as access to outer space and other remote locations, sample collection, measurement, data collection and storage, computation, and communication of information.

How Has Space Technology Benefited People?

The space program has led to many benefits. 🔑 **The space program has developed new technologies that help scientists work and new consumer products that people can use.**

Technology in Space Science Technology is essential for doing scientific research in outer space. Technology also helps scientists learn about remote locations, like the bottom of the ocean, the inside of a volcano, and the continent of Antarctica.

FIGURE 2 · · · · · · · · · · · · · · · ·

Technology in Science
Technology is used for the study of science in many varied ways.

✎ **Demonstrate Consumer Literacy Read about the different types of technology. Then assess how you might use one in your personal life.**

_____

_____

_____

_____

_____

❶ **Data Collection and Storage**
Space probes collect data. When scientists do experiments, they often write down data in lab notebooks, but space probes send back thousands of pages of data, far too much for one notebook.

Large computers can collect and store all these data from space probes, allowing scientists to analyze vast amounts of data.

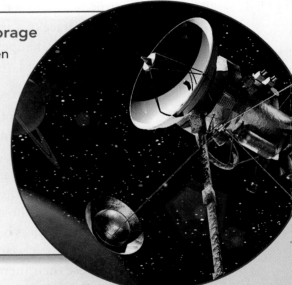

❷ **Sample Collection**
Collecting samples of soil and atmosphere from the moon and other planets is possible due to rockets and space probes. When astronauts traveled to the moon, they brought back samples of the moon's soil and moon rocks. Space probes that landed on Mars collected and tested samples of the Martian soil.

Technology is even required to collect samples on Earth. For example, in 1984 a group of scientists found a meteorite in Antarctica that they thought had traveled from Mars. In 1996 scientists theorized that the meteorite might show evidence of Martian life. Scientists relied on technology such as bags made of polytetrafluoroethylene (also known as Teflon) to collect the meteorite and keep it as sterile as possible.

❸ Computation

Space science can sometimes require complicated calculations. For example, it can be complex to figure out the correct time to launch a rocket for it to reach its destination on schedule. This period of time is called a launch window, and computers can help scientists calculate the best launch window.

❹ Measurement

Measurement is vital for scientific research. Measuring distances in space relies on telescopes, which collect light and other radiation from outer space. Scientists can use the data they get to figure out distances to faraway objects in the universe.

Lasers have also been used to take measurements. Astronauts on the moon set up an array of mirrors. Scientists fired lasers from Earth at these mirrors and measured the time it took for the light to return. This led to greater precision in our measurement of the distance to the moon.

❺ Communication of Information

Space probes use radio signals to send information back to scientists on Earth. Without radio, we'd have no way of knowing what space probes or space-based telescopes have found.

Once information arrives on Earth, scientists want to share it with each other and the public. NASA maintains a National Space Science Data Center Web site, an archive of space mission data, which anyone can use.

Design an Experiment Assess how you might use one of these technologies in an experiment.

_____

_____

_____

_____

_____

_____

Space Spinoffs The scientists and engineers who have worked on the space program have developed thousands of new materials and devices for use in space. Many of these items have proved useful on Earth as well. An item that has uses on Earth but was originally developed for use in space is called a **space spinoff.** Often such spinoffs are modified somewhat for use on Earth.

The tables on these pages show a few familiar examples.

Consumer Products

Space spinoffs include many devices used in consumer products. The joystick controller is one example. NASA scientists were looking for a way to control the Apollo lunar rover, and ended up developing the controller. The controller was then adapted for use in wheelchairs and in video games.

Materials	Use
Joystick controllers	Wheelchairs and video games
Scratch-resistant lenses	To make eyeglasses
Freeze-dried foods	Eaten by campers
Shock-absorbing helmets	Worn by cyclists
Shock-absorbing sneakers	Worn by runners

apply it!

Draw Conclusions Three items are shown in the top row that were developed for use in space. In the bottom row, write in the number for each item that corresponds to the space spinoff. Explain why you made each connection.

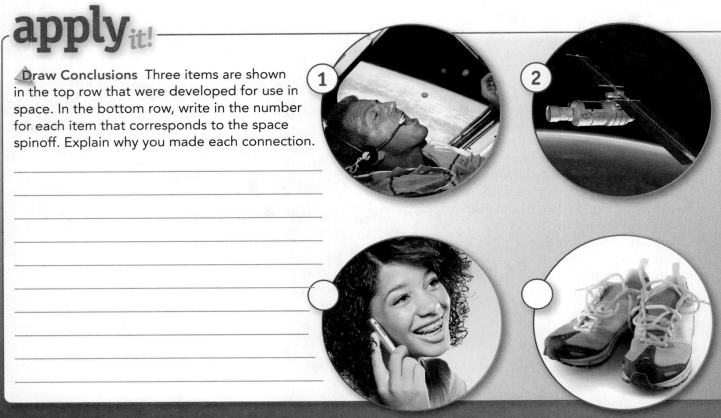

New Materials

A variety of materials were first developed by chemists and engineers for use in spacecraft.

Materials	Use
Composite materials	Tennis rackets and golf clubs
Memory metals	Flexible metal eyeglass frames
Clear, ceramic materials	Dental braces
Shielding materials	Houses, cars and trucks

Medical Devices

Medical science has benefited greatly from the technology of the space program.

Materials	Use
Computer-aided imaging techniques	By hospitals
Lasers	To clean clogged arteries
Pacemakers with longer-life batteries	For hearts

3

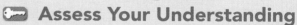

Do the Lab Investigation *Space Spinoffs.*

🔑 Assess Your Understanding

1a. Define What is a space spinoff?

_____

_____

_____

SC.8.N.4.2, SC.8.E.5.10

b. Assess How does science benefit from communication technology?

_____

_____

_____

_____

SC.8.N.4.2, SC.8.E.5.10

c. Compare and Contrast Choose one space spinoff and compare how it is used in space and on Earth.

_____

_____

_____

SC.8.N.4.2, SC.8.E.5.10

got it? ....

○ **I get it!** Now I know that the space program has developed _____

_____

_____

○ I need extra help with _____

Go to MY SCIENCE ⓢ COACH *online for help with this subject.*   SC.8.N.4.2, SC.8.E.5.10

FLORIDA NGSSS

SC.8.N.4.2 Explain how political, social, and economic concerns can affect science, and vice versa.

SC.8.E.5.10 Assess how technology is essential to science for such purposes as access to outer space and other remote locations, sample collection, measurement, data collection and storage, computation, and communication of information.

✎ **Identify the Main Idea**
In the paragraph at the right, underline the uses of observation satellites.

What Are Some Uses of Satellites Orbiting Earth?

When a World Cup soccer final is played, almost the entire world can watch! Today, hundreds of satellites are in orbit, relaying television signals from one part of the planet to another. Satellites also relay telephone signals and computer data. 🔑 **Satellites are used for communications and for collecting weather data and other scientific data.**

Observation satellites are used for many purposes, including tracking weather systems, mapping Earth's surface, and observing changes in Earth's environment. Observation satellites collect data using remote sensing, which is the collection of information about Earth and other objects in space without being in direct contact. Modern computers take the data collected by satellites and produce images for various purposes. For example, **Figure 3** shows a scientist studying weather data. Satellite data might also be used to analyze the amount of rainfall over a wide area, or to discover where oil deposits lie underground.

Satellite orbits are chosen to fit the purpose of the satellite. Most communications satellites are placed in a geostationary orbit. In a **geostationary orbit,** (jee oh STAY shuh ner ee) a satellite orbits Earth at the same rate as Earth rotates and thus stays over the same place over Earth's equator all the time.

FIGURE 3 ⋯⋯⋯⋯⋯⋯⋯⋯⋯⋯⋯⋯⋯⋯⋯⋯

Remote Sensing and Forest Fires
The scientist shown is studying weather data taken from a satellite by remote sensing.

✎ CHALLENGE How can remote sensing help fight forest fires?

_____

_____

_____

_____

_____

EXPLORE THE ESSENTIAL ?

Space Spinoffs

How does exploring space benefit people on Earth?

FIGURE 4 ....

> INTERACTIVE ART The word bank below shows space spinoffs.

✎ **Demonstrate Consumer Literacy** Choose three items, and describe three ways you might use them on Earth. Label the items shown on the page.

Freeze-dried food	Solar panels	Space helmet
Communications satellites	Radio telescope	Scratch-resistant lenses
Global Positioning System (GPS)	Light-emitting diodes	Tiny fuel pumps
Gas detector	Infrared cameras	Pressurized ink

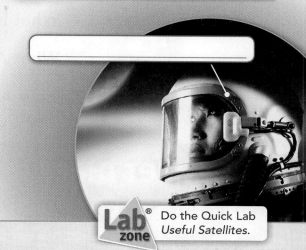

Lab zone® Do the Quick Lab *Useful Satellites.*

🔑 Assess Your Understanding

2a. Listing Name two uses of satellites that affect everyday life.

_____

_____

SC.8.N.4.2, SC.8.E.5.10

b. Infer What advantage would there be to placing a satellite in geostationary orbit?

_____

_____

SC.8.N.4.2, SC.8.E.5.10

c. ANSWER THE ESSENTIAL ? How does exploring space benefit people on Earth?

_____

_____

_____

SC.8.N.4.2, SC.8.E.5.10

got it? ....

○ **I get it!** Now I know that satellites are used

for _____

_____

○ **I need extra help with** _____

Go to my science s coach *online for help with this subject.*   SC.8.N.4.2, SC.8.E.5.10

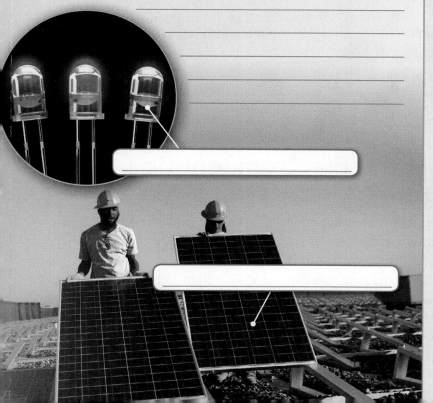

231

Exploring Space With Images

🔑 **What Is the Electromagnetic Spectrum?**
SC.8.E.5.11

🔑 **What Are Telescopes and How Do They Work?**
SC.8.E.5.11

🔑 **How Are Planetary Images and Satellite Photographs Made?**
SC.8.E.5.11

my PLANET DiARY

TECHNOLOGY

Infrared Goggles

Suppose you're a spy on a dark street, hoping to spot another spy. How would you see the other spy in the dark? Wear a pair of infrared goggles.

All objects give off radiation that you can't see. The glowing coils of an electric heater give off infrared radiation, which you feel as heat. Human beings also glow infrared, and with the infrared goggles you can see a green outline of a person in the dark. Some objects in space also give off invisible radiation that we can detect with special telescopes.

Communicate Answer the following question. Then discuss your answer with a partner.

In what other situations might you want to use infrared goggles?

_____

_____

_____

_____

_____

▶ **PLANET DIARY** Go to **Planet Diary** to learn more about telescopes.

Lab® zone
Do the Inquiry Warm-Up *How Does Distance Affect an Image?*

FLORIDA NGSSS

SC.8.E.5.11 Identify and compare characteristics of the electromagnetic spectrum such as wavelength, frequency, use, and hazards and recognize its application to an understanding of planetary images and satellite photographs.

What Is the Electromagnetic Spectrum?

To understand how we study space, it's useful to understand **electromagnetic radiation** (ih LEK troh mag NET ik), or energy that can travel through space in the form of waves.

Scientists call the light you can see **visible light.** Visible light is just one of several types of electromagnetic radiation. Many objects give off radiation that you can't see. Objects in space give off all types of electromagnetic radiation.

Vocabulary
- electromagnetic radiation • visible light • wavelength
- frequency • spectrum • refracting telescope
- reflecting telescope • satellite photograph
- pixel • planetary image

Skills
↩ Reading: Ask Questions
△ Inquiry: Infer

Spectrum Characteristics The distance between the crest of one wave and the crest of the next wave is called the **wavelength.** Visible light has very short wavelengths, less than one millionth of a meter. The **frequency** of a wave is the number of waves that pass a given point in a certain amount of time. Waves with the longest wavelengths have the lowest frequencies. Waves with the shortest wavelengths have the highest frequencies and highest energies.

If you shine white light through a prism, the light spreads out to make a range of different colors with different wavelengths, called a **spectrum.** The spectrum of visible light is made of the colors red, orange, yellow, green, blue, indigo, and violet. ⚷ **The electromagnetic spectrum includes the entire range of radio waves, microwaves, infrared radiation, visible light, ultraviolet radiation, X-rays, and gamma rays.**

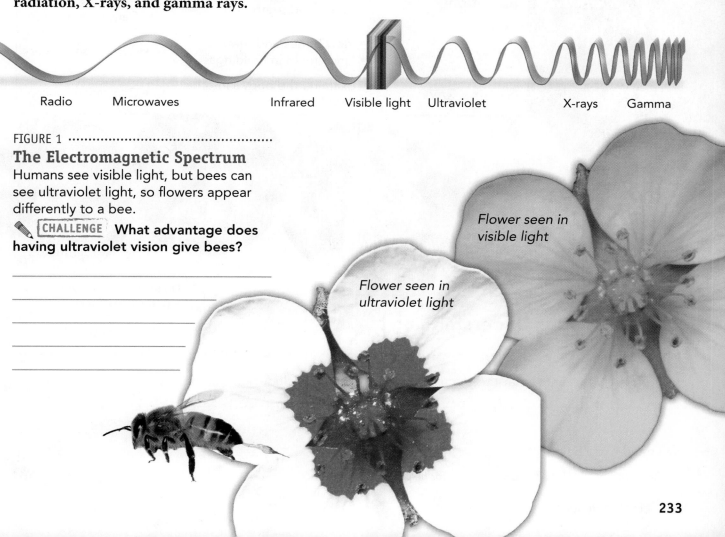

Radio Microwaves Infrared Visible light Ultraviolet X-rays Gamma

FIGURE 1 ·······························
The Electromagnetic Spectrum
Humans see visible light, but bees can see ultraviolet light, so flowers appear differently to a bee.

✎ CHALLENGE **What advantage does having ultraviolet vision give bees?**

_____

_____

_____

_____

Flower seen in visible light

Flower seen in ultraviolet light

233

FIGURE 2 ·····················

Properties of the Spectrum

✏ **Identify** Circle the names of two waves that you find useful and identify why they are useful.

_____

_____

_____

_____

Uses and Hazards The parts of the electromagnetic spectrum have a variety of uses, allowing us to watch television and cook our food. But these waves can also be hazardous. The table below lists the parts of the electromagnetic spectrum in order of increasing energy, and compares their uses and hazards.

Type of Wave	Uses	Hazards
Radio Waves	• Carry radio and TV signals	• None
Microwaves	• Microwave ovens • Cellular phone communication • Radar	• Could cause health issues at very high exposures
Infrared Radiation	• Heat lamps • Incubators • Photography	• Burns your skin
Visible Light	• Sight	• Bright light can damage eyes
Ultraviolet Radiation	• Helps skin cells to produce vitamin D, needed for healthy bones and teeth	• Burns your skin • Damages your eyes • Causes skin cancer
X-Rays	• View bones and teeth • Find cracks in buildings	• Can cause cancer
Gamma Rays	• Examine the body's internal structures	• Can cause cancer

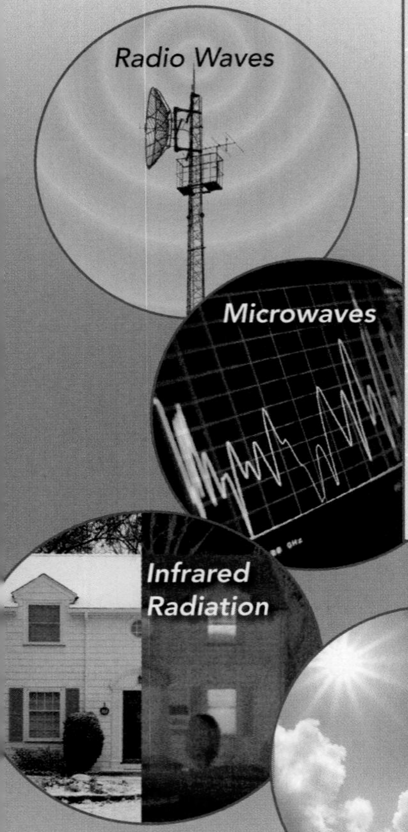

Radio Waves

Microwaves

Infrared Radiation

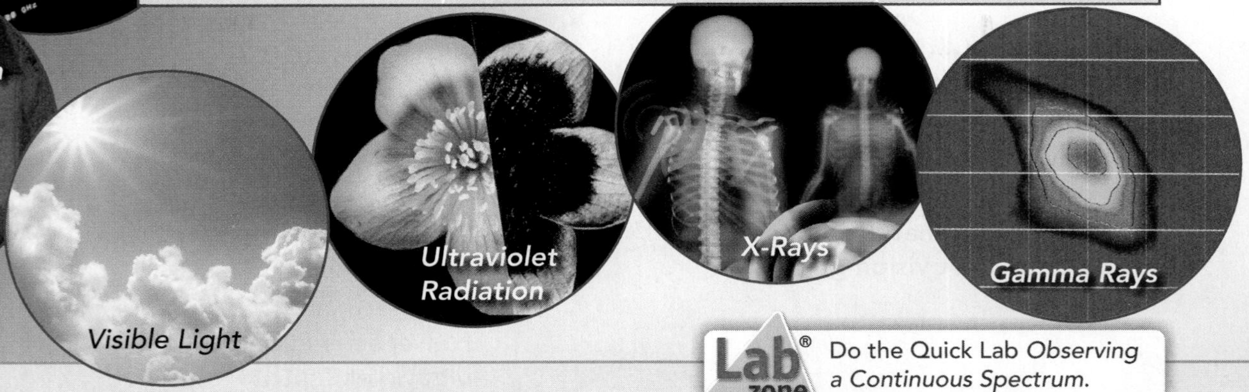

Visible Light

Ultraviolet Radiation

X-Rays

Gamma Rays

Lab zone® Do the Quick Lab _Observing a Continuous Spectrum._

🔑 Assess Your Understanding

got it? ···

○ **I get it!** Now I know that the electromagnetic spectrum includes _____

_____

○ **I need extra help with** _____

Go to MY SCIENCE ⬤ COACH online for help with this subject.

SC.8.E.5.11

What Are Telescopes and How Do They Work?

On a clear night, your eyes can see at most a few thousand stars. But with a telescope, you can see many millions. Why? The light from stars spreads out as it moves through space and your eyes are too small to gather much light from most stars.

🔑 **Telescopes are instruments that collect and focus light and other forms of electromagnetic radiation.** Telescopes make distant objects appear larger and brighter. A telescope that uses lenses or mirrors to collect and focus visible light is called an optical telescope.

Optical Telescopes
The two major types of optical telescopes are refracting telescopes and reflecting telescopes.

FLORIDA NGSSS

SC.8.E.5.11 Identify and compare characteristics of the electromagnetic spectrum such as wavelength, frequency, use, and hazards and recognize its application to an understanding of planetary images and satellite photographs.

FIGURE 3 ·····································

> INTERACTIVE ART **Refracting and Reflecting Telescopes**

A refracting telescope uses a lens to focus light. A reflecting telescope uses a curved mirror instead.

✎ **Infer** Which telescope would be better for viewing a faint, distant star? Why?

_____

_____

_____

Refracting Telescopes

A **refracting telescope** is a telescope that uses convex lenses to gather and focus light. A convex lens is a piece of glass that is curved, so the middle is thicker than the edges.

A refracting telescope has two convex lenses, one at each end of a long tube. Light enters the telescope through the large objective lens. This lens focuses the light at a certain distance, called the focal length of the lens. A larger objective lens can collect more light, making it easier to see faint objects.

The smaller lens at the lower end of a refracting telescope is the eyepiece lens. The eyepiece lens magnifies the image.

Objective lens

Eyepiece lens

Light rays

Reflecting Telescopes

In 1668, Isaac Newton built the first reflecting telescope. A **reflecting telescope** uses a curved mirror to collect and focus light. Like the objective lens in a refracting telescope, the curved mirror in a reflecting telescope focuses a large amount of light onto a small area. A larger mirror means that the telescope can collect more light.

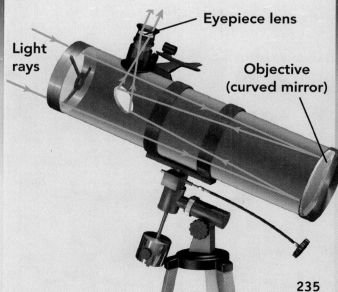

Eyepiece lens

Light rays

Objective (curved mirror)

235

✎ **Ask Questions** Write a question you would like answered about telescopes.

_____

_____

_____

Other Telescopes Telescopes are usually located in observatories. An observatory is a building that contains one or more telescopes. Many large observatories are located on the tops of mountains or in space. Why? Earth's atmosphere makes objects in space look blurry. The sky on some mountaintops is clearer than at sea level and is not brightened by city lights.

- Radio telescopes detect radio waves from objects in space. Most radio telescopes have curved, reflecting surfaces. These surfaces focus faint radio waves the way the mirror in a reflecting telescope focuses light waves. Radio telescopes need to be large to collect and focus more radio waves, because radio waves have long wavelengths. Some radio telescopes, like the one in **Figure 4**, are placed in valleys.
- The Spitzer Space Telescope, launched in 2003, produces images in the infrared portion of the spectrum.
- Very hot objects in space give off X-rays. The Chandra X-ray Observatory produces images in the X-ray portion of the spectrum. X-rays are blocked by Earth's atmosphere, so this telescope is located in outer space.

Some new telescopes are equipped with computer systems that correct images for problems such as telescope movement and changes in air temperature or mirror shape.

FIGURE 4

Arecibo Radio Telescope
The Arecibo telescope in Puerto Rico is 305 meters in diameter.

✎ **Evaluate the Design** Why are radio telescopes so large?

_____

_____

apply it!

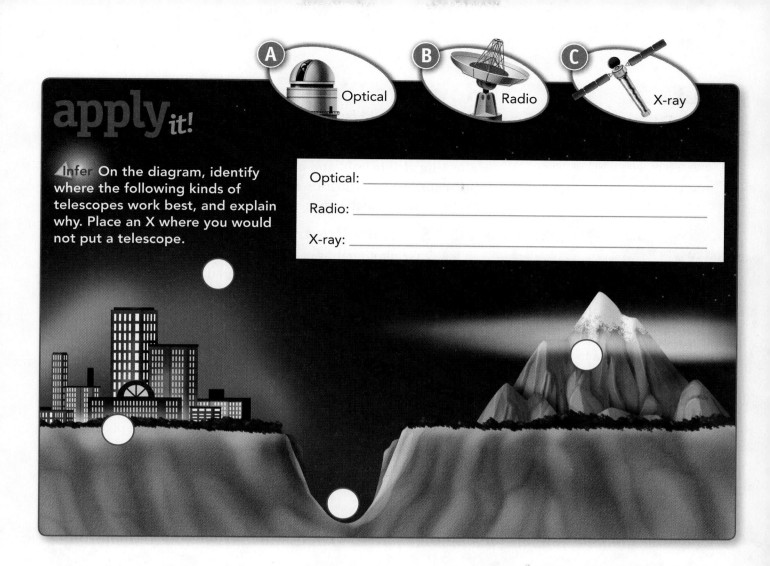

Infer On the diagram, identify where the following kinds of telescopes work best, and explain why. Place an X where you would not put a telescope.

Optical: _____

Radio: _____

X-ray: _____

A — Optical

B — Radio

C — X-ray

Lab zone® Do the Lab Investigation
Design and Build a Telescope.

🔑 Assess Your Understanding

1a. Sequence List the electromagnetic waves, from longest to shortest wavelength.

_____

_____

_____

_____

_____

SC.8.E.5.11

b. Identify Faulty Reasoning A student of astronomy suggests locating a radio telescope near a radio station. Is this a good idea? Why or why not?

_____

_____

_____

_____

_____

SC.8.E.5.11

got it? •••

○ **I get it!** Now I know that telescopes are _____

_____

○ **I need extra help with** _____

Go to MY SCIENCE ⓢ COACH *online for help with this subject.*

SC.8.E.5.11

FLORIDA NGSSS

SC.8.E.5.11 Identify and compare characteristics of the electromagnetic spectrum such as wavelength, frequency, use, and hazards and recognize its application to an understanding of planetary images and satellite photographs.

How Are Planetary Images and Satellite Photographs Made?

🔑 **Planetary images and satellite photographs are made by collecting visible light and other parts of the electromagnetic spectrum.** The information from the electromagnetic spectrum is then used to create the images and photographs.

Satellite Photographs Some satellites in orbit take photographs of Earth's surface. Many of the data used in computer mapping are gathered by these satellites. Mapping satellites use electronic devices to collect computer data about the land surface. Pictures of the surface based on computer data are called **satellite photographs.**

A satellite image is made up of thousands of tiny dots called **pixels.** Each pixel in a satellite image contains information on the color and brightness of a small part of Earth's surface. For example, the pixels that represent a forest differ in color and brightness from the pixels that represent farmland. The data in each pixel are stored on a computer. When the satellite image is printed, the computer translates these digitized data into colors.

FIGURE 5

Satellite Photographs

The left satellite photograph of the Florida Everglades is in visible light. The right photo is a false color image taken in red and infrared.

✏️ **Infer** What does blue represent in the photo at the right? What does that tell you about the Everglades?

_____

_____

_____

Planetary Images

Images of planets help scientists to understand how the solar system developed. Before film cameras were invented, scientists who studied planets through telescopes had to draw pictures of what they saw. With cameras, scientists could photograph the planets in visible light and study the images at their leisure. The images are more accurate than drawings.

Space probes make it easier to create pictures of planets, as they can fly very close to the planets and get clearer pictures. The Hubble Space Telescope also gets clear images of planets, as it orbits above Earth's atmosphere. But some probes and some telescopes collect forms of electromagnetic waves other than visible light. The information from these probes is used to create images that show structures that are otherwise not visible. A picture of a planet taken in visible light or in another form of electromagnetic radiation is called a **planetary image,** such as the one in **Figure 6**.

FIGURE 6 ....

Saturn in Ultraviolet Light

This planetary image was taken in ultraviolet radiation with the Hubble Space Telescope.

✎ **Ask Questions** Cloud bands, which cannot be seen easily in visible light, are evident when viewed in ultraviolet light. If you were a scientist, what would you ask about the cloud bands?

_____

_____

_____

Lab zone® Do the Quick Lab *Reading Satellite Images.*

🔑 Assess Your Understanding

1a. Explain A planetary image is _____

_____

_____

SC.8.E.5.11

b. Compare What are the advantages to using planetary images as opposed to drawings?

_____

_____

SC.8.E.5.11

got it? ....

○ **I get it!** Now I know that planetary images and satellite photographs are made by_____

_____

○ **I need extra help with** _____

Go to my science COACH online for help with this subject.   SC.8.E.5.11

LESSON 5

Space Exploration and Florida

UNLOCK THE ESSENTIAL ?

🔑 **How Has the Space Program Affected Florida?**

SC.8.N.4.1, SC.8.N.4.2, SC.8.E.5.12

my PLANET DiARY for Florida

Louise Kleba

Louise Kleba was born in Milwaukee but now works as a Flight Crew Representative at the Kennedy Space Center in Florida. As a child, she decided that she wanted to have a career in space science when she grew up. Today, she helps assemble and test the equipment that goes into space with the astronauts to make sure it works properly. Even so, things go wrong. Once a power cable that worked on Earth turned out to be too short, and the astronauts had to figure out how to connect it. Kleba is a firm believer in having people in space. As she says, "We are glad that we have people in space, since a robot couldn't fix some of the problems."

➡ To JEM

CAREERS

Communicate Discuss Kleba's career with a partner. Then answer the questions below.

1. Why does equipment to be used in space have to be tested on Earth?

_____

_____

2. Name a situation where you had to improvise because a tool didn't work properly.

_____

_____

▶ **PLANET DIARY** Go to **Planet Diary** to learn more about NASA.

 Lab zone ® Do the Inquiry Warm-Up *Space Jobs.*

FLORIDA NGSSS

SC.8.N.4.1 Explain that science is one of the processes that can be used to inform decision making at the community, state, national, and international levels.

SC.8.N.4.2 Explain how political, social, and economic concerns can affect science, and vice versa.

SC.8.E.5.12 Summarize the effects of space exploration on the economy and culture of Florida.

How Has the Space Program Affected Florida?

The history of space exploration has been connected to Florida from the very beginning. Even before NASA existed, the United States military decided to test launch missiles from Florida's east coast. 🔑 **The space program has been a boon to Florida's economy. It employs Florida's workers, uses Florida's businesses, and promotes tourism to the state. The space program has also encouraged interest in space exploration and technology.**

Vocabulary

- spaceport
- Space Coast

Skills

- Reading: Relate Cause and Effect
- Inquiry: Draw Conclusions

Economic Impact

In July 1958, President Dwight D. Eisenhower signed the National Aeronautics and Space Act, which established the National Aeronautics and Space Administration (NASA). Four years later, the agency created its Launch Operations Center in Brevard County on Florida's east coast. It was renamed the Kennedy Space Center in 1963. It is an example of a **spaceport,** a site for launching or receiving spacecraft.

The spaceport has been the launching site for all American manned missions. Also, hundreds of scientific spacecraft have launched from Florida. The Kennedy Space Center is the primary launch site for almost all of NASA's space missions.

The Kennedy Space Center employs almost 15,000 people. Its presence boosts the local economy in many ways. Both NASA and NASA's workers buy products and services from local businesses. In 2008, the Kennedy Space Center was responsible for almost $2 billion worth of spending in Florida. Tourism brings over a million people to the Kennedy Space Center each year.

NASA spending doesn't just help the residents of Brevard County. Taxes paid by the people who work at the Kennedy Space Center help everyone who lives in the state of Florida.

FIGURE 1 ·····················

Kennedy Space Center

A NASA report called Kennedy Space Center an "economic anchor for Brevard County and the surrounding Central Florida Region."

✎ **Make Generalizations** Why does the local presence of an industry create jobs outside that industry?

_____

_____

_____

_____

_____

_____

_____

Astronaut Guy Bluford at the Kennedy Space Center Visitor Complex

Kennedy Space Center Visitor Complex Rocket Garden

Buttons and patches honoring Apollo 11

Cultural Impact Before 1950, Florida was a very different state than it is today. More of the state was farmland. Tourists came primarily to enjoy the warmer weather in the winter. Today, people also come to Florida for space tourism. The space program has also made Florida into a technological center. It has improved the state's educational system and cultural institutions.

The **Space Coast** is the name given to the area where NASA's Kennedy Space Center is located in Brevard County. In the 1960s, many families moved to the area to work in the space program. This led to the development of Brevard County as a cultural center.

The Space Coast includes a variety of attractions related to the space program. The Kennedy Space Center has rides, exhibits, a simulated moon landing, and displays of spacecraft. The Valiant Air Command Warbird Museum includes a variety of aircraft. The U.S. Astronaut Hall of Fame honors the astronauts of the space program. Beyond the attractions of the space program, the area also includes art galleries, beaches, a zoo, and a symphony orchestra.

 **apply** *it!*

Draw Conclusions The space program has created many attractions along the Space Coast. In the circle, draw a possible attraction you think might be supported by the presence of NASA in Florida. Explain why.

_____

_____

_____

_____

_____

_____

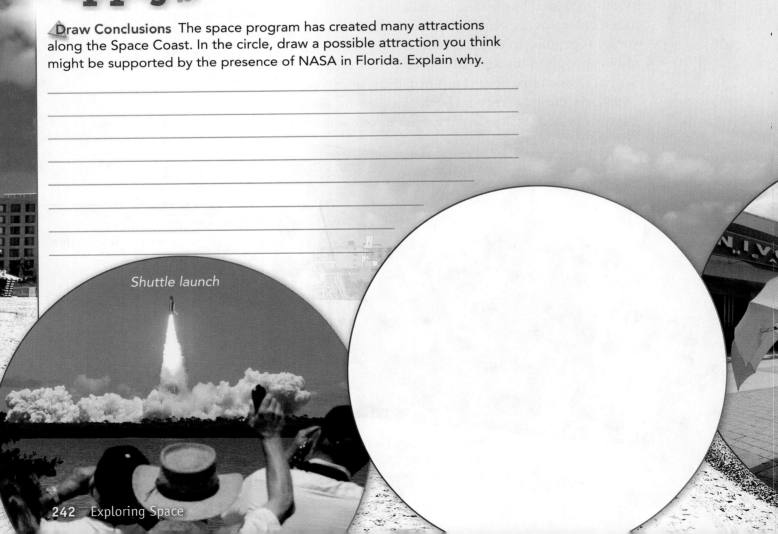

Shuttle launch

Florida's educational system has also benefited from the space program. Many Florida schools emphasize science education. NASA's presence has also created strong connections between science and engineering departments at local universities and NASA's labs. The Florida Institute of Technology is located an hour's drive from Cape Canaveral in Melbourne. It was founded in 1958 and grew quickly. Today over 6,000 students study science and engineering at Florida Tech.

Schools, parks, and streets have been named in honor of the space program. Even one of the telephone area codes for Brevard County was inspired by the space program. Area code 321 was chosen because it sounds like the end of a countdown for a rocket launch.

The influence of space exploration on Florida's culture can also be seen on a coin: the Florida quarter. The quarter includes a picture of a space shuttle to go along with the theme of "Gateway to Discovery."

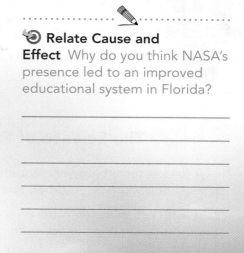

Relate Cause and Effect Why do you think NASA's presence led to an improved educational system in Florida?

_____

_____

_____

_____

_____

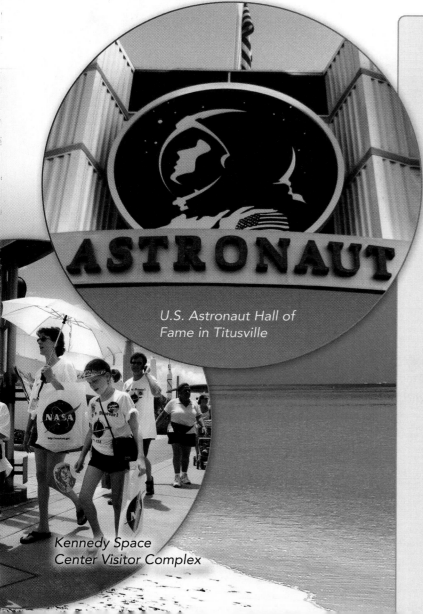

U.S. Astronaut Hall of Fame in Titusville

Kennedy Space Center Visitor Complex

Do the Quick Lab
Space and Florida.

🔑 Assess Your Understanding

1a. Describe What is a spaceport?

_____

_____

SC.8.N.4.2, SC.8.E.5.12

b. Summarize Why would the presence of a spaceport lead to improvements in the nearby area?

_____

_____

_____

_____

_____

_____

SC.8.N.4.1, SC.8.N.4.2, SC.8.E.5.12

got it? ....

O **I get it!** Now I know that space exploration has affected Florida's economy and culture by_____

_____

_____

O I need extra help with _____

Go to **my science COACH** *online for help with this subject.* SC.8.N.4.1, SC.8.N.4.2, SC.8.E.5.12

243

6 Study Guide

Space science benefits people on Earth through _____

_____

LESSON 1 The Science of Rockets

SC.8.N.4.2, SC.8.E.5.10

Rocket technology originated in China hundreds of years ago and gradually spread to other parts of the world.

A rocket moves forward when gases shooting out the back of the rocket push it in the opposite direction.

The main advantage of a multistage rocket is that the total weight of the rocket is greatly reduced as the rocket rises.

Vocabulary
• rocket • thrust • velocity
• orbital velocity • escape velocity

LESSON 2 The History of Space Exploration

SC.8.N.4.2, SC.8.E.5.10

The space race was a rivalry between the United States and the Soviet Union.

Space shuttles carry astronauts into space.

A space station is a place for experiments.

Space probes study the solar system.

Vocabulary
• satellite • space shuttle • space station
• space probe • remote sensing • rover

LESSON 3 Space and Technology

SC.8.N.4.2, SC.8.E.5.10

To help people live in space, engineers have created techology that provides air and insulation and the ability to work in microgravity.

The space program has developed new technologies for scientists and consumers.

Satellites are used for communications and for collecting scientific data.

Vocabulary
• vacuum • microgravity • space spinoff
• geostationary orbit

LESSON 4 Exploring Space With Images

SC.8.E.5.11

The electromagnetic spectrum includes radio waves through gamma rays.

Telescopes can collect and focus light for planetary images and satellite photographs.

Vocabulary
• electromagnetic radiation • visible light
• wavelength • frequency • spectrum
• refracting telescope • reflecting telescope
• satellite photograph • pixel • planetary image

LESSON 5 Space Exploration and Florida

SC.8.N.4.1, SC.8.N.4.2, SC.8.E.5.12

The space program has been a boon to Florida's economy by employing Florida's workers, using Florida's businesses, and promoting tourism to the state.

Vocabulary
• spaceport • Space Coast

Review and Assessment

LESSON 1 The Science of Rockets

1. Which term names a device that expels gas in one direction in order to move in the opposite direction?

   a. space station
   b. rover
   c. space probe
   d. rocket

   SC.8.E.5.10

2. **Classify** A jet airplane uses liquid fuel and oxygen from the atmosphere. The engine expels hot gases to the rear and the airplane moves forward. Is a jet a type of rocket? Explain.

   _____

   _____

   _____

   SC.8.N.4.2, SC.8.E.5.10

Use the illustration to answer the question below.

3. **Apply Concepts** The diagram shows a rocket lifting off. What does each arrow represent?

   _____

   _____

   SC.8.E.5.10

4. **math!** For every force there is an equal and opposite force. Describe a line graph that shows the relationship between a rocket's reaction force and thrust.

   _____

   _____

   _____

   SC.8.E.5.10

LESSON 2 The History of Space Exploration

5. What is any object that revolves around another object in space?

   a. rocket
   b. vacuum
   c. satellite
   d. shuttle

   SC.8.E.5.10

6. **Relate Cause and Effect** After the Soviet Union launched *Sputnik I*, American educators improved math and science education. Why?

   _____

   _____

   _____

   SC.8.N.4.2, SC.8.E.5.10

7. **Write About It** Suppose you are planning a Mars mission. List some major challenges the mission would face and suggest possible solutions. How will the crew's basic needs be met on the long journey?

   SC.8.N.4.2, SC.8.E.5.10, LA.8.4.2.2

LESSON 3 Space and Technology

8. **Classify** Name a space spinoff in each of the following categories: medical devices, materials, consumer products.

   _____

   _____

   _____

   _____

   _____

   _____

   _____

   _____

   _____

   _____

   SC.8.N.4.2, SC.8.E.5.10

245

6 Review and Assessment

Exploring Space With Images

9. What is visible light?

   a. gamma rays and X-rays

   b. the spectrum of rays

   c. a particular wavelength

   d. a form of electromagnetic radiation

                                      SC.8.E.5.11

10. Explain An optical telescope works by

_____

_____

_____

                                   SC.8.E.5.11

11. Draw Conclusions What advantage might there be in placing a telescope on the moon?

_____

_____

_____

                                   SC.8.E.5.11

Space Exploration and Florida

12. Describe What is a spaceport?

_____

_____

_____

                                   SC.8.E.5.12

13. Summarize Name one benefit Florida receives from the space program.

_____

_____

_____

_____

_____

_____

        SC.8.N.4.1, SC.8.N.4.2, SC.8.E.5.12

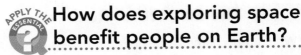 **How does exploring space benefit people on Earth?**

14. Suppose your car broke down in an unfamiliar place. Explain two ways that satellites in orbit could help you get assistance.

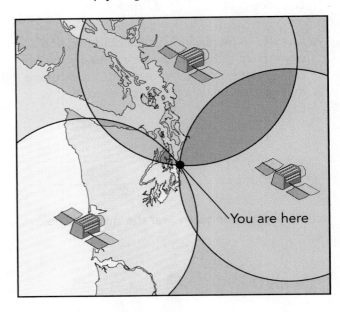

You are here

_____

_____

_____

_____

_____

_____

_____

_____

_____

_____

_____

_____

_____

_____

_____

_____

                                SC.8.N.4.2, SC.8.E.5.10

Florida Benchmarks Review

Circle the letter of the best answer.

1 The diagram below shows a rocket and the direction of four forces.

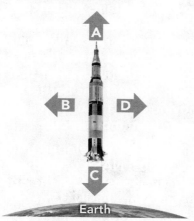

Which force represents an equal and opposite force to the thrust of the rocket?

A Force A **B** Force B
C Force C **D** Force D

SC.8.E.5.10

2 Which of the following is most responsible for rockets reaching the moon?

A explosives
B single-stage rockets
C gunpowder
D multistage rockets

SC.8.E.5.10

3 Which of the following groups of electromagnetic waves is listed correctly in order of increasing frequency?

A X-rays, visible light, radio waves
B radio waves, visible light, X-rays
C infrared rays, visible light, radio waves
D visible light, gamma rays, X-rays

SC.8.E.5.11

4 Which of these did the United States accomplish first during the space race?

A sending the first human being into space
B sending the first living creature into space
C landing the first human on the moon
D launching the first satellite into space

SC.8.N.4.2, SC.8.E.5.10

5 Which of the following is a spaceport?

A Kennedy Space Center
B Valiant Air Command Warbird Museum
C U.S. Astronaut Hall of Fame
D Florida Institute of Technology

SC.8.N.4.1, SC.8.N.4.2, SC.8.E.5.12

Object	Escape velocity (km/s)
MERCURY	4.3
VENUS	10.3
MOON	2.4
MARS	5.0

Object	Escape velocity (km/s)
JUPITER	59.5
SATURN	35.6
URANUS	21.2
NEPTUNE	23.6

6 The tables show the escape velocities needed for a rocket launch from different objects in the solar system. From which object would it be easiest to launch a rocket?

A Jupiter
B Saturn
C Mars
D Moon

SC.8.E.5.10

Cool It With Paint

Research It NASA technology has produced thousands of useful products, called "spinoffs." Use reference materials to make a list of other NASA technologies and their spinoffs. Include how these technologies have benefited society. Organize the information into a chart. Be sure to include a list of sources.

What if you could keep a house cooler and decrease air conditioning costs just by applying a coat of paint? You can, if you add an insulating powder to the paint. This powder contains microscopic ceramic beads filled with gas. Both the ceramic and gas in the beads are good insulators, or materials that do not conduct heat well. When these beads coat any surface, they form a protective barrier that prevents heat flow. In a warm climate, this barrier prevents warm air from moving into a house. In a cold climate, it prevents warm air from moving out.

This insulating mixture was developed using NASA technology. In the 1980s, NASA used the insulating paint to protect rocket boosters on the Space Shuttle. The boosters were easily damaged by hot exhaust and heat generated by wind resistance. Unfortunately, the insulation that NASA was using often chipped off during flight. It was also difficult to apply and expensive. So NASA engineers developed a new and improved coating. They combined insulators, such as glass and cork, with epoxy and paint to make an environmentally friendly spray-on powder. This new coating worked so well that engineers adapted it into a product that everyone could use!

The paint used on the building's exterior was mixed with insulating powder. The blues and greens in this thermal image show that very little heat is being lost from this building.

FLORIDA NGSSS

SC.8.N.4.2 Explain how political, social, and economic concerns can affect science, and vice versa.

SC.8.E.5.10 Assess how technology is essential to science for such purposes as access to outer space and other remote locations.

SC.8.E.5.12 Summarize the effects of space exploration on the economy and culture of Florida.

LA.8.4.2.2 The student will record information, such as notes and charts, related to a topic and attribute sources of information.

KEEPING TRACK OF TIME

▲ This sun stone is sometimes called the Aztec calendar. It shows the 20 days in the Aztec month. The Aztec calendar was a solar calendar, with a total of 365 days in a year.

What day of the week is your birthday this year? Better check the calendar.

Calendars were invented to keep track of important events, such as planting schedules and festivals.

Early people noticed certain patterns in nature. The seasons change. The sun rises and sets. The moon changes phases. These patterns became the basis for calendars even before people understood that Earth rotates on an axis and revolves around the sun or that the moon revolves around Earth.

Calendars were lunar (based on the moon), solar (based on the sun), or lunisolar (based on a combination). But none was completely accurate—important events shifted around from one year to the next.

The Gregorian calendar, introduced in 1582, is the standard calendar in use today. It is more accurate than most calendars, but even it requires some tinkering. We add an extra day almost every four years, giving us a leap year. Century years (like 2000) are not leap years unless they are divisible by 400.

Research It There are about 40 different kinds of calendars in use today. Pick a calendar and research it, including how it was developed. Write an essay describing the calendar and how it is different from the Gregorian calendar. What does the calendar tell you about the society that uses it?

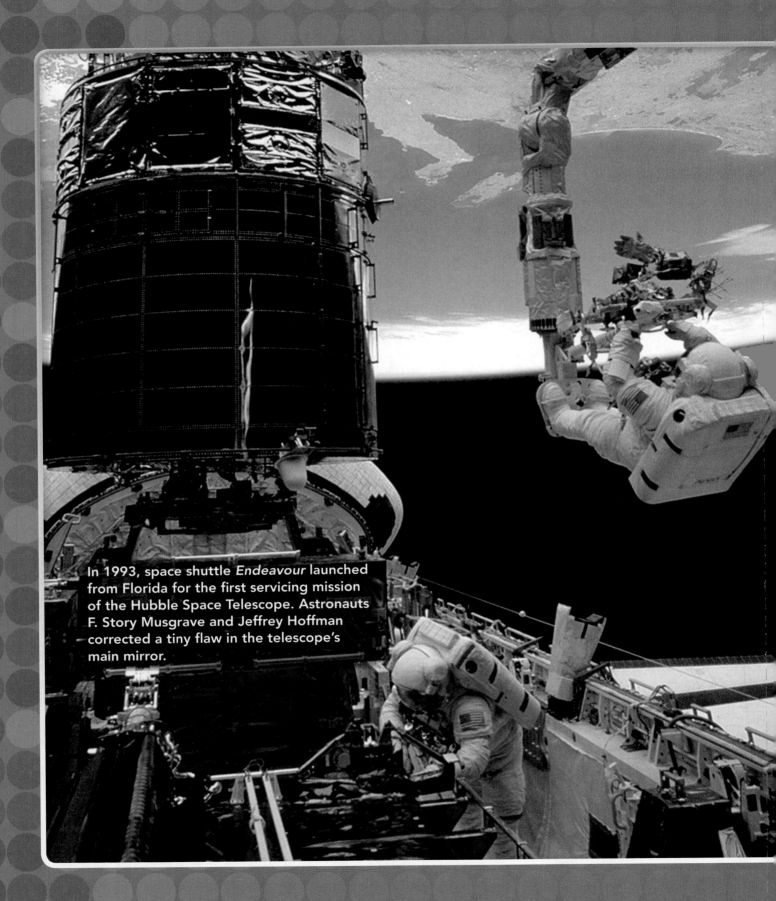

In 1993, space shuttle *Endeavour* launched from Florida for the first servicing mission of the Hubble Space Telescope. Astronauts F. Story Musgrave and Jeffrey Hoffman corrected a tiny flaw in the telescope's main mirror.

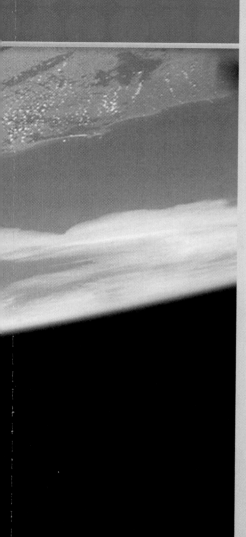

Summarizing

Earth Science

In the Earth Science unit, you learned about the objects that exist in the universe, including the objects in our galaxy and solar system and how they interact with each other. You also learned how the exploration of space benefits everyone on Earth, and how it helps the state of Florida.

How do the astronauts stay in orbit?

_____

_____

_____

_____

_____

_____

_____

_____

_____

What might the astronauts learn from their mission?

_____

_____

_____

_____

_____

_____

_____

_____

_____

What states of **MATTER** do you see in the photo?

What physical and chemical **CHANGES** is the fire causing?

A fire bomber makes a drop of fire retardant chemicals just above a brush fire.

Introducing

Physical Science

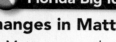

 Florida Big Idea 8

Properties of Matter

A. All objects and substances in the world are made of matter. Matter has two fundamental properties: matter takes up space and matter has mass which gives it inertia.

B. Objects and substances can be classified by their physical and chemical properties. Mass is the amount of matter (or "stuff") in an object. Weight, on the other hand, is the measure of force of attraction (gravitational force) between an object and Earth.

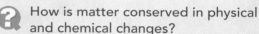

? How is matter described?

? What are the properties of matter?

? How is the periodic table organized?

? How can bonding determine the properties of a compound?

? What determines the properties of mixtures and pure substances?

Florida Big Idea 9

Changes in Matter

A. Matter can undergo a variety of changes.

B. When matter is changed physically, generally no changes occur in the structure of the atoms or molecules composing the matter.

C. When matter changes chemically, a rearrangement of bonds between the atoms occurs. This results in new substances with new properties.

? How is matter conserved in physical and chemical changes?

HOW DID THIS BUILDING TURN TO ICE?

Why does a substance change states?

Firefighters sprayed water on a blaze in this historic building in Maine. The air temperature was –14°F, which was uncomfortably cold. This made it difficult for firefighters to battle the flames. The building was in danger of falling down because it was covered in ice 6 to 10 inches thick. **Infer How did this building get covered in ice?**

_____

_____

_____

_____

_____

> UNTAMED SCIENCE Watch the **Untamed Science** video to learn more about changing states.

Introduction to Matter

FLORIDA | Next Generation Sunshine State Standards

Big Idea 3: SC.8.N.3.1
Big Idea 8: SC.8.P.8.1

Language Arts: LA.8.2.2.3
Mathematics: MA.6.A.3.6

Getting Started

Check Your Understanding

1. Background Read the paragraph below and then answer the question.

> The air **temperature** outside has been below freezing all week. The local pond has frozen over and is ready for ice skating. Ronnesia is excited just thinking about all the things she can do on the **ice.** She eats a good breakfast to get the **energy** she needs for ice skating.

> **Temperature** is a measure of the average energy of random motion of particles of matter.
>
> **Ice** is water in the solid form.
>
> **Energy** is the ability to do work or cause change.

- Why is the pond ready for ice skating?

_____

_____

> **MY READING WEB** If you had trouble completing the question above, visit **My Reading Web** and type in *Introduction to Matter.*

Vocabulary Skill

Suffixes A suffix is a letter or group of letters added to the end of a word to change its meaning and often its part of speech. In this chapter, you will learn vocabulary words that end in the suffixes *-ation*, *-ine*, and *-sion*.

Suffix	Meaning	Example
-ation	State of, process of, act of	Vaporization, evaporation, condensation, sublimation
-ine	Consisting of	Crystalline solid
-sion	State of, process of, act of	Surface tension

LA.8.1.6.7

2. Quick Check *Vapor* is another word for gas. Use the table above to predict the meaning of *vaporization*. Revise your definition as needed.

_____

_____

liquid

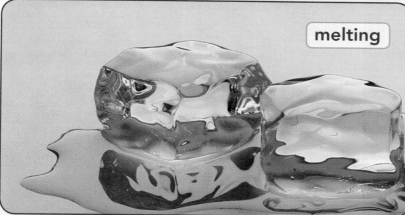

surface tension

melting

sublimation

Chapter Preview

LESSON 1

- matter
- chemistry
- substance
- element
- atom
- chemical bond
- molecule
- compound
- chemical formula
- mixture

↻ **Compare and Contrast**
△ **Infer**

LESSON 2

- solid
- crystalline solid
- amorphous solid
- liquid • fluid
- surface tension
- viscosity • gas
- pressure
- temperature

↻ **Relate Cause and Effect**
△ **Infer**

LESSON 3

- thermal energy
- heat
- physical property
- melting
- melting point
- freezing
- vaporization
- evaporation
- boiling
- boiling point
- condensation
- sublimation

↻ **Compare and Contrast**
△ **Predict**

> **VOCAB FLASH CARDS** For extra help with vocabulary, visit **Vocab Flash Cards** and type in *Introduction to Matter.*

1 Describing Matter

UNLOCK THE ESSENTIAL

🗝 **What Is Matter Made Of?**
SC.8.N.3.1, SC.8.P.8.1, LA.8.2.2.3

my planet diary

CAREER

Art Conservation Scientist

Science and art may seem like two very different interests, but they are both part of the job for an art conservation scientist. Over time, art can fade, decay, or get dirty. Conservation scientists find ways to restore art by examining its properties. They look at texture, color and age of the paint, the condition of the canvas, and materials used to make the paint. Then, the scientists can determine chemical properties of the painting. For example, they can predict how the painting will react to light, changes in temperature, and the use of chemicals for cleaning. Thanks to art conservation scientists, masterpieces of art can be enjoyed for many years.

Before

After

Write your answers to the questions below.

1. Why is it important for an art conservation scientist to study the properties of a painting before it's repaired?

_____

_____

_____

_____

2. Name another career that combines science with another interest.

_____

_____

Medusa by Caravaggio, about 1598. Uffizi Gallery, Florence, Italy

> **PLANET DIARY** Go to **Planet Diary** to learn more about matter.

 Do the Inquiry Warm-Up *Differences in Compounds.*

Vocabulary
- matter • chemistry • substance • element
- atom • chemical bond • molecule • compound
- chemical formula • mixture

Skills
↻ Reading: Compare and Contrast
△ Inquiry: Infer

What Is Matter Made Of?

You have probably heard the word *matter* used many times. "As a matter of fact . . ." or "Hey, what's the matter?" In science, **matter** is anything that has mass and takes up space. All the "stuff" around you is matter, and you are matter too. Air, plastic, metal, wood, glass, paper, and cloth are all matter.

Even though air and paper are both matter, you know they are different materials. Matter can have many different properties, or characteristics, that can be used to identify and classify it. Materials can be hard or soft, hot or cold, liquid, solid, or gas. Some materials catch fire easily, but others do not burn. **Chemistry** is the study of matter and how matter changes.

Substances Some types of matter are substances and some are not. In chemistry, a **substance** is a single kind of matter that is pure, meaning it always has a specific makeup, or composition. For example, table salt has the same composition and properties whether it comes from seawater or a salt mine. **Figure 1** shows two examples of water that appear to be very different. Water is a substance. Pure water is always the same, whether it comes from a glacier or from a geyser.

> **FLORIDA** NGSSS
>
> **SC.8.N.3.1** Select models useful in relating the results of their own investigations.
>
> **SC.8.P.8.1** Explore the scientific theory of atoms (also known as atomic theory) by using models to explain the motion of particles in solids, liquids, and gases.
>
> **LA.8.2.2.3** The student will organize information to show relationships among facts (e.g., representing key points within text through comparing/contrasting).

FIGURE 1 ···

Properties of Matter

✎ **Compare and Contrast** Complete the Venn diagram with the properties of water from a glacier and from a geyser.

Glacier   Geyser

Elements Why is one kind of matter different from another kind of matter? Around 450 B.C., a Greek philosopher named Empedocles attempted to answer these questions. He proposed that all matter was made of four "elements"—air, earth, fire, and water. Empedocles thought that all other matter was a combination of these elements. The idea of four elements was so convincing that people believed it for more than 2,000 years.

In the late 1600s, experiments by early chemists began to show that matter was made up of many more than four elements. Scientists know that all matter in the universe is made of more than 100 different substances, called elements. An **element** is a substance that cannot be broken down into any other substances by chemical or physical means. Elements are the simplest substances. Each element can be identified by its specific physical and chemical properties. You may already be familiar with some elements such as aluminum or tin. Elements are represented by one- or two-letter symbols, such as C for carbon, O for oxygen, and Ca for calcium.

apply it!

The elements make up all the matter in the universe.

❶ **Explore** How can you tell one element from another?

_____

_____

_____

❷ **Infer** Match the pictures on this page of items containing common elements to the element's name.

A) helium   B) gold   C) copper

D) iron   E) neon

❸ **CHALLENGE** Choose another element that you are familiar with and describe its properties.

_____

_____

_____

Atoms Imagine tearing a piece of aluminum foil in half over and over. Would you reach a point where you had the smallest possible piece of aluminum? The answer is yes. 🔑 **The scientific theory of atoms, also called the particle theory of matter, explains that all matter is made of atoms.** An **atom** is the basic particle from which all elements are made. An atom has a positively charged center, or nucleus, containing smaller particles. The nucleus is surrounded by a "cloud" of negative charge. The elements have different properties because their atoms are different.

Molecules Atoms of most elements are able to combine with other atoms. When atoms combine, they form a **chemical bond,** which is a force of attraction between two atoms. In many cases, atoms combine to form larger particles called molecules. A **molecule** (MAHL uh kyool) is a group of two or more atoms held together by chemical bonds. A molecule of water, for example, is made up of an oxygen atom chemically bonded to two hydrogen atoms. Two atoms of the same element can also combine to form a molecule. Oxygen molecules are made up of two oxygen atoms. **Figure 2** shows models of some common molecules.

✏️ **Compare and Contrast** How are atoms and molecules the same? How are they different?

_____

_____

_____

_____

_____

_____

LA.8.2.2.3

FIGURE 2 ··

Atoms and Molecules

Molecules are made up of groups of atoms.

✏️ **Use the molecule models to complete the activities.**

1. **Interpret Diagrams** Count the number of atoms of each element in the molecules and write it on the lines below.

2. [CHALLENGE] On the bottom line, write a representation for each molecule using letters and numbers.

Key

C = Carbon
H = Hydrogen
O = Oxygen
N = Nitrogen

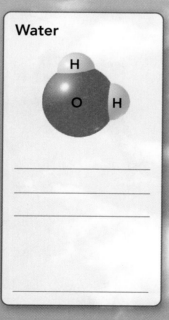

Carbon dioxide

_____

_____

[CHALLENGE]

_____

Water

_____

_____

_____

Oxygen

_____

_____

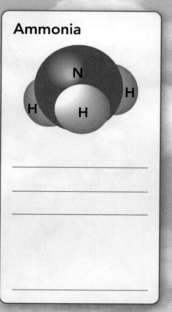

Ammonia

_____

_____

FIGURE 3 ·····················

> ART IN MOTION Compounds From Elements

When elements combine, the compound that forms has different properties than the original elements.

✎ **Describe** List the properties of copper, sulfur, and copper sulfide.

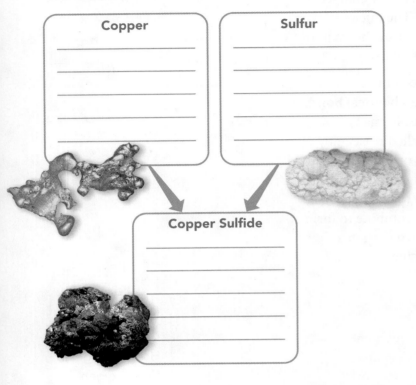

Copper	Sulfur

Copper Sulfide

FIGURE 4 ·····················

Fruit Mixtures

The fruit salad, fruit juice, and fruit smoothie are all different kinds of mixtures.

✎ **Interpret Photos** Label each fruit snack as a heterogeneous or homogeneous mixture.

Compounds

Water, ammonia, and carbon dioxide are all compounds. A **compound** is a substance made of two or more elements that are chemically combined in a set ratio. A compound is represented by a **chemical formula,** which shows the elements in the compound and the ratio of atoms. For example, the chemical formula for carbon dioxide is CO_2. The 2 below the O for oxygen tells you that the ratio of carbon atoms to oxygen atoms is 1 to 2. If there is no number after an element's symbol, it is understood that the number is 1. A different number of atoms in a formula represents a different compound. For example, the formula for carbon monoxide is CO. Here, the ratio of carbon atoms to oxygen atoms is 1 to 1.

When elements chemically combine, they form compounds with properties different from those of the elements. **Figure 3** shows that the element sulfur is a yellow solid and the element copper is a shiny metal. When copper and sulfur combine, they form a compound called copper sulfide. The new compound has different properties from both copper and sulfur.

Mixtures Elements and compounds are substances, but most materials are mixtures. **Figure 4** shows some common mixtures. A **mixture** is made of two or more substances that are together in the same place, but their atoms are not chemically bonded. Mixtures differ from compounds. Each substance in a mixture keeps its own properties. Also, the parts of a mixture are not combined in a set ratio.

Think of a handful of sand. If you look at sand closely, you will see particles of rock, bits of shells, and maybe even crystals of salt.

Heterogeneous Mixtures There are two types of mixtures. A mixture can be heterogeneous or homogeneous. In a heterogeneous mixture (het ur oh JEE nee us), you can usually see the different parts and they can be separated. The sand described above is a heterogeneous mixture. So is a salad. Think of how easy it is to see pieces of lettuce, tomatoes, onions, and other salad ingredients that can be mixed in countless ways.

Homogeneous Mixtures The substances of a homogeneous mixture (hoh moh JEE nee us), are so evenly mixed that you can't see the different parts. It is difficult to separate the parts of a homogeneous mixture. Air is a homogeneous mixture of gases. You know that oxygen is present in the air because you are able to breathe, but you cannot identify where the oxygen is in the air. A solution is another example of a homogeneous mixture. Solutions can be liquids, gases, or even solids.

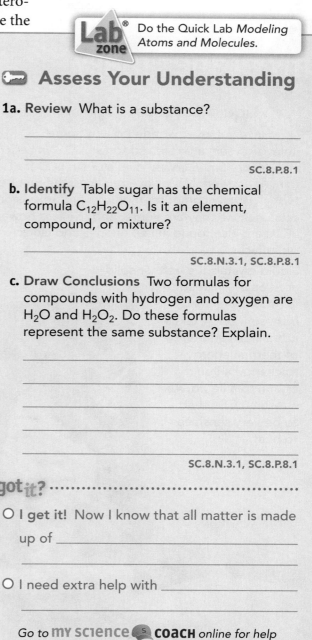

> **Lab zone®** Do the Quick Lab *Modeling Atoms and Molecules.*

Assess Your Understanding

1a. Review What is a substance?

_____

_____

SC.8.P.8.1

b. Identify Table sugar has the chemical formula $C_{12}H_{22}O_{11}$. Is it an element, compound, or mixture?

_____

SC.8.N.3.1, SC.8.P.8.1

c. Draw Conclusions Two formulas for compounds with hydrogen and oxygen are H_2O and H_2O_2. Do these formulas represent the same substance? Explain.

_____

_____

_____

_____

_____

SC.8.N.3.1, SC.8.P.8.1

got it? ....

○ **I get it!** Now I know that all matter is made up of _____

_____

○ **I need extra help with** _____

_____

Go to **MY SCIENCE** Ⓢ **COACH** *online for help with this subject.*   SC.8.N.3.1, SC.8.P.8.1

LESSON

2 States of Matter

UNLOCK THE ESSENTIAL

🔑 **How Do You Describe a Solid?**
SC.8.P.8.1

🔑 **How Do You Describe a Liquid?**
SC.8.P.8.1

🔑 **How Do You Describe a Gas?**
SC.8.P.8.1, MA.6.A.3.6

my planet diary

Liquid Crystals

Have you ever wondered why some television sets are referred to as LCD TVs? *LCD* stands for "liquid crystal display." An LCD is a thin, flat screen. LCDs have replaced the picture tubes in many computer monitors and television sets because they are lighter and use less power. LCDs are also found in cell phones and clock radio faces.

Liquid crystals are neither solid nor liquid—instead they fall somewhere in between. But it takes just a small amount of thermal energy to change a liquid crystal to a liquid. As a result, LCDs tend to be very sensitive to heat.

FUN FACTS

Communicate Discuss these questions with a classmate. Write your answers below.

1. List some objects that contain LCDs.

_____

_____

2. Why might you not want to leave a cell phone or a laptop computer outside on a hot day?

_____

_____

_____

_____

> PLANET DIARY Go to **Planet Diary** to learn more about solids, liquids, and gases.

 Lab zone Do the Inquiry Warm-Up *What Are Solids, Liquids, and Gases?*

LCD display with crystals cooling (background)

Vocabulary

- solid • crystalline solid • amorphous solid • liquid • fluid
- surface tension • viscosity • gas • pressure • temperature

Skills

⟳ Reading: Relate Cause and Effect

△ Inquiry: Infer

How Do You Describe a Solid?

Look at the bowl in **Figure 1.** It contains the metal ore azurite. Notice that the shape and size of the piece of azurite are different from the bowl's shape and size. What would happen if you took the azurite out of the bowl and placed it on a tabletop? Would it become flatter? What would happen if you put it in a larger bowl? Would it become larger? Of course not, because it's a solid. A **solid** has a definite shape and a definite volume. Your pencil is another example of a solid. If your pencil has a cylindrical shape and a volume of 6 cubic centimeters, it will keep this shape and volume in any position in any container.

FLORIDA NGSSS

SC.8.P.8.1 Explore the scientific theory of atoms (also known as atomic theory) by using models to explain the motion of particles in solids, liquids, and gases.

Particles in a Solid The particles that make up a solid are packed very closely together. Also, each particle is tightly fixed in one position. 🔑 **This fixed, closely packed arrangement of particles in a solid causes it to have a definite shape and volume.** Do the particles that make up a solid move at all? Yes, but not much. The particles in a solid are closely locked in position and can only vibrate in place. This means that the particles move back and forth slightly, like a group of people running in place.

Particles in a solid

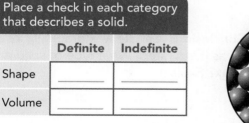

Place a check in each category that describes a solid.		
	Definite	**Indefinite**
Shape	_____	_____
Volume	_____	_____

FIGURE 1 ·····························

Solid

A solid does not take the shape or volume of its container.

✎ **Interpret Diagrams** Describe the arrangement of particles in a solid.

_____

_____

_____

265

FIGURE 2 ·······················

Types of Solids

Solids are either crystalline or amorphous. Butter is an amorphous solid. The mineral fluorite is a crystalline solid.

✎ **Compare and Contrast** Use the Venn diagram to compare the characteristics of amorphous and crystalline solids.

Types of Solids In many solids, the particles form a regular, repeating pattern. These patterns create crystals. Solids that are made up of crystals are called **crystalline solids** (KRIS tuh lin). Salt, sugar, and snow are examples of crystalline solids. The fluorite crystal shown in **Figure 2** is an example of a colorful crystalline solid. When a crystalline solid is heated, it melts at a distinct temperature.

In **amorphous solids** (uh MAWR fus), the particles are not arranged in a regular pattern. Unlike a crystalline solid, an amorphous solid does not melt at a distinct temperature. Instead, it may become softer and softer or change into other substances. Glass is an example of an amorphous solid. A glass blower can bend and shape glass that has been heated. Plastics and rubber are other examples of amorphous solids.

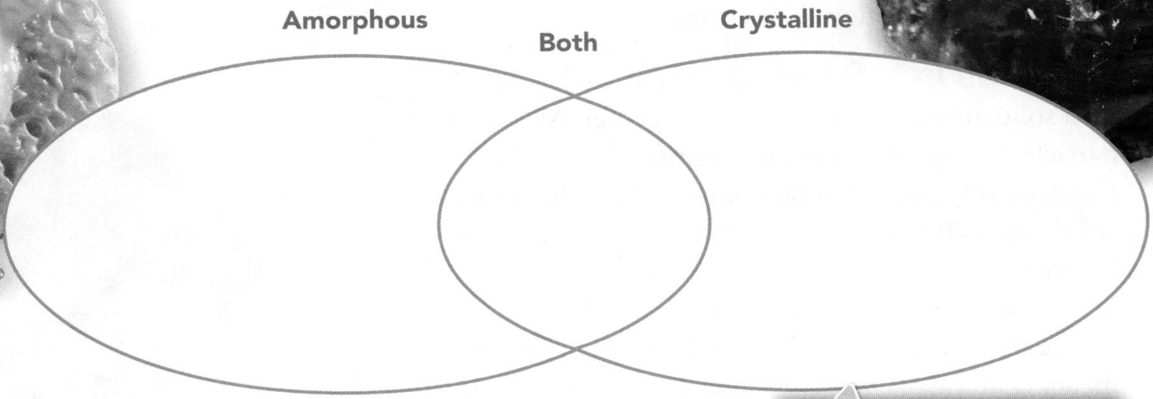

Amorphous   **Both**   **Crystalline**

Lab zone® Do the Quick Lab
Modeling Particles.

⚷ Assess Your Understanding

1a. Identify The two types of solids are

_____ and _____.

SC.8.P.8.1

b. Explore Are the particles in a solid motionless? Explain your answer.

_____

_____

SC.8.P.8.1

c. Draw Conclusions Candle wax gradually loses its shape as it is heated. What type of solid is candle wax? Explain.

_____

_____

_____

_____

SC.8.P.8.1

got it? ···

○ **I get it!** Now I know that a solid has a definite shape and volume because _____

_____

○ **I need extra help with** _____

Go to MY SCIENCE ⓢ COACH *online for help with this subject.*   SC.8.P.8.1

How Do You Describe a Liquid?

Without a container, a liquid spreads into a wide, shallow puddle. Like a solid, however, a liquid does have a constant volume. A **liquid** has a definite volume but no shape of its own. **Figure 3** shows equal volumes of grape juice in two different containers. The shape of a liquid may change with its container, but its volume remains the same.

Particles in a Liquid In general, the particles in a liquid are packed almost as closely together as those in a solid. However, the particles in a liquid move around one another freely. You can compare this movement to the way you might move a group of marbles around in your hand. Like the particles of a liquid, the marbles slide around one another but still touch. **Because its particles are free to move, a liquid has no definite shape. However, it does have a definite volume.** These freely moving particles allow a liquid to flow from place to place. For this reason, a liquid is also called a **fluid,** meaning a "substance that flows."

FLORIDA NGSSS

SC.8.P.8.1 Explore the scientific theory of atoms (also known as atomic theory) by using models to explain the motion of particles in solids, liquids, and gases.

↩ **Relate Cause and Effect**
Underline the cause and circle the effect in the boldface sentences.

Place a check in each category that describes a liquid.

	Definite	Indefinite
Shape	_____	_____
Volume	_____	_____

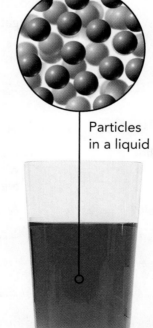

Particles in a liquid

FIGURE 3 ·····················

Liquid

Each container contains 300 cm³ of grape juice. The grape juice takes the shape of its container, but its volume does not change.

✎ **Interpret Diagrams** Describe the arrangement of particles in a liquid.

_____

_____

_____

_____

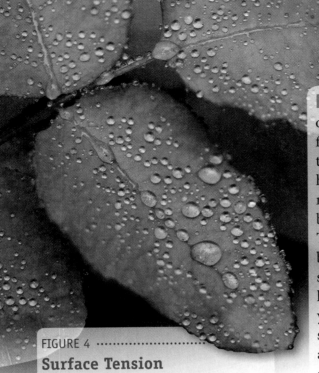

Properties of Liquids

One characteristic property of liquids is surface tension. **Surface tension** is an inward force, or pull, among the molecules in a liquid that brings the molecules on the surface closer together. You may have noticed that water forms droplets and can bead up on many surfaces, such as the leaves shown in **Figure 4.** That's because water molecules attract one another strongly. These attractions cause molecules at the water's surface to be pulled slightly toward the water molecules beneath its surface. Due to surface tension, the surface of water can act like a sort of skin. For example, a sewing needle floats when you place it gently on the surface of water, but it quickly sinks if you push it below the surface. Surface tension lets an insect called a water strider walk on the calm surface of a pond.

Another characteristic property of liquids is **viscosity** (vis KAHS uh tee), or a liquid's resistance to flowing. A liquid's viscosity depends on the size and shape of its particles and the attractions between the particles. Some liquids flow more easily than others. Liquids with high viscosity flow slowly. Honey is an example of a liquid with a very high viscosity. Liquids with low viscosity flow quickly. Water and vinegar have relatively low viscosities.

FIGURE 4 ·····················
Surface Tension
Infer Circle the correct answer.
Water beads up on the surface of the leaves because water molecules (attract/repel) each other strongly.

 **Lab** zone Do the Quick Lab
As Thick as Honey.

Assess Your Understanding

2a. Name A substance that flows is called a

_____
                                    SC.8.P.8.1

b. Describe Why is a liquid able to flow?

_____
_____
                                    SC.8.P.8.1

c. Compare and Contrast How do liquids with a high viscosity differ from liquids with a low viscosity?

_____
_____
_____
                                    SC.8.P.8.1

got it? ···

○ **I get it!** Now I know that a liquid has a definite volume but not a definite shape because _____

_____

○ I need extra help with _____

Go to MY SCIENCE ⓢ COACH online for help with this subject.   SC.8.P.8.1

How Do You Describe a Gas?

FLORIDA NGSSS

SC.8.P.8.1 Explore the scientific theory of atoms (also known as atomic theory) by using models to explain the motion of particles in solids, liquids, and gases.

MA.6.A.3.6 Construct and analyze equations to describe linear functions using algebraic notation.

Like a liquid, a gas is a fluid. Unlike a liquid, however, a **gas** has neither a definite shape nor a definite volume of its own. If a gas is in a closed container such as the flask in **Figure 5,** the gas particles will move and spread apart, taking the shape and volume of the container.

If you could see the particles that make up a gas, you would see them moving in all directions. 🔑 **As gas particles move, they spread apart, filling all the space available. Thus, a gas has neither definite shape nor definite volume.** When working with a gas, it is important to know its volume, temperature, and pressure. So what exactly do these measurements mean?

Volume Recall that volume is the amount of space that matter fills. Volume is measured in cubic centimeters (cm³), milliliters (mL), liters (L), and other units. Because gas particles move and fill all of the space available, the volume of a gas is the same as the volume of its container. For example, a large amount of helium gas can be compressed—or pressed together tightly— to fit into a metal tank. When you use the helium to fill balloons, it expands to fill many balloons that have a total volume much greater than the volume of the tank.

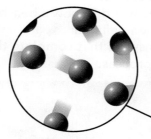

Place a check in each category that describes a gas.		
	Definite	**Indefinite**
Shape	_____	_____
Volume	_____	_____

Particles in a gas

FIGURE 5 ···
> INTERACTIVE ART **Gas**
A gas takes the shape and volume of its container.

✎ **Interpret Diagrams** Describe the arrangement of particles in a gas.

_____

_____

_____

_____

Calculating Pressure

When calculating pressure, force is measured in newtons (N). If the area is measured in square meters (m^2), pressure is expressed in pascals (Pa), where $1 Pa = 1 N/m^2$. Suppose a gas exerts a force of 252 N on a piston having an area of $0.430 m^2$. What is the pressure on the piston in Pascals?

$$Pressure = \frac{Force}{Area}$$

$$= \frac{252\ N}{0.430\ m^2}$$

$$= 586\ Pa$$

Practice Problem A gas exerts a force of 5,610 N over an area of $0.342 m^2$. What pressure does the gas exert in Pa?

_____

_____

_____

Pressure Gas particles constantly collide with one another and with the walls of their container. As a result, the gas pushes on the walls of the container. The **pressure** of the gas is the force of its outward push divided by the area of the walls of the container. Pressure is measured in units of pascals (Pa) or kilopascals (kPa) (1 kPa = 1,000 Pa).

$$Pressure = \frac{Force}{Area}$$

The firmness of a gas-filled object comes from the pressure of the gas. For example, the air inside an inflated ball has a higher pressure than the air outside. This higher pressure is due to the greater concentration of gas particles inside the ball than in the surrounding air. Concentration is the number of gas particles in a given unit of volume.

Why does a ball leak even when it has only a tiny hole? The higher pressure inside the ball results in gas particles hitting the inner surface of the ball more often. Therefore, gas particles inside the ball reach the hole and escape more often than gas particles outside the ball reach the hole and enter. Thus, many more particles go out than in. The pressure inside drops until it is equal to the pressure outside.

FIGURE 6 ·······························

Gas Pressure
Photos A and B show a beach ball being inflated and then deflated. ✎ **Interpret Photos** Circle the answers that complete the description of each process.

A
The concentration of gas particles inside the beach ball (increases/decreases). The gas pressure inside the beach ball (increases/decreases).

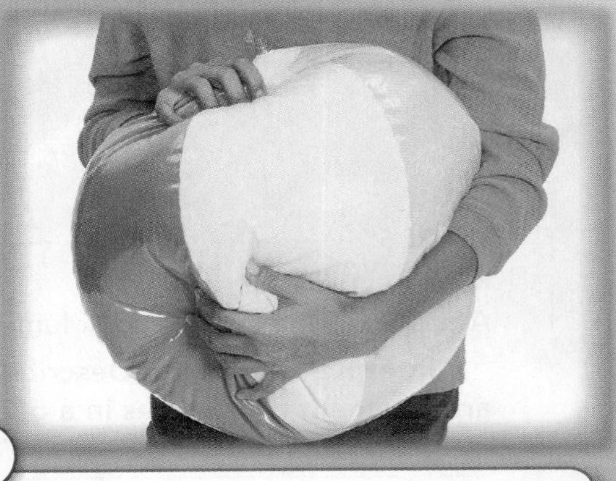

B
The concentration of gas particles inside the beach ball (increases/decreases). The gas pressure inside the beach ball (increases/decreases).

Faster-moving, hot gas particles

Slower-moving, cool gas particles

Temperature

The balloonists in **Figure 7** are preparing the balloon for flight. To do this, they use a propane burner to heat the air inside the balloon. Once the temperature of the air is hot enough, the balloon will start to rise. But what does the temperature tell you? All particles of matter are constantly moving. The average kinetic energy of the particles in a substance determines the object's **temperature,** which is a measure of how hot or cold something is. The faster the particles are moving, the greater their energy and the higher the temperature.

Even at room temperature, the average speed of particles in a gas is very fast. At about 20°C, the particles in a typical gas travel about 500 meters per second—more than twice the cruising speed of a jet plane!

FIGURE 7 ·····································

Temperature of a Gas

✎ **Explain** Why are the hot gas particles moving faster than the cool gas particles?

_____

_____

_____

Lab® zone   Do the Quick Lab *How Do the Particles in a Gas Move?*

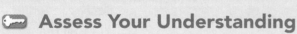 **Assess Your Understanding**

3a. Explore Explore how the motions of gas particles are related to the pressure exerted by the gas.

_____

_____

_____

_____

SC.8.P.8.1

b. Relate Cause and Effect Why does pumping more air into a basketball increase the pressure inside the ball?

_____

_____

_____

_____

SC.8.P.8.1

got it? ···

○ **I get it!** Now I know that a gas has neither a definite shape nor definite volume because _____

○ I need extra help with _____

Go to **MY SCIENCE** ⑤ **COACH** online for help with this subject

SC.8.P.8.1

Changes of State

UNLOCK THE ESSENTIAL ?

🔑 **What Happens When Heat Is Transferred to a Substance?**
SC.8.P.8.1

🔑 **What Happens to a Solid as It Melts?**
SC.8.P.8.1

🔑 **What Happens to a Substance That Becomes a Gas?**
SC.8.P.8.1, LA.8.2.2.3, MA.6.A.3.6

MY PLANET DIARY

On the Boil

You might have noticed that as an uncovered pot of water boils, the water level slowly decreases. The water level changes because the liquid is changing to a gas. As you heat the water, the thermal energy of its molecules increases. The longer you leave the pot on the hot stove, the more energy is absorbed by the water molecules. When the water molecules gain enough energy, they change state from a liquid to a gas.

The graph shows the temperature of a covered pot of water on a stove set to high heat. The starting temperature of the water is 20°C.

SCIENCE STATS

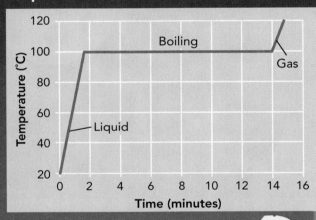

Liquid to a Gas

Graph: Temperature (°C) vs Time (minutes). Labels: Boiling, Gas, Liquid.

Answer the following questions.

1. How long does it take for the water to start boiling? At what temperature does the water boil?

_____

_____

_____

2. It takes more time to boil the water at 100°C into a gas than it takes to heat it up to 100°C. Which do you think takes more energy?

_____

_____

▶ PLANET DIARY Go to **Planet Diary** to learn more about changes of state.

 Lab® zone Do the Inquiry Warm-Up *What Happens When You Breathe on a Mirror?*

Vocabulary

- thermal energy • heat • physical property • melting
- melting point • freezing • vaporization • evaporation
- boiling • boiling point • condensation • sublimation

Skills

- Reading: Compare and Contrast
- Inquiry: Predict

What Happens When Heat Is Transferred to a Substance?

Have you ever boiled water to cook pasta? How can you better understand what happens in the pot of boiling water? Consider the concept of energy and how it relates to heat and temperature.

Thermal Energy and Heat Any object that is moving, no matter how small it is, has kinetic energy, or energy of motion. All matter is made up of tiny particles that are always moving, so these particles have kinetic energy. The more kinetic energy the particles in an object have, the hotter the object feels.

Recall that the average kinetic energy of the particles in an object determines the object's temperature. Temperature measures how hot or cold something is compared to a reference point. It is measured in different scales, such as Farenheit and Celsius.

Would two objects at the same temperature have the same total energy? Not necessarily. An object with more particles would have more energy. **Thermal energy** is the total kinetic and potential energy of the particles in an object.

Heat is the transfer of thermal energy from a warmer object to a cooler object. As an object heats up, its particles move faster. As a result, its temperature increases. However, sometimes the thermal energy doesn't go into increasing the temperature of the substance. At certain temperatures, the thermal energy would make the substance change its state. **When heat is transferred to a substance, the substance undergoes an increase in temperature, a change of state, or both.**

FLORIDA NGSSS

SC.8.P.8.1 Explore the scientific theory of atoms (also known as atomic theory) by using models to explain the motion of particles in solids, liquids, and gases.

FIGURE 1 ·······························

Thermal Energy

The two pots of hot water shown are both at 99°C, but one of them has about twice as much thermal energy as the other.

✎ **Explore** Why does the larger pot have more thermal energy?

_____

_____

_____

_____

_____

273

Physical Changes Every form of matter has physical properties. A **physical property** is a characteristic of a substance that can be observed without changing it into another substance. A physical change in a substance changes its characteristics without changing the substance itself.

An increase in temperature or a change of state is an example of a physical change. If a substance becomes hotter or colder, it is still the same substance, even if it is at a different temperature. If a solid substance becomes a liquid or a gas, it also remains the same substance.

In the case of a pot of boiling water, hot water is still just water, so the water has not changed into another substance. When the liquid water turns into gas, it is called water vapor, but water vapor is just another form of water, like ice.

FIGURE 2 ·······················
Physical Properties
✎ **Identify** Identify some of the physical properties of these rocks versus the sponge.

_____

_____

_____

_____

_____

_____

_____

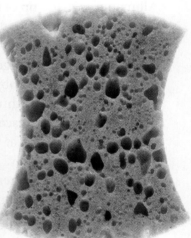

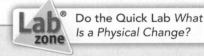
Do the Quick Lab *What Is a Physical Change?*

🔑 Assess Your Understanding

1a. Explain What determines an object's temperature?

_____

_____

SC.8.P.8.1

b. Compare and Contrast How does thermal energy differ from temperature?

_____

_____

_____

_____

_____

SC.8.P.8.1

got it?

○ **I get it!** Now I know that when heat is added to a substance, the substance_____

_____

_____

_____

○ **I need extra help with** _____

Go to **MY SCIENCE COACH** *online for help with this subject.*

SC.8.P.8.1

What Happens to a Solid as It Melts?

Particles of a liquid have more thermal energy than particles of the same substance in solid form. As a gas, the particles have even more thermal energy. A change from a solid to a liquid involves an increase in thermal energy. As you might guess, a change from a liquid to a solid is just the opposite: It involves a decrease in thermal energy.

Melting The change in state from a solid to a liquid is called **melting.** In pure, crystalline solids, melting occurs at a specific temperature, called the **melting point.** Because the melting point is a characteristic property of a substance, chemists often compare melting points when trying to identify an unknown material. The melting point of pure water, for example, is 0°C at sea level.

What happens to the particles of a solid as it melts? Think of an ice cube taken from the freezer. The energy needed to melt the ice comes mostly from the air in the room. At first, the added thermal energy makes the water molecules vibrate faster, raising their temperature. 🔑 **At a solid's melting point, its particles vibrate so fast that they break free from their fixed positions.** At 0°C, the temperature of the ice stops increasing. Any added energy continues to change the arrangement of the water molecules from ice crystals into liquid water. The ice melts.

FLORIDA NGSSS

SC.8.P.8.1 Explore the scientific theory of atoms (also known as atomic theory) by using models to explain the motion of particles in solids, liquids, and gases.

did you know?...

Dr. John Gorrie (1803–1855), a resident of Apalachicola, Florida, was granted the first U.S. Patent, in 1851, for mechanical refrigeration. A monument and a museum devoted to Gorrie are located in Apalachicola.

FIGURE 3 ·······················

Melting

✏️ **Relate Diagrams and Photos** Draw a line to match each illustration of water molecules to either ice or liquid water. Then describe how ice and liquid water differ in the arrangement of their molecules.

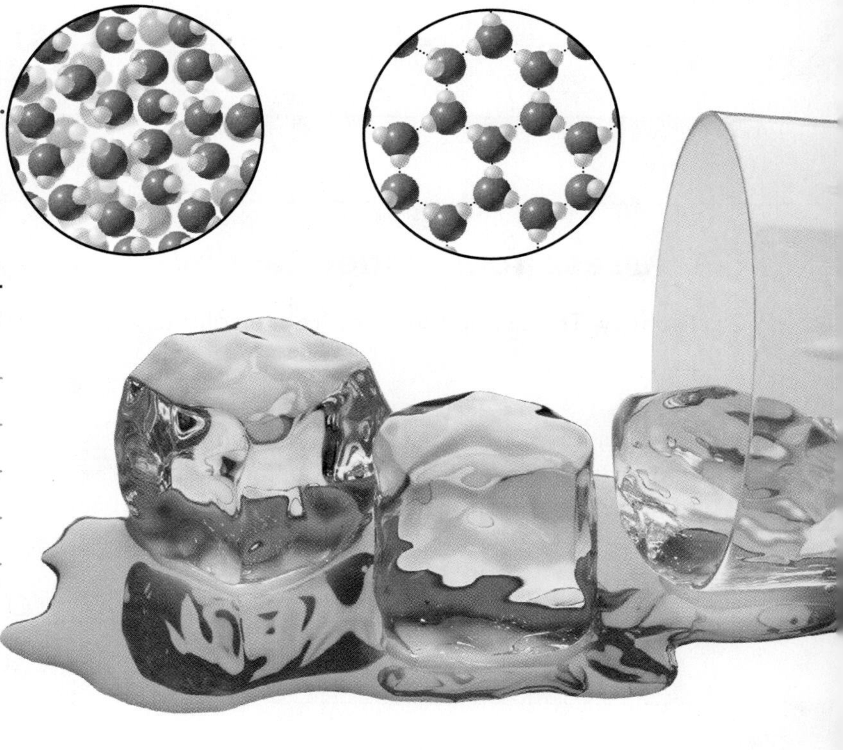

_____

_____

_____

_____

Freezing The change of state from a liquid to a solid is called **freezing.** It is just the reverse of melting. 🔑 **At a liquid's freezing point, its particles are moving so slowly that they begin to take on fixed positions.**

When you put liquid water into a freezer, for example, the water loses energy to the cold air in the freezer. The water molecules move more and more slowly as they lose energy. Over time, the water becomes solid ice. When water begins to freeze, its temperature stays at 0°C until freezing is complete. The freezing point of water, 0°C, is the same as its melting point.

apply it!

In metal casting, a liquid metal is poured into a container called a mold. The mold gives a shape to the metal when it cools and hardens.

1 Explain How does metal casting make use of the different characteristics of liquids and solids?

_____

_____

_____

_____

_____

2 [CHALLENGE] The melting point of copper is 1084°C. How does the energy of the particles in a certain amount of liquid copper compare to the energy of the molecules in the same amount of liquid water? Why?

_____

_____

_____

_____

_____

_____

> **Lab**® Do the Lab Investigation
> **zone** *Melting Ice.*

🔑 **Assess Your Understanding**

2a. Identify The change in state from a solid to a liquid is called _____

SC.8.P.8.1

b. Compare and Contrast How does what happens to the particles in a substance during melting differ from what happens in freezing?

_____

_____

_____

_____

_____

SC.8.P.8.1

got it?

○ **I get it!** Now I know that melting occurs when the particles in a solid _____

_____

_____

○ **I need extra help with** _____

Go to **my science** ⬢ **coach** *online for help with this subject.*

SC.8.P.8.1

What Happens to a Substance That Becomes a Gas?

Have you ever wondered how clouds form or why puddles dry up? To answer these questions, you need to look at what happens when changes occur between the liquid and gas states.

Evaporation and Boiling The change in state from a liquid to a gas is called **vaporization** (vay puhr ih ZAY shun). 🔑 **Vaporization occurs when the particles in a liquid gain enough energy to move independently and form a gas.** There are two main types of vaporization—evaporation and boiling.

Vaporization that takes place only on the surface of a liquid is called **evaporation** (ee vap uh RAY shun). A shrinking puddle is an example. Water in the puddle gains energy from the ground, the air, or the sun. The added energy enables some of the water molecules on the surface of the puddle to escape into the air, or evaporate.

Vaporization that takes place both below and at the surface of a liquid is called **boiling.** When water boils, vaporized water molecules form bubbles below the surface. The bubbles rise and eventually break the surface of the liquid. The temperature at which a liquid boils is called its **boiling point.** As with melting points, chemists use boiling points to help identify unknown substances.

FLORIDA NGSSS

SC.8.P.8.1 Explore the scientific theory of atoms by using models to explain the motion of particles in solids, liquids, and gases.

LA.8.2.2.3 The student will organize information to show understanding among facts (e.g., representing key points within text through comparing/contrasting).

MA.6.A.3.6 Analyze graphs to describe linear functions and other simple relations using common language.

⤷ **Compare and Contrast**
Compare and contrast the two types of vaporization.

_____

_____

_____

_____

_____

_____

_____

LA.8.2.2.3

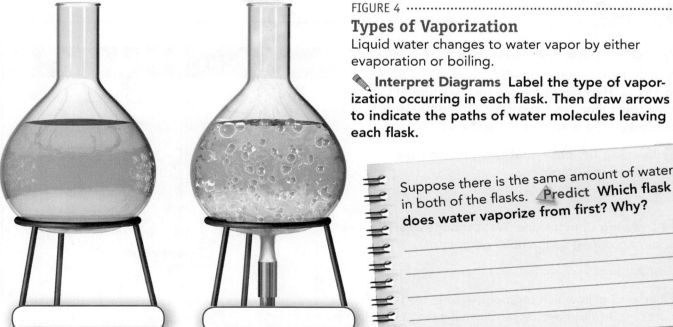

FIGURE 4 ·······························

Types of Vaporization

Liquid water changes to water vapor by either evaporation or boiling.

✎ **Interpret Diagrams** Label the type of vaporization occurring in each flask. Then draw arrows to indicate the paths of water molecules leaving each flask.

Suppose there is the same amount of water in both of the flasks. ⚠Predict Which flask does water vaporize from first? Why?

_____

_____

_____

_____

_____

Condensation Condensation is the reverse of vaporization. The change in state from a gas to a liquid is called **condensation.** You can observe condensation by breathing onto a mirror. When warm water vapor in your breath reaches the cooler surface of the mirror, the water vapor condenses into liquid droplets Condensation occurs when particles in a gas lose enough thermal energy to form a liquid.

Clouds typically form when water vapor in the atmosphere condenses into tiny liquid droplets. When the droplets get heavy enough, they fall to the ground as rain. Water vapor is a colorless gas that you cannot see. The steam you see above a kettle of boiling water is not water vapor, and neither are clouds or fog. What you see in those cases are tiny droplets of liquid water suspended in air.

FIGURE 5

Foggy Mirror

Explain Why does a mirror fog up after a hot shower?

_____

_____

_____

_____

do the math! Analyzing Data

Temperature and Changes of State

A sealed beaker of ice at –10°C was slowly heated to 110°C. The changes in the temperature of the water over time were recorded. The data were plotted on the graph, as shown here.

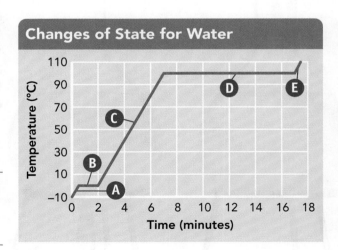

Changes of State for Water

❶ **Reading Graphs** What two variables are plotted on the graph?

_____

❷ **Drawing Conclusions** What change of state is occurring during segment B? Segment D?

_____

❸ **Inferring** In which segment, A or E, do the water molecules have more thermal energy? Explain your answer.

_____

MA.6.A.3.6, MA.8.A.1.1

Sublimation In places where the winters are cold, the snow may disappear even when the temperature stays well below freezing. This change is the result of sublimation. **Sublimation** occurs when the surface particles of a solid gain enough energy that they form a gas. **During sublimation, particles of a solid do not pass through the liquid state as they gain enough energy to move independently and form a gas.**

One example of sublimation occurs with dry ice. Dry ice is the common name for solid carbon dioxide. At ordinary atmospheric pressures, carbon dioxide cannot exist as a liquid. So instead of melting, solid carbon dioxide changes directly into a gas. As it sublimes, the carbon dioxide absorbs thermal energy. This property helps keep materials near dry ice cold and dry. For this reason, using dry ice is a way to keep the temperature low when a refrigerator is not available. Some fog machines use dry ice to create fog in movies or at concerts, as shown in **Figure 6.** When dry ice becomes a gas, it cools water vapor in the nearby air. The water vapor then condenses into a liquid, forming fog near the dry ice.

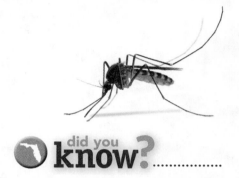

did you know?

Florida has about 80 different species of mosquitos, more than any other state. Mosquitos are attracted to the carbon dioxide gas you exhale during breathing. A mosquito trap baited with dry ice can attract up to five times as many mosquitos as traps baited with a light source alone.

FIGURE 6 ·······························
Dry Ice
A fog machine uses dry ice to create fog at this rock concert. **Explain** Why does fog form near dry ice?

_____
_____
_____
_____
_____

Dry ice subliming

The Changing States of Water

EXPLORE THE ESSENTIAL ?

Why does a substance change states?

FIGURE 7 ....

>VIRTUAL LAB Four examples of how water changes states—by melting, freezing, vaporization, and condensation—are shown here.

✎ **Review** Use what you have learned about states of matter to answer the questions.

FREEZING

This lake has frozen over due to the cold weather. As liquid water freezes, its molecules (gain/lose) thermal energy. How does the motion of the water molecules change during freezing?

_____

_____

_____

← Freezing

Melting →

Low Thermal Energy

MELTING

The air outside is so warm that this snow-man is melting. During melting, the water molecules (gain/lose) thermal energy. How does the motion of the molecules change during melting?

_____

_____

_____

_____

_____

These wet footprints are disappearing due to evaporation. As water evaporates, its molecules (gain/lose) thermal energy. How does the motion of the molecules change during evaporation?

_____

_____

_____

_____

_____

VAPORIZATION

High Thermal Energy

Condensation ◁

Vaporization ▷

CONDENSATION

During the night, water vapor in the air condensed on this spider web. As water vapor condenses, its molecules (gain/lose) thermal energy. How does the motion of the molecules change during condensation?

_____

_____

_____

_____

_____

Lab® zone Do the Quick Lab *Observing Sublimation.*

🔑 Assess Your Understanding

3a. Identify What is dry ice?

_____

_____

SC.8.P.8.1

b. 🖊 **Predict** If you allowed dry ice to stand in a bowl at room temperature for several hours, what would be left?

_____

_____

SC.8.P.8.1

c. Why does a substance change states?

_____

_____

_____

_____

_____

SC.8.P.8.1

got it? ....

○ **I get it!** Now I know that vaporization and sublimation occur when the particles in a liquid or solid_____

_____

_____

○ **I need extra help with** _____

Go to MY SCIENCE ⓢ COACH *online for help with this subject.*   SC.8.P.8.1

A substance (gains/loses) thermal energy when it melts or vaporizes.

A substance (gains/loses) thermal energy when it freezes or condenses.

LESSON 1 Describing Matter

SC.8.N.3.1, SC.8.P.8.1

🔑 The scientific theory of atoms, or the particle theory of matter, explains that all matter is made of atoms.

Vocabulary
- matter • chemistry • substance • element • atom • chemical bond • molecule
- compound • chemical formula • mixture

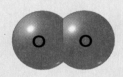

LESSON 2 States of Matter

SC.8.P.8.1

🔑 The fixed, closely packed arrangement of particles causes a solid to have a definite shape and volume.

🔑 Because its particles are free to move, a liquid has no definite shape. However, it does have a definite volume.

🔑 As gas particles move, they spread apart, filling all the space available. Thus, a gas has neither definite shape nor definite volume.

Vocabulary
- solid • crystalline solid • amorphous solid • liquid
- fluid • surface tension • viscosity • gas • pressure • temperature

---

LESSON 3 Changes of State

SC.8.P.8.1

🔑 When heat is transferred to a substance, the substance undergoes an increase in temperature, a change of state, or both.

🔑 At a solid's melting point, its particles vibrate so fast that they break free from their fixed positions.

🔑 Vaporization or sublimation occur when the particles in a liquid or solid gain enough energy to form a gas.

Vocabulary
- thermal energy • heat • physical property • melting
- melting point • freezing • vaporization • evaporation
- boiling • boiling point • condensation • sublimation

Review and Assessment

LESSON 1 Describing Matter

1. Classify Which of the following is a substance: table salt, seawater, or sand? Explain how you know.

_____

_____

_____

SC.8.P.8.1

Use the diagrams to answer Questions 2–4. Each diagram represents a different kind of matter. Each ball represents an atom. Balls of the same color are the same kind of atom.

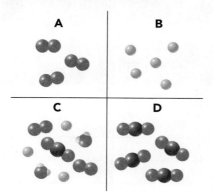

A   B

C   D

2. Interpret Diagrams Which diagram or diagrams represent a single element? Explain.

_____

_____

SC.8.P.8.1

3. Compare and Contrast How do the atoms in Diagram A differ from those in Diagram D?

_____

_____

_____

SC.8.P.8.1

4. Apply Concepts Which diagram or diagrams represent a mixture? Explain.

_____

_____

_____

SC.8.P.8.1

LESSON 2 States of Matter

5. A substance with a definite shape and definite volume is a

  a. solid.   **b.** liquid.

  c. gas.   **d.** fluid.

SC.8.P.8.1

6. Rubber is considered a(n) _____ solid because it does not melt at a distinct temperature.

SC.8.P.8.1

7. Compare and Contrast Why do liquids and gases take the shape of their containers while solids do not?

_____

_____

_____

SC.8.P.8.1

8. Predict What happens to the gas particles in an inflated ball when it gets a hole? Why?

_____

_____

_____

_____

_____

_____

SC.8.P.8.1

9. math! Earth's atmosphere exerts a force of 124,500 N on a kitchen table with an area of 1.5 m². What is the pressure in pascals?

_____

_____

_____

SC.8.P.8.1, MA.8.A.6.4

10. Write About It Write a short essay in which you create an analogy to describe particle motion. Compare the movements and positions of people dancing with the motions of water molecules in liquid water and in water vapor.

SC.8.P.8.1

283

LESSON 3 Changes of State

11. A puddle dries up by the process of

    a. melting.   **b.** freezing.

    c. condensation.   **d.** evaporation.

                                SC.8.P.8.1

12. When you see fog or clouds, you are seeing

water in the _____ state.

                                SC.8.P.8.1

13. Classify Label the correct change of state on top of the arrows in the diagram below.

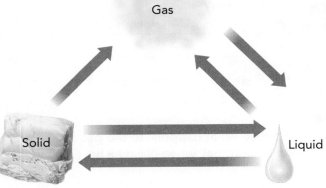

                                SC.8.P.8.1

14. Draw Conclusions At room temperature, table salt is a solid and mercury is a liquid. What conclusion can you draw about the melting points of these substances?

_____

_____

_____

_____

                                SC.8.P.8.1

15. Apply Concepts When you open a solid room air freshener, the solid slowly loses mass and volume. How do you think this happens?

_____

_____

_____

_____

_____

                                SC.8.P.8.1

APPLY THE ESSENTIAL ? Why does a substance change states?

16. A fog forms over a lake. What two changes of state must occur to produce the fog? Do the water molecules absorb or release energy during these changes of state? What happens to the motion of the water molecules as a result?

_____

_____

_____

_____

_____

_____

_____

_____

_____

_____

_____

_____

_____

_____

                                SC.8.P.8.1

Florida Benchmarks Review

Circle the letter of the best answer.

❶ The graph below shows changes in 1 g of a solid as energy is added.

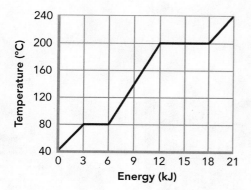

Based on the graph, what is the total amount of energy absorbed by the substance as it changes from a solid at 40°C to a gas at 200°C?

A 3 kJ   **B** 6 kJ
C 12 kJ   **D** 18 kJ

SC.8.P.8.1

❷ Which of the following correctly describes a solid?

A The particles do not move at all.
B The particles are closely locked in position and can only vibrate in place.
C The particles are free to move about independently, colliding frequently.
D The particles are closely packed but have enough energy to slide past one another.

SC.8.P.8.1

❸ A gas exerts a force of 1,000 N on a surface with an area of 5.0 m². What is the pressure on the area?

A 200 Pa
B 500 Pa
C 2,000 Pa
D 5,000 Pa

SC.8.P.8.1

❹ On a very cold day, the water in a glass turns into ice. This process is called

A melting.
B freezing.
C evaporation.
D sublimation.

SC.8.P.8.1

❺ A wet towel is hanging on a clothesline in the sun. The towel dries by the process of

A boiling.
B condensation.
C evaporation.
D sublimation.

SC.8.P.8.1

❻ The diagrams represent the molecules of water before and after a change of state. What change of state has occurred?

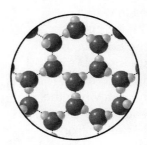 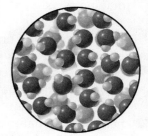

Before   After

A melting
B freezing
C evaporation
D sublimation

SC.8.P.8.1

WHAT ARE ALL OF THESE THINGS MADE OF?

What are the properties of matter?

Imagine relaxing at the beach with a cool drink in your hand. The ice cubes soon start to melt under the hot sun, but the glass your drink is in stays solid. You look across the water and notice that heavy fiberglass boats can float, while the small pebbles from the beach sink. What makes these materials so different from each other? **Classify** **Pick three materials found at the beach. Describe how the materials are different.**

> UNTAMED SCIENCE Watch the **Untamed Science** video to learn more about matter.

_____

_____

_____

_____

_____

Properties and Changes of Matter

FLORIDA Next Generation Sunshine State Standards

Big Idea 1: SC.8.N.1.6
Big Idea 8: SC.8.P.8.2, SC.8.P.8.3, SC.8.P.8.4, SC.8.P.8.5

Language Arts: LA.8.2.2.3
Mathematics: MA.6.S.6.2

Check Your Understanding

1. **Background** Read the paragraph below and then answer the question.

> Jorge decides to make a pitcher of lemonade. He mixes water with lemon juice in a **ratio** of six to one. He adds sugar and ice and stirs. The **properties** of the lemonade are that it is cold, yellow, and sweet. The lemon juice, sugar, and water are all examples of **matter.**

A **ratio** tells you the relationship between two or more things.

A **property** is a characteristic that belongs to a person or thing.

Matter is anything that has mass and takes up space.

- How would the properties of the lemonade change if the ratio of water to lemon juice were three to one? Assume the amount of sugar is the same.

_____

_____

▶ MY READING WEB If you had trouble completting the question above, visit **My Reading Web** and type in *Properties and Changes of Matter.*

Vocabulary Skill

Identify Multiple Meanings Familiar words may mean something else in science. Look at the different meanings of the words below.

Word	Everyday Meaning	Scientific Meaning
volume	*n.* the degree, strength, or loudness of sound Example: My brother asked me to turn down the volume of my radio.	*n.* the amount of space that matter occupies
property	*n.* something owned Example: The ball flew out of my yard and landed on the neighbor's property.	*n.* a characteristic that belongs to a person or thing

LA.8.1.6.9

2. **Quick Check** Write a sentence using the scientific definition of volume.

_____

_____

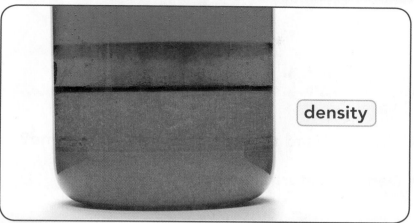

density

physical property

chemical property

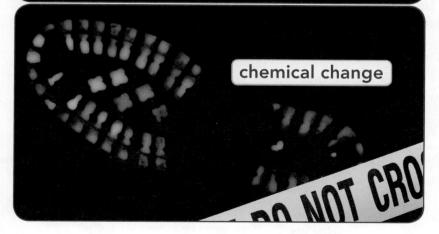

chemical change

Chapter Preview

LESSON 1
- weight
- mass
- International System of Units
- volume
- density

↻ **Identify the Main Idea**
△ **Calculate**

LESSON 2
- physical property
- chemical property

↻ **Summarize**
△ **Infer**

LESSON 3
- physical change
- chemical change

↻ **Compare and Contrast**
△ **Make Models**

▷ **VOCAB FLASH CARDS** For extra help with vocabulary, visit **Vocab Flash Cards** and type in *Properties and Changes of Matter.*

UNLOCK THE ESSENTIAL ?

🔑 **What Units Are Used to Express Mass and Volume?**
SC.8.P.8.2

🔑 **How Is Density Determined?**
SC.8.P.8.3, MA.6.S.6.2

MY PLANET DIARY   FIELD TRIP

Site: Lake Assal
Location: Djibouti, Republic of Djibouti

Travel to the eastern coast of Africa and you will find the country of Djibouti. There, you can visit one of the saltiest bodies of water in the world. Lake Assal is ten times saltier than the ocean. Its crystal white beaches are made up of salt. While on your visit to Lake Assal, be sure to take a dip in the clear blue waters. Take a book or magazine with you to read. Wait . . . what? Take a book into a lake? It might seem strange, but bodies of water with high salt contents, like Lake Assal or the Dead Sea in the Middle East, allow you to float so well that it's nearly impossible to sink below the surface of the water.

Salt water is denser than fresh water. Less-dense liquids float on top of more-dense liquids. You, too, will float on top of the salty water. In fact, it will be difficult even to swim, so what else can you do? Read a book while you float along!

Floating in the Dead Sea

Communicate **Write your answers to the questions below. Then discuss your answers with a partner.**

What water activities might be easier to do in Lake Assal's salty water? What activities could be more difficult?

_____

_____

_____

▶ PLANET DIARY Go to **Planet Diary** to learn more about density.

Lab zone Do the Inquiry Warm-Up
Which Has More Mass?

Vocabulary
- weight
- mass
- International System of Units
- volume
- density

Skills
- Reading: Identify the Main Idea
- Inquiry: Calculate

What Units Are Used to Express Mass and Volume?

Here's a riddle for you: Which weighs more, a pound of feathers or a pound of sand? If you answered "a pound of sand," think again. Both weigh exactly the same—one pound.

There are all sorts of ways to measure matter, and you use these measurements every day. Scientists rely on measurements as well. In fact, scientists work hard to make sure their measurements are as accurate as possible.

Weight Your **weight** is a measure of the force of gravity on you. On another planet, the force of gravity will be more if the planet is more massive than Earth and less if the planet is less massive than Earth. On the moon, you would weigh only about one sixth of your weight on Earth. On Jupiter, you would weigh more than twice your weight on Earth.

To find the weight of an object, you could place it on a scale like the ones shown in **Figure 1**. The object's weight pulls down on the mechanisms inside the scale. These mechanisms cause beams or springs inside the scale to move. The amount of movement depends on the weight of the object. From the movement of the beams, the scale displays the weight to you.

FLORIDA NGSSS

SC.8.P.8.2 Differentiate between weight and mass recognizing that weight is the amount of gravitational pull on an object and is distinct from, though proportional to, mass.

✎ **Identify the Main Idea**
Underline the sentence that describes how weight can be affected by location.

FIGURE 1 ·····················
Measuring Weight
✎ **Complete the tasks below.**

1. **Estimate** Use the weight of the first scale to estimate the weight of the fish on the other scales. Draw in the pointers.

2. **Describe** How would their weight change on a small planet like Mercury? Or a large planet like Neptune?

_____

_____

_____

_____

Mass How can you weigh less on the moon than on Earth when nothing about you has changed? Your weight is dependent on the gravity of the planet you are visiting. The amount of matter in an object is its **mass,** which does not change with location even if the force of gravity changes. If you travel to the moon, the amount of matter in your body—your mass—does not change. You are the same size. For this reason, scientists prefer to describe matter in terms of mass rather than weight. The mass of an object is a physical property.

To measure the properties of matter, scientists use a system called the **International System of Units** (abbreviated SI for the French name, *Système International d'Unités*). ⟶ **The SI unit of mass is the kilogram (kg).** If you weigh 90 pounds on Earth, your mass is about 40 kilograms. Often, a smaller unit is used to measure mass, the gram (g). There are 1,000 grams in a kilogram, or 0.001 kilogram in a gram. The table in **Figure 2** lists the masses of some common items.

Mass of Common Objects

Object	Mass (g)	Mass (kg)
Nickel	5	0.005
Baseball	150	_____
Pineapple	1,600	_____
Full can of soda	390	_____
Inflated balloon	3	_____

FIGURE 2 ···

Measuring Mass
The SI system uses grams and kilograms to measure mass.

✎ **Complete the following tasks about mass.**

1. ◢ Calculate In the table, convert the mass of each object from grams to kilograms.

2. [CHALLENGE] Suppose you are taking a flight to Europe. You are only allowed a 23-kg suitcase. How much is that in pounds? (*Hint:* 1 kg = 2.2 lb.)

   ○ 50.6 lb   ○ 46.2 lb   ○ 10.5 lb

Volume All matter has mass and takes up space. The amount of space that matter occupies is called its **volume.** It's easy to see that solids and liquids take up space, but gases have volume, too.

🔑 **The SI unit of volume is the cubic meter (m^3).** Other common SI units of volume include the cubic centimeter (cm^3), the liter (L), and the milliliter (mL). Common plastic soda bottles hold 2 liters of liquid. A milliliter is 1/1,000 of a liter and is exactly the same volume as 1 cubic centimeter. A teaspoonful of water has a volume of about 5 milliliters. In a lab, volumes of liquid are often measured with a graduated cylinder.

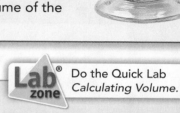

Calculating Volume

Suppose you want to know the volume of a rectangular object, like one of the suitcases shown in **Figure 3.** First, measure the length, width, and height (or thickness) of the suitcase. Then, multiply the measurements together.

Volume = Length × Width × Height

When you multiply the three measurements, you must also multiply the units.

Units = cm × cm × cm = cm^3

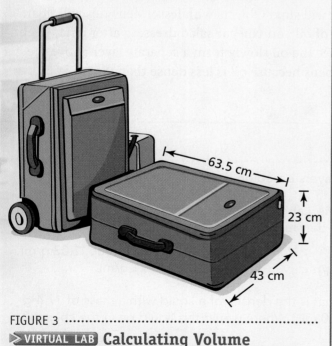

63.5 cm

23 cm

43 cm

FIGURE 3 ··
▷ VIRTUAL LAB **Calculating Volume**
⚠ **Calculate** Find the volume of the suitcase.

_____

_____

Measuring Irregular Objects

How do you measure the volume of an irregular object, such as a key or a raspberry? One way is to submerge the object in a liquid in a graduated cylinder. The liquid level will rise by an amount that is equal to the volume of the object in milliliters.

Lab ® Do the Quick Lab
zone *Calculating Volume.*

🔑 **Assess Your Understanding**

1. Describe Why is mass more useful than weight for measuring matter?

_____

_____

_____

_____

SC.8.P.8.2

got it? ··

○ **I get it!** Now I know that the SI unit for

mass is _____

and the SI unit for volume is _____

_____

○ **I need extra help with** _____

_____

Go to **my science** Ⓢ **coach** *online for help
with this subject.* SC.8.P.8.2

293

FLORIDA NGSSS

SC.8.P.8.3 Explore and describe the densities of various materials through measurement of their masses and volumes.

MA.6.S.6.2 Select and analyze the measures of central tendency to analyze a date set.

How Is Density Determined?

Remember the riddle about the sand and the feathers? Although they weigh the same, a kilogram of sand takes up much less space than a kilogram of feathers. The volumes differ because sand and feathers have different densities—an important property of matter.

Calculating Density Density is a measure of the mass of a material in a given volume. Density can be expressed as the number of grams in one cubic centimeter (g/cm^3). For example, the density of water at room temperature is stated as "one gram per cubic centimeter" ($1 \ g/cm^3$). Recall that volume can also be measured in milliliters. So the density of water can also be expressed as $1 \ g/mL$. 🔑 **You can determine the density of a sample of matter by dividing its mass by its volume.**

$$\text{Density} = \frac{\text{Mass}}{\text{Volume}}$$

Sinking or Floating? Suppose you have a block of wood and a block of iron of equal mass. When you drop both blocks into a tub of water, you see that the wood floats and the iron sinks. You know the density of water is $1 \ g/cm^3$. Objects with densities greater than that of water will sink. Objects with lesser densities will float.

Watch a bottle of oil and vinegar salad dressing after it has been shaken. You will see the oil slowly form a separate layer above the vinegar. This happens because oil is less dense than vinegar.

do the math!

MA.6.S.6.2

Liquids can form layers based on density.

❶ **Apply Concepts** Label the layers of colored liquid in the column according to their densities. Find and circle the median density.

Water: 1.00 g/mL   Honey: 1.36 g/mL   Dish soap: 1.03 g/mL
Corn syrup: 1.33 g/mL   Vegetable oil: 0.91 g/mL

❷ **Calculate** What is the density of a liquid with a mass of 17.4 g and a volume of 20 mL? Where would this liquid be in the column?

_____

_____

❸ Explain why the liquid with the median density floats where it does.

_____

_____

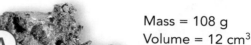

Using Density

Suppose you are a gold miner in the 1800s, like the men in **Figure 4.** One day, while panning through the sediment in a stream, you come across a shiny golden rock. How do you know if the rock is real gold? Since density is a physical property of a substance, it can be used to identify an unknown substance. You can measure the mass and volume of the rock and find its density. If it matches 19.3 g/cm³, the density of gold, then you have struck it rich!

FIGURE 4 ⋯⋯⋯⋯⋯⋯⋯⋯⋯⋯⋯⋯⋯⋯⋯⋯⋯⋯⋯⋯

▷ VIRTUAL LAB **Using Density**

Density can be used to identify substances.

✎ **Estimate** Hypothesize which rock sample is gold. Then, calculate the density of each sample. Circle the rock that is real gold.

My hypothesis is that the gold rock is:

◯ A ◯ B ◯ C

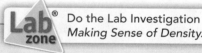

A

Mass = 108 g
Volume = 12 cm³

Density = _____

B

Mass = 126 g
Volume = 15 cm³

Density = _____

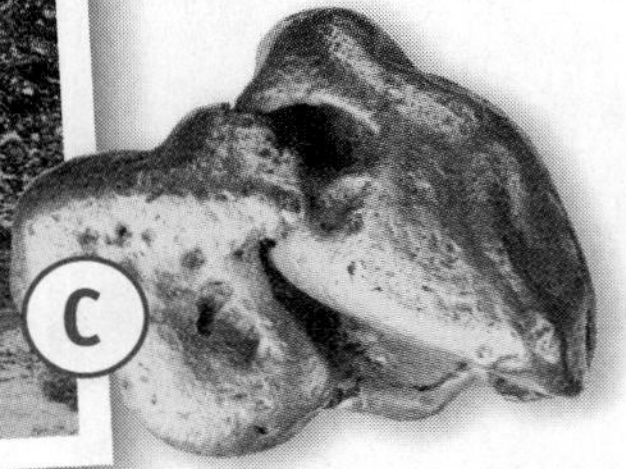

C

Mass = 386 g
Volume = 20 cm³

Density = _____

> **Lab zone®** Do the Lab Investigation
> *Making Sense of Density.*

🔑 Assess Your Understanding

2a. Identify Maple syrup will (float/sink) in water because its density is greater than 1 g/cm³.

SC.8.P.8.3

b. ⚠ **Calculate** What is the mass of a sample of a substance with a volume of 120 mL and a density of 0.75 g/mL?

_____

SC.8.P.8.3

c. CHALLENGE Liquid water and ice are the same substance, H₂O. How would you explain why ice floats in water?

_____

_____

_____

SC.8.P.8.3

got it? ⋯⋯⋯⋯⋯⋯⋯⋯⋯⋯⋯⋯⋯⋯⋯⋯⋯⋯⋯⋯⋯⋯⋯⋯⋯⋯⋯⋯⋯⋯⋯

◯ **I get it!** Now I know density is calculated by _____

◯ **I need extra help with** _____

  Go to **MY SCIENCE** ⑤ **COACH** *online for help with this subject.*

SC.8.P.8.3

Physical and Chemical Properties of Matter

UNLOCK THE ESSENTIAL ? Q

🔑 **Why Are Chemical and Physical Properties Useful?**
SC.8.N.1.6, SC.8.P.8.4, LA.8.2.2.3

MY PLANET DIARY
for Florida

FUN FACT

Manatees live all over the world, not just in the waters around Florida. Marine biologists classify the different species of manatee based on the animals' characteristics. Physical characteristics, such as coloring and size, differentiate Amazonian manatees from the West Indian manatees that inhabit Florida waters. The manatee below, Snooty, is a West Indian manatee. He lives at a Florida aquarium. At over 60 years old, Snooty is the oldest manatee in captivity.

Answer the questions below.

1. Besides appearances, what characteristics could marine biologists use to classify manatees?

2. What groups of objects do you classify based on their observable characteristics?

▷ PLANET DIARY Go to **Planet Diary** to learn more about chemical and physical properties.

 Lab zone® Do the Inquiry Warm-Up *How Do You Describe Matter?*

Vocabulary
- physical property
- chemical property

Skills
- Reading: Summarize
- Inquiry: Infer

Why Are Chemical and Physical Properties Useful?

Even though air and water are both matter, no one has to tell you they are different substances. Matter can have many different properties, or characteristics. Matter might be hard or soft, rough or smooth, hot or cold. Some matter may catch fire easily, while other matter does not. Matter can be any color of the rainbow—or have no color at all. Hardness, texture, flammability, and color are all examples of properties of matter.

Characteristic properties of matter can be used to identify unknown substances. Density, magnetism, melting and boiling points, and the abilities to conduct heat and electricity are some properties that hold true, independent of the amount of the sample. For example, at sea level ice melts into water at 0°C and boils at 100°C. The amount of ice does not change this property.

The amount of matter does not change the characteristic physical and chemical properties of the matter. For example, a piece of ice can be as small as an ice cube or as big as a glacier, as shown in **Figure 1.** In both cases, the substance is still water.

These are two kinds of properties of matter—physical properties and chemical properties. A physical property of oxygen is that it is a gas at room temperature. A chemical property of oxygen is that it reacts with iron to form rust. **Since characteristic chemical and physical properties for a given substance never change and are independent of the amount of the sample, you can use them to compare and classify matter.**

FLORIDA NGSSS

SC.8.N.1.6 Understand that scientific investigations involve collecting evidence and using logical reasoning to make sense of the collected evidence.

SC.8.P.8.4 Classify and compare substances on the basis of characteristic physical properties that can be demonstrated or measured; for example, density, thermal or electrical conductivity, solubility, magnetic properties, melting and boiling points, and know that these properties are independent of the amount of the sample.

LA.8.2.2.3 The student will organize information to show relationships among facts (e.g., representing key points within text through comparing/contrasting).

Vocab Skill Identify **Multiple Meanings** Write a sentence using the everyday meaning of "property."

FIGURE 1
Physical Properties
A small ice cube has many of the same physical properties as a giant glacier.
Observe Which of these is a characteristic property of ice?
- density
- mass
- volume

Physical Properties Suppose you want to know whether or not a substance is a metal. One way to find out is to compare the substance's physical properties to those of substances that you know are metals. A **physical property** is a characteristic of a substance that can be observed without changing it into another substance. Examples of physical properties include shininess, hardness, ability to attract a magnet, and the ability to dissolve in water, or solubility.

You probably already know some of the physical properties of metals. Metals are shiny. They are flexible, meaning that they can be bent into different shapes without breaking. They can conduct both thermal energy and electricity. If your substance has all of these properties, it is a metal. To find out which metal your substance is, you could compare its physical properties to those of other metals. Finding the melting points, boiling points, density, or color could all work. For example, if your substance is yellow and has a density of 19.3 g/cm³, it is likely to be gold.

apply it!

Each photo shows the application of a physical property.

1 Infer Beneath each photo, identify the physical property that is in use.

A. _____

_____

B. _____

_____

C. _____

_____

D. _____

_____

2 CHALLENGE Why is it important that the material around wire be made of a substance other than a metal?

_____

_____

_____

A

B

C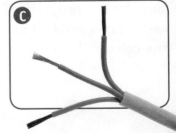

Chemical Properties

Chemical Properties Some properties of matter can't be seen or identified just by observation or touch. A **chemical property** is a characteristic of a substance that describes its ability to change into different substances. Like physical properties, chemical properties are used to classify substances. For example, a chemical property of fuels is that they can catch fire and burn. Wood, gas, and the charcoal shown in **Figure 2,** are all examples of fuels. When a fuel burns it combines with oxygen in the air and changes into the substances water and carbon dioxide. The ability to burn, or flammability, is a chemical property.

One chemical property of iron is that it will combine slowly with water and oxygen to form a different substance, rust. Silver reacts with sulfur and air to form tarnish. In contrast, a chemical property of gold is that it does not react easily with oxygen or sulfur. Gold can keep its shininess and color forever.

✐ Summarize What is the main difference between chemical and physical properties?

_____

_____

_____

_____

LA.8.2.2.3

FIGURE 2 ·······························

Chemical Properties

Use these photos to complete the activities.

1. **Identify** Label the chemical property shown in each photo.

2. **Interpret Photos** What substance must be present in order to observe the chemical properties shown in the photos? Explain.

   _____

   _____

   _____

3. **Compare and Contrast** Based on your observations, how are the chemical properties of iron and glass similar? How are they different?

   _____

   _____

   _____

   _____

   _____

INDIANA JANE

AND THE
INVESTIGATION OF MATTER

What are the properties of matter?

FIGURE 3 ....

> **INTERACTIVE ART** Indiana Jane is hunting for lost treasures of matter. Join her in following clues to describe different types of matter.

✐ **Classify** Answer questions about Indiana's findings along the way. Then, complete the logbook with information you've gathered about the properties of matter.

Arrowhead This arrowhead, most likely carved by an ancient hunter, was discovered in a pile of rocks. **Describe how you would determine the volume of this arrowhead.**

_____

_____

_____

_____

_____

_____

Yellowed, torn map
Field notes: The paper of this ancient map has survived over time, including a fire, which seems to have burned its edges. —IJ

Tarnished coins I found these coins near the opening of a foul-smelling cave. I believe they were a shiny metal at one point, perhaps silver, platinum, or aluminum. I've determined the mass of each coin to be 315 g and the volume to be 30 cm³.

What element are the coins made of?

○ Aluminum (density = 2.7 g/cm³)

○ Silver (density = 10.5 g/cm³)

○ Platinum (density = 21.5 g/cm³)

Mummy An exciting find today—a 3,000-year-old mummy encased in a precious metal sarcophagus! It required our entire team to lift it because it has a mass of 180 kg. I also noticed that it was very warm and that it had no effect on magnets. When a small chip of the sarcophagus broke off, it landed in a bucket of water and sunk right to the bottom.

Name the properties of the sarcophagus described by Indiana Jane. Which properties can be used to identify what substance the sarcophagus is made of? Explain.

_____

_____

_____

_____

_____

_____

_____

_____

Indiana Jane has to bring all the artifacts back to the museum. Describe at least one physical and one chemical property of the objects listed.

Object	Properties	Changes Undergone
1. Metal Pot		
2. Coins		
3. Map		

Metal pot Field notes: I've come across some ancient iron pots. They look like they've changed from so many years of being exposed to the air. —IJ

Wax statue I believe we have found the remains of the famous Carved Dove wax statue. It would have been a valuable artifact, but it has melted into a puddle of liquid.
Describe what has happened to the wax statue. Is this a physical or chemical property of wax? Explain.

_____
_____
_____
_____
_____

Lab zone® Do the Quick Lab *Observing Physical Properties*

🔑 Assess Your Understanding

1a. Explain Why can chemical and physical properties be used to classify matter?

_____
_____

SC.8.N.1.6, SC.8.P.8.4

b. ANSWER THE ESSENTIAL ? What are the properties of matter?

_____
_____
_____
_____
_____
_____
_____
_____

SC.8.N.1.6, SC.8.P.8.4

got it? ....

○ **I get it!** Now I know that substances can be classified by their _____

_____

○ **I need extra help with** _____

_____

Go to **MY SCIENCE** Ⓢ **COACH** *online for help with this subject.* SC.8.N.1.6, SC.8.P.8.4

301

Physical and Chemical Changes

 **How Can Matter Change?**
SC.8.P.8.5

MY PLANET DIARY

BLOG

Posted by: Dylan
Location: Fountain Valley, California

Whenever I go to the beach, I spend a majority of my time building a sand castle. I try to build it after a high tide comes. That way I have a lot of time to build up the walls and they will not be destroyed as quickly by the water.

Even though the waves will eventually destroy the castle and take the sand with them back to the ocean, the sand could be easily separated from the ocean. At the end of the day when I leave and kick and stomp on my sand castle, it is still sand. Only its appearance changes.

Write your answers to the questions below.

1. Describe the differences in the ways the sand castle is changed by an ocean wave and by Dylan stomping on it.

_____

_____

_____

_____

2. Dylan changed a formless pile of sand into a sand castle. What other natural materials can be changed into art?

_____

_____

> PLANET DIARY Go to **Planet Diary** to learn more about changes in matter.

 Do the Inquiry Warm-Up *Is a New Substance Formed?*

Vocabulary
- physical change
- chemical change

Skills
- Reading: Compare and Contrast
- Inquiry: Make Models

How Does Matter Change?

How does the matter in a piece of paper change when you fold it into a shape like the origami frog in **Figure 1**? How does the matter in that paper change if it is burned? Substances can undergo two types of changes—physical and chemical changes. **A substance that undergoes a physical change is still the same substance after the change. A substance that undergoes a chemical change produces a new substance with new properties.** Changes in matter are important because they produce all of the different compounds that you encounter in the natural world. There are only a finite number of elements. Atoms of these elements combine in many ways to produce new compounds and substances.

Physical Change As you know, matter occurs in three states—solid, liquid, and gas. A puddle of liquid water left in the sun will not be there two hours later. The water won't disappear but a physical change will happen. The liquid water changes into water vapor, a gas. When the appearance or form of a substance has changed but no new substance is produced, the matter has undergone a **physical change**. All changes in the state of matter of a substance are physical changes. Other examples of physical changes are bending, crushing, breaking, and dissolving. The methods of separating mixtures, such as filtration and distillation, also involve physical changes.

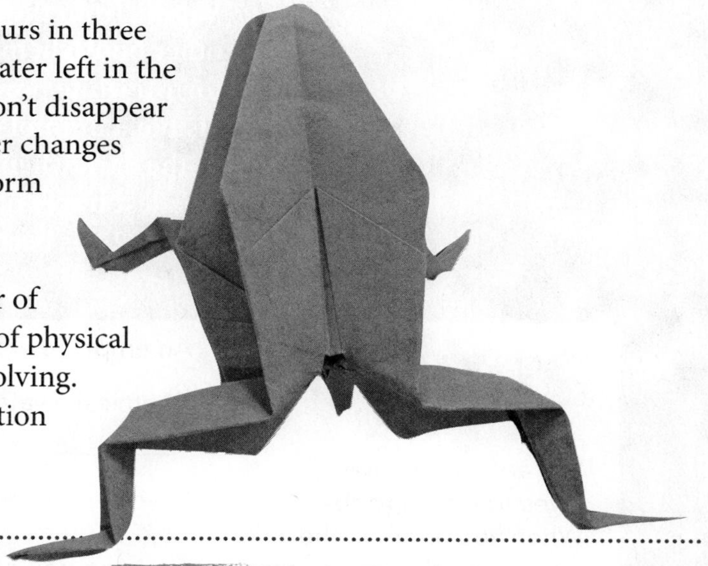

FLORIDA NGSSS

SC.8.P.8.5 Recognize that there are a finite number of elements and that their atoms combine in a multitude of ways to produce compounds that make up all of the living and nonliving things that we encounter.

Compare and Contrast On this page, underline the differences between chemical and physical changes.

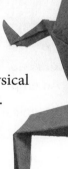

FIGURE 1 ....

Changes in Appearance
The Japanese art of folding origami paper involves physical changes.

Complete the following tasks.

1. **Make Models** Using the corner of this page or a separate sheet, make two physical changes to the paper.

2. **Communicate** Ask a classmate to identify and list below the changes you made.

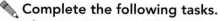

3. **CHALLENGE** Is it correct to say that dissolving a packet of juice powder in water makes a new substance, fruit punch, and so it must not be a physical change?

_____

_____

_____

_____

303

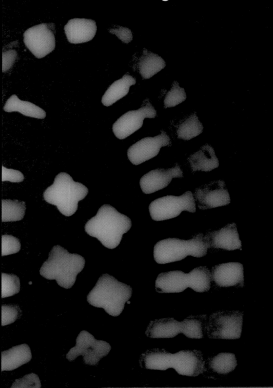

FIGURE 2 ·······························

Chemical Changes
The prints are visible because of chemical change.

Chemical Change A change in matter that produces one or more new substances is a **chemical change,** or chemical reaction. In some chemical changes, a substance breaks down into two or more other substances. For example, hydrogen peroxide breaks down into water and oxygen gas when it's poured on a cut on your skin. In other chemical changes, two or more substances combine to form different substances. Everything you encounter is made up of some combination of a finite set of elements. Atoms from two or more of these elements can combine in many ways. Photosynthesis is a chemical change that happens naturally in plants. Several compounds combine using energy from the sun to produce new compounds. All living and nonliving things are made up of substances that formed through a wide variety of chemical changes of the elements.

Figure 2 shows chemical changes that forensic scientists use to collect evidence. To make fingerprints more visible, they heat a chemical found in super-strong glue. Vapors from the glue react with sweat or other body chemicals in a fingerprint to form a white powder, making the print visible. Luminol is a chemical that glows in the dark when it reacts with even the smallest traces of blood. The footprint in Figure 2 has been treated with luminol.

apply it!

You are a detective investigating a robbery. When you arrive at the scene, you do not find many clues that can help you solve the crime. You're able to write down a few observations.

Solve Problems
Determine how you could use chemical changes to gather evidence at the crime scene.

An empty jewelry box is knocked over on a table.

Chemical treatment: _____

_____

_____

An open box of bandages is on the floor. Bandage wrappers are found nearby.

Chemical treatment: _____

_____

_____

Shattered glass from a window is scattered across the floor.

Chemical treatment: _____

_____

_____

Examples of Chemical Change

Examples of Chemical Change
One common chemical change is the burning of natural gas on a gas stove. When it burns, the methane (CH_4) in natural gas combines with oxygen in the air and forms new substances. These new substances include carbon dioxide gas (CO_2) and water vapor (H_2O). Both of these substances can be identified by their properties, which are different from those of methane. The chemical change that occurs when fuels, such as natural gas, candle wax, or wood, burn in air is called combustion. The table in **Figure 3** describes other processes that result in chemical changes.

Chemical Change	Description	Example
Combustion	Rapid combination of a fuel with oxygen; produces heat, light, and new substances	Gas, oil, or coal burning in a furnace
Electrolysis	Use of electricity to break a compound into elements or simpler compounds	Breaking down water into hydrogen and oxygen
Oxidation	Combination of a substance with oxygen	Rusting of an iron fence
Tarnishing	Slow combination of a bright metal with sulfur or another substance, producing a dark coating on the metal	Tarnishing of brass

Copper: before

Copper: after

FIGURE 3 ··

> INTERACTIVE ART **Types of Chemical Change**
The copper in the Statue of Liberty is exposed to oxygen in the air.

✎ **Observe** What chemical change did the Statue of Liberty likely undergo? Describe the properties before and after the chemical change.

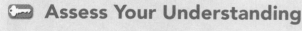

SC.8.P.8.5

Lab zone® Do the Quick Lab
Physical and Chemical Changes.

⚷ Assess Your Understanding

1a. Identify Melting butter for popcorn is a (physical/chemical) change.

SC.8.P.8.5

b. Predict What kind of chemical change do you think occurs when a banana peel turns brown in the open air? Explain.

SC.8.P.8.5

got it?

○ I get it! Now I know that physical changes _____

while chemical changes _____

○ I need extra help with _____

Go to **MY SCIENCE ⓢ COACH** online for help with this subject.

SC.8.P.8.5

Study Guide

A _____ property of charcoal is that it can catch fire and burn. A _____ property of water is that it boils at 100°C. The _____ of water is 1 g/cm³.

LESSON 1 Measuring Matter
SC.8.P.8.2, SC.8.P.8.3

🔑 The SI unit of mass is the kilogram (kg).

🔑 The SI unit of volume is the cubic meter (m³).

🔑 You can determine the density of a sample of matter by dividing its mass by its volume.

Vocabulary
• weight • mass • International System of Units • volume • density

LESSON 2 Physical and Chemical Properties of Matter
SC.8.N.1.6, SC.8.P.8.4

🔑 Since characteristic chemical and physical properties for a given substance never change and are independent of the amount of the sample, you can use them to compare and classify matter.

Vocabulary
• physical property
• chemical property

LESSON 3 Physical and Chemical Changes
SC.8.P.8.5

🔑 A substance that undergoes a physical change is still the same substance after the change. A substance that undergoes a chemical change produces a new substance with new properties.

Vocabulary
• physical change   • chemical change   • law of conservation of mass
• temperature   • thermal energy   • endothermic change
• exothermic change   • chemical energy

Review and Assessment

Measuring Matter

1. What is the SI unit of mass?

a. milliliter   b. kilogram

c. pound   d. cubic centimeter

SC.8.P.8.2

2. The density of a substance is calculated by

_____

_____

SC.8.P.8.3

3. Make Judgments Which measurement shown in the diagram is not needed to find the volume of the box? Explain.

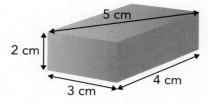

5 cm

2 cm

3 cm   4 cm

_____

_____

_____

SC.8.P.8.3

4. math! A piece of metal has a volume of 38 cm³ and a mass of 277 g. Calculate the density of the metal and identify it based on the information in the table below.

Density of Common Metals	
Iron	7.9 g/cm³
Lead	11.3 g/cm³
Tin	7.3 g/cm³
Zinc	7.1 g/cm³

SC.8.P.8.3

Physical and Chemical Properties of Matter

5. Which of the following is an example of a chemical property?

a. density   b. flammability

c. hardness   d. luster

SC.8.P.8.4

6. A substance can be classified by its physical properties, which are properties that

_____

_____

_____

SC.8.P.8.4

7. Classify You have a list of chemical and physical properties for known materials and an object made of an unknown material. Explain how you could figure out what material the object is made of.

_____

_____

_____

_____

SC.8.P.8.4

8. Interpret Tables Write a title that describes the table below.

Helium	Colorless; less dense than air
Iron	Attracted to magnets; melting point of 1,535°C
Oxygen	Odorless; gas at room temperature

SC.8.P.8.4

9. **Write About It** Write an e-mail to a friend explaining why the melting point of a substance is a physical property but flammability is a chemical property. Use examples to explain.

SC.8.P.8.4

307

LESSON 3 Physical and Chemical Changes

10. Which of the following is a physical change?

a. burning   b. rusting

c. freezing   d. oxidation

SC.8.P.8.5

11. Infer Copper statues, like the one shown above, are often made from sheets of copper. Infer what physical changes had to happen to the copper sheets to turn them into a statue.

_____

_____

_____

_____

SC.8.P.8.5

12. Predict What chemical changes could happen to the copper statue if it is left outside? How do you know these are chemical changes?

_____

_____

_____

_____

SC.8.P.8.5

13. Solve Problems How could you prove that dissolving table salt in water is a physical change, not a chemical change?

_____

_____

_____

SC.8.P.8.5

APPLY THE ESSENTIAL **What are the properties of matter?**

14. Choose a substance you're familiar with. What are its physical and chemical properties? How would you measure its density? What are some physical and chemical changes it can undergo?

_____

_____

_____

_____

_____

_____

_____

_____

_____

_____

_____

_____

_____

_____

_____

_____

_____

_____

_____

_____

_____

_____

SC.8.P.8.4

Florida Benchmarks Review

Circle the letter of the best answer.

1 Suppose you had three blocks of wood, as shown below. Which of the following statements is true for these three blocks?

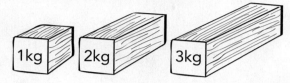

A Their masses and volumes are the same.

B Their densities are different.

C Their masses and volumes are different but their characteristic physical properties are the same.

D The smallest block will float but the others will not.   SC.8.P.8.4

2 If you went to the moon, which of the following statements would be true?

A Your mass would stay the same and your weight would decrease.

B Your mass would stay the same and your weight would increase.

C Your weight would stay the same and your mass would increase.

D Neither your mass nor your weight would change.   SC.8.P.8.2

3 The density of a substance equals its mass divided by its volume. The density of sulfur is 2.0 g/cm^3. What is the mass of a sample of sulfur with a volume of 6.0 cm^3?

A 3.0 g   **B** 4.0 g

C 8.0 g   **D** 12.0 g

SC.8.P.8.3

4 The abilities to dissolve in water and to conduct electric current are examples of

A physical properties.

B chemical properties.

C physical changes.

D chemical bonding.

SC.8.P.8.4

5 Which two pieces of laboratory equipment would be the *most* useful for measuring the mass and volume of a rectangular block?

A a metric ruler and a stopwatch

B a balance and a metric ruler

C a graduated cylinder and a metric ruler

D a balance and a stop watch

SC.8.P.8.3

6 You put away a clean fork. Later you take it out and it is tarnished, like the fork below. Which statement best describes what happened?

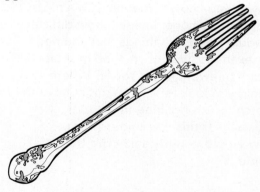

A Tarnish particles drifted through the air and settled on the fork.

B Elements in the air and the fork combined to form tarnish.

C The fork started to decay.

D Dust stuck to the fork and changed into tarnish.

SC.8.P.8.5

HOW WOULD YOU

SORT OUT THIS MESS?

Maybe you know someone with a messy room like this one. Imagine how difficult it would be to find things that you need. For example, what if you had misplaced your homework in this room? Where would you look for it? You might have to search for a long, long time!

Classify If this were your room, how would you organize the things inside it?

_____

_____

_____

_____

_____

_____

> **UNTAMED SCIENCE** Watch the **Untamed Science** video to learn more about organizing matter.

Atoms and the Periodic Table

FLORIDA Next Generation Sunshine State Standards

Big Ideas 1, 3: SC.8.N.1.4, SC.8.N.1.6, SC.8.N.3.2
Big Idea 8: SC.8.P.8.6, SC.8.P.8.7

Language Arts: LA.8.2.2.3, LA.8.4.2.2
Mathematics: MA.6.A.3.6

Getting Started

Check Your Understanding

1. Background Read the paragraph below and then answer the question.

> Katherine and her family are having a barbecue. They are burning charcoal in the grill to provide heat to cook their food. Charcoal is made mostly of the **element** carbon. As the charcoal burns, it reacts with oxygen **molecules** in the air. Each oxygen molecule contains two **atoms.**

An **element** is a pure substance that cannot be broken down into any other substances by chemical or physical means.

A **molecule** is a group of two or more atoms held together by chemical bonds.

An **atom** is the basic particle from which all elements are made.

- How can oxygen be both an element and a molecule?

_____

_____

▶ **MY READING WEB** If you had trouble completing the question above, visit **My Reading Web** and type in *Atoms and the Periodic Table.*

Vocabulary Skill

Greek Word Origins Many science words in English come from Greek. For example, the word *autograph* comes from the Greek words *auto,* meaning "self," and *graph,* meaning "written." An *autograph* is one's name written in one's own handwriting. Look at the Greek origins and their meanings below.

Greek Origin	Meaning	Examples
atomos	Cannot be cut, indivisible	Atom, atomic number, atomic mass
di	Two, double	Diatomic molecule

LA.8.1.6.7

2. Quick Check Predict the meaning of the term *diatomic molecule.*

_____

_____

Ga	Ge	As	Se	Br	Kr
Gallium 69.72	Germanium 72.59	Arsenic 74.922	Selenium 78.96	Bromine 79.904	Krypton 83.80

periodic table

In 49	Sn	Sb	Te 52	I 53	Xe 54
Indium 114.82	Tin 118.69	Antimony 121.75	Tellurium 127.60	Iodine 126.90	Xenon 131.30
81	82	83	84	85	86

corrosion

semiconductor

noble gas

Chapter Preview

LESSON 1
- atomic mass • periodic table
- nucleus • proton
- atomic number • neutron
- electron • chemical symbol
- period • group

↻ **Relate Text and Visuals**
▲ **Predict**

LESSON 2
- metal • luster • malleable
- ductile • thermal conductivity
- electrical conductivity • reactivity
- corrosion • alkali metal
- alkaline earth metal
- transition metal

↻ **Ask Questions**
▲ **Infer**

LESSON 3
- nonmetal • diatomic molecule
- halogen • noble gas • metalloid
- semiconductor

↻ **Summarize**
▲ **Classify**

LESSON 4
- energy level
- isotope • mass number

↻ **Compare and Contrast**
▲ **Make Models**

> **VOCAB FLASH CARDS** For extra help with vocabulary, visit **Vocab Flash Cards** and type in *Atoms and the Periodic Table.*

Organizing the Elements

UNLOCK THE ESSENTIAL ?

🗝 **What Did Mendeleev Discover?**
SC.8.N.1.6, SC.8.P.8.6

🗝 **What Information Does the Periodic Table Contain?**
SC.8.P.8.6, LA.8.2.2.3

🗝 **How Is the Periodic Table Useful?**
SC.8.P.8.6

mY planeT DiaRY

VOICES FROM HISTORY

Dmitri Mendeleev

The Russian chemist Dmitri Mendeleev (men duh LAY ef) is given credit for creating the first version of the periodic table in 1869. By arranging the elements according to their atomic masses, he predicted that new elements would be discovered:

> We must expect the discovery of many yet unknown elements—for example, elements analogous [similar] to aluminum and silicon—whose atomic weight [mass] would be between 65 and 75.

Within 17 years, chemists had discovered these missing elements.

Communicate Discuss these questions with a group of classmates. Write your answers below.

1. What did Mendeleev predict?

_____

_____

_____

_____

2. Make a prediction based on an observation or a pattern you recognize.

_____

_____

_____

_____

▶ PLANET DIARY Go to **Planet Diary** to learn more about the periodic table.

Lab zone®

Do the Inquiry Warm-Up
Which Is Easier?

🌴 **FLORIDA** NGSSS

SC.8.N.1.6 Understand that scientific investigations involve collecting evidence and using reasoning to devise hypotheses, predictions, explanations, and models.

SC.8.P.8.6 Recognize that elements are grouped in the periodic table according to similarities in their properties.

What Did Mendeleev Discover?

By 1869, a total of 63 elements had been discovered. A few were gases. Two were liquids. Most were solid metals. Some reacted explosively as they formed compounds. Others reacted slowly. Scientists wondered if the properties of elements followed a pattern. Dmitri Mendeleev discovered a set of patterns that applied to all the elements.

Vocabulary
- atomic mass • periodic table • nucleus • proton
- atomic number • neutron • electron
- chemical symbol • period • group

Skills
↪ Reading: Relate Text and Visuals
△ Inquiry: Predict

Mendeleev's Work Mendeleev knew that some elements had similar chemical and physical properties. For example, silver and copper are both shiny metals. Mendeleev thought these similarities were important clues to a hidden pattern.

To find that pattern, Mendeleev wrote each element's melting point, density, and color on an individual card. He also included the element's atomic mass. The **atomic mass** of an element is the average mass of all the isotopes of that element. (Isotopes are different forms of the same element. You will learn more about isotopes later in the chapter.) Using the information he had, Mendeleev tried arranging the cards in different ways.

🔑 **Mendeleev noticed that a pattern of properties appeared when he arranged the elements in order of increasing atomic mass. He found that the properties repeated regularly.** For example, lithium, sodium, and potassium showed several common properties. As you can see in **Figure 1,** each of these elements reacts with water in a similar way. (The letters *amu* mean "atomic mass units.") Mendeleev lined up the cards for these elements to form their own group. He did the same with other elements that shared similar properties.

FIGURE 1 ······························

Metals That React With Water
Lithium, sodium, and potassium all react with water.

✏️ **Observe** Write down your observations of each reaction.

| Lithium |
| Atomic mass = 7 amu |

| Sodium |
| Atomic mass = 23 amu |

| Potassium |
| Atomic mass = 39 amu |

Relate Text and Visuals
Using **Figure 2**, predict an element that would react with water as lithium (Li), sodium (Na), and potassium (K) did. Explain.

_____

_____

_____

_____

_____

_____

_____

The Periodic Table
Mendeleev created the first periodic table in 1869. A **periodic table** is an arrangement of elements showing the repeating pattern of their properties. (The word *periodic* means "in a regular, repeated pattern.") The periodic table shown in **Figure 2** was an improved version published in 1871.

FIGURE 2 ···

Mendeleev's Periodic Table
In his periodic table, Mendeleev left blank spaces. He predicted the spaces would be filled by elements that had not yet been discovered.

Group I	Group II	Group III	Group IV	Group V	Group VI	Group VII	Group VIII
H = 1							
Li = 7	Be = 9.4	B = 11	C = 12	N = 14	O = 16	F = 19	
Na = 23	Mg = 24	Al = 27.3	Si = 28	P = 31	S = 32	Cl = 35.5	
K = 39	Ca = 40	— = 44	Ti = 48	V = 51	Cr = 52	Mn = 55	Fe = 56, Co = 59, Ni = 59, Cu = 63.
(Cu = 63)	Zn = 65	— = 68	— = 72	As = 75	Se = 78	Br = 80	
Rb = 85	Sr = 87	Yt = 88	Zr = 90	Nb = 94	Mo = 96	— = 100	Ru = 104, Rh = 104, Pd = 106, Ag = 108.
(Ag = 108)	Cd = 112	In = 113	Sn = 118	Sb = 122	Te = 125	I = 127	
Cs = 133	Ba = 137	Di = 138	Ce = 140	—	—	—	— — —
(—)	—	—	—	—	—	—	
—	—	Er = 178	La = 180	Ta = 182	W = 184	—	Os = 195, Ir = 197, Pt = 198, Au = 199.
(Au = 199)	Hg = 200	Tl = 204	Pb = 207	Bi = 208			
—	—	—	Th = 231	—	U = 240		

apply it!

A pattern can be described as a recognizable design or relationship. Mendeleev organized elements using patterns in their properties. From these patterns, he was able to make predictions about unknown elements. See if you can do the same with a group of buttons.

1 Classify Identify a pattern that helps you sort the buttons into two or more groups. Write the letters of the buttons in each group. Then tell what pattern you used.

_____

_____

_____

2 Predict If you were to add another button to each group in Step 1, what would each of the new buttons look like?

_____

_____

_____

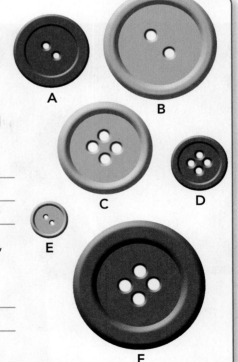

Mendeleev's Predictions You can see from the table on the opposite page where Mendeleev left blanks. For example, no element is written in Group III for atomic weight 68 or in Group IV for atomic weight 72. Mendeleev left these spaces open because no known elements fit the patterns in these groups. He predicted that an element with atomic weight 68 would have properties very much like aluminum (Al). He also predicted that an element with atomic weight 72 would have properties like silicon (Si).

Mendeleev was so sure about his predictions that he even gave these unknown elements temporary names. He called one "eka-aluminum" and the other "eka-silicon." (The prefix *eka* means "first" in Sanskrit, a language of India. Mendeleev thought these elements would be the first ones to follow aluminum and silicon in his periodic table.) When these elements were later discovered, their names became gallium and germanium. And they did, indeed, match Mendeleev's predictions!

did you know? ....

Before 1869, other ways to organize the elements were tried, but none was widely used. Mendeleev's table succeeded because he could explain how it was useful. A Russian postage stamp of his image (above) and an element that was later named for him (mendelevium) are two ways that his work has been honored.

Lab zone ® Do the Quick Lab *Classifying.*

🔑 **Assess Your Understanding**

1a. Review In what order did Mendeleev arrange the elements in his periodic table?

_____

_____

SC.8.P.8.6

b. Understand Scientific Investigations Why do you think that looking for patterns can be useful when doing scientific investigations?

_____

_____

_____

SC.8.N.1.6, SC.8.P.8.6

c. Recognize Groupings How could Mendeleev predict the properties of elements that had not yet been discovered?

_____

_____

_____

SC.8.P.8.6

d. Pose Questions What is one thing you would like to know about how the periodic table that is used today differs from Mendeleev's?

_____

_____

_____

SC.8.P.8.6

got it? ....

○ **I get it!** Now I know that when Mendeleev arranged the elements in order of increasing atomic mass, __

○ **I need extra help with** _____

Go to MY SCIENCE ⓢ COACH *online for help with this subject.*

SC.8.N.1.6, SC.8.P.8.6

FLORIDA NGSSS

SC.8.P.8.6 Recognize that elements
are grouped in the periodic table
according to similarities in their
properties.

LA.8.2.2.3 The student will organize
information to show understanding
(e.g., representing main ideas within
text through charting).

What Information Does the Periodic Table Contain?

As scientists discovered new elements, the periodic table changed. The organization of the table also changed when people learned more about atoms. To understand the periodic table, you need to know something about atoms, too.

The Parts of an Atom Atoms were once thought of as the smallest particles of matter. But starting in the late 1800s, scientists found that atoms are made of even smaller parts. Look at the simple model of an atom shown in **Figure 3,** as you continue to read.

The Nucleus and Protons At the very center of an atom, is the **nucleus** (NOO klee us; plural, *nuclei*). It contains positively charged particles called **protons.** Every atom of the same element has the same number of protons, called the **atomic number.** Elements can be identified by their atomic number.

In the early 1900s, chemists recognized that the number of protons in the nucleus determines the chemical properties of an element. Modern periodic tables are arranged in order of increasing atomic number rather than by atomic weight.

The nucleus also contains particles, called **neutrons,** that have no charge. Protons and neutrons have about the same atomic mass and make up most of the mass of an atom.

Electrons Moving around in the space outside the nucleus are negatively charged particles called **electrons.** A neutral atom has the same number of electrons as it has protons. You will learn more about electrons later in this chapter.

FIGURE 3 ·······

Structure of an Atom
Knowing something about atoms can help you understand the periodic table of elements.

✎ **Use the diagram of an atom to complete the tasks.**

1. **Chart** In each box, write one thing you have learned about that part of the atom.

2. **Infer** What do you know about two atoms if their atomic numbers are different?

_____

_____

LA.8.2.2.3

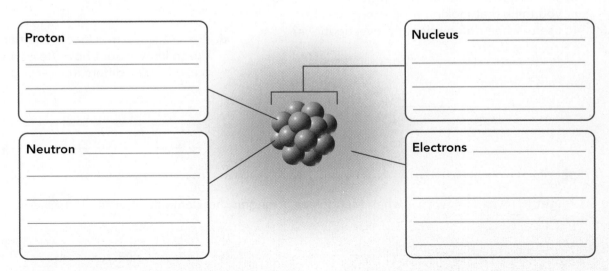

Proton _____

Nucleus _____

Neutron _____

Electrons _____

Reading the Periodic Table The periodic table contains information about each of the known elements. 🔑 **In this book, the periodic table includes the atomic number, chemical symbol, name, and atomic mass for each element.** The information that the periodic table lists about potassium is shown below in **Figure 4**.

❶ Atomic Number The first piece of information is the number 19, the atomic number of potassium. Every potassium atom has 19 protons in its nucleus.

❷ Chemical Symbol Just below the atomic number is the letter K—the **chemical symbol** for potassium. Chemical symbols contain either one or two letters. Often, an element's symbol is an abbreviation of the element's name in English. Other elements have symbols that are abbreviations of their Latin names.

❸ Atomic Mass The last piece of information is the average atomic mass. For potassium, this value is 39.098 amu (atomic mass units). The atomic mass is an average because most elements consist of a mixture of isotopes, or different forms.

The modern periodic table is shown in **Figure 5** on the next two pages. Can you find potassium in the table?

FIGURE 4 ·····································

Potassium

Potassium has atomic number 19 and an atomic mass of 39.098 amu. Bananas are rich in potassium.

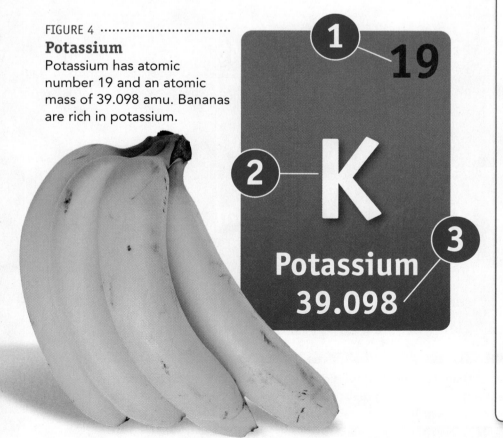

apply it!

The entry for silicon (Si) in the periodic table looks like this. ⟶

14

Si

Silicon
28.086

❶ The atomic number of silicon is _____.

❷ 🔺 **Predict** Without looking at the periodic table, do you think that any other element has the same atomic number as silicon? Explain.

_____
_____
_____
_____
_____
_____
_____
_____

319

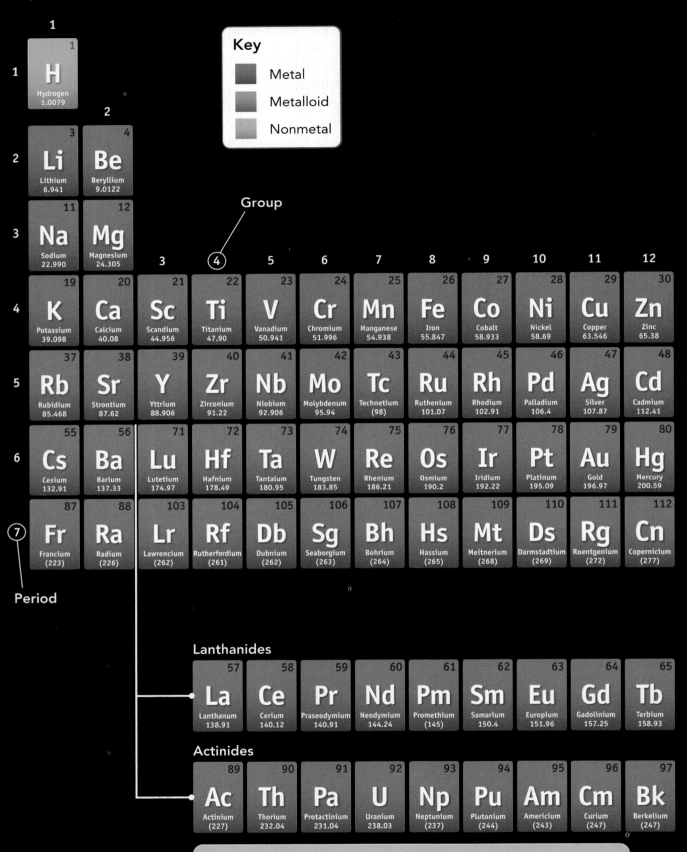

Key
- Metal
- Metalloid
- Nonmetal

Group

1

1	
H	
Hydrogen	
1.0079	

2

2	
3	4
Li	Be
Lithium	Beryllium
6.941	9.0122

3	
11	12
Na	Mg
Sodium	Magnesium
22.990	24.305

3	4	5	6	7	8	9	10	11	12
21	22	23	24	25	26	27	28	29	30
Sc	Ti	V	Cr	Mn	Fe	Co	Ni	Cu	Zn
Scandium 44.956	Titanium 47.90	Vanadium 50.941	Chromium 51.996	Manganese 54.938	Iron 55.847	Cobalt 58.933	Nickel 58.69	Copper 63.546	Zinc 65.38

4

19	20
K	Ca
Potassium 39.098	Calcium 40.08

5

37	38	39	40	41	42	43	44	45	46	47	48
Rb	Sr	Y	Zr	Nb	Mo	Tc	Ru	Rh	Pd	Ag	Cd
Rubidium 85.468	Strontium 87.62	Yttrium 88.906	Zirconium 91.22	Niobium 92.906	Molybdenum 95.94	Technetium (98)	Ruthenium 101.07	Rhodium 102.91	Palladium 106.4	Silver 107.87	Cadmium 112.41

6

55	56	71	72	73	74	75	76	77	78	79	80
Cs	Ba	Lu	Hf	Ta	W	Re	Os	Ir	Pt	Au	Hg
Cesium 132.91	Barium 137.33	Lutetium 174.97	Hafnium 178.49	Tantalum 180.95	Tungsten 183.85	Rhenium 186.21	Osmium 190.2	Iridium 192.22	Platinum 195.09	Gold 196.97	Mercury 200.59

7

87	88	103	104	105	106	107	108	109	110	111	112
Fr	Ra	Lr	Rf	Db	Sg	Bh	Hs	Mt	Ds	Rg	Cn
Francium (223)	Radium (226)	Lawrencium (262)	Rutherfordium (261)	Dubnium (262)	Seaborgium (263)	Bohrium (264)	Hassium (265)	Meitnerium (268)	Darmstadtium (269)	Roentgenium (272)	Copernicium (277)

Period

Lanthanides

57	58	59	60	61	62	63	64	65
La	Ce	Pr	Nd	Pm	Sm	Eu	Gd	Tb
Lanthanum 138.91	Cerium 140.12	Praseodymium 140.91	Neodymium 144.24	Promethium (145)	Samarium 150.4	Europium 151.96	Gadolinium 157.25	Terbium 158.93

Actinides

89	90	91	92	93	94	95	96	97
Ac	Th	Pa	U	Np	Pu	Am	Cm	Bk
Actinium (227)	Thorium 232.04	Protactinium 231.04	Uranium 238.03	Neptunium (237)	Plutonium (244)	Americium (243)	Curium (247)	Berkelium (247)

The lanthanides and the actinides are placed off the table to save space and to make the rest of the table easier to read. Follow the line to see how they fit in the table.

Many periodic tables include a zigzag line that separates the metals from the nonmetals. Metalloids, found on either side of the line, share properties of both metals and nonmetals.

13	14	15	16	17	18
					2 He Helium 4.0026
5 B Boron 10.81	6 C Carbon 12.011	7 N Nitrogen 14.007	8 O Oxygen 15.999	9 F Fluorine 18.998	10 Ne Neon 20.179
13 Al Aluminum 26.982	14 Si Silicon 28.086	15 P Phosphorus 30.974	16 S Sulfur 32.06	17 Cl Chlorine 35.453	18 Ar Argon 39.948
31 Ga Gallium 69.72	32 Ge Germanium 72.59	33 As Arsenic 74.922	34 Se Selenium 78.96	35 Br Bromine 79.904	36 Kr Krypton 83.80
49 In Indium 114.82	50 Sn Tin 118.69	51 Sb Antimony 121.75	52 Te Tellurium 127.60	53 I Iodine 126.90	54 Xe Xenon 131.30
81 Tl Thallium 204.37	82 Pb Lead 207.2	83 Bi Bismuth 208.98	84 Po Polonium (209)	85 At Astatine (210)	86 Rn Radon (222)
113 (284)	114 (289)	115 (288)	116 (292)		118 (294)

The discoveries of elements 113 and above have not yet been officially confirmed. Atomic masses in parentheses are those of the most stable isotopes.

66 Dy Dysprosium 162.50	67 Ho Holmium 164.93	68 Er Erbium 167.26	69 Tm Thulium 168.93	70 Yb Ytterbium 173.04
98 Cf Californium (251)	99 Es Einsteinium (252)	100 Fm Fermium (257)	101 Md Mendelevium (258)	102 No Nobelium (259)

FIGURE 5

INTERACTIVE ART **The Periodic Table**

The periodic table is one of a chemist's most valuable tools. **Interpret Tables** **Find the element identified by the atomic number 25 on the periodic table. Use the information to fill in the blanks below.**

Name of element: ____________________

Chemical symbol: ____________________

Atomic mass: ____________________

Lab zone® Do the Quick Lab *Using the Periodic Table.*

Assess Your Understanding

2a. Compare and Contrast Describe two differences between Mendeleev's periodic table and the modern periodic table.

____

____

____

____

____

SC.8.P.8.6

b. Interpret Tables An atom of which element has 47 protons in its nucleus?

____

SC.8.P.8.6

got it?

○ **I get it!** Now I know that information found in the periodic table for each element includes ____________________

____

____

____

○ I need extra help with ____________________

Go to **MY SCIENCE COACH** *online for help with this subject.* SC.8.P.8.6

How Is the Periodic Table Useful?

Look at the periodic table on the previous two pages. Notice that the atomic numbers increase from left to right. Also notice that each color-coded region corresponds to a different class of elements—metals, nonmetals, and metalloids.

As you look across a row, the elements' properties change in a predictable way. 🔑 **An element's properties can be predicted from its location in the periodic table.** This predictability is the reason that the periodic table is so useful to chemists.

Periods The periodic table is arranged in rows called **periods.** A period contains a series of different elements. From left to right, the properties of the elements change in a pattern. Metals are shown on the left of the table and nonmetals are located on the right. Metalloids are found between the metals and nonmetals. This pattern is repeated in each period. **Figure 6** shows the elements of Period 3.

ELEMENT SCRAMBLE

Rearrange the chemical symbols to form a word.

Example:

53	3	1	6
I	Li	H	C

C H I Li

56	5	20	32
Ba	B	Ca	Ge

1	49	15	89	16
H	In	P	Ac	S

18	47	15	16	33	92
Ar	Ag	P	S	As	U

Answers: CaBBaGe, SPInAcH, AsPArAGUS

FIGURE 6 ···

Elements of Period 3

The properties of the Period 3 elements change as you look across the period.

✏️ **Classify Use three different colors to fill in the key below. Then color in each element in Period 3 according to your key.**

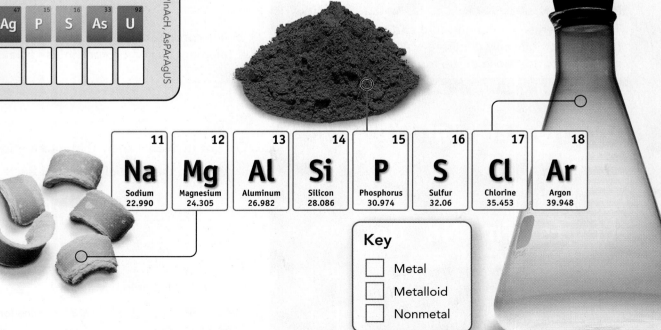

11	12	13	14	15	16	17	18
Na	**Mg**	**Al**	**Si**	**P**	**S**	**Cl**	**Ar**
Sodium	Magnesium	Aluminum	Silicon	Phosphorus	Sulfur	Chlorine	Argon
22.990	24.305	26.982	28.086	30.974	32.06	35.453	39.948

Key

☐ Metal

☐ Metalloid

☐ Nonmetal

Groups The modern periodic table has 7 periods, which form 18 columns. The elements in a column form a **group.** Groups are also known as families. The groups are numbered from Group 1 on the left of the table to Group 18 on the right.

The pattern of properties repeats in each period, so the elements in each group have similar characteristics. For example, except for hydrogen, the elements in Group 1 are all metals that react violently with water. Group 17 elements are very reactive, but Group 18 elements are generally nonreactive. The elements of Group 10 are shown in **Figure 7.**

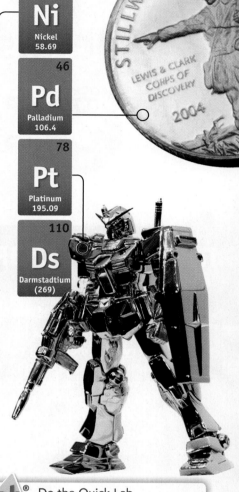

| 28 |
| Ni |
| Nickel |
| 58.69 |

| 46 |
| Pd |
| Palladium |
| 106.4 |

| 78 |
| Pt |
| Platinum |
| 195.09 |

| 110 |
| Ds |
| Darmstadtium |
| (269) |

FIGURE 7 ·····················

Elements of Group 10
The elements of Group 10 include nickel (Ni), palladium (Pd), platinum (Pt), and darmstadtium (Ds). Darmstadtium is not found in nature, but scientists believe it exhibits properties similar to the other Group 10 metals.

✏️ **CHALLENGE** Look at the photos of nickel, palladium, and platinum. What properties would you predict for darmstadtium?

_____

_____

Lab zone ® Do the Quick Lab
Expanding the Periodic Table.

🔑 **Assess Your Understanding**

3a. Name The rows in the periodic table are

called _____. The columns in the

periodic table are called _____.

SC.8.P.8.6

b. Recognize What do elements in the same group in the periodic table have in common?

_____

_____

SC.8.P.8.6

c. Predict Use the periodic table to name two elements that you would expect to have properties very much like those of calcium (Ca).

_____

_____

_____

_____

SC.8.P.8.6

got it? ··

○ **I get it!** Now I know that the periodic table is useful because _____

○ **I need extra help with** _____

Go to MY SCIENCE ⓢ COACH *online for help with this subject.*   SC.8.P.8.6

What Are the Properties of Metals?
SC.8.P.8.6, LA.8.2.2.3

How Are Metals Classified?
SC.8.P.8.6, MA.6.A.3.6

my planet diary

Recycling Metals

You can find metals in many items that you use every day, including cell phones, computers, appliances, and money. In 2006, the supply of metal in the United States was more than 150 million metric tons. (One metric ton equals 1,000 kilograms.) Many of these metals can be recycled. Recycling helps conserve energy and reduces the amount of waste in landfills.

Metal	Percent of U.S. Supply That Came From Recycling
Aluminum	43
Copper	32.3
Iron and steel	48
Nickel	43
Zinc	24.5

SCIENCE STATS

Communicate Answer the question below. Then discuss your answer with a partner.

Beverage cans contain mostly aluminum. Estimate the percent of beverage cans that you recycle. What other objects that contain metal do you think can be recycled?

_____
_____
_____
_____
_____

> PLANET DIARY Go to **Planet Diary** to learn more about recycling.

Lab zone Do the Inquiry Warm-Up *Why Use Aluminum?*

Vocabulary

- metal • luster • malleable • ductile • thermal conductivity
- electrical conductivity • reactivity • corrosion • alkali metal
- alkaline earth metal • transition metal

Skills

↻ Reading: Ask Questions

△ Inquiry: Infer

What Are the Properties of Metals?

It's hard to imagine modern life without metals. The cars and buses you ride in are made of steel, which is mostly iron (Fe). Airplanes are covered in aluminum (Al). Copper (Cu) wires carry electric current to lamps, stereos, and computers. Can you identify the objects that contain metals in **Figure 1** below?

Elements can be classified by their properties, including melting point, density, hardness, and thermal and electrical conductivity. Metals are elements that are good conductors of electric current and heat. They also tend to be shiny and bendable—like copper wire, for instance. The majority of elements in the periodic table are metals. The metals begin on the left side and extend across the periodic table.

FLORIDA NGSSS

SC.8.P.8.6 Recognize that elements are grouped in the periodic table according to similarities in their properties.

LA.8.2.2.3 The student will organize information to show understanding (e.g., representing main ideas within text through charting).

FIGURE 1 ·······················

Metals

Many of the objects around you contain metals.

✎ **Communicate** Circle the objects that will set off the metal detector. Then, with a partner, look around your classroom and make a list of the objects you see that contain metals.

_____

_____

_____

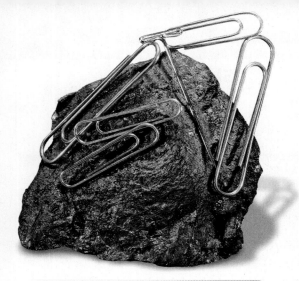

This stone, called magnetite, is made out of a compound of iron.

_____

_____

Gold can be pounded into coins.

_____

_____

Copper is often used for electrical wires.

_____

_____

FIGURE 2 ··

Physical Properties of Metals

Metals have certain physical properties.

✎ **Chart** After reading about the physical properties of metals below, identify the property or properties exhibited by each of the objects above.   LA.8.2.2.3

Physical Properties **Figure 2** shows some common metal objects. 🔑 **The physical properties of metals include luster, malleability, ductility, and conductivity.** A material that has a high **luster** is shiny and reflective. A **malleable** (MAL ee uh bul) material is one that can be hammered or rolled into flat sheets or other shapes. A **ductile** material is one that can be pulled out, or drawn, into long wires. Copper is both malleable and ductile. It can be made into thin sheets or drawn into wires.

Thermal conductivity is the ability of an object to transfer heat. The ability of an object to carry electric current is called **electrical conductivity.** Most metals are good thermal conductors and electrical conductors. Metals also generally have low specific heats. The specific heat is the amount of energy required to raise the temperature of 1 gram of a material by 1 kelvin. Having a low specific heat means that only a small amount of thermal energy is required to raise the temperature of a metal.

Some metals are magnetic. Iron, cobalt (Co), and nickel (Ni) are attracted to magnets and can be made into magnets. Most metals are solids at room temperature. Only mercury (Hg) is a liquid at room temperature.

FIGURE 3 ·······················
Reactivity of Metals
This iron chain is coated with rust after being exposed to air and water.

Chemical Properties
The ease and speed with which an element combines, or reacts, with other substances is called its **reactivity.** Metals usually react by losing electrons to other atoms. Some metals are very reactive. For example, sodium (Na) reacts strongly with water. By comparison, gold (Au) and platinum (Pt) do not react easily with other substances.

The reactivities of other metals fall somewhere between those of sodium and gold. Iron, for example, reacts slowly with oxygen in the air, forming iron oxide, or rust. The iron chain in **Figure 3** is coated with reddish brown rust. The deterioration of a metal due to a chemical reaction in the environment is called **corrosion.**

apply it!

The forks shown are made of silver (Ag).

❶ Some of the silver forks shown have lost their luster—they have become tarnished. This is an example of _____.

❷ Infer What properties of gold and platinum make these metals desirable for jewelry?

_____

_____

_____

Lab zone® Do the Lab Investigation *Copper or Carbon? That Is the Question.*

🔑 Assess Your Understanding

1a. Explain What does the term *thermal conductivity* mean?

_____

_____

_____

_____

SC.8.P.8.6

b. Infer What property of metals led to the use of plastic or wooden handles on many metal cooking utensils? Explain.

_____

_____

_____

_____

_____

SC.8.P.8.6

got it? ···

○ I get it! Now I know that the physical properties of metals include _____

○ I need extra help with _____

Go to MY SCIENCE ⓢ COACH *online for help with this subject.*

SC.8.P.8.6

FLORIDA NGSSS

SC.8.P.8.6 Recognize that elements are grouped in the periodic table according to similarities in their properties.

MA.6.A.3.6 Construct and analyze tables, graphs, and equations to describe simple relations.

FIGURE 4 ····················
Fireworks
Compounds containing potassium are used in fireworks.

FIGURE 5 ····················
X-Ray of Healthy Bones
Calcium compounds are an essential part of teeth and bones.

20
Ca
Calcium
40.08

How Are Metals Classified?

The metals in a group have similar properties. Properties within a group change gradually as you look across the periodic table. For example, the reactivity of metals tends to decrease from left to right across the table. **In the periodic table, metals are classified as alkali metals, alkaline earth metals, transition metals, metals in mixed groups, lanthanides, and actinides.**

Alkali Metals
The metals of Group 1, from lithium (Li) to francium (Fr), are called the **alkali metals.** These metals are the most reactive metals in the periodic table. Alkali metals are so reactive that they are never found as uncombined elements in nature. They are found only in compounds. Compounds that contain potassium (K) are used in fireworks, such as those shown in **Figure 4.**

In the laboratory, chemists can isolate alkali metals from their compounds. As pure, uncombined elements, some of the alkali metals are shiny and so soft you can cut them with a plastic knife. These elements have low densities and low melting points. For example, sodium melts at 98°C, and it has a density of 0.97 g/cm³—less than that of water.

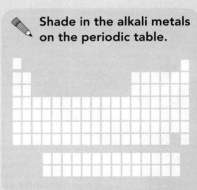

Shade in the alkali metals on the periodic table.

Alkaline Earth Metals
The metals of Group 2 are called the **alkaline earth metals.** These metals are harder and denser, and melt at higher temperatures than the alkali metals. For example, magnesium (Mg) is a hard metal that melts at 648.8°C.

Alkaline earth metals are very reactive, though not as reactive as the alkali metals. These metals are also never found uncombined in nature. Calcium (Ca) is one of the most common alkaline earth metals. Calcium compounds are essential for bone health. **Figure 5** shows an X-ray of healthy bones.

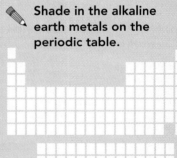

Shade in the alkaline earth metals on the periodic table.

do the math! Analyzing Data

Melting Points in a Group of Elements

Properties of elements in a single group in the periodic table often change according to a certain pattern. The graph shows the melting points of the Group 1 elements, or the alkali metals.

1 **Read Graphs** The melting points of the alkali metals (increase/decrease) from lithium to francium.

2 **Interpret Data** Which of the alkali metals are liquids at 50°C?

_____

3 CHALLENGE If element 119 were discovered, it would fall below francium in Group 1. Predict the approximate melting point of element 119.

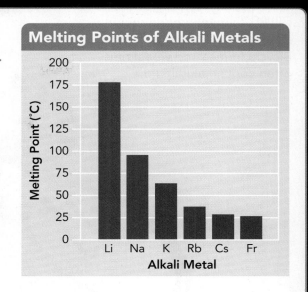

Melting Points of Alkali Metals

(Bar graph: y-axis "Melting Point (°C)" from 0 to 200; x-axis "Alkali Metal" with bars for Li, Na, K, Rb, Cs, Fr. Li ≈ 180, Na ≈ 98, K ≈ 63, Rb ≈ 39, Cs ≈ 28, Fr ≈ 27)

MA.6.A.3.6

Transition Metals

The elements in Groups 3 through 12 are called the **transition metals.** The transition metals include iron, copper, nickel, gold, and silver. Most of these metals are hard and shiny solids. However, mercury is a liquid at room temperature. Except for mercury, the transition metals often have high melting points and high densities. They are also good conductors of heat and electric current, and are very malleable. As shown in **Figure 6**, gold is sometimes used to coat an astronaut's visor.

The transition metals are less reactive than the metals in Groups 1 and 2. When iron reacts with air, forming rust, it sometimes takes many years to react completely.

> ✏ Shade in the transition metals on the periodic table.

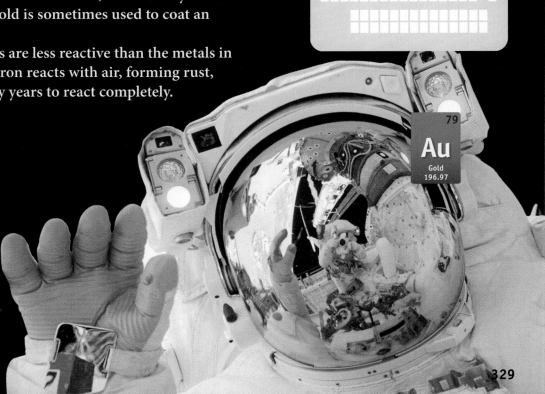

79
Au
Gold
196.97

FIGURE 6 ....
Astronaut Visor
The gold film in an astronaut's visor protects the eyes and face from the sun without interfering with vision.

329

FIGURE 7 ⋯⋯⋯⋯⋯⋯⋯⋯⋯

Aluminum Bicycle Frame

Bicycle frames and wheel rims often contain aluminum.

Al 13 Aluminum 26.982

✏ Shade in the metals in mixed groups on the periodic table.

Metals in Mixed Groups

Bicycle frames, such as the one in **Figure 7**, often contain aluminum because it is durable but light. Aluminum is in Group 13 of the periodic table. Only some of the elements in Groups 13 through 16 are metals. Other metals in these groups that you may be familiar with are tin (Sn) and lead (Pb). A thin coating of tin protects steel from corrosion in some cans of food. Lead was once used in paints and water pipes. Lead is no longer used for these purposes because it was found to be poisonous. Now its most common use is in automobile batteries.

✏ Shade in the lanthanides and actinides on the periodic table.

Lanthanides and Actinides

Two rows of elements are placed below the main part of the periodic table. The elements in the top row are the lanthanides (LAN thuh nydz). Compounds containing the lanthanide neodymium (Nd) are used to make laser light. These lasers are used for surgery, for cutting metals, and in laser range finders, such as the one shown in **Figure 8.**

The elements below the lanthanides are called actinides (AK tuh nydz). Many of these elements are not found in nature but are made artificially in laboratories.

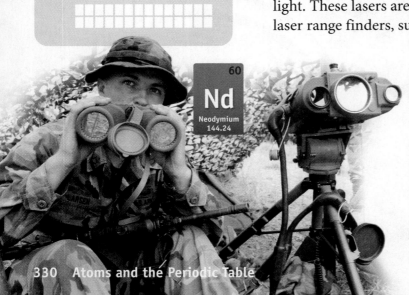

Nd 60 Neodymium 144.24

FIGURE 8 ⋯⋯⋯⋯⋯⋯⋯⋯⋯⋯⋯⋯⋯⋯⋯⋯⋯

Laser Range Finder

A compound containing neodymium is used to produce the laser light in a range finder. The range finder uses a laser beam to determine the distance to an object.

Transuranium Elements Elements that follow uranium (U) in the periodic table are transuranium elements. These elements are made, or synthesized, when nuclear particles are forced to crash into one another. They are sometimes called synthetic elements. For example, plutonium (Pu) is synthesized by bombarding nuclei of uranium-238 with neutrons in a nuclear reactor.

To make elements with atomic numbers above 95, scientists use devices called particle accelerators that move atomic nuclei at extremely high speeds. If these nuclei crash into the nuclei of other elements with enough energy, the particles can combine into a single nucleus. An example of a particle accelerator is shown in **Figure 9.**

In general, the difficulty of synthesizing new elements increases with atomic number. So new elements have been synthesized only as more powerful particle accelerators have been built. Elements in the periodic table with atomic numbers greater than 111 do not yet have permanent names or symbols. In the future, scientists around the world will agree on permanent names and symbols for these elements.

✐ **Ask Questions** Before reading about transuranium elements, ask a *What* or *How* question. As you read, write the answer to your question.

_____

_____

_____

_____

_____

_____

FIGURE 9 ···
Particle Accelerator
The heaviest synthetic elements are synthesized using particle accelerators.

Lab **zone**® Do the Quick Lab *Finding Metals.*

🔑 Assess Your Understanding

2a. Identify Which family in the periodic table contains the most reactive metals?

_____

_____
SC.8.P.8.6

b. Infer Period 4 of the periodic table contains the elements potassium, calcium, and copper. Which is the least reactive?

_____

_____
SC.8.P.8.6

c. Apply Concepts How is plutonium made?

_____

_____

_____
SC.8.P.8.6

got it?

⊙ **I get it!** Now I know that metals are classified in the periodic table as _____

_____

_____

_____

_____

⊙ **I need extra help with** _____

_____

Go to MY SCIENCE 🅢 COACH *online for help with this subject.*
SC.8.P.8.6

LESSON

3 Nonmetals and Metalloids

UNLOCK THE ESSENTIAL

🔑 **What Are the Properties of Nonmetals?**
SC.8.P.8.6

🔑 **What Are the Families Containing Nonmetals?**
SC.8.P.8.6, LA.8.4.2.2

my planeT DiaRY

MISCONCEPTION

Something in the Air

A common misconception is that the air in the atmosphere is mostly oxygen.

Fact: At sea level, air is actually only about 21 percent oxygen by volume. Nitrogen makes up about 78 percent of the atmosphere. The remaining one percent is made up of several gases, including argon and carbon dioxide.

Evidence:
Oxygen is toxic at high concentrations. If you breathed in pure oxygen, you would eventually get very sick.

Communicate Write your answer to each question below. Then discuss your answers with a partner.

1. Why don't scuba divers fill their tanks with pure oxygen?

_____

_____

_____

_____

_____

2. Can you think of anything else that is good for you in small amounts but bad for you in large amounts?

_____

_____

_____

_____

> **PLANET DIARY** Go to **Planet Diary** to learn more about nonmetals.

Lab zone® Do the Inquiry Warm-Up *What Are the Properties of Charcoal?*

Vocabulary
- nonmetal   • diatomic molecule   • halogen
- noble gas   • metalloid   • semiconductor

Skills
↻ Reading: Summarize
△ Inquiry: Classify

What Are the Properties of Nonmetals?

Life on Earth depends on many nonmetals. For example, carbon (C), nitrogen (N), phosphorus (P), hydrogen (H), and oxygen (O) are all nonmetal elements found in your body's DNA. A model of DNA is shown in **Figure 1.** While many compounds made with nonmetals are essential to life, some nonmetals are poisonous and highly reactive. Still others are nonreactive. Compared to metals, nonmetals have a much wider variety of properties. However, nonmetals do have several properties in common.

Physical Properties   A **nonmetal** is an element that lacks most of the properties of a metal. Except for hydrogen, the non-metals are found on the right side of the periodic table. 🗝 **In general, most nonmetals are poor conductors of electric current and heat. Solid nonmetals tend to be dull and brittle.** If you were to hit most solid nonmetals with a hammer, they would break or crumble into a powder. Also, nonmetals usually have lower densities than metals.

Many nonmetals are gases at room temperature. The air you breathe contains mostly nitrogen and oxygen. Some nonmetal elements, such as carbon, sulfur (S), and iodine (I), are solids at room temperature. Bromine (Br) is the only nonmetal that is a liquid at room temperature.

FLORIDA NGSSS

SC.8.P.8.6 Recognize that elements are grouped in the periodic table according to similarities in their properties.

Key

⬤ Hydrogen
⬤ Carbon
⬤ Nitrogen
⬤ Oxygen
⬤ Phosphorus

FIGURE 1 ···
DNA
DNA, which is made up of atoms of nonmetals, is essential to life.

✎ **Identify** Can you think of other substances essential to life that contain nonmetals?

_____

_____

_____

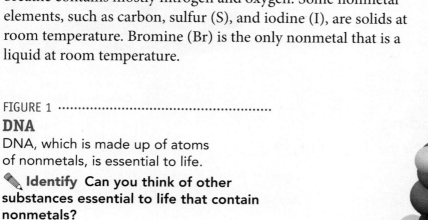

Chemical Properties Atoms of nonmetals usually gain or share electrons when they react with other atoms. When nonmetals and metals react, electrons move from the metal atoms to the nonmetal atoms. For example, when sodium and chlorine react to form table salt (NaCl), an electron moves from the sodium atom to the chlorine atom.

Many nonmetals can form compounds with other nonmetals. In these types of compounds, the atoms share their electrons, forming bonds. When two or more atoms bond this way, they form a molecule. A water (H_2O) molecule consists of two hydrogen atoms and one oxygen atom.

apply it!

Most properties of nonmetals are the opposite of the properties of metals.

❶ Compare and Contrast Complete the table about the properties of metals and nonmetals.

❷ Observe Sulfur, shown at the right, is a nonmetal. What properties can you observe from the photo? What additional properties can you predict?

_____

_____

_____

_____

Properties of Metals	Properties of Nonmetals
Shiny	Dull
Malleable	_____
Good conductors of electric current	_____ _____ _____
_____ _____ _____	Poor conductors of heat

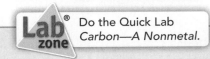

Do the Quick Lab
Carbon—A Nonmetal.

🔑 Assess Your Understanding

1a. Identify What property of nonmetals is the opposite of being *malleable* and *ductile*?

_____

SC.8.P.8.6

b. Make Generalizations What happens to the atoms of most nonmetals when they react with other elements?

_____

_____

_____

_____

SC.8.P.8.6

got it?

○ **I get it!** Now I know that the physical

properties of nonmetals are that _____

_____

_____

○ **I need extra help with** _____

_____

Go to **MY SCIENCE** 🗪 **COACH** *online for help with this subject.*

SC.8.P.8.6

What Are the Families Containing Nonmetals?

Look back at the periodic table. There are nonmetals in Group 1 and in Groups 14–18. 🔑 **The families containing nonmetals include the carbon family, the nitrogen family, the oxygen family, the halogen family, the noble gases, and hydrogen.**

FLORIDA NGSSS

SC.8.P.8.6 Recognize that elements are grouped in the periodic table according to similarities in their properties.

LA.8.4.2.2 The student will record information (e.g., charts) related to a topic, including visual aids to organize and record information.

Before you read about the families containing nonmetals, refer to the periodic table to complete the table below.

Family	Group	Nonmetals in Family
Carbon family	14	
Nitrogen family	15	
Oxygen family	16	
Halogen family	17	
Noble gases	18	
Hydrogen	1	

The Carbon Family In Group 14, only carbon is a nonmetal. Carbon is especially important in the chemistry of life. Proteins, carbohydrates, DNA, and fats all contain carbon.

Most of the fuels that are burned to yield energy contain carbon. Coal contains large amounts of carbon. Gasoline is made from crude oil, which is a mixture of many carbon compounds. Some of these compounds consist of molecules made of long chains of carbon atoms. A diamond, shown in **Figure 2**, is made of pure carbon.

✏️ Shade in the nonmetal in Group 14 on the periodic table.

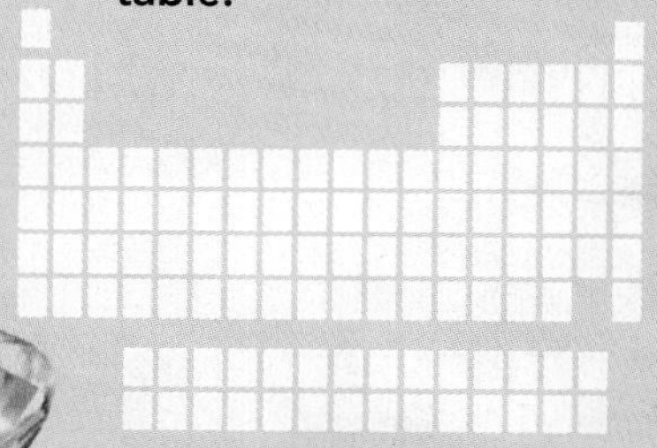

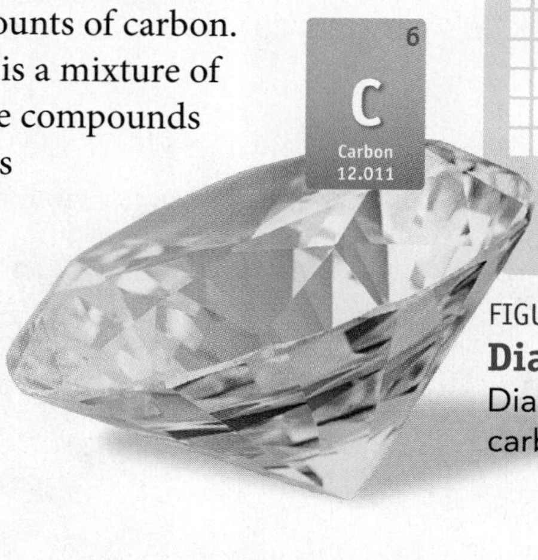

6
C
Carbon
12.011

FIGURE 2 ·····························

Diamond
Diamonds are made of pure carbon.

335

The Nitrogen Family

Group 15, the nitrogen family, contains two nonmetals, nitrogen and phosphorus. Nitrogen makes up about 78 percent of Earth's atmosphere by volume. In nature, nitrogen exists as two nitrogen atoms bonded together to form a diatomic molecule, N_2. A **diatomic molecule** is made up of two atoms. In this form, nitrogen is not very reactive.

Although living things need nitrogen, most of them are unable to use nitrogen from the air. However, certain kinds of bacteria can use the nitrogen from the air to form compounds. This process is called nitrogen fixation. Plants can then take in these nitrogen compounds formed by the bacteria in the soil. Farmers also add nitrogen compounds to the soil in the form of fertilizers. Lightning, shown in **Figure 3,** also converts nitrogen in the atmosphere into a form that can be used by plants.

Phosphorus is the other nonmetal in the nitrogen family. Much more reactive than nitrogen, phosphorus in nature is always found in compounds.

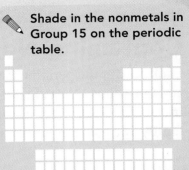

Shade in the nonmetals in Group 15 on the periodic table.

FIGURE 3

Lightning
The energy released in the atmosphere in the form of lightning is able to break the bonds between nitrogen atoms, causing them to react with oxygen. Plants are able to use the nitrogen in this form.

CHALLENGE **How do you get the nitrogen you need?**

did you know?

Over 85 percent of Florida's tropical fruits are grown in soils that contain compounds made of calcium, carbon, and oxygen. These soils often lack nutrients that plants need. Florida agricultural scientists usually suggest that farmers working with these soils add fertilizers that are rich in the nonmetals nitrogen and phosphorus, as well as the metal potassium.

7

N

Nitrogen
14.007

The Oxygen Family

The Oxygen Family Group 16, the oxygen family, contains three nonmetals—oxygen, sulfur, and selenium (Se). Oxygen is a gas at room temperature, whereas sulfur and selenium are both solids.

You are using oxygen right now. With every breath, oxygen travels into your lungs. There, it is absorbed into your bloodstream, which distributes it all over your body. Like nitrogen, oxygen (O_2) is a diatomic molecule. Oxygen is relatively reactive, so it can combine with almost every other element.

If you have ever smelled the odor of a rotten egg, then you are already familiar with the smell of some sulfur compounds. Sulfur is used in the manufacturing of rubber for rubber bands and automobile tires, like the one shown in **Figure 4.**

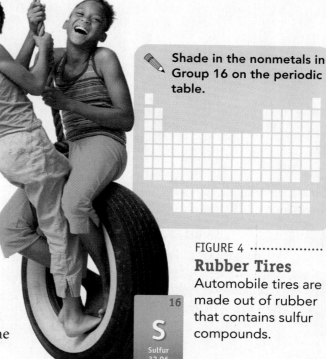

🖉 Shade in the nonmetals in Group 16 on the periodic table.

FIGURE 4 ⋯⋯⋯⋯⋯
Rubber Tires
Automobile tires are made out of rubber that contains sulfur compounds.

16
S
Sulfur
32.06

The Halogen Family Group 17 nonmetals include fluorine (F), chlorine (Cl), bromine (Br), and iodine (I). These elements are also known as the **halogens,** which means "salt forming." The properties of astatine (At) are unknown because it is extremely rare.

🖉 Shade in the nonmetals in Group 17 on the periodic table.

All of the halogens are very reactive. Fluorine is the most reactive of all the elements. It is so reactive that it reacts with almost every known substance, including water. Chlorine gas is extremely dangerous, but it is used in small amounts to kill bacteria in water supplies.

Though the halogen elements are dangerous, many of the compounds that halogens form are quite useful. Compounds of fluorine make up the nonstick coating on cookware. Fluorine compounds are also found in toothpaste, shown in **Figure 5,** because they help prevent tooth decay.

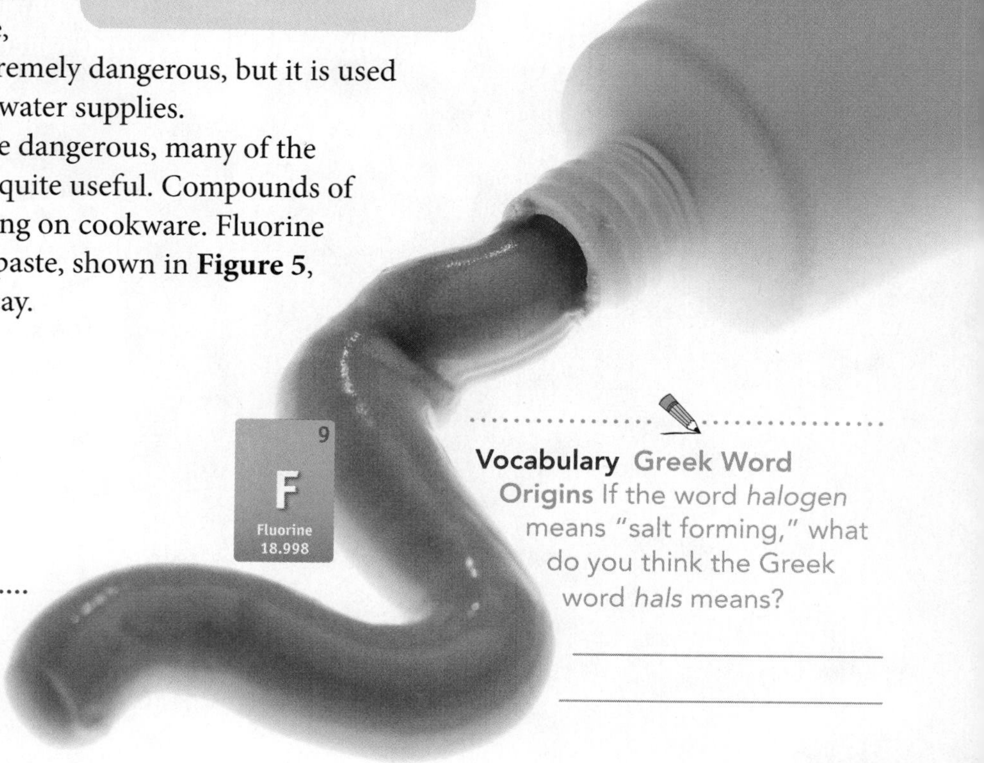

9
F
Fluorine
18.998

Vocabulary Greek Word **Origins** If the word *halogen* means "salt forming," what do you think the Greek word *hals* means?

_____

_____

FIGURE 5 ⋯⋯⋯⋯⋯⋯
Toothpaste
Toothpastes often contain fluorine compounds.

He Ne Ar Kr Xe

FIGURE 6 ·················
Neon Lights
Glowing electric lights are often called "neon lights" even though they are usually filled with other noble gases or mixtures of them. The lights above show the symbols for helium (He), neon (Ne), argon (Ar), krypton (Kr), and xenon (Xe).

The Noble Gases The elements in Group 18 are known as the noble gases. They do not ordinarily form compounds because atoms of noble gases do not usually gain, lose, or share electrons. As a result, the noble gases are usually nonreactive. Even so, scientists have been able to synthesize some noble gas compounds in the laboratory.

You have probably seen a floating balloon filled with helium (He). Noble gases are also used in glowing electric lights, such as the ones shown in Figure 6.

Hydrogen Alone in the upper left corner of the periodic table is hydrogen—the element with the simplest atoms. The chemical properties of hydrogen are very different from those of the other elements, so it cannot be grouped in with a family.

Hydrogen makes up more than 90 percent of the atoms in the universe. Stars—like the sun, shown in **Figure 7**—contain massive amounts of hydrogen. But, hydrogen makes up only 1 percent of the mass of Earth's crust, oceans, and atmosphere. Hydrogen is rarely found on Earth as a pure element. Most hydrogen is combined with oxygen in water.

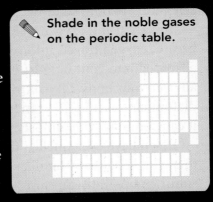

Shade in the noble gases on the periodic table.

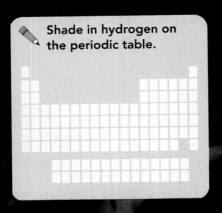

Shade in hydrogen on the periodic table.

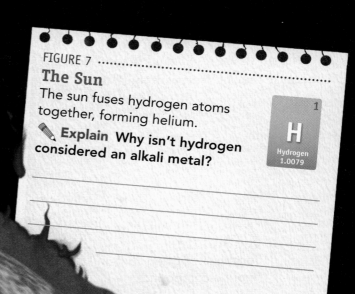

FIGURE 7 ·················
The Sun
The sun fuses hydrogen atoms together, forming helium.

Explain Why isn't hydrogen considered an alkali metal?

_____

_____

_____

| 1 |
| H |
| Hydrogen |
| 1.0079 |

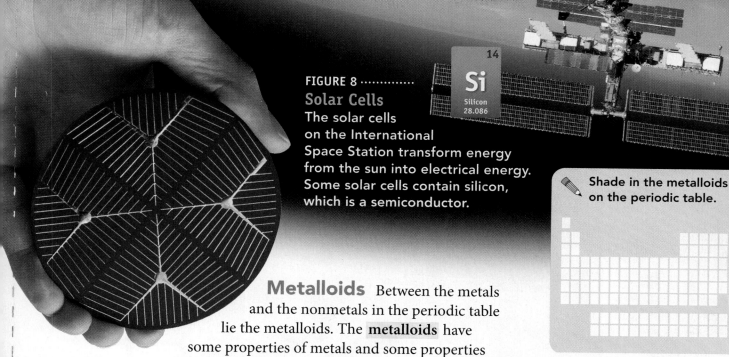

FIGURE 8 ·············
Solar Cells
The solar cells on the International Space Station transform energy from the sun into electrical energy. Some solar cells contain silicon, which is a semiconductor.

14
Si
Silicon
28.086

Metalloids Between the metals and the nonmetals in the periodic table lie the metalloids. The **metalloids** have some properties of metals and some properties of nonmetals. All metalloids are solids at room temperature. The metalloids are brittle, hard, and somewhat reactive.

The most common metalloid is silicon (Si). Ordinary sand, which is mostly silicon dioxide, (SiO_2) is the main component of glass. A compound of boron (B) and oxygen is added during the process of glassmaking to make heat-resistant glass.

A metalloid's most useful property is the ability to conduct electric current. The conductivity of a metalloid can depend on temperature, exposure to light, or the presence of impurities. For this reason, metalloids such as silicon and germanium (Ge) are used to make semiconductors. **Semiconductors** are substances that can conduct electric current under some conditions but not under other conditions. Semiconductors are used to make computer chips, transistors, and lasers. Semiconductors are also used in solar cells, such as the ones shown in **Figure 8**.

🖉 Shade in the metalloids on the periodic table.

·········· 🖉 ··········

⌾ **Summarize** Summarize the properties of the metalloids.

_____

_____

_____

_____

_____

_____

apply it!

Use this portion of the periodic table to answer the questions.

❶ △**Classify** List the chemical symbols of the nonmetals:

_____. The remaining

elements are classified as _____

❷ Selenium has properties similar to (sulfur/bromine) because they are in the same (period/group).

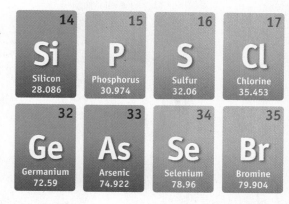

14	15	16	17
Si Silicon 28.086	**P** Phosphorus 30.974	**S** Sulfur 32.06	**Cl** Chlorine 35.453
32	**33**	**34**	**35**
Ge Germanium 72.59	**As** Arsenic 74.922	**Se** Selenium 78.96	**Br** Bromine 79.904

Alien Periodic Table

How is the periodic table organized?

FIGURE 9 ···

▶ **VIRTUAL LAB** Imagine that inhabitants of another planet send a message to Earth that contains information about 30 elements. However, the message contains different names and symbols for these elements than those used on Earth.

✎ Infer Using the clues provided, fill in the periodic table with these "alien" names. LA.8.4.2.2

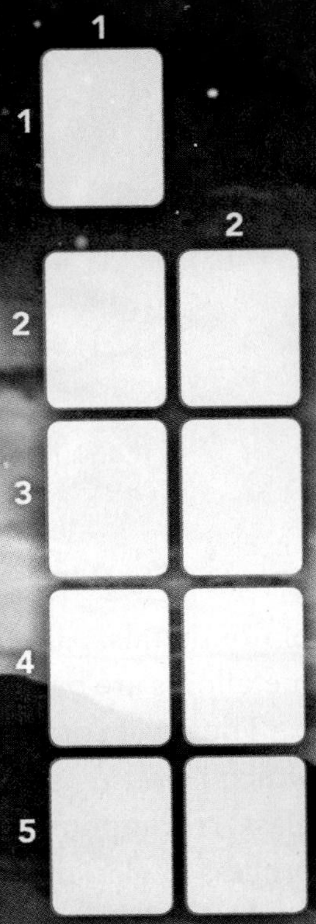

Alien Elements

The noble gases are **bombal** (Bo), **wobble** (Wo), **jeptum** (J), and **logon** (L). Among these gases, wobble has the greatest atomic mass and bombal the least. Logon is lighter than jeptum.

The most reactive group of metals are **xtalt** (X), **byyou** (By), **chow** (Ch), and **quackzil** (Q). Of these metals, chow has the lowest atomic mass. Quackzil is in the same period as wobble.

Apstrom (A), **vulcania** (Vc), and **kratt** (Kt) are non-metals in Group 17. Vulcania is in the same period as quackzil and wobble.

The metalloids are **ernst** (E), **highho** (Hi), **terriblum** (T), and **sississ** (Ss). Sississ is the metalloid with the greatest atomic mass. Ernst is the metalloid with the lowest atomic mass. Highho and terriblum are in Group 14. Terriblum has more protons than highho. **Yazzer** (Yz) touches the zigzag line, but it's a metal, not a metalloid.

The lightest element of all is called **pfsst** (Pf). The heaviest element in the group of 30 elements is **eldorado** (El). The most chemically active non-metal is apstrom. Kratt reacts with byyou to form table salt.

13	14	15	16	17	18

The element **doggone** (D) has only 4 protons in its atoms.

Floxxit (Fx) is important in the chemistry of life. It forms compounds made of long chains of atoms.

Rhaatrap (R) and **doadeer** (Do) are metals in the fourth period, but rhaatrap is less reactive than doadeer.

Magnificon (M), **goldy** (G), and sississ are all members of Group 15. Goldy has fewer electrons than magnificon.

Urrp (Up), **oz** (Oz), and **nuutye** (Nu) are in Group 16. Nuutye is found as a diatomic molecule and has the same properties as a gas found in Earth's atmosphere. Oz has a lower atomic number than urrp.

The element **anatom** (An) has atoms with a total of 49 electrons. **Zapper** (Z) and **pie** (Pi) are both members of Group 2. Zapper has fewer protons than pie.

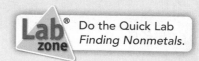

Do the Quick Lab
Finding Nonmetals.

Assess Your Understanding

2a. List What are the nonmetals in Group 16 of the periodic table?

_____

_____

_____

SC.8.P.8.6

b. Compare and Contrast How do the chemical properties of the halogens compare to those of the noble gases?

_____

_____

_____

SC.8.P.8.6

c. ANSWER THE ESSENTIAL ? How is the periodic table organized?

_____

_____

_____

_____

_____

_____

_____

_____

_____

SC.8.P.8.6

got it? ....

○ **I get it!** Now I know that the families containing nonmetals include _____

_____

_____

_____

○ **I need extra help with** _____

Go to MY SCIENCE COACH *online for help with this subject.*   SC.8.P.8.6

341

Models of Atoms

How Did Atomic Theory Develop?
SC.8.N.1.4, SC.8.N.1.6, SC.8.N.3.2, SC.8.P.8.7

What Is the Modern Model of the Atom?
SC.8.N.1.6, SC.8.P.8.7, LA.8.2.2.3

my PLANET DiARY

Nanowhiskers

What's more than 16,000 times thinner than a human hair, and, when added to fabric, able to repel spills, stains, and the smell of the sweatiest of socks? It's a nanowhisker!

Nanowhiskers are tiny threads that measure about 10 nanometers (nm) in length and 1.5 nanometers in diameter (1 nm equals 0.000000001 m). They are often made of carbon or silver atoms. Scientists have found a way to bond nanowhiskers to individual threads of cloth. The nanowhiskers are so small and so close together that they form a barrier that prevents substances from ever touching the fabric. Nanowhiskers made from silver can even kill bacteria on your feet and stop socks from smelling!

DISCOVERY

Communicate Write your answer to each question below. Then discuss your answers with a partner.

1. Why are nanowhiskers used to repel stains on fabrics?

_____

_____

_____

_____

_____

2. What uses for nanowhiskers can you imagine?

_____

_____

> **PLANET DIARY** Go to **Planet Diary** to learn more about atomic structure.

Lab zone Do the Inquiry Warm-Up *What's in the Box?*

Vocabulary
- energy level
- isotope
- mass number

Skills
- ↻ Reading: Compare and Contrast
- ⚠ Inquiry: Make Models

How Did Atomic Theory Develop?

If you could see a single atom, what would it look like? Studying atoms is difficult because atoms are so small. The smallest visible speck of dust may contain 10 million billion atoms! Scientists have created models to describe atoms because they are so small. Models of the atom have changed many times.

Around 430 B.C., the Greek philosopher Democritus proposed that matter was formed of small pieces that could not be cut into smaller parts. He used the word *atomos,* meaning "uncuttable," for these smallest possible pieces. In modern terms, an atom is the smallest particle that still can be considered an element.

The idea of atoms began to develop again in the 1600s. As people did experiments, atomic theory began to take shape. **🔑 Atomic theory grew as a series of models that developed from experimental evidence. As more evidence was collected, the theory and models were revised.**

Dalton's Atomic Theory
Using evidence from many experiments, John Dalton, an English chemist, inferred that atoms had certain characteristics. Dalton thought that atoms were like smooth, hard balls that could not be broken into smaller pieces. The main ideas of Dalton's theory are summarized in **Figure 1.**

FLORIDA NGSSS

SC.8.N.1.4 Explain how hypotheses are valuable if they lead to further investigations, even if they turn out not to be supported by the data.

SC.8.N.1.6 Understand that scientific investigations involve collecting evidence and using reasoning to devise hypotheses, predictions, explanations, and models.

SC.8.N.3.2 Explain why theories may be modified but are rarely discarded.

SC.8.P.8.7 Explore the scientific theory of atoms by recognizing that atoms are the smallest unit of an element and are composed of sub-atomic particles.

FIGURE 1 ·····················

Dalton's Model
Dalton thought that atoms were smooth, hard balls.

✏ **Predict** Read the summary of Dalton's theory. Based on this theory, would you expect a carbon atom to have the same mass as an oxygen atom? Explain.

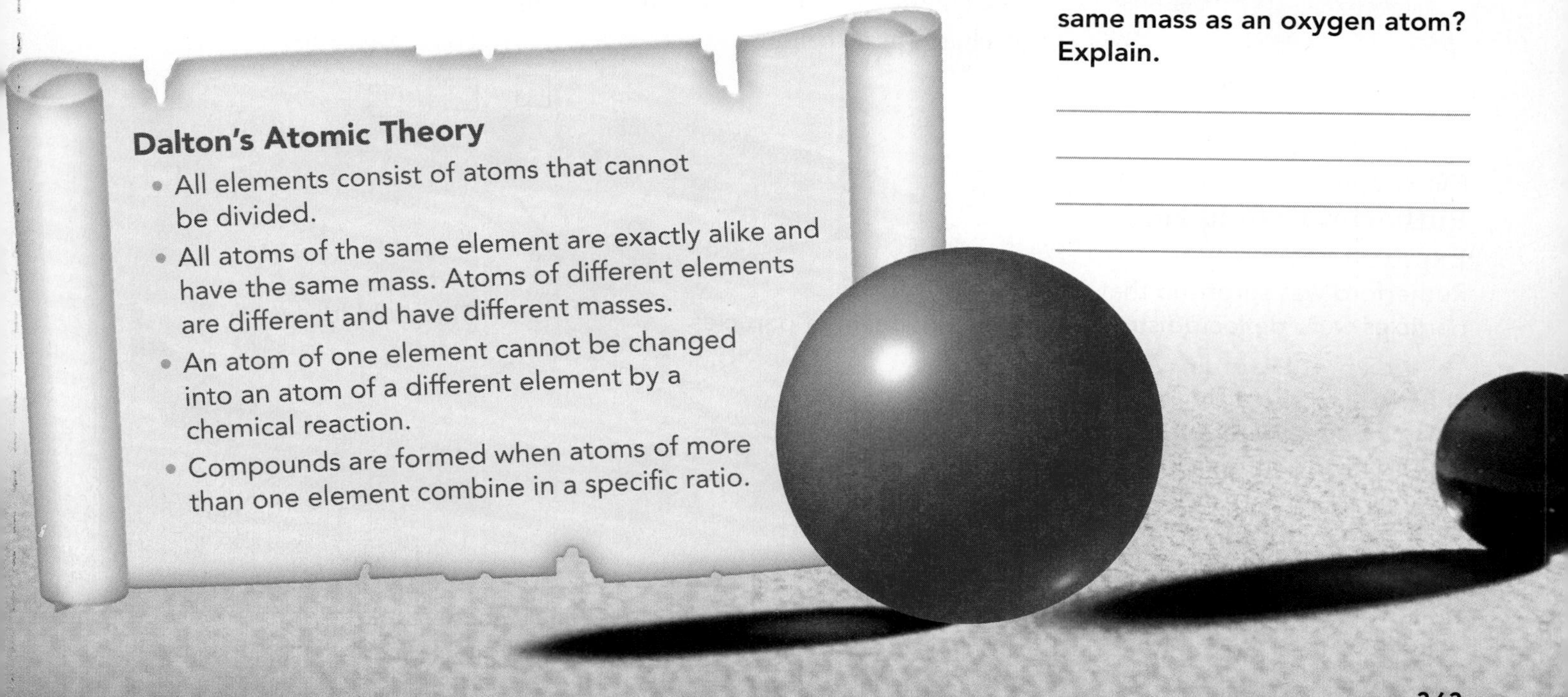

_____

_____

_____

Dalton's Atomic Theory
- All elements consist of atoms that cannot be divided.
- All atoms of the same element are exactly alike and have the same mass. Atoms of different elements are different and have different masses.
- An atom of one element cannot be changed into an atom of a different element by a chemical reaction.
- Compounds are formed when atoms of more than one element combine in a specific ratio.

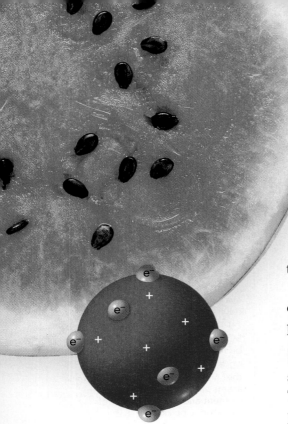

Thomson's Model

Dalton's atomic theory has some similarities to today's models, but there are many differences. One important change is that atoms are now known to be made of even smaller parts. In 1897, J.J. Thomson discovered that atoms contain negatively charged particles called electrons. Yet scientists knew that atoms themselves had no electrical charge. So Thomson reasoned that atoms must also contain some sort of positive charge. This positive charge must balance the negative charge of the electrons.

Thomson proposed a model like the one shown in **Figure 2**. He described an atom that had electrons scattered throughout a ball of positive charge—something like seeds in a watermelon.

Rutherford's Model

In 1911, one of Thomson's former students, Ernest Rutherford, found evidence that challenged Thomson's model. Rutherford's research team aimed a beam of positively charged particles at a thin sheet of gold foil. A diagram of the experiment is shown in **Figure 3**. Rutherford and his team predicted that, if Thomson's model were correct, the charged particles would pass straight through the foil. They also predicted that the paths of some particles would bend, or deflect, slightly. The particles would be only slightly deflected because the positive charge was thought to be spread out in the gold atoms.

Rutherford observed that most of the particles passed straight through the foil with little or no deflection. But to everyone's surprise, a few particles were deflected by the gold foil at very large angles. Based on the results of his experiment, Rutherford suggested that the atom is mostly empty space but has a positive charge at its center.

FIGURE 2 ....

Thomson's Model

Thomson suggested that atoms had negatively charged electrons set in a positive sphere. Each electron is represented above by the symbol e⁻.

FIGURE 3 ....

Rutherford's Gold Foil Experiment

Rutherford was surprised that a few particles were deflected strongly.

✎ **Interpret Diagrams** Place a check (✔) to show the paths of the particles that were not predicted by Thomson's atomic model.

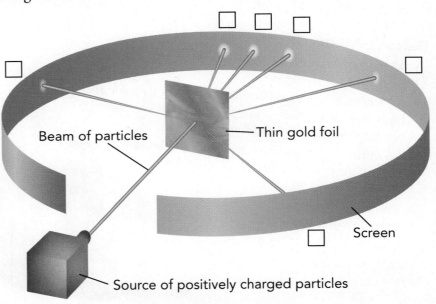

Beam of particles

Thin gold foil

Screen

Source of positively charged particles

Like charges repel each other. So Rutherford inferred that an atom's positive charge must be packed within a small region in its center. Any particle that was deflected strongly had been repelled by what Rutherford termed a gold atom's nucleus. Rutherford's new model of the atom, which is shown in **Figure 4,** is like a cherry. The pit models the nucleus of the atom. The rest of the fruit is the space taken up by the electrons. Later research suggested that the nucleus was made up of one or more positively charged particles. Rutherford called the positively charged particles in an atom's nucleus protons.

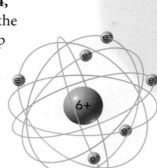

FIGURE 4 ·····························

Rutherford's Model
According to Rutherford's model, an atom was mostly open space. The "6+" in the model means that there are six protons in the nucleus.

✎ **Explain** How was Thomson's model of the atom valuable, even though Rutherford's experiment showed that the model was wrong?

_____

_____

_____

SC.8.N.1.4

apply it!

Use the diagrams below to compare the expected and observed results of Rutherford's gold foil experiment. Part **a** shows the expected paths of the charged particles through the atoms of the gold foil. In part **b**, draw the observed paths of the charged particles. Show at least one particle that is deflected strongly.

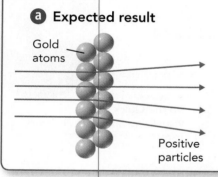

a Expected result

Gold atoms

Positive particles

b Observed result

Nucleus of gold atom

Bohr's Model One of Rutherford's students was Niels Bohr, a Danish scientist. In 1913, Bohr revised the atomic model again. Bohr suggested that electrons are found only in specific orbits around the nucleus. The orbits in Bohr's model look like planets orbiting the sun or the rings of a tree, as shown in **Figure 5.** Each possible electron orbit in Bohr's model has a fixed energy.

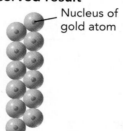

FIGURE 5 ······························

Bohr's Model
Niels Bohr suggested that electrons move in specific orbits around the nucleus of an atom.

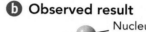
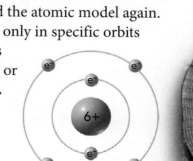

Cloud Model

Cloud Model In the 1920s, the atomic model changed again. Scientists determined that electrons do not orbit the nucleus like planets, as Bohr suggested. Instead, electrons move rapidly within a cloudlike region around the nucleus. Look at **Figure 6.** The orange "cloud" is a visual model. It represents where electrons are likely to be found. An electron's movement is related to its **energy level,** or the specific amount of energy it has. Electrons that have different energy levels are likely to be found in different places.

FIGURE 6 ·····················

Cloud Model
Electrons move rapidly in different directions around the nucleus.

apply it!

Scientists have used models to help them understand atoms. You can too!

1 **Make Models** Match each object with the atomic model that the object most closely represents.

2 **CHALLENGE** An object is missing for one of the atomic models listed. In the space provided, draw an object that represents this model. SC.8.N.1.6

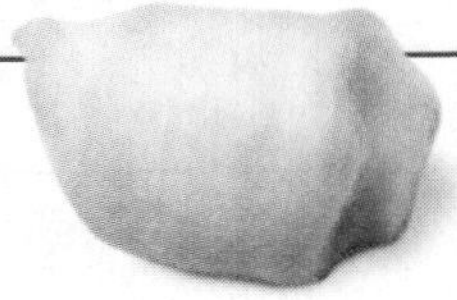

Dalton's Model

Thomson's Model

Bohr's Model

Cloud Model

Lab zone® Do the Quick Lab *Visualizing an Electron Cloud.*

🔑 Assess Your Understanding

1a. 🔄 **Compare and Contrast** How is the cloud model of the atom different from Bohr's model?

_____

_____

_____

_____

SC.8.N.1.6, SC.8.P.8.7

b. Explain How did Dalton's atomic theory lead to the different model scientists have today?

_____

_____

_____

_____

SC.8.N.3.2, SC.8.P.8.7

got it? ·····················

○ **I get it!** Now I know that atomic theory changed with time because _____

_____

○ **I need extra help with** _____

Go to **MY SCIENCE** 🔊 **COACH** *online for help with this subject.* SC.8.P.8.7

What Is the Modern Model of the Atom?

In 1932, English scientist James Chadwick showed that another particle exists in the nucleus of atoms. This particle, called a neutron, was hard to find because it has no electric charge.

Scientists have learned more about the atom since then. One modern model of the atom is shown in **Figure 7**.  **At the center of the atom is a tiny, dense nucleus containing protons and neutrons. Surrounding the nucleus is a cloudlike region of moving electrons.**

Most of an atom's volume is the space in which the electrons move. This space is huge compared to the space taken up by the nucleus. Imagine holding a pencil while standing in the middle of a stadium. If the nucleus were the size of the pencil's eraser, the electrons would reach as far away as the top row of seats!

New research supports the modern model of the atom. However, scientists still don't know the details of the smallest scales of matter. Who will develop the next model of the atom? Maybe it will be you!

> **FLORIDA** NGSSS
>
> **SC.8.N.1.6** Understand that scientific investigations involve collecting evidence and using reasoning to devise hypotheses, predictions, explanations, and models.
>
> **SC.8.P.8.7** Explore the scientific theory of atoms by recognizing that atoms are the smallest unit of an element and are composed of sub-atomic particles.
>
> **LA.8.2.2.3** The student will organize information to show understanding or relationships among facts, ideas, and events (e.g., comparing/contrasting).

FIGURE 7 ·······························

Modern Model of an Atom
A carbon atom has a nucleus made up of positively charged protons and neutral neutrons. The nucleus is surrounded by a cloud of negatively charged electrons.

✎ **Identify** How many protons are in the carbon atom?

_____

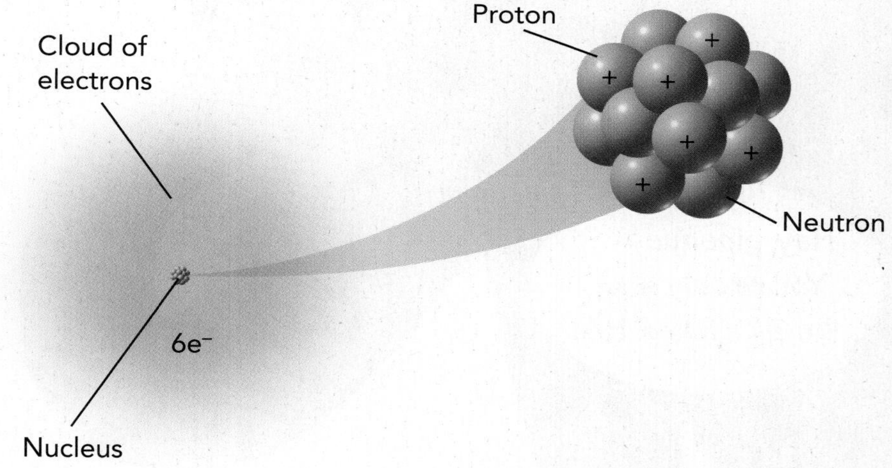

Cloud of electrons

Proton

Neutron

$6e^-$

Nucleus

Particle Charges In **Figure 7**, protons are shown by a plus sign (+). Electrons are shown by the symbol e^-. According to the scale used for measuring charge in atoms, protons have a charge of +1. Electrons have exactly the opposite charge. So electrons have a charge of −1. If you count the number of protons in **Figure 7**, you'll see there are six. The number of protons equals the number of electrons. As a result, the positive charge from the protons equals the negative charge from the electrons. The charges balance, making the atom neutral. Neutrons don't affect the charge of an atom because they have a charge of zero.

·············· ✎ ··············
🔁 Compare and Contrast

A proton has a charge of _____.

An electron has a charge of _____.

A neutron has a charge of _____.

LA.8.2.2.3

Comparing Particle Masses

Comparing Particle Masses Although electrons may balance protons charge for charge, they can't compare when it comes to mass. It takes almost 1,840 electrons to equal the mass of one proton. A proton and a neutron are about equal in mass. Together, the protons and neutrons make up almost all the mass of an atom.

Figure 8 compares the charges and masses of the three atomic particles. Atoms are too small to be described by everyday units of mass, such as grams or kilograms. Sometimes scientists use units known as atomic mass units (amu). A proton or a neutron has a mass equal to about one amu.

Atomic Number Every atom of an element has the same number of protons. For example, every carbon atom has 6 protons and every iron atom has 26 protons. The number of protons in the nucleus of an atom is the atomic number of that atom's element. The definition of an element is based on its atomic number. Carbon's atomic number is 6 and iron's is 26.

Hey, pipsqueak... You're only 4 kg. I'm 8,000 kg! HA!

Relative to an elephant, I'm about the same mass as an electron is relative to a proton. Meow!

FIGURE 8 ·································

▶ INTERACTIVE ART Particles in an Atom
An atom is made up of protons, neutrons, and electrons.

✎ **Review** Complete the table by filling in the correct charge for each atomic particle.

Particles in an Atom

Particle	Symbol	Charge	Mass (amu)	Model
Proton	p^+	_____	1	●
Neutron	n	_____	1	●
Electron	e^-	_____	$\frac{1}{1,840}$	•

Isotopes All atoms of an element have the same number of protons. However, the number of neutrons can vary. Atoms with the same number of protons and different numbers of neutrons are called **isotopes** (EYE suh tohps). **Figure 9** shows three isotopes of carbon.

An isotope is identified by its **mass number,** which is the sum of the protons and neutrons in the atom. The most common isotope of carbon has a mass number of 12 (6 protons + 6 neutrons) and may be written as "carbon-12." About 99 percent of naturally occurring carbon is carbon-12. Two other isotopes are carbon-13 and carbon-14. Despite their different mass numbers, all three carbon isotopes react the same way chemically. The same is true for the isotopes of any other element.

FIGURE 9 ·······························

Isotopes of Carbon
All isotopes of carbon contain 6 protons. They differ in the number of neutrons.

✎ **Relate Text and Visuals** Fill in the missing information for each isotope below.

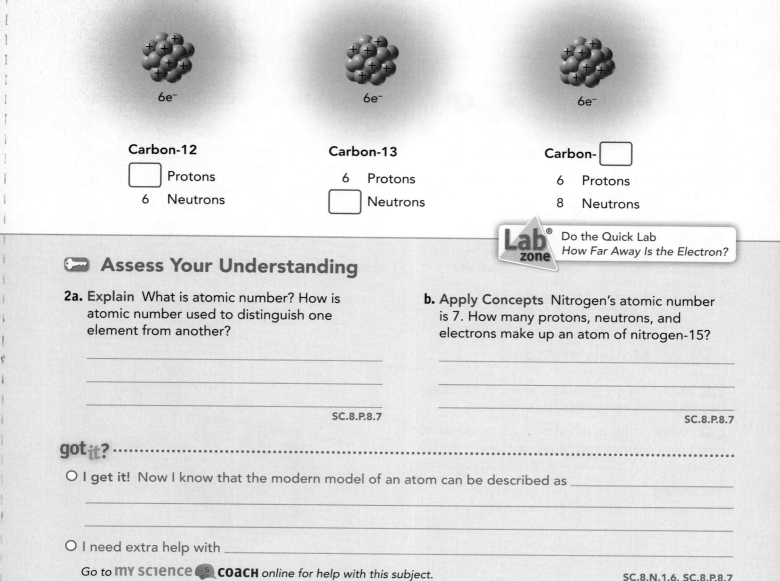

Carbon-12
[ ] Protons
6 Neutrons

Carbon-13
6 Protons
[ ] Neutrons

Carbon-[ ]
6 Protons
8 Neutrons

Lab zone ® Do the Quick Lab
How Far Away Is the Electron?

🔑 Assess Your Understanding

2a. Explain What is atomic number? How is atomic number used to distinguish one element from another?

_____

_____

SC.8.P.8.7

b. Apply Concepts Nitrogen's atomic number is 7. How many protons, neutrons, and electrons make up an atom of nitrogen-15?

_____

_____

SC.8.P.8.7

got it? ···

○ **I get it!** Now I know that the modern model of an atom can be described as _____

_____

○ I need extra help with _____

Go to MY SCIENCE 🗨S COACH *online for help with this subject.*

SC.8.N.1.6, SC.8.P.8.7

Study Guide

In the periodic table, the elements are organized in order of _____ atomic number.

The properties of the elements repeat in each _____.

LESSON 1 Organizing the Elements
SC.8.N.1.6, SC.8.P.8.6

🗝 Mendeleev noticed a pattern of properties in elements arranged by increasing atomic mass.

🗝 The periodic table includes each element's atomic number, symbol, name, and atomic mass.

🗝 The properties of an element can be predicted from its location in the periodic table.

Vocabulary
• atomic mass • periodic table • nucleus
• proton • atomic number • neutron
• electron • chemical symbol • period • group

LESSON 2 Metals
SC.8.P.8.6

🗝 The physical properties of metals include luster, malleability, ductility, and conductivity.

🗝 Metals are classified as alkali metals, alkaline earth metals, transition metals, metals in mixed groups, lanthanides, and actinides.

Vocabulary
• metal • luster • malleable • ductile
• thermal conductivity • electrical conductivity
• reactivity • corrosion • alkali metal
• alkaline earth metal • transition metal

LESSON 3 Nonmetals and Metalloids
SC.8.P.8.6

🗝 Most nonmetals are poor conductors. Solid nonmetals tend to be dull and brittle.

🗝 The families containing nonmetals include the carbon family, the nitrogen family, the oxygen family, the halogen family, the noble gases, and hydrogen.

Vocabulary
• nonmetal • diatomic molecule • halogen
• noble gas • metalloid • semiconductor

LESSON 4 Models of Atoms
SC.8.N.1.4, SC.8.N.1.6, SC.8.N.3.2, SC.8.P.8.7

🗝 Atomic theory grew as a series of models that developed from experimental evidence.

🗝 At the center of the atom is a tiny, dense nucleus containing protons and neutrons. Surrounding the nucleus is a cloudlike region of moving electrons.

Vocabulary
• energy level • isotope • mass number

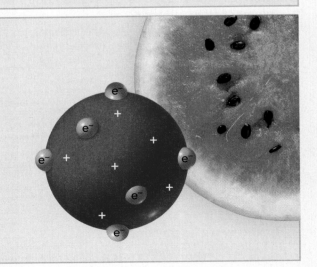

Review and Assessment

LESSON 1 **Organizing the Elements**

1. The rows in the periodic table are called

   a. groups.   **b.** periods.

   c. nonmetals.   **d.** metals.

   SC.8.P.8.6

2. Dmitri Mendeleev constructed the first periodic table, which is _____

   _____

   _____

   SC.8.P.8.6

3. **Apply Concepts** Why was Mendeleev able to use his periodic table to make predictions?

   _____

   _____

   _____

   _____

   SC.8.N.1.6, SC.8.P.8.6

4. **Interpret Diagrams** Below is an entry taken from the periodic table. Identify the type of information given by each labeled item.

   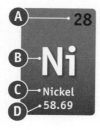

   A → 28
   B → Ni
   C → Nickel
   D → 58.69

   _____

   _____

   _____

   _____

   SC.8.P.8.6

5. **Write About It** Write an advertisement that you could use to sell copies of Mendeleev's periodic table to chemists in 1869. Be sure to emphasize the benefits of the table to the chemical profession. Remember, the chemists have never seen such a table.

   SC.8.P.8.6

LESSON 2 **Metals**

6. Of the following, the group that contains elements that are the most reactive is the

   a. alkali metals.   **b.** alkaline earth metals.

   c. carbon family.   **d.** noble gases.

   SC.8.P.8.6

7. A property of metals is high thermal conductivity, which is _____

   _____

   SC.8.P.8.6

8. **Predict** Using the periodic table, predict which element—potassium, aluminum, or iron—is most reactive. Explain your answer.

   _____

   _____

   _____

   _____

   SC.8.P.8.6

LESSON 3 **Nonmetals and Metalloids**

9. Unlike metals, solid nonmetals are

   a. good conductors of heat and electric current.

   b. malleable.

   c. dull and brittle.

   d. ductile.

   SC.8.P.8.6

10. Two elements that have properties similar to those of chlorine are _____

    _____

    SC.8.P.8.6

11. **Infer** What property of the materials used in computer chips makes them useful as switches that turn electric current on and off?

    _____

    _____

    _____

    _____

    _____

    SC.8.P.8.6

LESSON 4 **Models of Atoms**

12. The atomic number of an element is determined by the number of

    a. protons.   **b.** electrons.

    c. neutrons.   **d.** isotopes.

                                   SC.8.P.8.7

13. Two isotopes of an element have the same

   number of _____ but different

   numbers of _____.

                                     SC.8.P.8.7

14. Relate Cause and Effect How can an atom be electrically neutral when it contains particles that are charged?

_____

_____

_____

_____

                                     SC.8.P.8.7

15. Relate Evidence and Explanation How did Rutherford's experimental evidence lead to the development of a new atomic model?

_____

_____

_____

_____

_____

_____

_____

_____

_____

                      SC.8.N.1.6, SC.8.P.8.7

16. Write About It Write a letter that Thomson might have sent to another scientist explaining why an atom must contain positive charges as well as negative charges. The letter should also explain why Thomson proposed the atomic model that he did.

                      SC.8.N.1.6, SC.8.P.8.7

APPLY THE ESSENTIAL **How is the periodic table organized?**

5	6	7	8
B	**C**	**N**	**O**
Boron 10.81	Carbon 12.011	Nitrogen 14.007	Oxygen 15.999
13	14	15	16
Al	**Si**	**P**	**S**
Aluminum 26.982	Silicon 28.086	Phosphorus 30.974	Sulfur 32.06

17. A portion of the periodic table is shown above. Which element on the periodic table has properties that are most similar to those of nitrogen (N) and which element has properties that are the least similar? Explain your reasoning.

_____

_____

_____

_____

_____

_____

_____

_____

_____

_____

_____

_____

_____

_____

_____

_____

                      SC.8.N.1.6, SC.8.P.8.7

Florida Benchmarks Review

Circle the letter of the best answer.

1 A portion of the periodic table is shown below.

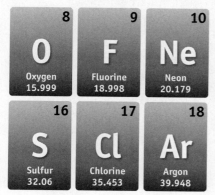

Which elements are noble gases?

A oxygen, fluorine, and neon
B sulfur, chlorine, and argon
C fluorine and chlorine
D neon and argon

SC.8.P.8.6

2 Why is the mass of a carbon atom greater than the total mass of its protons and electrons?

A The mass of a proton is greater than the mass of an electron.
B A proton is positively charged and an electron is negatively charged.
C Most of the atom's volume is the sphere-shaped cloud of electrons.
D The neutrons in the nucleus add mass to the atom.

SC.8.P.8.7

3 Elements that are gases at room temperature are likely to be classified as which of the following?

A metals
B nonmetals
C metalloids
D semiconductors

SC.8.P.8.6

4 Which property of aluminum makes it a suitable metal for soft-drink cans?

A It has good electrical conductivity.
B It can be hammered into a thin sheet (malleability).
C It can be drawn into long wires (ductility).
D It can reflect light (luster).

SC.8.P.8.6

5 Mendeleev's periodic table was a useful tool because it enabled him to

A observe the properties of undiscovered elements.
B construct the periodic table that is used today.
C make predictions about the properties of undiscovered elements.
D understand the structure of atoms.

SC.8.N.1.6, SC.8.P.8.6

6 Which model of the atom is represented by the diagram below?

A the modern cloud model
B the Bohr model
C the Rutherford model
D the Thomson model

SC.8.N.1.6, SC.8.P.8.7

WHAT IS GROWING IN THIS CAVE?

How can bonding determine the properties of a compound?

Mexico's Cave of Crystals contains the world's largest natural crystals. These rocks are made of the mineral gypsum. They grew under water for as many as 500,000 years. The water was pumped out to reveal thousands of giant crystals up to 11 meters in length and 50,000 kilograms in mass. The cave might appear to be a fun place to climb around, but temperatures inside can reach 65°C (hotter than a desert afternoon). This makes it deadly for human exploration without specialized equipment.

Form Operational Definitions Based on the photograph of the Cave of Crystals, how would you define a crystal?

_____

_____

_____

> **UNTAMED SCIENCE** Watch the **Untamed Science** video to learn more about chemical bonding.

Bonding and Chemical Compounds

FLORIDA Next Generation Sunshine State Standards

Big Idea 3: SC.8.N.3.1
Big Idea 8: SC.8.P.8.5, SC.8.P.8.6, SC.8.P.8.8

Language Arts: LA.8.2.2.3

10 Getting Started

Check Your Understanding

1. Background Read the paragraph below and then answer the question.

Marcy fills an ice cube tray with water and places it in a freezer. The temperature in the freezer is −18°C, which is lower than the **melting point** of water (0°C.) When Marcy opens the freezer a few hours later, she finds that the water has frozen into **solid** ice cubes.

> The **melting point** of a substance is the temperature at which the substance changes from a solid to a liquid.
>
> A **solid** has a definite volume and a definite shape.

- What will happen to an ice cube if it is left oustide on a warm, sunny day? Explain.

_____

_____

▶ **MY READING WEB** If you have trouble completing the question above, visit **My Reading Web** and type in *Bonding and Chemical Compounds.*

Vocabulary Skill

High-Use Academic Words High-use academic words are words you are likely to encounter while reading textbooks. Look for the following words in context as you read this chapter.

Word	Definition	Example Sentence
stable	*adj.* not easily or quickly changed from one state to another	Gold is a *stable* metal that does not rust or tarnish.
symbol	*n.* a written sign that stands for something else	The *symbol* for the element oxygen is O.

LA. 8.1.6.5

2. Quick Check Choose the word that best completes the sentence.

- The letter H is the _____ for hydrogen.
- Platinum jewelry lasts a long time because the metal is very

_____

ionic compound

I want it!

I want it more!

polar bond

crystal

acid

Chapter Preview

LESSON 1
- valence electron
- electron dot diagram
- chemical bond

↻ **Relate Cause and Effect**
△ **Predict**

LESSON 2
- ion
- ionic bond
- ionic compound
- chemical formula
- subscript
- covalent bond
- molecular compound
- molecule
- nonpolar bond
- polar bond
- metallic bond

↻ **Compare and Contrast**
△ **Interpret Data**

LESSON 3
- crystal
- acid
- indicator
- base
- neutralization
- salt
- pH scale

↻ **Summarize**
△ **Infer**

▷ **VOCAB FLASH CARDS** For extra help with vocabulary, visit **Vocab Flash Cards** and type in *Bonding and Chemical Compounds.*

Atoms and Bonding

 What Determines an Element's Chemistry?

SC.8.N.3.1, SC.8.P.8.5, SC.8.P.8.6, LA.8.2.2.3

my planet diary

FUN FACTS

Elemental Effects

Many people enjoy fireworks displays. Did you know that chemistry plays a big part in the beauty and the noise? The different colors and effects produced depend on the properties of the elements in the chemical compounds used in each firework rocket. These compounds produce smoke, color bursts, loud noises, or a combination of these effects when they are detonated.

The table below lists some elements found in the compounds used in rockets. It shows the effects these elements produce.

Using what you know about the periodic table, answer the questions below. After you finish the lesson, check your answers.

What elements do you think were used to produce the fireworks display in the photo? What groups of the periodic table do these elements belong to?

_____

_____

_____

> PLANET DIARY Go to **Planet Diary** to learn more about elements.

Element	Effect
Strontium	Red color
Barium	Green color
Copper	Blue color
Sodium	Yellow color
Magnesium or aluminum	White color
Potassium or sodium	Whistling sound
Potassium and sulfur	White smoke

Lab zone Do the Inquiry Warm-Up *What Are the Trends in the Periodic Table?*

Vocabulary
- valence electron
- electron dot diagram
- chemical bond

Skills
- ↻ Reading: Relate Cause and Effect
- △ Inquiry: Predict

What Determines an Element's Chemistry?

When atoms combine, they form compounds. Certain atom combinations make certain compounds. For example, when two nonmetal atoms combine, they often form compounds with low melting points. Or, when a nonmetal atom combines with a metal atom, the resulting compound conducts electric current when dissolved in water. The different ways atoms combine contribute to the diversity of all living and nonliving things. How atoms form compounds has to do with electrons and their energy levels.

Valence Electrons The number of protons in a neutral atom equals the number of electrons. The electrons of an atom are found in different energy levels. Electrons at higher energy levels have higher amounts of energy. The **valence electrons** (VAY luns) of an atom are those electrons that have the highest energy. Valence electrons are involved in chemical bonding. 🔑 **The number of valence electrons in each atom helps determine the chemical properties of that element.**

Electron Dot Diagrams Each atom of an element has a certain number of valence electrons. Different elements can have from 1 to 8 valence electrons. **Figure 1** demonstrates one way to show the number of valence electrons in an element. An **electron dot diagram** includes the symbol for the element surrounded by dots. Each dot stands for one valence electron.

Bonding Atoms tend to be more stable if they have 8 valence electrons. The noble gases have 8 valence electrons. They are nonreactive, or stable. Helium is stable with 2 electrons. Hydrogen also needs only 2 to be stable. When atoms bond, valence electrons may be transferred from one atom to another. Or they may be shared between the atoms. A **chemical bond** is the force of attraction that holds atoms together as a result of the rearrangement of electrons between them.

FLORIDA NGSSS

SC.8.N.3.1 Select models useful in relating the results of investigations.

SC.8.P.8.5 Recognize that there are a finite number of elements and that their atoms combine in a multitude of ways to produce compounds.

SC.8.P.8.6 Recognize that elements are grouped in the periodic table according to similar properties.

LA.8.2.2.3 The student will organize information such as charting, to show understanding.

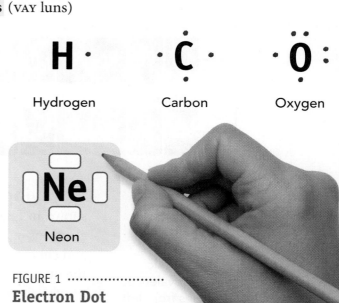

H⋅   ⋅Ċ⋅   ⋅Ö⋅

Hydrogen   Carbon   Oxygen

Ne

Neon

FIGURE 1 ⋯⋯⋯⋯⋯⋯
Electron Dot Diagrams
The valence electrons of an atom are shown as dots around the symbol of the element.

✎ **Interpret Diagrams** Complete the electron dot diagram for neon by drawing the correct number of dots.
SC.8.N.3.1

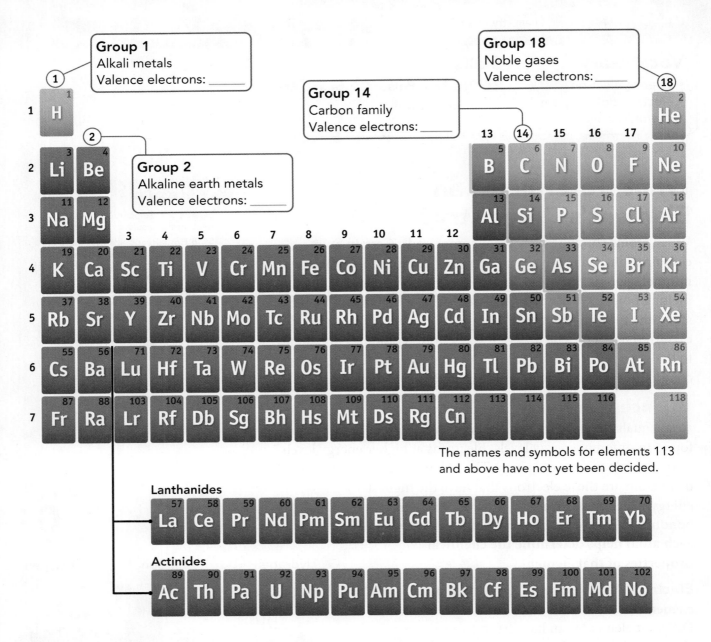

Group 1
Alkali metals
Valence electrons: _____

Group 2
Alkaline earth metals
Valence electrons: _____

Group 14
Carbon family
Valence electrons: _____

Group 18
Noble gases
Valence electrons: _____

The names and symbols for elements 113 and above have not yet been decided.

Lanthanides

Actinides

FIGURE 2 ⋯⋯⋯⋯⋯⋯⋯⋯⋯

▶ INTERACTIVE ART **Periodic Table of the Elements**
The periodic table is arranged in order of increasing atomic number. The number of valence electrons also increases from left to right across a period.

✏ **Recognize** As you read the lesson, fill in the number of valence electrons for each group circled above.

Applying the Periodic Table The periodic table is shown in **Figure 2**. It gives you information about the valence electrons in atoms. The table is organized into rows, called periods, and columns, called groups. The atomic number of an element is the number of protons in each atom of that element.

The elements in the periodic table are in order by increasing atomic number. The number of valence electrons increases from left to right across each period. Each period begins with an element that has 1 valence electron and ends with an element that has 8 valence electrons. Period 1 is an exception, ending with helium, which has 2 valence electrons. This repeating pattern means that the elements within a group always have the same number of valence electrons. As a result, the elements in each group have similar properties.

Each element in Periods 2 and 3 has one more valence electron than the element to its left. Group 1 elements have 1. Group 2 elements have 2. Group 13 elements have 3 valence electrons. Group 14 elements have 4, and so on. (Elements in Groups 3 to 12 follow a slightly different pattern.)

apply it!

The symbols for the elements in Periods 2 and 3 are shown below. The correct electron dot diagrams are shown for only half of the elements.

1 Make Models Complete the electron dot diagrams for nitrogen, oxygen, fluorine, sodium, magnesium, aluminum, silicon, and argon.

2 Fluorine (F) and Chlorine (Cl) are in Group ____. A fluorine atom has _____ valence electrons. A chlorine atom has _____ valence electrons.

3 Predict How many valence electrons does a bromine (Br) atom have? _____

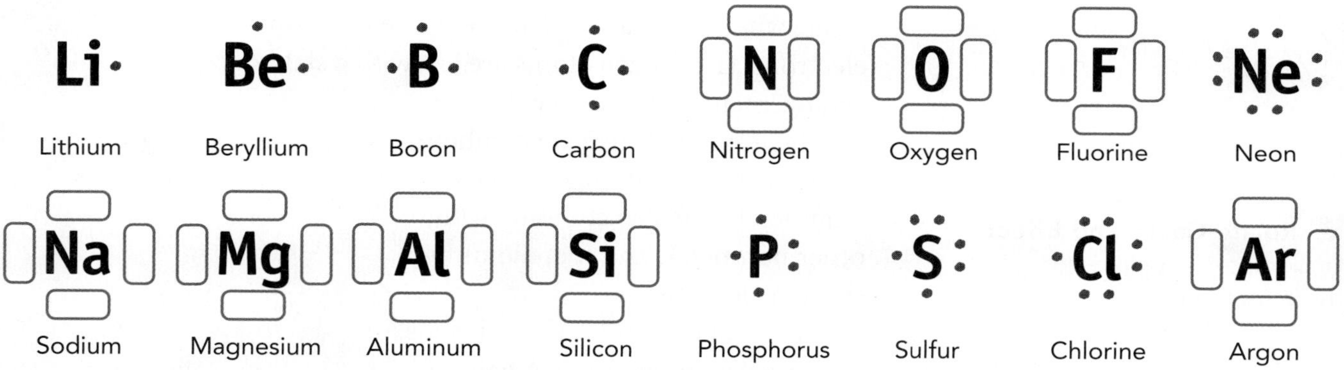

Li·	Be·	·B·	·Ċ·	N	O	F	:Ne:
Lithium	Beryllium	Boron	Carbon	Nitrogen	Oxygen	Fluorine	Neon
Na	Mg	Al	Si	·P:	·S̈·	·Cl:	Ar
Sodium	Magnesium	Aluminum	Silicon	Phosphorus	Sulfur	Chlorine	Argon

SC.8.N.3.1

Noble Gases The Group 18 elements are the noble gases. Atoms of the noble gases have 8 valence electrons, except for helium, which has 2. Atoms with 8 valence electrons (or 2, in the case of helium) are stable. They are unlikely to gain or lose electrons or to share electrons with other atoms. Noble gases do not react easily with other elements. Some don't react at all. But, chemists have been able to make some noble gases form compounds with a few other elements.

FIGURE 3 ·······················
Camera Flashes
Argon, a noble gas, is used to produce camera flashes.

Vocabulary **High-Use Academic Words** Use the word *stable* to explain why the alkali metals tend to lose 1 valence electron.

_____

_____

_____

_____

_____

_____

_____

Metals The metals are the elements in the blue section of the periodic table in **Figure 2**. Metal atoms react by losing their valence electrons. In general, the reactivity of a metal depends on how easily its atoms lose valence electrons. The reactivity of metals decreases from left to right across the periodic table.

At the far left side of the periodic table is Group 1, the alkali metals. Each alkali metal is the most reactive element in its period. Atoms of the alkali metals have 1 valence electron. Except for lithium (Li), when a Group 1 atom loses an electron, it is left with a stable arrangement of 8 electrons in the highest energy level. These electrons are in a lower energy level than the 1 valence electron that was lost. (Lithium atoms are left with a stable arrangement of 2 electrons.) The alkali metals are so reactive that they can cause an explosion when added to water!

Nonmetals The elements in the orange section of the periodic table in **Figure 2** are the nonmetals. Nonmetal atoms become stable when they gain or share enough electrons to have 8 valence electrons. (Hydrogen atoms are left with a stable arrangement of 2 electrons.)

The nonmetals usually combine with metals by gaining electrons. Nonmetals can also combine with other nonmetals and metalloids by sharing electrons.

Atoms of Group 17, the halogens, have 7 valence electrons. A gain of one more electron gives these atoms a stable 8 electrons. The halogens react easily with other elements. **Figure 4** shows the reaction of bromine (Br), a halogen, with aluminum (Al).

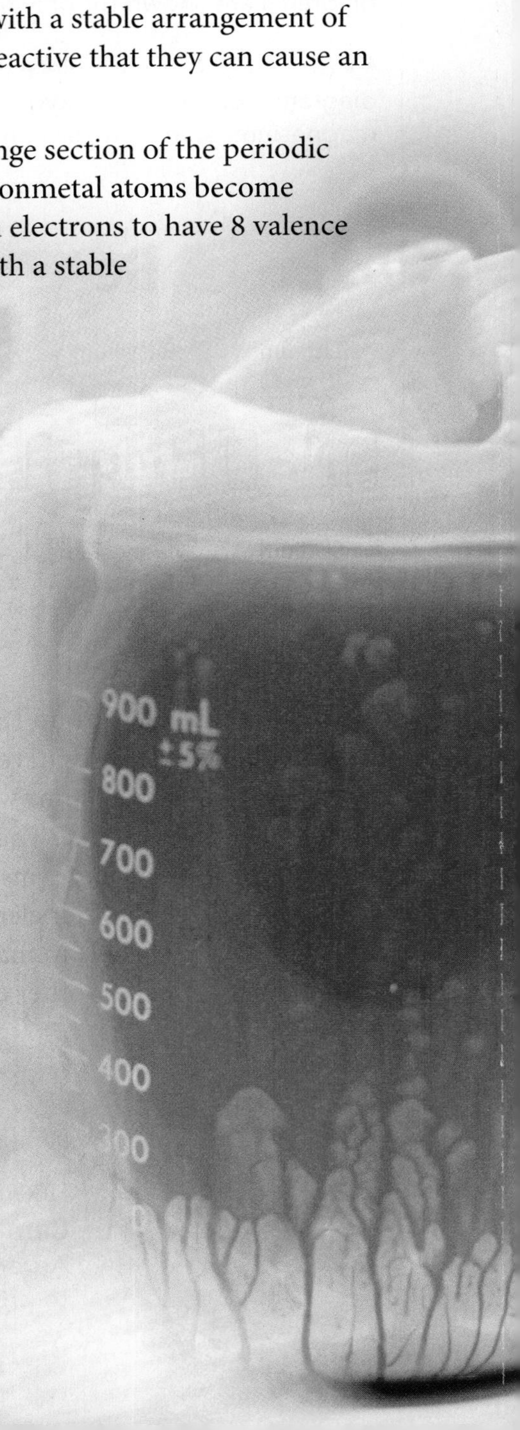

FIGURE 4
VIRTUAL LAB **Reactivity of Bromine**
Aluminum reacts violently with bromine to produce aluminum bromide.

CHALLENGE What would happen if an alkali metal was combined with a halogen? Explain.

_____

_____

_____

900 mL
±5%
800
700
600
500
400
300

Complete the table about groups of elements in the periodic table.

Group Number	Group Name	Number of Valence Electrons	Reactivity (High/Low)
1	Alkali metals	_____	_____
17	Halogens	_____	_____
18	Noble gases	_____	_____

LA.8.2.2.3

Metalloids The metalloids lie along the zigzag line in the periodic table, between the metals and the nonmetals. Atoms of the metalloids can either lose or share electrons when they combine with other elements. Each metalloid has some of the properties of metals and some of the properties of nonmetals.

Hydrogen Hydrogen (H) is placed in Group 1 in the periodic table because it has 1 valence electron, but hydrogen is considered to be a nonmetal. The properties of hydrogen are very different from the properties of the alkali metals. Hydrogen shares its electron when forming compounds with other non-metals to obtain a stable arrangement of 2 electrons.

FIGURE 5
Computer Chip
Silicon, a metalloid, is one of the most abundant elements on Earth. It is used to make computer processor chips.

Lab zone® Do the Quick Lab *Element Chemistry.*

Assess Your Understanding

1a. Define What are valence electrons?

_____

_____

SC.8.P.8.5

b. Explain Why do the properties of elements change in a regular way across a period?

_____

_____

_____

SC.8.P.8.6

c. Relate Cause and Effect Explain the reactivity of the noble gases in terms of valence electrons.

_____

_____

_____

_____

_____

SC.8.P.8.6

got it?

○ **I get it!** Now I know that the chemical properties of an element are determined by _____

_____

○ **I need extra help with** _____

Go to MY SCIENCE ⓢ COACH *online for help with this subject.*

SC.8.P.8.6

Elements Forming Compounds

LESSON 2

UNLOCK THE ESSENTIAL ?

🔑 **How Do Ionic Compounds Form?**
SC.8.N.3.1, SC.8.P.8.8, LA.8.2.2.3

🔑 **How Do Molecular Compounds Form?**
SC.8.P.8.8

🔑 **What Determines the Properties of Metals?**
SC.8.P.8.8

MY PLANET DIARY for Florida

FIELD TRIP

Site: Atlantic Coast to Gulf of Mexico **Location:** Florida

The coral reefs that surround the coasts of Florida are unique because they are the only extensive reefs in the continental United States. They are formed when polyps of living coral take calcium from the seawater and combine it with carbon dioxide to make the ionic compound calcium carbonate, also known as limestone. It's the calcium carbonate that forms the reef. Individual coral colonies can grow up to seven inches a year. From the expanse of the Florida reefs, scientists believe the reefs are between 5,000 and 7,000 years old.

Communicate Write your answers to the questions below. Then discuss your answers with a partner.

1. Egg shells, chalk, and cement all contain calcium carbonate. Using these examples, determine some of the properties of calcium carbonate.

_____
_____
_____

2. What other object do you think might contain the compound calcium carbonate?

_____
_____

▷ **PLANET DIARY** Go to **Planet Diary** to learn more about elements forming compounds.

 Lab zone Do the Inquiry Warm-Up *How Do Ions Form?*

Vocabulary
- ion • ionic bond • ionic compound
- chemical formula • subscript • covalent bond
- molecular compound • molecule • nonpolar bond
- polar bond • metallic bond

Skills
Reading: Compare and Contrast
Inquiry: Interpret Data

How Do Ionic Compounds Form?

You and a friend walk past a market that sells apples for 40 cents each and pears for 50 cents each. You have 45 cents and want an apple. Your friend also has 45 cents but wants a pear. If you give your friend a nickel, she will have 50 cents and can buy a pear. You will have 40 cents left to buy an apple. Transferring the nickel gets both of you what you want. In a simple way, your actions model what can happen between atoms. 🔑 **When a neutral atom transfers one or more electrons to another atom, it results in the formation of an ionic compound.**

Ions An **ion** (EYE ahn) is an atom or group of atoms that has an electric charge. When a neutral atom loses a valence electron, it loses a negative charge. It becomes a positive ion. When a neutral atom gains an electron, it gains a negative charge. It becomes a negative ion.

Metal atoms tend to lose enough electrons to have a stable arrangement of 8 valence electrons at a lower energy level. A potassium (K) atom easily loses its 1 valence electron to become more stable, as shown in **Figure 1.** Nonmetal atoms are likely to gain electrons so that they have 8 valence electrons. A fluorine (F) atom gains 1 electron to have a stable arrangement of 8 valence electrons.

FLORIDA NGSSS

SC.8.N.3.1 Select models useful in relating the results of investigations.

SC.8.P.8.8 Identify basic examples of and compare and classify the properties of compounds, including acids, bases, and salts.

LA.8.2.2.3 The student will organize information, such as charting, to show understanding.

Two Atoms Talking Together

I'm about to lose an electron!
Are you sure?
I'm positive!

K F

K⁺ F⁻

FIGURE 1 ······························

How Ions Form
Ions form when electrons are transferred between atoms.

✎ **Interpret Diagrams**
Complete the electron dot diagrams for potassium (K) and fluorine (F) before and after the electron is transferred.

Common Ions and Their Charges

Name	Charge	Symbol or Formula
Lithium	1+	Li^+
Sodium	1+	Na^+
Potassium	1+	K^+
Ammonium	1+	NH_4^+
Calcium	2+	Ca^{2+}
Magnesium	2+	Mg^{2+}
Aluminum	3+	Al^{3+}
Fluoride	1–	F^-
Chloride	1–	Cl^-
Iodide	1–	I^-
Bicarbonate	1–	HCO_3^-
Nitrate	1–	NO_3^-
Oxide	2–	O^{2-}
Sulfide	2–	S^{2-}
Carbonate	2–	CO_3^{2-}
Sulfate	2–	SO_4^{2-}

Common Ions **Figure 2** lists the names of some common ions. Notice that some ions are made of several atoms. The ammonium ion is made of 1 nitrogen atom and 4 hydrogen atoms. Ions that are made of more than 1 atom are called polyatomic ions (pahl ee uh TAHM ik). The prefix *poly-* means "many," so *polyatomic* means "many atoms." Like other ions, polyatomic ions have an overall positive or negative charge.

Ionic Bonds When atoms that easily lose electrons react with atoms that easily gain electrons, valence electrons are transferred from one type of atom to another. The transfer gives each type of atom a more stable arrangement of electrons. Look at **Figure 3** to see how sodium atoms and chlorine atoms react to form sodium chloride (table salt).

❶ The sodium atom has 1 valence electron. The chlorine atom has 7 valence electrons.

❷ The valence electron of the sodium atom is transferred to the chlorine atom. Both atoms become ions. The sodium atom becomes a positive ion (Na^+). The chlorine atom becomes a negative ion (Cl^-).

❸ Oppositely charged particles attract and form an **ionic bond.** When oppositely charged ions bond, the result is an ionic compound. An **ionic compound** is made up of positive and negative ions, but the overall charge on the compound is zero. The positive Na^+ ion and the negative Cl^- form the ionic compound, NaCl, which has no charge.

FIGURE 3 ·····································

Formation of an Ionic Bond
Follow the steps to see how an ionic bond forms between a sodium atom and a chlorine atom.

✎ **Infer** Complete the electron dot diagrams for the sodium and chlorine atoms and their ions.

SC.8.N.3.1

▲ Sodium metal

Transfer of an electron

▲ Chlorine gas

Sodium ion   Chloride ion

Formulas of Ionic Compounds

You will often see a compound represented by its chemical formula. A **chemical formula** is a group of symbols that shows the ratio of elements in a compound. The formula for calcium chloride is $CaCl_2$. When ionic compounds form, the ions combine to balance the charges on the ions. The chemical formula for the compound reflects this balance. Look at the formula for calcium chloride.

Chemical symbols → $CaCl_2$ ← Subscript

The table in **Figure 2** shows that the charge on the calcium ion is 2+. The charge on each chloride ion is 1−. Two chloride ions balance the charge on the calcium ion. The number "2" in the formula is a subscript. **Subscripts** tell the ratio of elements in a compound. The ratio of calcium ions to chloride ions in $CaCl_2$ is 1 to 2. To write the formula for an ionic compound, write the symbol of the positive ion and then the symbol of the negative ion. Add the subscripts that are needed to balance the charges.

If no subscript is written, it is understood that the subscript is 1. The formula NaCl tells you that there is a 1-to-1 ratio of sodium ions to chloride ions. Formulas for compounds of polyatomic ions are similar. Magnesium carbonate has the formula $MgCO_3$. There is one magnesium ion (Mg^{2+}) for each carbonate ion (CO_3^{2-}).

did you know?

Calcium oxide (CaO), also known as lime, gives off a white light when heated. Theaters once used special lamps to focus this bright light on a single actor. So, the expression *in the limelight* describes a person who receives favorable attention.

FIGURE 4 ·····················
Athletic Chalk

Athletes, such as gymnasts, weight lifters, and rock climbers, use chalk to lubricate their hands and dry up sweat. The white powdery chalk is actually an ionic compound called magnesium carbonate.

✎ Identify Circle the part of the formula representing the carbonate ion. Then write the charge of each ion in the compound.

$MgCO_3$

Green, leafy vegetables contain sodium nitrite.

Naming Ionic Compounds Calcium chloride, sodium bicarbonate, sodium oxide—where do these names come from? For an ionic compound, the name of the positive ion is first, followed by the name of the negative ion. The positive ion is usually a metal, but a few positive polyatomic ions exist, such as the ammonium ion (NH_4^+). If the negative ion is a single element, the end of its name changes to *-ide*. For example, CaO is named calcium oxide. If the negative ion is polyatomic, its name usually ends in *-ate* or *-ite*, as in the compound ammonium nitrate (NH_4NO_3).

apply it!

Chemists refer to compounds by either their names or their chemical formulas.

⚠ **Interpret Data** Use the periodic table and **Figure 2** to fill in the table.

▢ **CHALLENGE** What is the chemical formula for magnesium nitrate?

_____

Name	Positive Ion	Negative Ion	Formula
Magnesium chloride	Mg^{2+}	Cl^-	$MgCl_2$
Sodium bromide	___	___	
_____	___	___	Li_2O
_____	Mg^{2+}	S^{2-}	___
Aluminum fluoride	___	___	___
_____	___	___	KNO_3
_____	NH_4^+	Cl^-	___

LA.8.2.2.3

Lab zone Do the Quick Lab *Ion Formation.*

🔑 **Assess Your Understanding**

1a. Review An atom that loses a valence electron becomes a (positive/negative) ion. An atom that gains a valence electron becomes a (positive/negative) ion.

SC.8.P.8.8

b. Explain The formula for sodium sulfide is Na_2S. Explain what this formula means.

_____

_____

SC.8.P.8.8

c. Apply Concepts What is the name of the compound KI? Why is it electrically neutral?

_____

_____

_____

_____

SC.8.P.8.8

got it?

○ **I get it!** Now I know that ionic compounds form when _____

_____

○ **I need extra help with** _____

Go to **MY SCIENCE COACH** online for help with this subject.

SC.8.P.8.8

How Do Molecular Compounds Form?

You and a friend want to buy a sandwich that sells for one dollar. But each of you has only 50 cents. If you combine your money, you can buy the sandwich and share it. Similarly, 2 atoms can form a bond by sharing electrons. The chemical bond formed when 2 atoms share electrons is called a **covalent bond.** Covalent bonds usually form between nonmetal atoms.

Electron Sharing
Atoms of some nonmetals can bond with each other. **Figure 5** shows how 2 oxygen atoms can react by sharing pairs of electrons. **Covalent bonds between the shared electrons of each atom hold the atoms together to form a molecular compound.** A **molecular compound** is a compound that is made up of molecules. The 2 bonded oxygen atoms form a **molecule,** a neutral group of atoms joined by covalent bonds.

How Many Bonds?
Look at the first electron dot diagram in **Figure 5.** Hydrogen has 1 valence electron. Oxygen has 6 valence electrons. In a water molecule, oxygen forms one covalent bond with each of 2 hydrogen atoms. As a result, the oxygen atom has a stable arrangement of 8 valence electrons. Each hydrogen atom forms one bond because it needs only 2 electrons to be stable.

Look again at the electron dot diagram of the oxygen molecule (O_2) in **Figure 5.** This time, the 2 atoms share 2 pairs of electrons forming a double bond. Atoms of some elements, such as nitrogen, can share 3 pairs of electrons, forming a triple bond.

FLORIDA NGSSS

SC.8.P.8.8 Identify basic examples of and compare and classify the properties of compounds, including acids, bases, and salts.

FIGURE 5 ·······························

Covalent Bonds
Atoms can form single, double, and triple covalent bonds by sharing one or more pairs of electrons.

CHALLENGE In a carbon dioxide (CO_2) molecule, the carbon atom forms a double bond with each of the 2 oxygen atoms. Draw the electron dot diagram for CO_2 below.

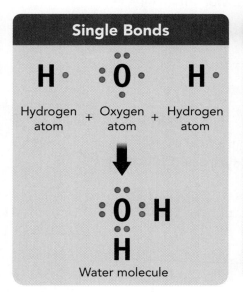

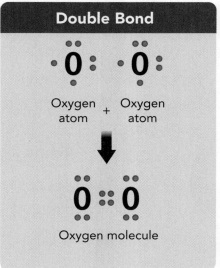

Nonpolar Bonds and Polar Bonds

Have you ever played tug-of-war? When one team pulls the rope with more force than the other team, the rope moves toward the side of the stronger team. The same is true of electrons in a covalent bond. Atoms of some elements pull more strongly on the shared electrons of a covalent bond than do atoms of other elements. As a result, the electrons are shared unequally. Unequal sharing of electrons causes covalently bonded atoms to have slight electric charges. These charges are weaker compared to those of ions.

If 2 atoms pull equally on the electrons, neither atom becomes charged. This happens when identical atoms are bonded. A covalent bond in which electrons are shared equally is a **nonpolar bond.** The hydrogen molecule (H_2), shown in **Figure 6,** has a nonpolar bond.

When electrons in a covalent bond are shared unequally, the atom with the stronger pull gains a slightly negative charge. The atom with the weaker pull gains a slightly positive charge. A covalent bond in which electrons are shared unequally is a **polar bond.** Hydrogen fluoride (HF), also shown in **Figure 6,** has a polar bond.

Compare and Contrast In a nonpolar bond electrons are shared (equally/unequally). In a polar bond electrons are shared (equally/unequally).

FIGURE 6 ·······················

> ART IN MOTION **Nonpolar and Polar Bonds**
Hydrogen forms a nonpolar bond with another hydrogen atom. In hydrogen fluoride, fluorine attracts electrons more strongly than hydrogen does. The bond formed is polar.

Round 1: H_2

Round 2: HF

I want it!

I want it more!

Communicate Imagine you're a sportscaster. Write a commentary describing each of the "tug-of-war" matchups at the left.

Round 1: Hydrogen (H_2)

_____

_____

_____

Round 2: Hydrogen Fluoride (HF)

_____

_____

_____

◀ Intermolecular forces allow a gecko's feet to grip onto smooth surfaces, such as glass.

Polar Bonds in Molecules

A molecule is polar if it has a positively charged end and a negatively charged end. However, not all molecules containing polar bonds are polar overall. In a carbon dioxide molecule, the bonds between the oxygen and carbon atoms are polar. But, as you can see in **Figure 7,** a carbon dioxide molecule has a straight-line shape. The two oxygen atoms pull with equal strength in opposite directions. The attractions cancel out, so the molecule is nonpolar overall.

A water molecule, with its two polar bonds, is itself polar. As you can see in **Figure 7,** a water molecule has a bent shape. The two hydrogen atoms are at one end of the molecule. The oxygen atom is at the other end of the molecule. The oxygen atom attracts electrons more strongly than do the hydrogen atoms. As a result, the end of the molecule with the oxygen atom has a slight negative charge. The end of the molecule with the hydrogen atoms has a slight positive charge.

Attractions Between Molecules

Opposite charges attract. Polar molecules are connected to each other by weak attractions between their slight negative and slight positive charges. These attractions are called intermolecular forces. The negatively charged oxygen ends of the polar water molecules attract the positively charged hydrogen ends of nearby water molecules. Intermolecular forces pull water molecules toward each other.

The properties of polar and nonpolar compounds are different because of differences in attractions between their molecules. The melting point and boiling point of water are much higher than the melting point and boiling point of oxygen. The attractions between the polar water molecules require more energy to overcome than the attractions between the nonpolar oxygen molecules.

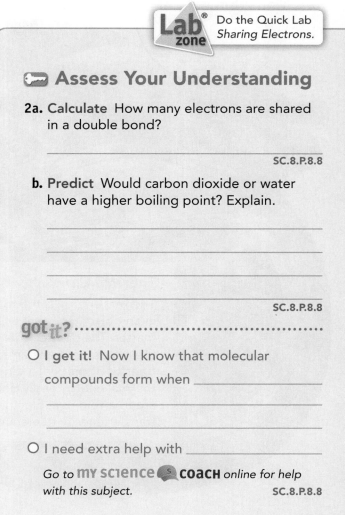

Nonpolar Molecule
Carbon dioxide

Polar Molecule
Water

Opposite pulling cancels.

Electrons pulled toward oxygen

FIGURE 7 ···
Nonpolar and Polar Molecules
Both carbon dioxide and water molecules contain polar bonds. But only water is a polar molecule.

✎ **Interpret Diagrams** Draw a positive (+) sign next to the atoms that gain a slight positive charge. Draw a negative (–) sign next to the atoms that gain a slight negative charge.

Lab zone® Do the Quick Lab *Sharing Electrons.*

⚷ Assess Your Understanding

2a. Calculate How many electrons are shared in a double bond?

_____
SC.8.P.8.8

b. Predict Would carbon dioxide or water have a higher boiling point? Explain.

_____
_____
_____
_____
SC.8.P.8.8

got it? ··

○ **I get it!** Now I know that molecular compounds form when _____
_____

○ **I need extra help with** _____

Go to MY SCIENCE COACH *online for help with this subject.* SC.8.P.8.8

FLORIDA NGSSS

SC.8.P.8.8 Identify basic examples of and compare and classify the properties of compounds, including acids, bases, and salts.

What Determines the Properties of Metals?

Properties of metals include a shiny luster, and high levels of malleability, ductility, electrical conductivity, and thermal conductivity. **Each property of metals is determined by the structure of metal atoms and the bonding between their valence electrons.**

When metal atoms combine chemically with atoms of other elements, they usually lose valence electrons. Metal atoms easily lose electrons because they do not hold onto their valence electrons very strongly. The loosely held valence electrons result in a type of bonding that happens in metals. Most metals are crystalline solids. A metal solid is composed of closely packed, positively charged metal ions. The valence electrons drift among the ions. Each metal ion is held together by a **metallic bond**—an attraction between a positive metal ion and the electrons surrounding it. The atomic model in **Figure 8** illustrates the metallic bonds that hold together aluminum foil. Metallic bonding explains many of the common physical properties of metals.

Atomic model of
metallic bonding

Luster

Polished metals have a shiny, reflective luster, called metallic luster. The luster of a metal is due to its valence electrons. When light strikes these electrons, they absorb the light and then re-emit the light.

Thermal Conductivity

Thermal energy is the total energy of the motion of the particles in an object. Thermal energy flows from warmer matter to cooler matter. The greater energy of the particles in the warmer parts of the material is transferred to the particles in the cooler parts. This transfer of thermal energy is known as heat. Metals conduct thermal energy easily because the valence electrons within a metal are free to move. Electrons in the warmer part of the metal can transfer energy to electrons in the cooler part of the metal.

FIGURE 8 ···

Heavy Metal Bonding

This motorcycle displays many of the properties of metals.

✎ **Identify** For each property of metals, circle the sentence that describes how electrons of the metal determine the property.

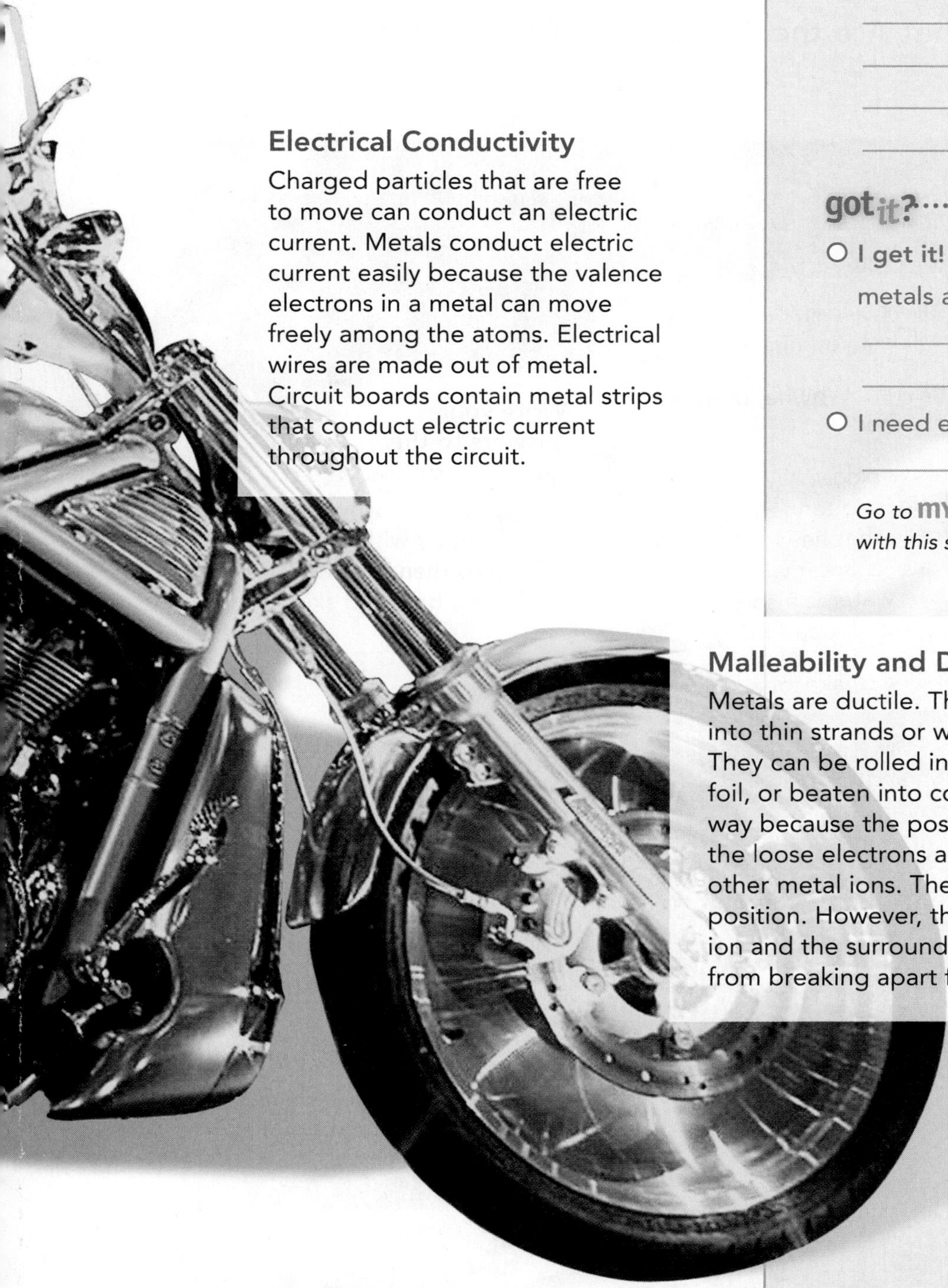

Electrical Conductivity

Charged particles that are free to move can conduct an electric current. Metals conduct electric current easily because the valence electrons in a metal can move freely among the atoms. Electrical wires are made out of metal. Circuit boards contain metal strips that conduct electric current throughout the circuit.

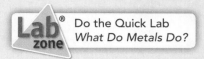

Lab zone Do the Quick Lab
What Do Metals Do?

🔑 Assess Your Understanding

3. Infer Why is it safer to use a nonmetal mixing spoon when cooking something on the stove?

_____

_____

_____

_____

SC.8.P.8.8

got it? ···

○ **I get it!** Now I know that the properties of metals are determined by _____

_____

○ **I need extra help with** _____

_____

Go to my science COACH *online for help with this subject.*

SC.8.P.8.8

Malleability and Ductility

Metals are ductile. They can be bent easily and pulled into thin strands or wires. Metals are also malleable. They can be rolled into thin sheets, as with aluminum foil, or beaten into complex shapes. Metals act this way because the positive metal ions are attracted to the loose electrons all around them rather than to other metal ions. These ions can be made to change position. However, the metallic bonds between the ion and the surrounding electrons keep the metal ions from breaking apart from one another.

Classifying Chemical Compounds

What Are the Properties of Ionic and Molecular Compounds?
SC.8.P.8.8

What Are the Properties of Acids, Bases, and Salts?
SC.8.P.8.8, LA.8.2.2.3

my planeT DiaRY

VOICES FROM HISTORY

Bog Bodies

Even in Shakespeare's time it was known that tanning, the process of making leather, preserves body tissues. Hundreds of years later, the body of a 2,300-year-old man was found in the peat bogs of Europe. The man is a bog body. Bog bodies are the remains of human bodies that have been preserved in the highly acidic conditions of peat bogs around the world. The bog acids are similar in strength to vinegar. They naturally pickle the human bodies. A lack of oxygen and cold temperatures cause the acids to saturate body tissues before they decay. As a result, the organs, hair, and skin are all preserved. The acids may dissolve the bones of the bog bodies, but details like tattoos and fingerprints can still be seen on some of the bodies. Bog bodies from Windover Pond in Florida have even been found with their brains preserved.

GRAVE DIGGER. ...A tanner will last you nine year.

HAMLET. Why he, more than another?

GRAVE DIGGER. Why, sir, his hide is so tanned with his trade that he will keep out water a great while, and your water is a sore decayer of your...dead body.

—Shakespeare, *Hamlet*

Write your answers to the questions below.

1. Hypothesize why bog acids react differently with the bones of the bodies than they do with the organs, hair, and skin.

_____
_____
_____
_____
_____
_____

2. How are pickles similar to bog bodies?

_____
_____

> PLANET DIARY Go to **Planet Diary** to learn more about compounds.

Lab zone® Do the Inquiry Warm-Up *What Color Does Litmus Turn?*

Vocabulary
- crystal • acid • indicator • base • neutralization
- salt • pH scale

Skills
↻ Reading: Summarize
△ Inquiry: Infer

What Are the Properties of Ionic and Molecular Compounds?

Compounds have properties that are different from their component elements. As you have learned, ionic compounds are made up of ions. Molecular compounds are made of molecules containing atoms that are covalently bonded. These differences result in the different properties of ionic and molecular compounds. 🔑 **In general, ionic compounds form hard crystals with high melting points and conduct electric current when dissolved in water or melted. Molecular compounds usually do not conduct electric current when melted or dissolved in water and usually have lower melting points and boiling points.**

Crystals Ionic compounds form solids by building up repeating patterns of ions. The ions form an orderly, three-dimensional arrangement called a **crystal.** Sodium chloride, or table salt, forms an ionic crystal of Na^+ and Cl^- ions. Every Na^+ ion is attracted to the Cl^- ions that surround it. The pattern is the same no matter what the size of the crystal. In a single grain of salt, the crystal pattern extends for millions of ions in every direction. Many crystals of ionic compounds are hard and brittle. This is due to the strength of their ionic bonds and the attractions among all the ions. Some molecular compounds, such as table sugar ($C_{12}H_{22}O_{11}$), also form crystals. But the forces between molecules are much weaker than the forces between ions. As a result, molecular crystals can be broken down much easier.

Melting Points and Boiling Points The ions in an ionic compound must break apart for the compound to melt. It takes a huge amount of thermal energy to separate the ions in a crystal, because the attraction between positive and negative ions is so great. As a result, ionic compounds have high melting points.

Compared to an ionic compound, a molecular compound needs less heat to separate the molecules because the forces holding them together are weaker than those of an ionic compound. As a result, molecular compounds usually have much lower melting and boiling points. For example, table salt melts at 801°C, but table sugar melts at about 190°C.

FLORIDA   NGSSS

SC.8.P.8.8 Identify basic examples of and compare and classify the properties of compounds, including acids, bases, and salts.

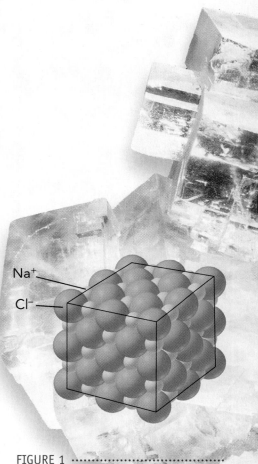

FIGURE 1 ....
Halite
Some crystals have a cubic shape, like these crystals of halite, or sodium chloride.

Calculate If the crystal pattern for halite expanded in every direction, how many chloride ions would surround each sodium ion?

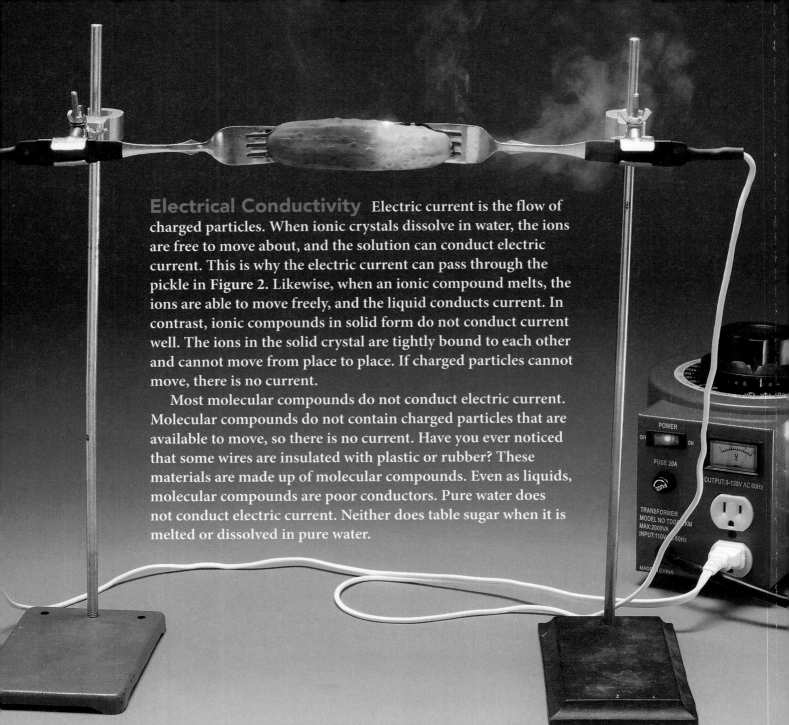

Electrical Conductivity Electric current is the flow of charged particles. When ionic crystals dissolve in water, the ions are free to move about, and the solution can conduct electric current. This is why the electric current can pass through the pickle in Figure 2. Likewise, when an ionic compound melts, the ions are able to move freely, and the liquid conducts current. In contrast, ionic compounds in solid form do not conduct current well. The ions in the solid crystal are tightly bound to each other and cannot move from place to place. If charged particles cannot move, there is no current.

Most molecular compounds do not conduct electric current. Molecular compounds do not contain charged particles that are available to move, so there is no current. Have you ever noticed that some wires are insulated with plastic or rubber? These materials are made up of molecular compounds. Even as liquids, molecular compounds are poor conductors. Pure water does not conduct electric current. Neither does table sugar when it is melted or dissolved in pure water.

FIGURE 2 ···

Glowing Pickle
Electric current can be conducted through a pickle because pickles contain salt water. After a time, the pickle becomes hot and begins to glow.

✎ Complete the tasks about conducting electric current.

1. Identify What ions are present in solution inside the pickle?

_____

2. Communicate With a partner, list some other foods you think may be able to conduct electric current.

_____

The table shows the melting points and boiling points of a few molecular and ionic compounds.

❶ **Infer** Use the data table to determine if a compound is ionic or molecular. Circle the ionic compounds. Underline the molecular compounds.

❷ **Compare and Classify** Ammonia (NH_3) has a melting point of −78°C and a boiling point of −34°C. This suggests that ammonia is a(n) (molecular/ionic) compound.

❸ CHALLENGE Which kinds of compounds have the greatest difference between their melting point and their boiling point? What does this suggest about the energy needed to change a solid to a liquid to a gas?

Substance	Formula	Melting Point (°C)	Boiling Point (°C)
Calcium chloride	$CaCl_2$	775	1,935
Isopropyl alcohol	C_3H_8O	−87.9	82.3
Octane	C_8H_{18}	−56.8	125.6
Sodium chloride	NaCl	800.7	1,465
Water	H_2O	0	100

_____

_____

_____

_____

Lab zone Do the Lab Investigation *Shedding Light on Ions.*

🔑 Assess Your Understanding

1a. Define Both ionic and molecular compounds form three-dimensional, repeating patterns called _____.

SC.8.P.8.8

b. Draw Conclusions Why are almost all ionic compounds solid at room temperature?

_____

_____

_____

SC.8.P.8.8

got it? ....

○ **I get it!** Now I know that the properties of ionic compounds include _____

_____

_____

and the properties of molecular compounds include _____

_____

_____

○ **I need extra help with** _____

Go to MY SCIENCE ⓢ COACH *online for help with this subject.*

SC.8.P.8.8

FLORIDA NGSSS

SC.8.P.8.8 Identify basic examples of and compare and classify the properties of compounds, including acids, bases, and salts.

LA.8.2.2.3 The student will organize information, such as summarizing, to show understanding.

What Are the Properties of Acids, Bases, and Salts?

Did you have any fruit to eat today? What about a muffin? If so, acids, bases, and salts were probably part of your meal. These compounds are an important part of our lives.

Acids Many common items contain acids. Folic acid is found in green, leafy vegetables. Hydrochloric acid in your stomach helps with digestion. Sulfuric acid is used in certain batteries, giving it the nickname "battery acid." Acids are compounds with specific characteristic properties. 🔑 **An acid reacts with metals and carbonates, tastes sour, and turns blue litmus paper red.**

Reactions with Metals Acids react with some metals to produce hydrogen gas. Platinum and gold don't react with most acids, but copper, zinc, and iron do. When they react, acids can "wear away" these metals. This is one reason acids are described as corrosive.

Acids can also corrode materials containing the carbonate ion (CO_3^{2-}). The carbonate ion is found in shells, chalk, and limestone. One product of the reaction of an acid with a carbonate is carbon dioxide gas.

Sour Taste If you've ever tasted a lemon you've had firsthand experience with the sour taste of acids. Citrus fruits, such as lemons and oranges, contain citric acid. Although sour taste is a characteristic of acids, scientists never taste chemicals.

Reactions With Indicators
Chemists use indicators to test acids. Litmus paper is one type of **indicator**, a compound that changes color when it comes in contact with an acid. Acids turn blue litmus paper red.

Litmus Paper

FIGURE 3 ··········
Reactions With Metals
Acids are used to test the purity of precious metals.

✎ **Infer** What could you determine about a gold charm that bubbles when it's exposed to an acid?

_____

_____

_____

FIGURE 4 ··········
Reactions With Carbonates
This sculpture is carved from limestone.

✎ **Predict** Describe what a geologist would observe if she poured acid on the sculpture.

_____

_____

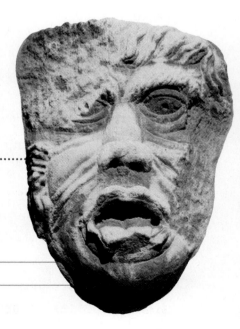

Bases Another group of compounds that can be identified by their properties are **bases**. 🔑 **A base tastes bitter, feels slippery, and turns red litmus paper blue.** Common bases include ammonia, found in household cleaners, and baking soda, or sodium bicarbonate, which causes baked goods to rise. Unlike acids, bases don't react with metals or carbonates. The lack of a reaction can be a useful property for identifying bases.

Bitter Taste Have you ever tasted tonic water? The base, quinine, causes the slightly bitter taste. Bases taste bitter. Other foods that contain bases include bitter melon, almonds, and cocoa beans.

Slippery Feel Many soaps and detergents contain bases. The slippery feel of your shampoo is a property of the bases it contains. Just as you avoid tasting chemicals, you wouldn't want to touch one either. Strong bases can irritate your skin.

Reactions With Indicators Litmus paper can also be used to test bases. Unlike acids, however, bases turn red litmus paper blue. An easy way to remember this is to think of the letter *b*. **B**ases turn litmus paper **b**lue.

▲ Cocoa beans

🖉 ⤴ **Summarize** What are some uses of bases? LA.8.2.2.3

_____

_____

_____

_____

FIGURE 5 ················

Acid and Base Properties

🖉 **Compare and Classify** Draw an arrow from each item to the word "acid" or "base" that describes its properties.

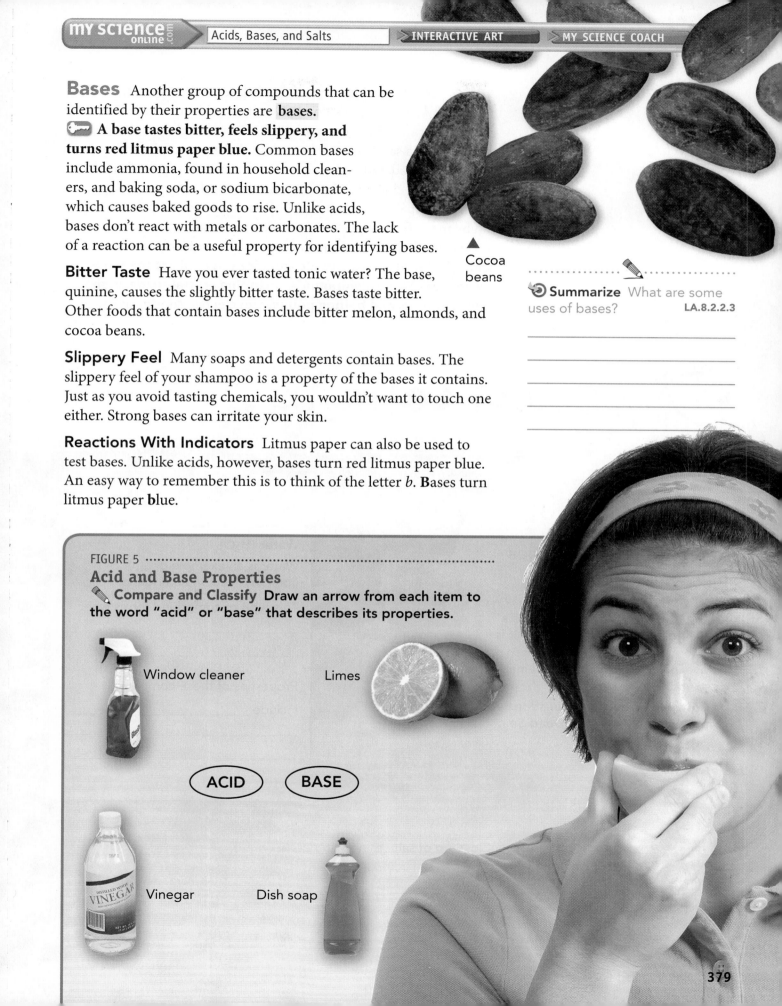

Window cleaner

Limes

(ACID)   (BASE)

Vinegar   Dish soap

Salts Are you curious about what happens when you mix an acid and a base? A reaction between an acid and a base is called **neutralization** (noo truh lih ZAY shun) and it results in the formation of a salt. *Salt* may be the familiar name of the stuff you sprinkle on food, but table salt is actually only one type of salt, called sodium chloride. To a chemist, the word *salt* refers to a specific group of compounds. A **salt** is any ionic compound that can be made from a neutralization reaction. Salt compounds are made from the positive ion of a base and the negative ion of an acid. 🔑 **Since salts are made from ions, they share the same properties of ionic compounds, including crystal shape, high melting points and boiling points, and electric conductivity.**

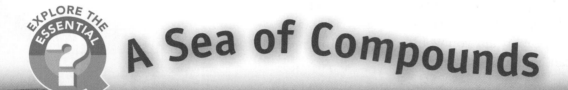

EXPLORE THE ESSENTIAL ❓

A Sea of Compounds

How can bonding determine the properties of a compound?

FIGURE 6 ·············
▶ INTERACTIVE ART The Dead Sea is a saltwater lake in the Middle East. It is so salty that neither fish nor plants can survive in it. The water contains many dissolved compounds.

✎ **Review** Answer the questions about compounds found in the Dead Sea.

LA.8.2.2.3

Close-up of salt

Water (H_2O)

Water is an example of a(n) (ionic/molecular) compound.

This type of compound forms when

_____

_____

Properties of these compounds

include _____

_____

_____

(0) (1) (2) (3) (4) (5) (6) (7) (8) (9) (10) (11) (12) (13) (14)

 Do the Quick Lab
pHone Home.

The pH Scale Acids and bases can be measured using the pH scale. The **pH scale** ranges from 0 to 14. The most acidic substances are found at the low end of the scale, while basic substances are found at the high end. You can find the pH of a substance using indicator paper, which changes a different color for each pH value. Matching the color of the paper with the colors on the scale tells you the substance's pH. A pH lower than 7 is acidic. A pH higher than 7 is basic. If the pH is exactly 7, the substance is neutral, meaning it's neither an acid nor a base. Pure water and salts are both neutral.

Sodium Chloride (NaCl)

Sodium chloride is an example of a(n) (ionic/molecular) compound.

This type of compound forms when _____

_____

_____

Properties of these compounds include _____

_____

_____

_____

_____

Acids and Bases

Salt is formed in a (neutralization/molecular) reaction between an acid and a base.

To form the salt compound, the acid

contributes _____

_____

The base contributes _____

_____

Assess Your Understanding

2a. Review A substance that tastes bitter and has a pH of 9 is most likely a(n) (acid/base).
SC.8.P.8.8

b. Describe Why are acids considered corrosive?

_____

_____
SC.8.P.8.8

c. ANSWER THE ESSENTIAL **?** How can bonding determine the properties of a compound?

_____

_____

_____

_____

_____

_____

_____

_____

_____

_____
SC.8.P.8.8

got it? ....

○ **I get it!** Now I know that the properties of

acids include _____

_____

_____

The properties of bases include _____

_____

_____

The properties of salts are the same as the

properties of _____

○ **I need extra help with** _____

Go to **MY SCIENCE** Ⓢ **COACH** online for help
with this subject.   SC.8.P.8.8

10 Study Guide

Compared to molecular compounds, ionic compounds have _____ melting points.

Ionic compounds conduct electric current when _____.

LESSON 1 Atoms and Bonding
SC.8.N.3.1, SC.8.P.8.5, SC.8.P.8.6

The number of valence electrons in each atom helps determine the chemical properties of that element.

Vocabulary
• valence electron   • electron dot diagram
• chemical bond

LESSON 2 Elements Forming Compounds
SC.8.N.3.1, SC.8.P.8.8

When a neutral atom transfers one or more electrons to another atom, the result is an ionic compound.

Covalent bonds between the shared electrons of atoms hold the atoms together to form a molecular compound.

Each property of metals is determined by the structure of metal atoms and the bonding between their valence electrons.

Vocabulary
• ion   • ionic bond   • ionic compound   • chemical formula   • subscript   • covalent bond
• molecular compound   • molecule   • nonpolar bond   • polar bond   • metallic bond

LESSON 3 Classifying Chemical Compounds
SC.8.N.4.2, SC.8.P.8.8

Ionic compounds form hard crystals with high melting points and can conduct electric current. Molecular compounds do not conduct electric current and have low melting and boiling points.

An acid reacts with metals and carbonates, tastes sour, and turns blue litmus paper red.

A base tastes bitter, feels slippery, and turns red litmus paper blue.

Salts are ionic compounds with ionic properties.

Vocabulary
• crystal   • acid   • indicator   • base
• neutralization   • salt   • pH scale

Review and Assessment

LESSON 1 Atoms and Bonding

1. An electron dot diagram shows an atom's number of

    a. protons   **b.** electrons

    c. valence electrons   **d.** chemical bonds

SC.8.P.8.5

2. When atoms react, they form a chemical bond, which is defined as _____

_____

_____

SC.8.P.8.5

Use the diagrams to answer Questions 3 and 4.

Calcium   Argon   Sodium

Nitrogen   Oxygen   Chlorine

3. Infer Which of these elements can become stable by losing 1 electron? Explain.

_____

_____

_____

_____

SC.8.P.8.6

4. Draw Conclusions Which of these elements is least likely to react with other elements? Explain.

_____

_____

_____

SC.8.P.8.6

5. ⟨**Write About It**⟩ Go to your local grocery store and observe how the products on the shelves are organized. Write a paragraph comparing how food products are organized in a grocery store and how elements are organized in the periodic table.

SC.8.P.8.6

LESSON 2 Elements Forming Compounds

6. When an atom loses or gains electrons, it becomes a(n)

    a. ion   **b.** formula

    c. crystal   **d.** subscript

SC.8.P.8.8

7. Polished metals have a metallic luster, which means that _____

_____

SC.8.P.8.8

8. Interpret Tables Use the periodic table to find the number of valence electrons for calcium (Ca), aluminum (Al), oxygen (O), and iodine (I). Then predict the formula for the following compounds: calcium oxide, aluminum iodide, and aluminum oxide.

_____

_____

_____

SC.8.P.8.8

9. Interpret Diagrams Identify each molecule below as either a polar or nonpolar molecule. Explain your reasoning.

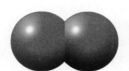   

  Oxygen   **Carbon dioxide**

_____

_____

_____

_____

_____

_____

_____

_____

_____

SC.8.P.8.8

LESSON 3 Classifying Chemical Compounds

How can bonding determine the properties of a compound?

10. Which of the following is a property of bases?

 a. sour taste

 b. slippery feel

 c. turns blue litmus paper red

 d. reacts with some metals

 SC.8.P.8.8

11. Litmus paper is an example of an indicator

 because _____

 _____

 SC.8.P.8.8

12. **Relate Cause and Effect** Solid table salt does not conduct electric current. How does dissolving salt in water allow electric current to flow?

 _____

 _____

 _____

 _____

 _____

 SC.8.P.8.8

13. **Design Experiments** A student has a sample of a white powdery substance. She needs to know if it is an ionic compound or a molecular compound. Describe a method she could use to determine what kind of compound the substance is.

 _____

 _____

 _____

 _____

 SC.8.P.8.8

14. **Write About It** A bottle of acid is missing from the lab. Design a "Missing Acid" poster describing the properties of the acid. Include examples of tests that could be done to check if the bottle that is found contains acid.

 SC.8.P.8.8

15. An ice cube and a scoop of salt are left outside on a warm, sunny day. Explain why the ice cube melts and the salt does not.

_____

_____

_____

_____

_____

_____

_____

_____

_____

_____

_____

 SC.8.P.8.8

Florida Benchmarks Review

Circle the letter of the best answer.

1 The table below lists some ions and their charges.

Ions and Their Charges		
Name	**Charge**	**Symbol/Formula**
Sodium	1+	Na^+
Calcium	2+	Ca^{2+}
Chloride	1−	Cl^-
Phosphate	3−	PO_4^{3-}

How many sodium ions are needed to balance the charge of one phosphate ion?

A 1
B 2
C 3
D 4

SC.8.P.8.5, SC.8.P.8.6

2 Ionic crystals have higher melting points than molecular crystals because

A ionic crystals are usually made up of two metal atoms.
B only ionic crystals have a regular, repeating pattern.
C ionic crystals can conduct electric current.
D the ionic bonds of an ionic crystal are stronger than the covalent bonds of a molecular crystal.

SC.8.P.8.8

3 Glass is a material made up of molecular compounds. Why would it be a useful insulator?

A Molecular compounds have low melting points.
B Molecular compounds do not conduct electric current.
C Molecular compounds can dissolve easily in water.
D Molecular compounds have high boiling points.

SC.8.P.8.8

4 A scientist observes that an unknown solution turns blue litmus paper red and reacts with zinc to produce hydrogen gas. Which of the following *best* describes the unknown solution?

A an ionic compound
B an acid
C a base
D a molecular compound

SC.8.P.8.8

5 All of the following are characteristics of metallic compounds except

A the tendency to form hard, brittle crystals.
B the ability to conduct electric current.
C the ability to be hammered into sheets.
D luster.

SC.8.P.8.8

6 Predict the type of compound that forms and its properties from the process shown in the diagram.

A Acid; sour taste, reacts with metals and carbonates
B Base; bitter taste, slippery feel
C Ionic; crystal shape, high melting point, conducts electric current
D Molecular; low melting point, cannot conduct electric current

SC.8.P.8.8

HOW DID THIS SINKHOLE APPEAR?

What determines the properties of mixtures and pure substances?

You might be wondering, "What is a sinkhole?" A sinkhole forms when the ground suddenly collapses. Sometimes sinkholes are caused by human activities like mining or by broken water pipes. In this photograph, divers are exploring a sinkhole that happened naturally when the underground rock, called limestone, mixed with slightly acidic water. The water actually dissolved the rock!

Predict **Do you think pure water would have the same effect on the rock as the mixture of acidic water? Explain.**

_____

_____

_____

_____

> **UNTAMED SCIENCE** Watch the **Untamed Science** video to learn more about solutions.

Mixtures and Solutions

FLORIDA Next Generation Sunshine State Standards

Big Idea 2: SC.8.N.2.1

Big Idea 4: SC.8.N.4.1, SC.8.N.4.2

Big Idea 8: SC.8.P.8.9

Language Arts: LA.8.2.2.3

Mathematics: MA.6.A.3.6

11 Getting Started

Check Your Understanding

1. Background Read the paragraph below and then answer the question.

> When we breathe, we take in oxygen (O_2) and exhale carbon dioxide (CO_2). The bonds between the oxygen atoms in O_2 are **nonpolar bonds.** The bonds between the carbon and oxygen atoms in CO_2 are **polar bonds.** However, carbon dioxide is a nonpolar molecule.

> A covalent bond in which electrons are shared equally is a **nonpolar bond.**
>
> A covalent bond in which electrons are shared unequally is a **polar bond.**

• Carbon monoxide (CO) is an air pollutant. What type of bonds are in carbon monoxide?

_____

> **MY READING WEB** If you had trouble completing the question above, visit **My Reading Web** and type in *Mixtures and Solutions.*

Vocabulary Skill

Identify Related Word Forms You can expand your vocabulary by learning the related forms of a word. For example, the common verb *to bake* is related to the noun *baker* and the adjective *baked.*

Verb	Noun	Adjective
indicate to show; to point	**indicator** something that shows or points to	**indicative** serving as a sign; showing
saturate to fill up as much as possible	**saturation** the condition of holding as much as possible	**saturated** to be full; to hold as much as is possible

LA.8.1.6.5

2. Quick Check Review the words related to *saturate.* Complete the following sentences with the correct form of the word.

• The _____ sponge could hold no more water.

• He continued to add water to the point of _____

mixture

solution

colloid

saturated solution

Chapter Preview

LESSON 1

- pure substance
- mixture
- heterogeneous mixture
- homogeneous mixture
- ↻ Ask Questions
- △ Design Experiments

LESSON 2

- solution
- solvent
- solute
- colloid
- suspension
- ↻ Identify Supporting Evidence
- △ Interpret Data

LESSON 3

- dilute solution
- concentrated solution
- solubility
- saturated solution
- ↻ Identify the Main Idea
- △ Calculate

> VOCAB FLASH CARDS For extra help with vocabulary, visit **Vocab Flash Cards** and type in *Mixtures and Solutions.*

Exploring Pure Substances and Mixtures

🔑 **How Are Mixtures Different From Pure Substances?**
SC.8.P.8.9

🔑 **What Are Two Types of Mixtures?**
SC.8.P.8.9

my planeт DiaRY for Florida

BLOG

Posted by: Bethany
Location: Indialantic, Florida

Last night, I made dinner: chicken noodle soup. You make it by heating the broth in a pot, then adding all the ingredients. Chicken noodle soup is a mixture because the ingredients are together, but could be separated easily. Some of the ingredients in chicken noodle soup include chicken, broth, noodles, carrots, and other vegetables. This is one of my favorite mixtures because it tastes great.

Communicate Discuss the questions with a classmate. Then write your answers below.

1. Bethany says that soup is a mixture because it can be separated easily. How would you separate the parts of chicken noodle soup?

_____

_____

_____

_____

_____

2. Describe another food mixture. What are the different ingredients that make up the mixture?

_____

_____

_____

_____

> PLANET DIARY Go to **Planet Diary** to learn more about mixtures and pure substances.

Lab zone ® Do the Inquiry Warm-Up *What Is a Mixture?*

Vocabulary
- pure substance • mixture • heterogeneous mixture
- homogenous mixture

Skills
↪ Reading: Ask Questions
△ Inquiry: Design Experiments

How Are Mixtures Different From Pure Substances?

If you have ever made cookies from scratch, then you know that you combine several ingredients to make dough. The ingredients for your cookies probably included water, sugar, salt, and baking soda. When you put them together, along with other ingredients, they formed a new combination. Water, sugar, salt, and baking soda are all pure substances. A **pure substance** is a single kind of matter that has a specific makeup, or composition. On the other hand, when you combined the ingredients, a mixture formed. A **mixture** is two or more substances that are together in the same place, but their atoms are not chemically bonded. ☞ **Pure substances cannot be separated easily or sometimes, at all. But, mixtures can be physically separated.** Using various methods, the cookie dough could be separated back into water, sugar, salt, and baking soda. However, separating the sodium and chlorine that make up salt can only be done by a chemical reaction.

Pure Substances Recall that elements and compounds are the two types of pure substances. Elements are made of only one type of matter. Compounds are made up of more than one element in which the atoms are chemically bonded.

FLORIDA NGSSS

SC.8.P.8.9 Distinguish among mixtures (including solutions) and pure substances.

FIGURE 1 ·····························

Mixture or Pure Substance?
The Florida Keys provide miles of beautiful beaches.

✎ **Distinguish** For each example found at the beach, circle whether the substance is pure or a mixture.

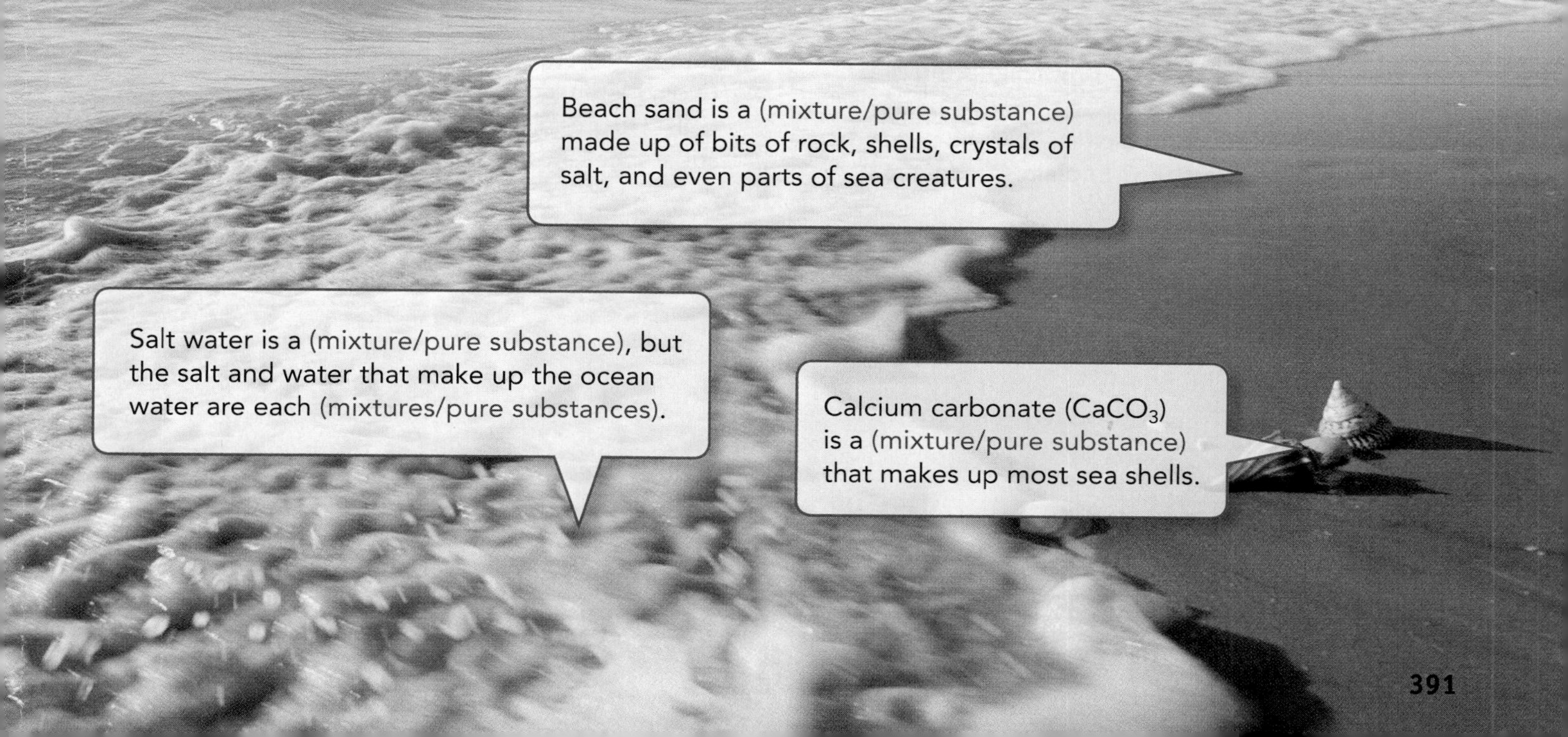

Beach sand is a (mixture/pure substance) made up of bits of rock, shells, crystals of salt, and even parts of sea creatures.

Salt water is a (mixture/pure substance), but the salt and water that make up the ocean water are each (mixtures/pure substances).

Calcium carbonate ($CaCO_3$) is a (mixture/pure substance) that makes up most sea shells.

391

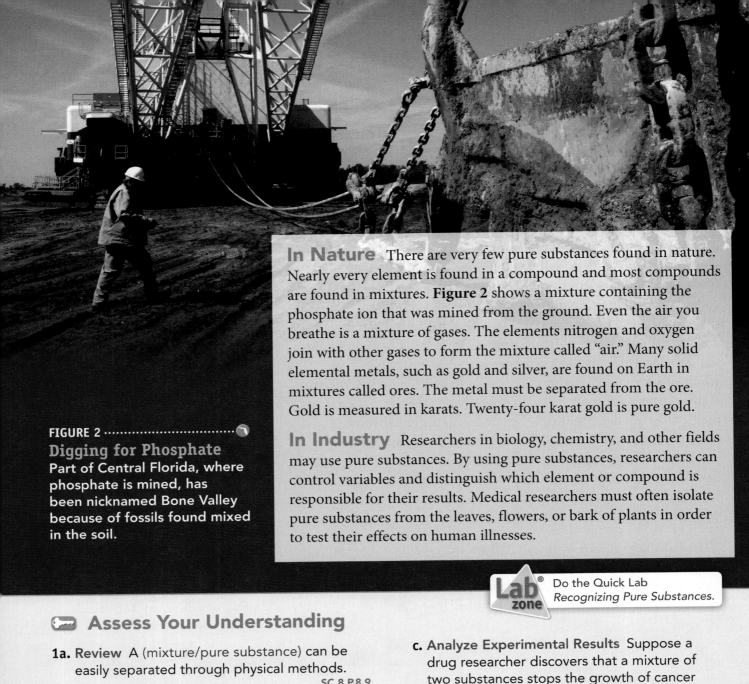

In Nature There are very few pure substances found in nature. Nearly every element is found in a compound and most compounds are found in mixtures. **Figure 2** shows a mixture containing the phosphate ion that was mined from the ground. Even the air you breathe is a mixture of gases. The elements nitrogen and oxygen join with other gases to form the mixture called "air." Many solid elemental metals, such as gold and silver, are found on Earth in mixtures called ores. The metal must be separated from the ore. Gold is measured in karats. Twenty-four karat gold is pure gold.

In Industry Researchers in biology, chemistry, and other fields may use pure substances. By using pure substances, researchers can control variables and distinguish which element or compound is responsible for their results. Medical researchers must often isolate pure substances from the leaves, flowers, or bark of plants in order to test their effects on human illnesses.

FIGURE 2 ·······
Digging for Phosphate
Part of Central Florida, where phosphate is mined, has been nicknamed Bone Valley because of fossils found mixed in the soil.

Lab® Do the Quick Lab
zone *Recognizing Pure Substances.*

Assess Your Understanding

1a. Review A (mixture/pure substance) can be easily separated through physical methods.

SC.8.P.8.9

b. Distinguish Is carbon dioxide (CO_2) a pure substance or a mixture? Explain.

_____

_____

_____
SC.8.P.8.9

c. Analyze Experimental Results Suppose a drug researcher discovers that a mixture of two substances stops the growth of cancer cells. How could she determine which of the substances stopped the cancer?

_____

_____

_____

_____
SC.8.P.8.9

got it? ·······················

O **I get it!** Now I know that mixtures differ from pure substances because _____

_____

O **I need extra help with** _____

Go to MY SCIENCE ⓢ COACH online for help with this subject.
SC.8.P.8.9

What Are Two Types of Mixtures?

You are more likely to find mixtures in your everyday life than pure substances. Mixtures are everywhere, from the trail mix in your lunch bag to the sand at the beach. Sometimes it is difficult to recognize a mixture because its component parts are blended together so well. 🔑 **Two types of mixtures are heterogeneous mixtures and homogeneous mixtures.**

FLORIDA NGSSS

SC.8.P.8.9 Distinguish among mixtures (including solutions) and pure substances.

Heterogeneous Mixtures
Trail mix and beach sand are both examples of heterogeneous mixtures. A mixture in which you can see the different parts and can easily separate them out is a **heterogeneous mixture.** Just think how easy it would be to separate the peanuts from the pretzels and raisins in your bag of trail mix. The different parts are easily seen and they keep their properties even when they're mixed together.

Homogeneous Mixtures
Separating the parts of a homogeneous mixture is not quite as easy as separating the parts of a heterogeneous mixture. A **homogeneous mixture** is so evenly mixed that you can't differentiate the parts simply by looking at the mixture. Suppose you stir a spoonful of sugar into a glass of lemonade. After stirring for a little while, the sugar dissolves, and you can no longer see crystals of sugar in the lemonade. You know the sugar is there, though, because the lemonade tastes sweet. As in all mixtures, the parts keep their properties. The sugar kept its property of tasting sweet. Lemonade is an example of a solution. Solutions are homogeneous mixtures. Not all solutions are liquid, however. They can be gases and solids, as well. Brass is an alloy. It is a solution of the elements copper and zinc.

Honey

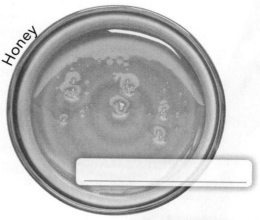

Guacamole

Soy sauce

FIGURE 3 ···

Mix It Up
Many foods are mixtures of several ingredients.

✏️ **Interpret Photos** Label each food as a heterogeneous or homogeneous mixture.

CHALLENGE Is ketchup a heterogeneous or homogeneous mixture? Explain your reasoning.

Ketchup

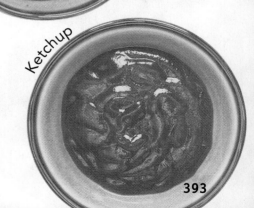

_____

_____

_____

393

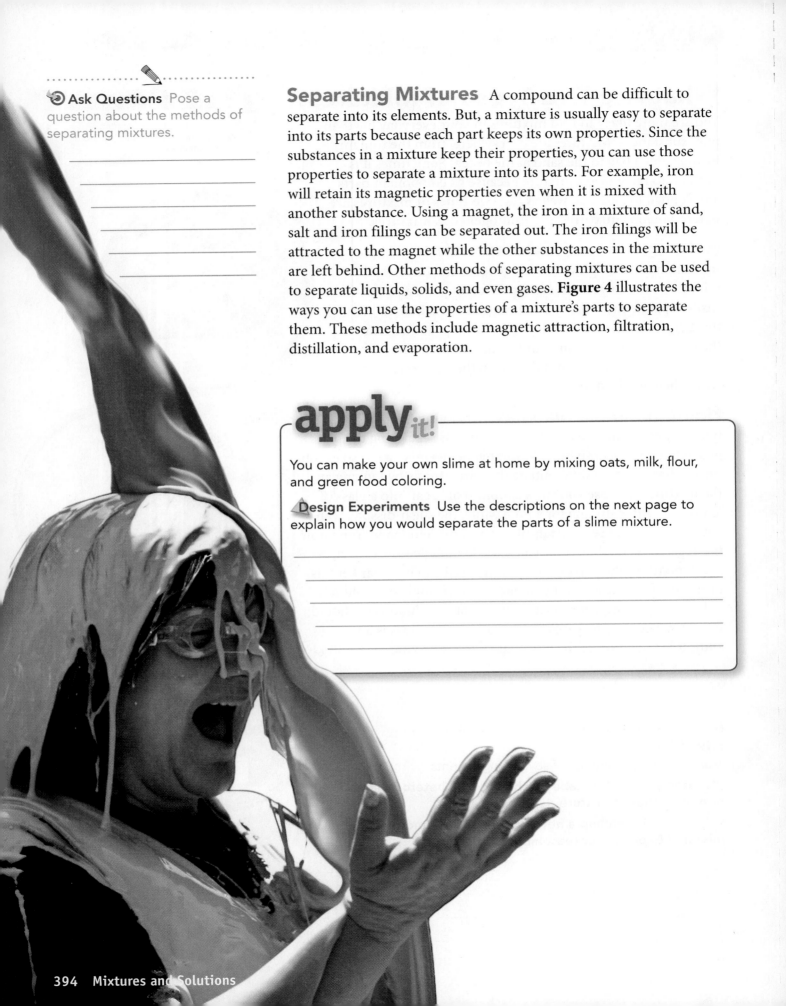

Separating Mixtures A compound can be difficult to separate into its elements. But, a mixture is usually easy to separate into its parts because each part keeps its own properties. Since the substances in a mixture keep their properties, you can use those properties to separate a mixture into its parts. For example, iron will retain its magnetic properties even when it is mixed with another substance. Using a magnet, the iron in a mixture of sand, salt and iron filings can be separated out. The iron filings will be attracted to the magnet while the other substances in the mixture are left behind. Other methods of separating mixtures can be used to separate liquids, solids, and even gases. **Figure 4** illustrates the ways you can use the properties of a mixture's parts to separate them. These methods include magnetic attraction, filtration, distillation, and evaporation.

apply it!

You can make your own slime at home by mixing oats, milk, flour, and green food coloring.

Design Experiments Use the descriptions on the next page to explain how you would separate the parts of a slime mixture.

_____

_____

_____

_____

_____

Sulfur and water mixture

Water

FIGURE 4 ··

> REAL-WORLD INQUIRY

Separating a Mixture

Various methods can be used to separate mixtures.

✎ **Identify** Using the list in the last sentence of the previous page, name the type of separation method being used in each photo.

Solids can be separated from liquids by pouring the mixture through a filter.

Iron objects can be separated from a mixture using a magnet.

Liquids can be separated from each other by heating them up to the temperature at which one of the liquids boils. The liquid boils into a gas. Then the gas cools, forming the separated liquid.

When left in the open air, liquid solutions can change to gas, leaving solid components behind.

Salt water → Table salt

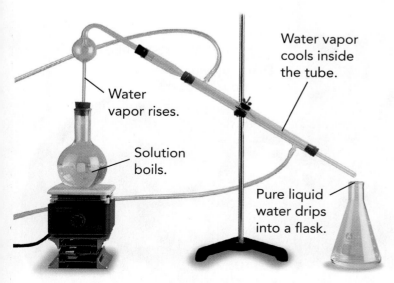

Water vapor rises.

Solution boils.

Water vapor cools inside the tube.

Pure liquid water drips into a flask.

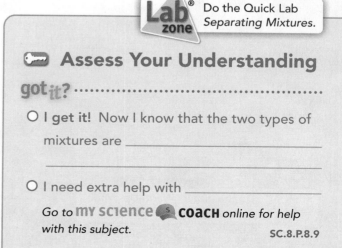

Lab zone Do the Quick Lab *Separating Mixtures.*

🔑 Assess Your Understanding

got it? ··

○ **I get it!** Now I know that the two types of mixtures are _____

_____

○ **I need extra help with** _____

Go to **MY SCIENCE** 🔍 **COACH** *online for help with this subject.*

SC.8.P.8.9

LESSON
2 Solutions

 How Are Mixtures Classified?
SC.8.N.2.1, SC.8.P.8.9, LA.8.2.2.3

 How Does a Solution Form?
SC.8.N.4.1, SC.8.P.8.9, MA.6.A.3.6

my planet diary

MISCONCEPTION

Killer Quicksand?

Misconception: You may have watched scenes in a movie like the one below. It's a common misconception that if you fall into a pit of quicksand, it is nearly impossible to escape its muddy clutches.

Fact: Although it is real, quicksand is not as deadly as it's often made out to be. Quicksand is a mixture of sand and water and is rarely more than a few feet deep. It forms when too much water mixes with loose sand. Water molecules surround the individual grains of sand, reducing the friction between them. The sand grains easily slide past each other and can no longer support any weight.

Fortunately, a human body is less dense than quicksand, which means you can float on it. By relaxing and lying on your back, you'll eventually float to the top.

Write your answer to the question below. SC.8.N.2.1

Quicksand can be frightening until you understand how it works. Describe something that seemed scary to you until you learned more about it.

_____

_____

_____

_____

_____

_____

_____

> **PLANET DIARY** Go to **Planet Diary** to learn more about solutions.

Lab zone Do the Inquiry Warm-Up *What Makes a Mixture a Solution?*

Vocabulary
- solution • solvent
- solute • colloid
- suspension

Skills
- Reading: Identify Supporting Evidence
- Inquiry: Interpret Data

How Are Mixtures Classified?

What do peanut butter, lemonade, and salad dressing have in common? All of these are examples of different types of mixtures. **A mixture is classified as a solution, colloid, or suspension based on the size of its largest particles.**

Solutions Grape juice is one example of a mixture called a solution. A **solution** is a mixture containing a solvent and at least one solute and has the same properties throughout. The **solvent** is the part of a solution usually present in the largest amount. It dissolves the other substances. The **solute** is the substance that is dissolved by the solvent. Solutes can be gases, liquids, or solids. Water is the solvent in grape juice. Sugar and other ingredients are the solutes. A solution has the same properties throughout. It contains solute, molecules or ions that are too small to see.

Water as a Solvent In many common solutions, the solvent is water. Water dissolves so many substances that it is often called the "universal solvent." Life depends on water solutions. Nutrients used by plants are dissolved in water in the soil. Water is the solvent in blood, saliva, sweat, urine, and tears.

FLORIDA NGSSS

SC.8.N.2.1 Distinguish between scientific and pseudoscientific ideas.

SC.8.P.8.9 Distinguish among mixtures (including solutions) and pure substances.

LA.8.2.2.3 The student will organize information, such as charting and comparing and contrasting, to show understanding or relationships.

apply it!

Soda Water (A)   Salt Water (B)   Grape Juice (C)

There are many common solutions in daily life.

1 Define In a solution, the substance present in the greatest amount is the (solute/solvent).

2 Infer Answer the questions below about the solutions shown above.

Which solution(s) has a gas solute? _____

In which solution(s) is water the solvent? _____

Which solution(s) has two or more solutes? _____

3 CHALLENGE What are some of the solutes in low-fat chocolate milk?

_____

_____

_____

_____

Other Solvents Although water is the most common solvent, it is certainly not the only one. Many solutions are made with solvents other than water, as shown in the table in **Figure 1.** For example, gasoline is a solution of several different liquid fuels. Solvents don't even have to be liquids. A solution may be a combination of gases, liquids, or solids. Air is an example of a solution that is made up of nitrogen, oxygen, and other gases. Solutions can even be made up of solids. Metal alloys like bronze, brass, and steel are solutions of different solid elements.

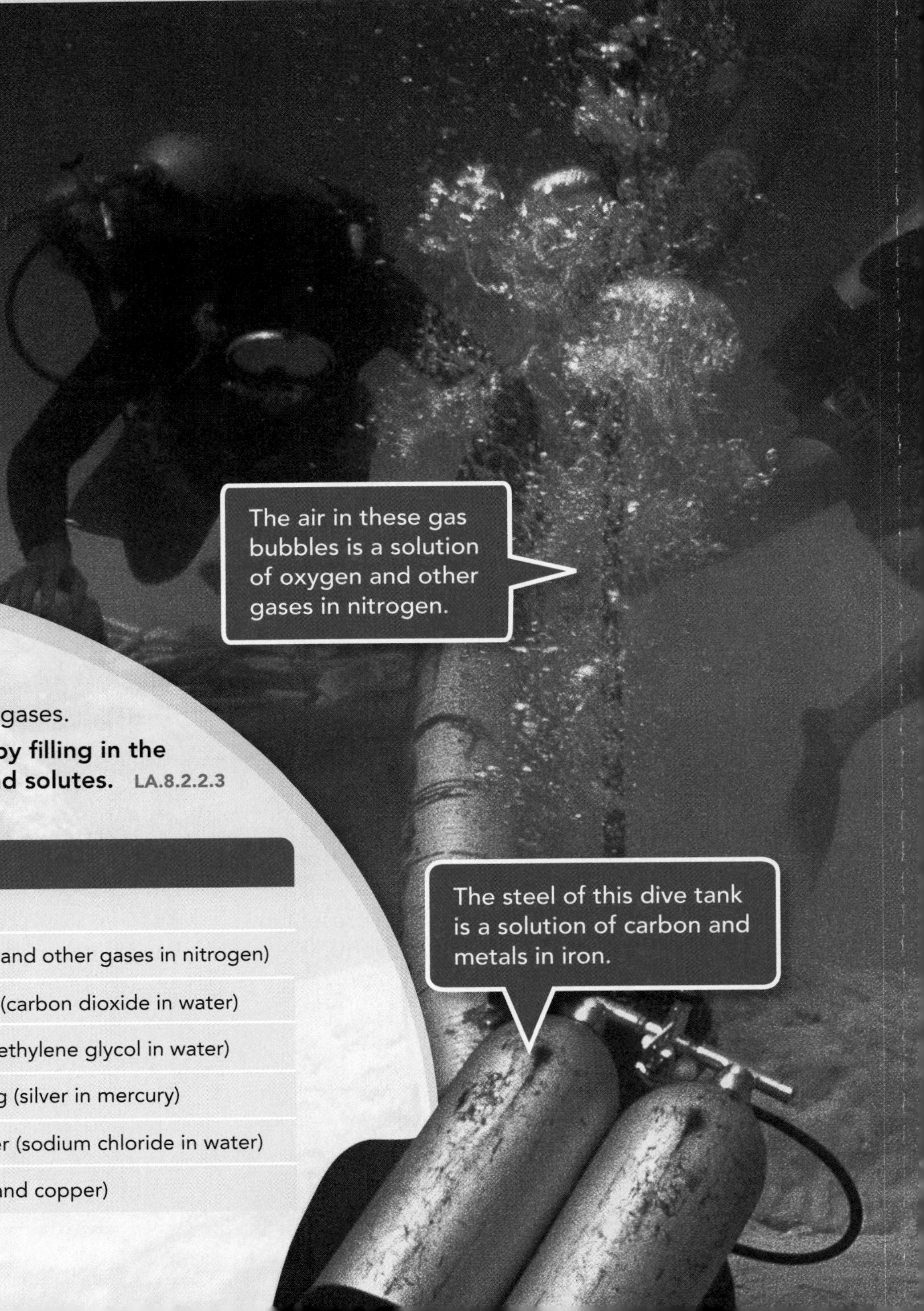

🔄 **Identify Supporting Evidence** Underline evidence in the text that shows water is not the only solvent.

Sea water is a solution of sodium chloride and other compounds in water.

The air in these gas bubbles is a solution of oxygen and other gases in nitrogen.

FIGURE 1 ·····································

Solutions

Solutions can be made from any combination of solids, liquids, and gases.

✏️ **Identify Complete the table by filling in the state of matter of the solvents and solutes.** LA.8.2.2.3

The steel of this dive tank is a solution of carbon and metals in iron.

Common Solutions		
Solute	Solvent	Solution
_____	_____	Air (oxygen and other gases in nitrogen)
_____	_____	Soda water (carbon dioxide in water)
Liquid	_____	Antifreeze (ethylene glycol in water)
_____	Liquid	Dental filling (silver in mercury)
_____	_____	Ocean water (sodium chloride in water)
Solid	_____	Brass (zinc and copper)

Colloids Not all mixtures are solutions. As shown in **Figure 2**, a **colloid** (KAHL oyd) is a mixture containing small, undissolved particles that do not settle out. The particles in a colloid are too small to be seen without a microscope, yet they are large enough to scatter a beam of light. For example, fog is a colloid that is made up of water droplets in air. Fog scatters the headlight beams of cars. Milk, shaving cream, and smoke are some other examples of colloids. Because they scatter light, most colloids are not clear, unlike many solutions.

Suspensions If you tried to mix sand in water, you would find that the sand never dissolves completely, no matter how much you stir it. Sand and water make up a suspension. A **suspension** (suh SPEN shun) is a mixture in which particles can be seen and easily separated by settling or filtration. Unlike a solution, a suspension does not have the same properties throughout. It contains visible particles that are larger than the particles in solutions or colloids.

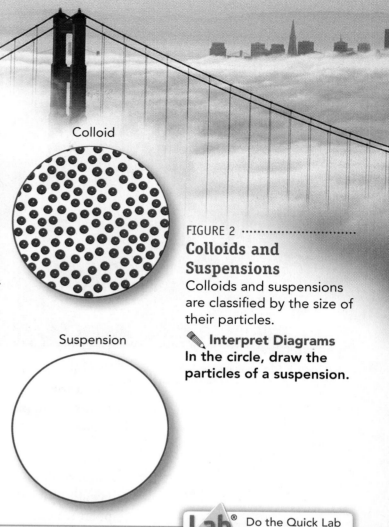

Colloid

Suspension

FIGURE 2 ·····························

Colloids and Suspensions
Colloids and suspensions are classified by the size of their particles.

✎ **Interpret Diagrams**
In the circle, draw the particles of a suspension.

Lab zone® Do the Quick Lab *Scattered Light*.

🔑 Assess Your Understanding

1a. Review What is a solution?

_____

_____

SC.8.P.8.9

b. Compare and Contrast How are colloids and suspensions different from solutions?

_____

_____

SC.8.P.8.9, LA.8.2.2.3

c. Distinguish Suppose you mix food coloring in water to make it blue. Have you made a solution or a suspension? Explain.

_____

_____

_____

_____

_____

SC.8.P.8.9

got it? ···

○ **I get it!** Now I know that classifying mixtures as solutions, colloids, and suspensions is based on _____

_____

○ **I need extra help with** _____

Go to MY SCIENCE S COACH *online for help with this subject.*

SC.8.P.8.9

FLORIDA NGSSS

SC.8.N.4.1 Explain that science is one of the processes that can be used to inform decision making at the community level.

SC.8.P.8.9 Distinguish among mixtures (including solutions) and pure substances.

MA.6.A.3.6 Analyze tables and graphs to describe simple relations.

FIGURE 3 ·······························

▶ INTERACTIVE ART

Forming a Solution

✎ **Sequence** Explain what occurs as sodium chloride, an ionic solid, dissolves in water.

How Does a Solution Form?

If it were possible to see the particles of a solution, you could see how a solute behaves when it's mixed in a solution. 🔑 **A solution forms when particles of the solute separate from each other and become surrounded by particles of the solvent.**

Ionic and Molecular Solutes **Figure 3** shows an ionic solid, sodium chloride (NaCl), mixed with water. The positive and negative ions of the solute are attracted to the partially charged polar water molecules. Eventually, water molecules will surround all of the ions and the solid crystal will be completely dissolved.

Molecular compounds, such as table sugar, break up into individual neutral molecules in water. The polar water molecules attract the polar sugar molecules. This causes the sugar molecules to move away from each other. The covalent bonds within the molecules remain unbroken.

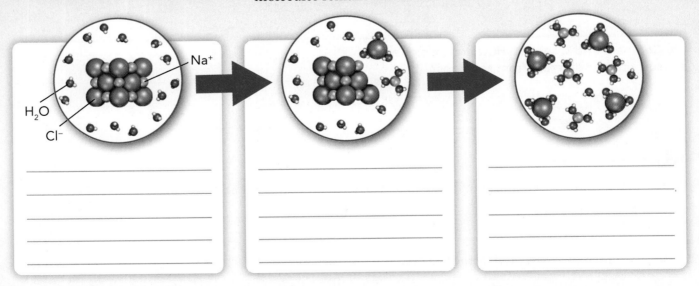

do the math! Analyzing Data

Airplane de-icing fluids are typically solutions of ethylene glycol in water. The freezing point of pure water is 0°C.

1 Explain How is the percent of ethylene glycol in de-icing fluid related to water's freezing point?

_____

_____

_____

2 Read Graphs How much does a 45% solution of de-icing fluid lower the freezing point of water?

_____

3 Interpret Data Would you allow a plane to take off in −20°C weather if it were de-iced with a solution of 30% ethylene glycol? Explain.

_____

_____

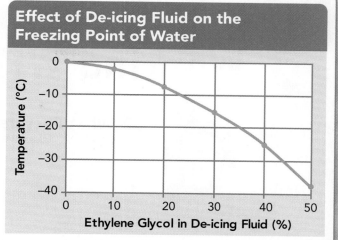

Effect of De-icing Fluid on the Freezing Point of Water

Temperature (°C) vs. Ethylene Glycol in De-icing Fluid (%)

MA.6.A.3.6, MA.8.A.6.4

Solutes and Conductivity
How could you find out if the solute of a water solution was salt or sugar? Ionic compounds in water conduct electric current, but a solution of molecular compounds may not. If ions are present, electric current will flow and you'll know the solute is salt.

Effects of Solutes
Solutes raise the boiling point of a solution above that of the solvent. As the temperature of a liquid rises, the molecules gain energy and escape as gas. In a liquid solution, the solute particles prevent the solvent molecules' escape. The temperature must go above the boiling point of the solvent in order for the solution to boil. However, the temperature increases only slightly and is not enough to cook food faster.

Solutes lower the freezing point of a solution below that of the solvent alone. When pure liquid water freezes at 0°C, the molecules pack together to form crystals of ice. In a solution, the solute particles get in the way of the water molecules forming ice crystals. The temperature must drop below 0°C in order for the solution to freeze.

Lab zone® Do the Lab Investigation *Speedy Solutions.*

🔑 Assess Your Understanding

2. Apply Concepts What benefits does sprinkling salt on icy roads give to drivers?

_____

_____

_____

_____

_____

SC.8.N.4.1, SC.8.P.8.9

got it? ....

○ **I get it!** Now I know that in a solution the particles of solute _____

_____

_____

○ **I need extra help with** _____

Go to **MY SCIENCE** S **COACH** online for help with this subject. SC.8.P.8.9

Working With Solubility

What Factors Affect Solubility?

SC.8.N.4.2, SC.8.P.8.9, LA.8.2.2.3

MY PLANET DIARY
for Florida

DISCOVERY

Even Whales Get the Bends

Decompression sickness, or "the bends" as it's commonly known, is a fear for many scuba divers. Under the extreme pressure of the deep ocean, nitrogen and other gases from the air dissolve in a diver's body tissues. If the diver rises too quickly, the sudden decrease in pressure causes the dissolved gas to bubble out of the tissue. The bubbles can enter a blood vessel and cause intense pain, and sometimes more severe injury.

But what if the diver is a whale? Previously, it was thought that whales did not suffer from the bends. Scientists have discovered evidence in beached whales off the coast of Florida of nitrogen bubbles expanding and damaging vital organs. It is believed that sonar waves from nearby ships in the coastal waters may have frightened the whales, causing them to surface too quickly. This can result in the bends.

Write your answers to the questions below.

1. Scientists have found small gashes in the bones of whale fossils, which are a sign of the bends. What conclusions can you draw from these fossils?

_____

_____

_____

_____

_____

2. Do you think restrictions should be placed on ships' sonar testing to protect whales? Why or why not?

_____

_____

_____

_____

_____

SC.8.N.4.2

> **PLANET DIARY** Go to **Planet Diary** to learn more about solubility.

Lab zone® Do the Inquiry Warm-Up *Does It Dissolve?*

Vocabulary

- dilute solution • concentrated solution
- solubility • saturated solution

Skills

↻ **Reading:** Identify the Main Idea

△ **Inquiry:** Calculate

What Factors Affect Solubility?

Suppose you add sugar to a cup of hot tea. If you add a small amount of sugar, the tea will not be very sweet. A mixture that has only a little solute dissolved in a certain amount of solvent is called a **dilute solution.** However, if you were to add a lot of sugar to sweeten the tea, it would become concentrated. A **concentrated solution** is a mixture that has a lot of solute dissolved in the solvent. But is there a limit to how sweet you can make the tea? Yes, at some point, no more sugar will dissolve. **Solubility** is a measure of how much solute can dissolve in a solvent at a given temperature. ➤ **Factors that can affect the solubility of a substance include pressure, the type of solvent, and temperature.**

When you've added so much solute that no more dissolves, you have a **saturated solution.** If you can continue to dissolve more solute in a solution, then the solution is unsaturated.

Working With Solubility

Look at the table in **Figure 1.** It compares the solubilities of familiar compounds in 100 grams of water at 20°C. You can see that only 9.6 grams of baking soda will dissolve in these conditions. However, 204 grams of table sugar will dissolve in the same amount of water at the same temperature.

Solubility can be used to help identify a substance. It is a characteristic property of matter. Suppose you had a white powder that looked like table salt or sugar. Since you never taste unknown substances, how could you identify the powder? You could measure its solubility in 100 grams of water at 20°C. Then compare the results to the data in **Figure 1** to identify the substance.

FIGURE 1 ·······

Solubility

Pickling requires saturated solutions of salt in water.

✎ △ **Calculate** Using the table, determine the amount of sodium chloride you would need to make pickles using 500 grams of water.

_____

_____

FLORIDA NGSSS

SC.8.N.4.2 Explain how political, social, and economic concerns can affect science, and vice versa.

SC.8.P.8.9 Distinguish among mixtures (including solutions) and pure substances.

LA.8.2.2.3 The student will organize information, such as representing key points to show understanding.

Vocabulary Identify Related Word Forms To concentrate is the verb form of the adjective concentrated. Write a sentence about solutions using the verb concentrate.

_____

_____

_____

_____

_____

Solubility in 100 g of Water at 20°C	
Compound	Solubility (g)
Baking soda (sodium bicarbonate, $NaHCO_3$)	9.6
Table salt (sodium chloride, NaCl)	35.9
Table sugar (sucrose, $C_{12}H_{22}O_{11}$)	204

Factors Affecting Solubility

You have already read that there is a limit to solubility. By changing certain conditions, you can change a substance's solubility.

Pressure The solubility of a gas solute in a liquid solvent increases as the pressure of the gas over the solution increases. To increase the carbon dioxide concentration in soda water, the gas is added to the liquid under high pressure. Opening the bottle or can reduces the pressure. The escaping gas makes the fizzing sound you hear.

Scuba divers must be aware of the effects of pressure on gases if they want to avoid decompression sickness. Under water, divers breathe from tanks of compressed air. The air dissolves in their blood in greater amounts as they dive deeper. If divers return to the surface too quickly, the gases can bubble out of solution. The bubbles can block blood flow. Divers double over in pain, which is why you may have heard this condition called "the bends."

Solvents Sometimes you just can't make a solution because the solute and solvent are not compatible, as shown in **Figure 2**. This happens with motor oil and water. Have you ever tried to mix oil and water? If so, you've seen how quickly they separate into layers after you stop mixing them. Oil and water separate because water is a polar compound and oil is nonpolar. Some polar and nonpolar compounds do not mix very well.

For liquid solutions, ionic and polar compounds usually dissolve in polar solvents. Nonpolar compounds do not usually dissolve in very polar solvents, but they will dissolve in nonpolar solvents.

◄ Polar water mixed with nonpolar motor oil

FIGURE 2 ···

Solvents and Solubility

Some polar and nonpolar compounds form layers when they are mixed together.

✎ CHALLENGE Determine which of these liquids are polar and which are nonpolar by the way they form layers or mix together. The first answer is given.

A. Polar

B. _____

C. _____

D. _____

E. _____

F. _____

Temperature For most solid solutes, solubility increases as temperature increases. For example, the solubility of table sugar in 100 grams of water at 0°C is 180 grams. However, the solubility increases to 231 grams at 25°C and 487 grams at 100°C.

Cooks use this increased solubility of sugar to make candy. At room temperature, not enough sugar for candy can dissolve in the water. Solutions must be heated for all the sugar to dissolve.

When heated, a solution can dissolve more solute than it can at cooler temperatures. If a heated, saturated solution cools slowly, the extra solute may remain dissolved to become a supersaturated solution. It has more dissolved solute than is predicted by its solubility at the given temperature. If you disturb a supersaturated solution, the extra solute will quickly come out of solution. You can see an example of a supersaturated solution in **Figure 3.**

Unlike most solids, gases become less soluble when the temperature goes up. For example, more carbon dioxide can dissolve in cold water than in hot water. If you open a warm bottle of soda water, carbon dioxide escapes the liquid in greater amounts than if the soda water had been chilled. Why does a warm soda taste "flat" when it's opened? It contains less gas. If you like soda water that's very fizzy, open it when it's cold!

FIGURE 3 ⋯⋯⋯⋯⋯⋯⋯⋯⋯⋯⋯⋯
Supersaturated Solution
Dropping a crystal of solute into a supersaturated solution causes the extra solute to rapidly come out of solution.

⋯⋯⋯⋯⋯⋯✏⋯⋯⋯⋯⋯⋯

✍ Identify the Main Idea
Underline the sentences on this page that explain how increasing temperature affects the solubility of both solid and gas solutes.

LA.8.2.2.3

apply it!

Crystallized honey, a supersaturated solution, can be more than 70 percent sugar.

❶ Calculate How many grams of sugar could be in 50 grams of crystallized honey?

❷ Develop Hypotheses How would you explain why certain types of honey rarely crystallize?

❸ CHALLENGE Is there a way to turn crystallized honey back into liquid honey? Explain.

EXPLORE THE ESSENTIAL ?

Cooking With Chemistry

What determines the properties of mixtures and pure substances?

FIGURE 4 ···

▶ INTERACTIVE ART At the Chemistry Café, mixtures and pure substances are found everywhere on the menu. In order to serve his customers, the chef must know the properties of both mixtures and pure substances.

✎ **Solve Problems** Use what you know about mixtures and pure substances to help the chef in the kitchen.

Quick Cooking!

The chef is in a hurry and needs the pasta to cook fast. He adds a handful of salt to the pot of water to raise the boiling point. Explain whether the chef's plan to cook the pasta faster will work or not.

_____

_____

_____

_____

_____

_____

Fizzy!

A customer orders sparkling water to drink, which is a combination of carbon dioxide (CO_2) and water (H_2O). Determine what parts of the drink are mixtures and which are pure substances. Explain.

_____

_____

_____

_____

_____

_____

Mix It Up!

The chef is making salad dressing with vinegar, olive oil, and pepper, but the ingredients are not mixing together. Why?

_____

_____

_____

_____

_____

Sweet!

The chef makes the best iced tea. His secret is to saturate the tea with sugar. Refer back to the table in **Figure 1** to determine how much sugar the chef will need if he wants to make 3,000 grams of tea at 20°C.

- ○ 1,470 grams
- ○ 6,120 grams
- ○ 14,700 grams
- ○ 61,200 grams

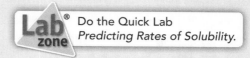

Lab zone Do the Quick Lab *Predicting Rates of Solubility.*

🔑 Assess Your Understanding

1a. Review How can you tell when a solution is saturated?

_____

_____

SC.8.P.8.9

b. Control Variables You are given two white powdery substances. How would you use solubility to identify them?

_____

_____

_____

_____

_____

_____

_____

SC.8.P.8.9

c. ANSWER THE ESSENTIAL ❓ What determines the properties of mixtures and pure substances?

_____

_____

_____

_____

_____

_____

_____

_____

SC.8.P.8.9

got it? ···

○ **I get it!** Now I know that the solubility of a substance can be affected by _____

_____

_____

○ **I need extra help with** _____

Go to MY SCIENCE ⑤ COACH *online for help with this subject.* SC.8.P.8.9

Solutions contain a _____ and at least one _____ . The solubility of a substance depends on _____ .

LESSON 1 Exploring Pure Substances and Mixtures

SC.8.P.8.9

🔑 Pure substances cannot be separated easily or sometimes, at all. Mixtures can be physically separated.

🔑 Two types of mixtures are heterogeneous mixtures and homogeneous mixtures.

Vocabulary
- pure substance • mixture
- heterogeneous mixture
- homogeneous mixture

LESSON 2 Solutions

SC.8.N.2.1, SC.8.N.4.1, SC.8.P.8.9

🔑 A mixture is classified as a solution, colloid, or suspension based on the size of its largest particles.

🔑 A solution forms when particles of the solute separate from each other and become surrounded by particles of the solvent.

Vocabulary
- solution • solvent • solute
- colloid • suspension

LESSON 3 Working With Solubility

SC.8.P.8.9

🔑 Factors that can affect the solubility of a substance include pressure, the type of solvent, and temperature.

Vocabulary
- dilute solution • concentrated solution
- solubility • saturated solution

Review and Assessment

LESSON 1 Exploring Pure Substances and Mixtures

1. Pancake syrup is an example of a

  a. homogeneous mixture.

  b. heterogeneous mixture.

  c. colloid.

  d. suspension.

  SC.8.P.8.9

2. The only way to separate a compound into its elements is by a _____

  SC.8.P.8.9

3. Summarize Four methods that can be used to separate mixtures are _____

  _____

  _____

  SC.8.P.8.9

4. Distinguish Which of the following is a pure substance: sugar, salt water, or pepper? Explain how you know.

  _____

  _____

  _____

  _____

  SC.8.P.8.9

5. Make Models Using blue spheres and red spheres, draw a model of a pure substance compound and a model of a mixture.

Compound	Mixture

  SC.8.P.8.9

LESSON 2 Solutions

6. Which of the following is an example of a solution?

  a. fog   **b.** soda water

  c. milk   **d.** mud

  SC.8.P.8.9

7. A mixture of pepper and water is a suspension because _____

  _____

  _____

  SC.8.P.8.9

8. Apply Concepts The table below shows the main components of Earth's atmosphere. What is the solvent in air? What are the solutes?

Composition of Earth's Atmosphere

Compound	Percent Volume
Argon (Ar)	0.93
Carbon dioxide (CO_2)	0.03
Nitrogen (N_2)	78.08
Oxygen (O_2)	20.95
Water vapor (H_2O)	0 to 3

  _____

  _____

  _____

  _____

  SC.8.P.8.9

9. Predict Suppose you put equal amounts of pure water and salt water into separate ice cube trays of the same size and shape. What would you expect to happen when you put both trays in the freezer? Explain.

  _____

  _____

  _____

  _____

  SC.8.P.8.9

LESSON 3 **Working With Solubility**

10. A solution in which no more solute can be added is

a. dilute.

b. concentrated.

c. saturated.

d. unsaturated.

SC.8.P.8.9

11. Most gases become more soluble in liquid as the temperature _____

SC.8.P.8.9

12. Interpret Diagrams Which of the diagrams below shows a dilute solution? Which one shows a concentrated solution? Explain.

Solution A

Solute particle

Solution B

Solvent particle

_____

_____

_____

_____

_____

SC.8.P.8.9

13. **Write About It** Imagine you work for a bottling company and the cola your company produces keeps coming out flat. Write an e-mail to your boss describing changes she should make in order to have the ideal conditions for bottling fizzy cola.

SC.8.P.8.9

APPLY THE ESSENTIAL

What determines the properties of mixtures and pure substances?

14. You are given three beakers of unidentified liquids. One beaker contains pure water. One contains salt water. One contains a mixture of rubbing alcohol and water. How could you use the methods of separation to identify the pure substance?

_____

_____

_____

_____

_____

_____

_____

_____

_____

_____

_____

_____

_____

_____

_____

_____

_____

SC.8.P.8.9

Florida Benchmarks Review

Circle the letter of the best answer.

1 Each diagram below represents a different kind of matter. Each ball represents an atom. Balls of the same size and shade are the same atom.

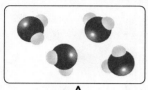

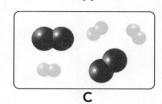
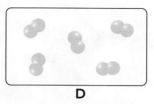

A   B

C   D

Which diagram **best** represents a mixture of two kinds of molecules?

A Diagram A   **B** Diagram B
C Diagram C   **D** Diagram D

SC.8.P.8.9

2 What is the best method for separating two different liquids that are mixed together?

A distillation
B filtration
C evaporation
D magnetic attraction

SC.8.P.8.9

3 Three sugar cubes are placed in a beaker containing 50 milliliters of water at 20°C. Which action would speed up the rate at which the sugar cubes dissolve in the water?

A Use less water.
B Transfer the contents to a larger beaker.
C Cool the water and sugar cubes to 5°C.
D Heat and stir the contents of the beaker.

SC.8.P.8.9

4 Why are candy sprinkles an example of a heterogenous mixture?

A The individual atoms are chemically bonded.
B It cannot be separated into its individual parts.
C The parts are so evenly mixed, it is difficult to differentiate them.
D It is easy to see and separate out its individual parts.

SC.8.P.8.9

5 A scientist mixes an unknown solid in water. He notices that the particles of the solid solute do not completely dissolve in the solvent and he could easily separate them out using filtration. Which of the following **best** describes this type of mixture?

A a solution
B a colloid
C a suspension
D a pure substance

SC.8.P.8.9

Use the diagram below and your knowledge of science to help you answer Question 6.

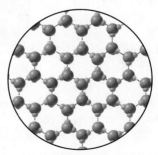
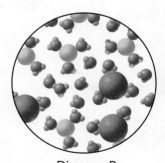

Diagram A   Diagram B

6 Which diagram represents a pure substance? Explain your reasoning.

A A; the atoms are chemically bonded together.
B A; the atoms are near each other but not bonded.
C B; the atoms are chemically bonded together.
D B; the atoms are near each other but not bonded.

SC.8.P.8.9

HOW DO BEES MAKE HONEY?

 How is matter conserved in physical and chemical changes?

Honeybees drink nectar from flowers. They store the nectar in a honey sac found inside their bodies. Nectar begins changing into honey in the honey sac. Nectar is mostly water, which evaporates during the honey-making process.

After collecting nectar, the honeybees return to the hive where they spit the nectar into the mouths of house bees. Chemicals in the mouths of the house bees continue changing the nectar into honey until it is ready to be stored in the honeycomb.

Draw Conclusions **Explain why bees must collect more nectar than actual honey that is produced.**

_____

_____

_____

> UNTAMED SCIENCE Watch the **Untamed Science** video to learn more about chemical reactions.

Chemical Reactions

FLORIDA Next Generation Sunshine State Standards

Big Idea 2: SC.8.N.2.2
Big Idea 3: SC.8.N.3.1
Big Idea 9: SC.8.P.9.1, SC.8.P.9.2, SC.8.P.9.3

Language Arts: LA.8.2.2.3
Mathematics: MA.6.A.3.6

12 Getting Started

Check Your Understanding

1. Background Read the paragraph below and then answer the question.

Alex is doing an experiment to see how vinegar reacts with **ionic compounds.** He measures the **mass** of a sample of baking soda. Alex records the measurement in his lab book next to the **chemical formula** for baking soda, $NaHCO_3$.

> An **ionic compound** consists of positive and negative ions.
>
> **Mass** is the amount of material in an object.
>
> A **chemical formula** shows the ratio of elements in a compound.

- Which substance is an ionic compound in the experiment that Alex is conducting?

_____

_____

> ► **MY READING WEB** If you had trouble completing the question above, visit **My Reading Web** and type in *Chemical Reactions.*

Vocabulary Skill

Identify Multiple Meanings Some familiar words have more than one meaning. Words you use every day may have different meanings in science.

Word	Everyday Meaning	Scientific Meaning
matter	*n.* a subject of discussion, concern, or action **Example:** We had an important *matter* to discuss in the meeting.	*n.* anything that has mass and takes up space **Example:** Solids, liquids, and gases are states of *matter.*
product	*n.* anything that is made or created **Example:** Milk and cheese are dairy *products.*	*n.* a substance formed as a result of a chemical reaction **Example:** In a chemical reaction, substances can combine or split up to form *products.*

LA.8.1.6.9

2. Quick Check Circle the sentence below that uses the scientific meaning of the word *product.*

- She brought napkins and other paper *products* to the picnic.
- Table salt is the *product* of the reaction of sodium and chlorine.

chemical change

law of conservation of mass

precipitate

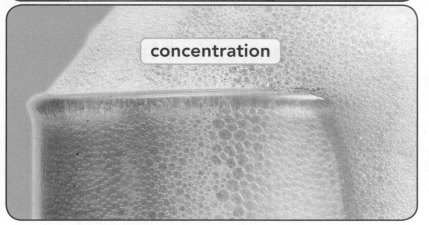

concentration

Chapter Preview

LESSON 1

- physical change
- chemical change
- reactant
- product
- law of conservation of mass
- exothermic reaction
- endothermic reaction
- precipitate

↻ **Compare and Contrast**
△ **Graph**

LESSON 2

- chemical equation
- coefficient

↻ **Summarize**
△ **Make Models**

LESSON 3

- activation energy
- concentration
- catalyst
- enzyme
- inhibitor

↻ **Ask Questions**
△ **Predict**

▷ **VOCAB FLASH CARDS** For extra help with vocabulary, visit **Vocab Flash Cards** and type in *Chemical Reactions.*

LESSON

1

Identifying Physical and Chemical Changes

UNLOCK THE ESSENTIAL ?

🔑 **How Can Changes in Matter Be Described?**
SC.8.N.2.2, SC.8.P.9.1, SC.8.P.9.2

🔑 **How Do You Tell a Chemical Change From a Physical Change?**
SC.8.P.9.2, LA.8.2.2.3, MA.6.A.3.6

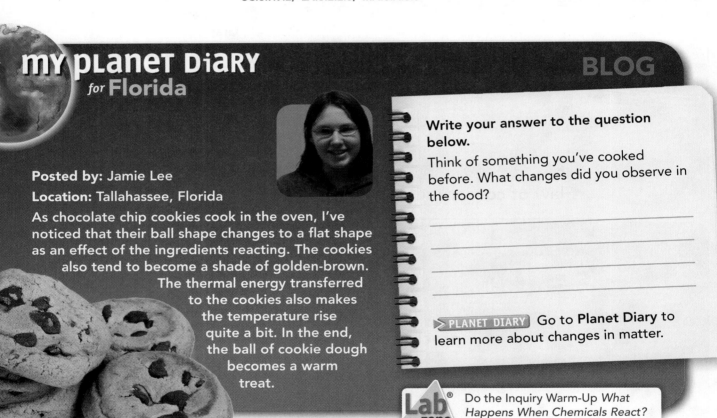

my pLaneT DiaRY for Florida

BLOG

Posted by: Jamie Lee
Location: Tallahassee, Florida

As chocolate chip cookies cook in the oven, I've noticed that their ball shape changes to a flat shape as an effect of the ingredients reacting. The cookies also tend to become a shade of golden-brown. The thermal energy transferred to the cookies also makes the temperature rise quite a bit. In the end, the ball of cookie dough becomes a warm treat.

Write your answer to the question below.

Think of something you've cooked before. What changes did you observe in the food?

_____

_____

_____

_____

> PLANET DIARY Go to **Planet Diary** to learn more about changes in matter.

Lab® **zone** Do the Inquiry Warm-Up *What Happens When Chemicals React?*

FLORIDA NGSSS

SC.8.N.2.2 Discuss what characterizes science and its methods.

SC.8.P.9.1 Explore the Law of Conservation of Mass by demonstrating and concluding that mass is conserved when substances undergo physical and chemical changes.

SC.8.P.9.2 Differentiate between physical and chemical changes.

How Can Changes in Matter Be Described?

Picture yourself frying an egg. You crack open the shell and the yolk and egg white spill into the pan. As the egg heats up, the white changes from a clear liquid to a white solid. The egg, the pan, and the stove are all examples of matter. Recall that matter is anything that has mass and takes up space. Matter is often described by its properties and how it changes.

Vocabulary

- physical change • chemical change • reactant • product
- law of conservation of mass
- exothermic reaction • endothermic reaction • precipitate

Skills

↻ Reading: Compare and Contrast

△ Inquiry: Graph

Changes in Matter

Like properties of matter, there are two types of changes in matter. ⊙ **Changes in matter can be described in terms of physical changes and chemical changes.** A physical change is any change that alters the form or appearance of a substance but does not change it into another substance. In a physical change, some of the physical properties of the material may be altered, but the chemical composition remains the same. Bending, crushing, and cutting are all physical changes. Changes in the state of matter, such as melting, freezing, and boiling, are also physical changes.

Sometimes when matter changes, its chemical composition is changed. For example, when a cut apple is left out in the air, it turns brown, as shown in **Figure 1**. Compounds in the apple react with the oxygen in the air to form new compounds. A change in matter that produces one or more new substances is a chemical change, or chemical reaction. When a substance undergoes a chemical change, it results in different physical properties as well. Burning and rusting are both chemical changes. Substances that undergo the chemical changes are called **reactants.** The new substances that form are the **products.**

FIGURE 1 ·······························

> **INTERACTIVE ART**

Changes in Matter

Matter can undergo both physical and chemical changes.

✎ **Differentiate** Label each apple with the type of change it has undergone.

FIGURE 2 ·······························

Physical and Chemical Changes

Changes in matter occur everywhere in your daily life.

✎ **Complete the tasks below.**

1. **Apply Concepts** Paper that has been (torn/burned) has undergone a chemical change.

2. **CHALLENGE** In the correct box, draw or explain how the palm frond will look if it undergoes a physical change and if it undergoes a chemical change.

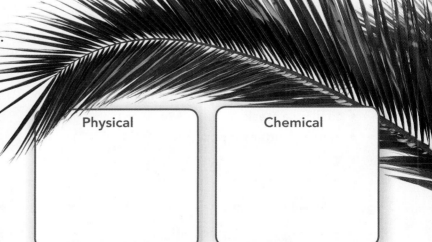

Physical

Chemical

FIGURE 3 ·····················

Conservation of Mass

✏ **Explore** Fill in the number of atoms of each element before and after the chemical change. Is mass conserved in this reaction? Explain.

_____

_____

_____

_____

Conservation of Mass

Does water disappear when it evaporates? Does a piece of paper weigh less when it's shredded into pieces? Scientists answered these questions long ago. In the 1770s, a French chemist, Antoine Lavoisier, measured mass both before and after a chemical change. His data showed that no mass was lost or gained during the change. The fact that matter is not created or destroyed in any chemical or physical change is called the **law of conservation of mass.** This law is also called the law of conservation of matter since mass is a measurement of matter.

Suppose you could measure all of the carbon dioxide and water produced when methane burns. You would find that it equals the mass of the original methane plus the mass of the oxygen from the air that was used in the burning. **Figure 3** demonstrates that during a chemical change, atoms are not lost or gained, only rearranged.

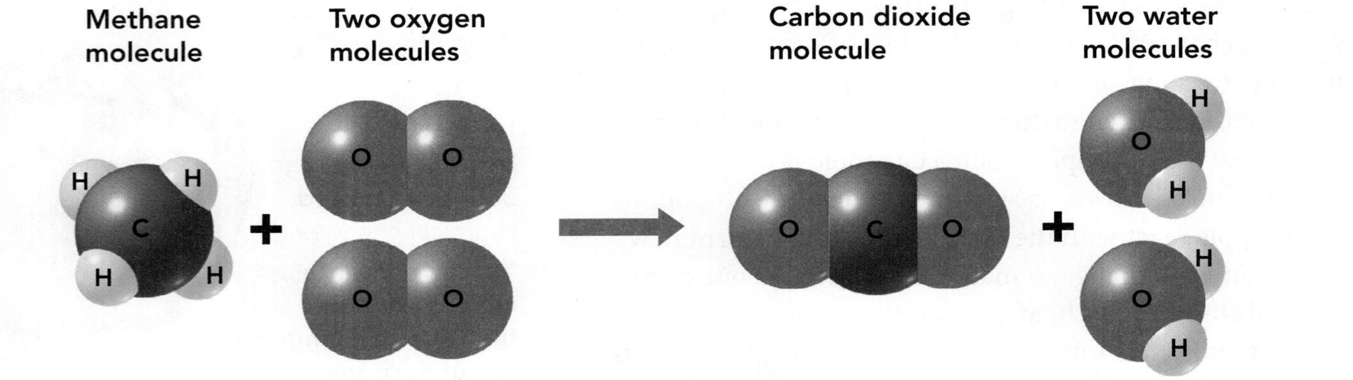

Methane molecule	Two oxygen molecules		Carbon dioxide molecule	Two water molecules

☐ Carbon atom(s)	☐ Hydrogen atom(s)	☐ Oxygen atom(s)	☐ Carbon atom(s)	☐ Hydrogen atom(s)	☐ Oxygen atom(s)

Lab® zone Do the Quick Lab *Observing Change.*

🔑 Assess Your Understanding

1a. Classify Circle the physical changes and underline the chemical changes listed below.

- drying wet clothes
- lighting a match from a matchbook
- cooking a steak
- melting butter for popcorn

SC.8.P.9.2

b. CHALLENGE Refer to Lavoisier's methods to explain why the mass of a rusted nail is greater than the mass of a nail before it rusted.

_____

_____

_____

SC.8.N.2.2, SC.8.P.9.1

got it? ···

○ **I get it!** Now I know that two types of changes in matter are _____

○ **I need extra help with** _____

Go to MY SCIENCE 🔊 COACH *online for help with this subject.* SC.8.P.9.1, SC.8.P.9.2

How Do You Tell a Chemical Change From a Physical Change?

How can you tell when a chemical change has occurred?
🔑 **Unlike a physical change, during a chemical change, a new substance is formed.** Evidence of a chemical change can include a change in energy and a change in chemical and physical properties.

Changes in Energy Chemical changes occur when bonds between atoms break and new bonds form. Breaking bonds requires energy, while forming bonds releases energy.

In an **exothermic reaction,** energy is released, usually as heat. For example, the reactions between oxygen and fuels that produce fire, such as wood or oil, are exothermic reactions.

Some chemical reactions require more energy than they release. **Endothermic reactions** absorb energy from nearby matter, which can cause the surroundings to become cooler. Baking soda undergoes an endothermic reaction when it is mixed with vinegar. The reaction absorbs energy so it feels cold. Some endothermic reactions occur only when heat is constantly added, as when you fry an egg.

 FLORIDA NGSSS

SC.8.P.9.2 Differentiate between physical and chemical changes.
LA.8.2.2.3 The student will organize information, such as comparing and contrasting, to show understanding.
MA.6.A.3.6 Construct and analyze tables and graphs to describe simple relations.

↪ **Compare and Contrast**
In the text, underline the details that describe the difference between endothermic and exothermic reactions. Then, describe how the two types of reactions are alike.

_____
_____
_____

LA.8.2.2.3

do the math! Analyzing Data

A student adds magnesium oxide to hydrochloric acid. She measures the temperature of the reaction every minute. Her data are recorded in the table.

❶ **Graph** Plot the data from the table onto the graph. Then name the graph.

❷ **Interpret Data** Is the reaction endothermic or exothermic? Explain.

_____
_____
_____
_____
_____

Time (min)	Temperature (°C)
0	20
1	24
2	27
3	29
4	29

❸ **Read Graphs** In which time interval did the temperature increase the most?

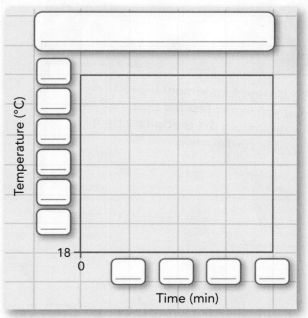

MA.6.A.3.6, MA.8.A.1.5

Vocabulary Identify Multiple Meanings Precipitation can mean rain, snow, or hail. In chemistry, precipitation is the formation of a solid from

_____

_____

Changes in Properties One way to detect chemical reactions is to observe changes in the physical properties of the materials. **Figure 4** shows some changes in properties that can result when new substances form. For instance, formation of a precipitate, gas production, and a color change are all possible evidence that a chemical reaction has taken place. Many times, physical properties such as texture and hardness also change in a chemical reaction.

Changes in physical properties can be easy to recognize in a chemical reaction, but what about the chemical properties? During a chemical reaction, reactants interact to form products with different chemical properties. For example, sodium (Na) and chlorine (Cl_2) react to form an ionic compound, sodium chloride (NaCl). Both reactants are very reactive elements. However, the product, sodium chloride, is a very stable compound.

Although you may observe a change in matter, the change does not always indicate that a chemical reaction has taken place. Sometimes physical changes give similar results. For example, when water boils, the gas bubbles you see are made of molecules of water, just as the liquid was. Boiling is a physical change. The only sure evidence of a chemical reaction is that one or more new substances are produced.

❶ Formation of a Precipitate

The mixing of two liquids may form a precipitate. A **precipitate** (pree SIP uh tayt) is a solid that forms from liquids during a chemical reaction. For example, the precipitate seen in this curdled milk has formed from the liquids milk and lemon juice.

FIGURE 4 ·····································

▷ VIRTUAL LAB **Evidence of Chemical Reactions**
Many kinds of change provide evidence that a chemical reaction has occurred.

Design Experiments Describe how you would test the best method for separating the precipitate from the liquid in curdled milk.

_____

_____

_____

_____

_____

_____

_____

❷ Gas Production

Another observable change is the formation of a gas from solid or liquid reactants. Often, the gas formed can be seen as bubbles.

✏️ **Observe** Bread dough rises from gas bubbles produced when yeast reacts with sugar. What evidence in a slice of bread shows the presence of gas?

_____
_____
_____
_____
_____

❸ Color Change

A color change can signal that a new substance has formed. For example, avocados turn brown when they react with oxygen in the air.

✏️ **Differentiate** Adding food coloring to water causes a color change. Is this a chemical or physical change? Explain.

_____
_____
_____
_____
_____

Lab ® zone   Do the Lab Investigation *Where's the Evidence?*

🔑 Assess Your Understanding

2. Apply Concepts What evidence of a chemical change is observed when wood burns?

_____
_____
_____

SC.8.P.9.2

got it? ....

O **I get it!** Now I know that during a chemical

change _____

_____

Go to **my science** 🅢 **coach** *online for help with this subject.*

SC.8.P.9.2

Describing Chemical Reactions

🔑 **What Information Does a Chemical Equation Contain?**
SC.8.N.3.1, SC.8.P.9.1, LA.8.2.2.3

🔑 **How Is Mass Conserved During Chemical and Physical Changes?**
SC.8.N.3.1, SC.8.P.9.1, LA.8.2.2.3

my planet diary

FUN FACTS

Lifesaving Reactions

What moves faster than 300 km/h, inflates in less than a second, and saves lives? An airbag, of course! Did you know that the "air" in an airbag is made by a chemical reaction? A compound called sodium azide (NaN_3) breaks down into sodium metal (Na) and nitrogen gas (N_2). The nitrogen gas fills the airbag and cushions the passengers in an accident.

It's important that the correct amount of sodium azide is used. The mass of sodium azide in the airbag before the collision will equal the mass of sodium and nitrogen that is made by the reaction. If too little or too much nitrogen gas is made, the airbag will not inflate properly.

Write your answer to the question below.

What might happen if an airbag doesn't contain the correct amount of sodium azide?

_____

_____

_____

_____

_____

▷ **PLANET DIARY** Go to **Planet Diary** to learn more about the law of conservation of mass.

 Do the Inquiry Warm-Up *Did You Lose Anything?*

FLORIDA NGSSS

SC.8.N.3.1 Select models useful in relating results of investigations.

SC.8.P.9.1 Explore the Law of Conservation of Mass in physical and chemical changes.

LA.8.2.2.3 The student will organize information, such as summarizing, to show understanding.

What Information Does a Chemical Equation Contain?

Cell phone text messages often use symbols and abbreviations to express ideas in shorter form. A type of shorthand is used in chemistry, too. A **chemical equation** is a way to show a chemical reaction, using symbols instead of words. Chemical equations are shorter than sentences, but they contain plenty of information. In chemical equations, chemical formulas and other symbols are used to summarize a reaction.

Vocabulary
- chemical equation
- coefficient

Skills
- Reading: Summarize
- Inquiry: Make Models

Formulas in an Equation

Recall that a chemical formula is a combination of symbols that represents the elements in a compound. CO_2 is the formula for carbon dioxide. It tells you that each carbon dioxide molecule has 1 carbon atom and 2 oxygen atoms. **Figure 1** lists the formulas of other familiar compounds.

Structure of an Equation

Suppose you are building some skateboards for your friends. **Figure 2** shows all the parts you will need. Similarly, a chemical equation summarizes everything needed for a chemical reaction. **A chemical equation tells you the substances you start with in a reaction or the reactants, and the new substances that are formed at the end, the products.**

Reactants are written on the left, followed by an arrow. You read the arrow as "yields." Products are written to the right of the arrow. When there are two or more reactants or products, they are separated by plus signs. The basic structure of a chemical equation is:

$$\text{Reactant} + \text{Reactant} \rightarrow \text{Product} + \text{Product}$$

The number of reactants and products can vary. For example, the reaction that occurs when calcium carbonate ($CaCO_3$) is heated has one reactant and two products (CaO and CO_2).

$$CaCO_3 \rightarrow CaO + CO_2$$

FIGURE 1
Chemical Formulas

The formula of a compound identifies the elements in the compound and the ratio in which their atoms or ions are present.

✎ **Interpret Tables Complete the table by filling in the missing chemical formulas.**

Formulas of Familiar Compounds	
Compound	Formula
Propane	C_3H_8
Sugar (sucrose)	$C_{12}H_{22}O_{11}$
Rubbing alcohol	C_3H_8O
Ammonia	NH_3
Baking soda	$NaHCO_3$
Water	_____
Carbon dioxide	_____
Sodium chloride	_____

FIGURE 2
Modeling a Chemical Equation

Like a skateboard, a chemical equation has a basic structure.

△ **Make Models Complete the equation by filling in the number of the skateboard parts shown. Determine the number of complete skateboards that can be made and draw them as the product.** SC.8.N.3.1

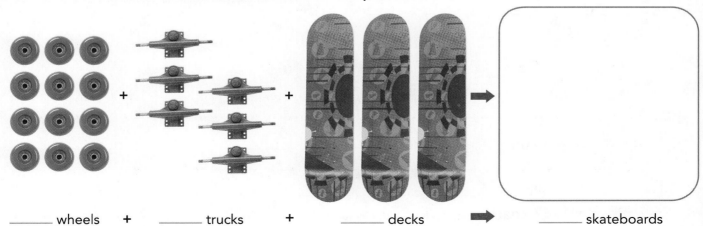

_____ wheels + _____ trucks + _____ decks ➡ _____ skateboards

apply it!

Molecules of nitrogen (N_2) and hydrogen (H_2) react to form ammonia (NH_3).

1 Identify Indicate the number of N_2 and H_2 molecules needed to yield two molecules of NH_3.

2 Make Models Draw the correct number of reactant molecules in the boxes on the left side of the equation.

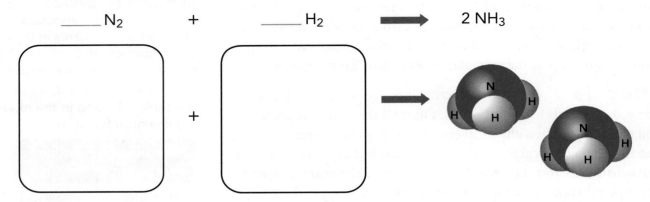

_____ N_2 +   _____ H_2 ➡ $2 NH_3$

+

3 CHALLENGE What bonds of the reactants are broken in this reaction? What bonds are formed in the product?

_____

_____

_____

_____

SC.8.N.3.1

Do the Quick Lab *Information in a Chemical Equation.*

🔑 Assess Your Understanding

1a. 🔄 Summarize What do the formulas, arrows, and plus signs tell you in a chemical equation?

_____

_____

_____

_____

_____

SC.8.P.9.1, LA.8.2.2.3

b. Interpret Data Write the chemical equation for the following reaction: The elements carbon and oxygen combine to yield the compound carbon dioxide.

_____

SC.8.P.9.1

got it?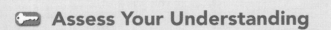

○ **I get it!** Now I know that a chemical equation tells you _____

_____

○ **I need extra help with** _____

    Go to MY SCIENCE ⑤ COACH *online for help with this subject.*

SC.8.P.9.1

How Is Mass Conserved During Chemical and Physical Changes?

Look at the reaction below in **Figure 3**. Iron and sulfur can react to form iron sulfide (FeS). Can you predict the mass of iron sulfide, knowing the mass of the reactants? It might help you to recall the law of conservation of mass. This principle, first demonstrated by the French chemist Antoine Lavoisier in 1774, states that matter is not created or destroyed during any physical or chemical change.

The idea of atoms explains the conservation of mass. 🔑 **All of the atoms present before a physical or chemical change are present after the change.** Atoms are not created or destroyed. However, they may be rearranged to form new substances or have their appearance altered. Look again at **Figure 3**. Suppose 1 atom of iron reacts with 1 atom of sulfur. At the end of the reaction, you have 1 iron atom bonded to 1 sulfur atom in the compound iron sulfide (FeS). All the atoms in the reactants are present in the products. The amount of matter does not change. According to the law of conservation of mass, the total mass stays the same before and after the reaction.

FLORIDA NGSSS

SC.8.N.3.1 Select models useful in relating results of investigations.

SC.8.P.9.1 Explore the Law of Conservation of Mass in physical and chemical changes.

LA.8.2.2.3 The student will organize information, such as summarizing, to show understanding.

did you know?

Antoine Lavoisier is known as the father of modern chemistry, but he was also a lawyer and a tax collector. Despite his support for reform, his connection to tax collection led to his unfortunate beheading in 1794 during the French Revolution.

FIGURE 3 ·······························

> INTERACTIVE ART **Conservation of Mass**

In a chemical reaction, matter is not created or destroyed.

✎ **Calculate** On the balance, write the mass of iron sulfide produced by this reaction.

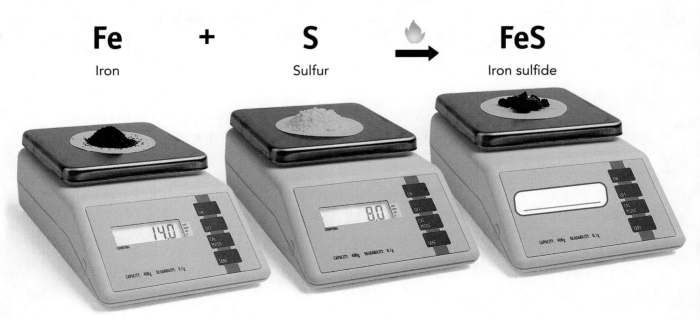

Fe + S 🔥➡ FeS

Iron   Sulfur   Iron sulfide

Balancing Chemical Equations The principle of conservation of mass means that the total number of atoms of each element in the reactants must equal the total number of atoms of each element in the products. To be accurate, a chemical equation must show the same number of atoms of each element on both sides of the equation. Chemists say an equation is balanced when conservation of mass is correctly shown. How can you write a balanced chemical equation?

STEP 1 Write the Equation Suppose you want to write a balanced chemical equation for the reaction between hydrogen and oxygen that forms water. To begin, write the correct chemical formulas for both reactants and the product. Place the reactants, H_2 and O_2, on the left side of the arrow, separated by a plus sign. Then write the product, H_2O, on the right side of the arrow.

Hydrogen	+	Oxygen	→	Water

STEP 2 Count the Atoms Count the number of atoms of each element on each side of the equation. Recall that a subscript tells you the ratio of elements in a compound.

Hydrogen atom(s) + Oxygen atom(s) → Hydrogen atom(s) / Oxygen atom(s)

After counting, you find 2 atoms of oxygen in the reactants but only 1 atom of oxygen in the product. How can the number of oxygen atoms on both sides of the equation be made equal? You cannot change the formula for water to H_2O_2 because H_2O_2 is the formula for hydrogen peroxide, a completely different compound. So how can you show that mass is conserved?

STEP 3 **Use Coefficients to Balance Atoms** To balance the equation, use coefficients. A **coefficient** (koh uh FISH unt) is a number placed in front of a chemical formula in an equation. It tells you the amount of a reactant or a product that takes part in a reaction. The coefficient applies to every atom of the formula it is in front of. If the coefficient is 1, you don't need to write it.

Balance the number of oxygen atoms by changing the coefficient of H_2O to 2. Again, count the number of atoms on each side of the equation.

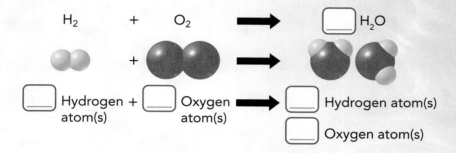

H_2 + O_2 ⟶ ☐ H_2O

☐ Hydrogen + ☐ Oxygen ⟶ ☐ Hydrogen atom(s)
atom(s)   atom(s)   ☐ Oxygen atom(s)

Balancing the oxygen atoms "unbalances" the number of hydrogen atoms. There are now 2 hydrogen atoms in the reactants and 4 in the product. How can you balance the hydrogen? Try changing the coefficient of H_2 to 2. Then, count the atoms again.

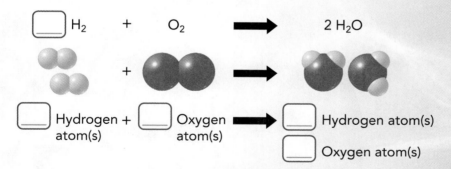

☐ H_2 + O_2 ⟶ 2 H_2O

☐ Hydrogen + ☐ Oxygen ⟶ ☐ Hydrogen atom(s)
atom(s)   atom(s)   ☐ Oxygen atom(s)

STEP 4 **Look Back and Check** Is the number of atoms of each element in the reactants equal to the number of atoms of each element in the products? If so, mass is conserved and the equation is balanced. The balanced equation tells you 2 hydrogen molecules react with 1 oxygen molecule to yield 2 water molecules.

✏️

🔁 **Summarize** Describe the steps to balancing a chemical equation.

_____
_____
_____
_____
_____
_____
_____
_____
_____
LA.8.2.2.3

do the
math! Sample Problem
....

Apply Concepts Balance the equations.

❶ $KClO_3$ ⟶ $KCl + O_2$
_____

❷ $NaBr + Cl_2$ ⟶ $NaCl + Br_2$
_____

❸ $Na + Cl_2$ ⟶ $NaCl$
_____

❶ Write the equation.
Mg + O$_2$ ⟶ MgO

❷ Count the atoms.
Mg + O$_2$ ⟶ MgO
  1   2   1 1

❸ Use coefficients to balance.
2 Mg + O$_2$ ⟶ 2 MgO
   2   2   2 2

❹ Look back and check.
MA.6.A.3.6

How Can Chemical Reactions Generate *SPEED*?

How is matter conserved in physical and chemical changes?

FIGURE 4 ···

> **INTERACTIVE ART** One day, you might be able to drink the exhaust from your car! Sounds gross, right? Well, it could be possible with hydrogen fuel cells. Hydrogen fuel cells use a chemical reaction between hydrogen and oxygen to generate energy for running a car. In the process, water is produced.

✎ **Review** Use what you've learned about chemical reactions to answer questions about fuel cells.

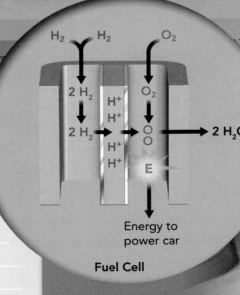

1 **Endothermic or Exothermic?**
The reaction in a fuel cell is used to power cars and other devices. Is it an endothermic or exothermic reaction? Explain.

2 **Conservation of Mass**
Inside a fuel cell, hydrogen is converted into H^+ ions. These ions combine with oxygen to produce energy for the car and water as exhaust. Describe how the fuel cell obeys the law of conservation of mass.

H_2 H_2 O_2

$2\ H_2$ O_2

H^+
H^+

$2\ H_2$ O $2\ H_2O$
O

H^+
H^+

E

Energy to power car

Fuel Cell

Hydrogen gas

3 Changes

When hydrogen gas forms liquid water in a fuel cell, it undergoes both physical and chemical changes. Describe both types of changes the hydrogen undergoes.

Physical:

_____

_____

Chemical:

_____

_____

4 Balance the Chemical Equation

Hydrogen must be obtained from decomposing fuels like methane (CH_4). Balance the equation for generating hydrogen for fuel cells.

$$CH_4 + H_2O \rightarrow CO + H_2$$

_____

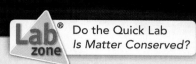

Do the Quick Lab
Is Matter Conserved?

🔑 Assess Your Understanding

2a. Infer If the total mass of the products in a reaction is 90 grams, what was the total mass of the reactants?

_____

SC.8.P.9.1

b. Demonstrate Explore the law of conservation of mass by balancing the equations.

- $Al + CuO \rightarrow Al_2O_3 + Cu$
- $Fe_2O_3 + C \rightarrow Fe + CO_2$
- $SO_2 + O_2 \rightarrow SO_3$

_____

_____

_____

SC.8.P.9.1

c. How is matter conserved in physical and chemical changes?

_____

_____

_____

_____

_____

_____

_____

SC.8.P.9.1

got it? ·

○ **I get it!** Now I know that during a physical change or chemical change, the mass of the reactants must _____

_____

○ **I need extra help with** _____

Go to **MY SCIENCE 🅢 COACH** *online for help with this subject.* SC.8.P.9.1

Controlling Chemical Reactions

🔑 **How Do Reactions Get Started?**
SC.8.P.9.3, MA.6.A.3.6

🔑 **What Affects the Rate of a Chemical Reaction?**
SC.8.P.9.3, LA.8.2.2.3

my planet Diary
for Florida

FIELD TRIP

Site: Kennedy Space Center

Location: Cape Canaveral, Florida

"We are a go for launch...start ignition...3, 2, 1, liftoff!" These might be the words of mission control as a rocket prepares to launch from NASA's Kennedy Space Center at Cape Canaveral. Rockets rely on the thrust of high speed, high pressure gas to launch. But where does that gas and the energy contained within it come from? Rocket fuels are often combusted, or burned, in the presence of chemicals like oxygen to produce thrust. This exothermic reaction produces gas and huge amounts of energy that help launch the rocket into space. This same type of reaction also powers cars, burns wood in your fireplace, and makes fireworks explode.

Communicate **Write your answer to the question below. Then discuss your answer with a partner.**

Rocket launches are often cancelled, or "scrubbed," if conditions are not exactly right for a launch. Why do you think the situation must be ideal to begin the reaction that launches a rocket?

_____

_____

_____

_____

Lab zone® Do the Inquiry Warm-Up *Can You Speed Up or Slow Down a Reaction?*

▶ **PLANET DIARY** Go to **Planet Diary** to learn more about controlling chemical reactions.

Vocabulary
- activation energy
- concentration
- catalyst
- enzyme
- inhibitor

Skills
- ⟳ Reading: Ask Questions
- △ Inquiry: Predict

How Do Reactions Get Started?

Suppose you're a snowboarder, like the one shown in **Figure 1.** You know that the only way to ride down the mountain is to first get to the top. One way to get there is by riding the chairlift. Once you reach the top of the mountain, you can get off the lift and enjoy the ride down. If you never get to the top, you will never be able to go down the mountain.

Activation Energy Chemical reactions can be like snow-boarding. A reaction won't begin until the reactants have enough energy to push them to the "top of the mountain." The energy is used to break the chemical bonds of the reactants. Then the atoms form the new bonds of the products. **Activation energy** is the minimum amount of energy needed to start a chemical reaction. 🔑 **All chemical reactions need a certain amount of activation energy to get started.** Usually, once a few molecules react, the rest will quickly follow. The first few reactions provide the activation energy for more molecules to react.

Hydrogen and oxygen can react to form water. However, if you just mix the two gases together, nothing happens. For the reaction to start, activation energy must be added. An electric spark or adding heat can provide that energy. A few of the hydrogen and oxygen molecules will react, producing energy. That energy will provide the activation energy needed for even more molecules to react.

FLORIDA NGSSS

SC.8.P.9.3 Investigate and describe how temperature influences chemical changes.

MA.6.A.3.6 Construct and analyze graphs to describe simple relations.

✏️ ⟳ **Ask Questions** Is it clear where chemical reactions get activation energy from? Write a question about this topic that you want answered.

_____

_____

_____

_____

_____

FIGURE 1 ⋯⋯⋯⋯⋯⋯⋯
Activation Energy
✏️ A chemical reaction needs a push to the "top of the mountain" to get started.

1. **Infer** Place an arrow at the point where enough activation energy has been added to start the reaction.

2. **Interpret Diagrams** Where does the snowboarder get the activation energy needed to reach the top of the mountain?

_____

431

Graphing Changes in Energy Every chemical reaction needs activation energy to start. Whether or not a reaction still needs more energy from the environment to keep going depends on whether it is exothermic or endothermic.

Exothermic reactions follow the pattern you can see in **Figure 2A.** The dotted line marks the energy of the reactants before the reaction begins. The peak on the graph shows the activation energy. Notice that at the end of the reaction, the products have less energy than the reactants. This type of reaction results in a release of energy. The burning of fuels, such as wood, natural gas, or oil, is an example of an exothermic reaction.

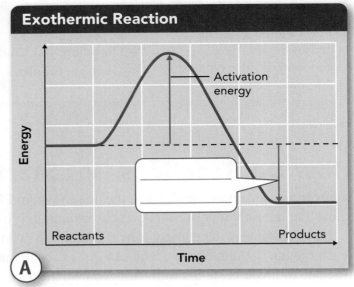

A

FIGURE 2 ....

>ART IN MOTION **Graphs of Exothermic and Endothermic Reactions**
Each of the graphs shows the amount of energy before and after the reaction.

✎ **Analyze Graphs** On each graph, label whether energy is absorbed or released. MA.6.A.3.6

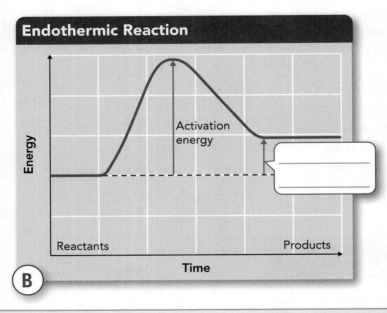

B

Now look at the graph of an endothermic reaction in **Figure 2B.** Endothermic reactions also need activation energy to get started. In addition, they need energy to continue. Notice that the energy of the products is greater than the energy of the reactants. This means that the reaction must continually absorb energy to keep going. Some endothermic reactions draw energy from the surroundings, leaving the area feeling cold. However, most endothermic reactions require continuous energy. For example, cooking a hamburger requires adding energy constantly until the meat is done.

Lab zone Do the Quick Lab Modeling Activation Energy.

🔑 **Assess Your Understanding**

got it? ....

○ **I get it!** Now I know that in order for reactions to get started _____

_____

○ **I need extra help with** _____

Go to **MY SCIENCE COACH** *online for help with this subject.* SC.8.P.9.3

What Affects the Rate of a Chemical Reaction?

Chemical reactions don't all occur at the same rate. Some, like explosions, are very fast. Others, like the rusting of iron in air, are slow. A particular reaction can occur at different rates depending on the conditions.

If you want to make a chemical reaction happen faster, the particles of the reactants need to collide either more quickly or with more energy. Also, if more particles are available to react, the reaction will happen faster. To slow down a reaction, you need to do the opposite. **Factors that can affect rates of reactions include surface area, temperature, concentration, and the presence of catalysts and inhibitors.**

Surface Area
Look at the burning building in **Figure 3**. It used to be a sugar factory. The factory exploded when sugar dust ignited in the air above the stored piles of sugar. Although the sugar itself doesn't react violently in air, the dust can. This difference is related to surface area. When a piece of solid substance reacts with a liquid or gas, only the particles on the surface of the solid come into contact with the other reactant. If you break the solid into smaller pieces, more particles are exposed to the surface and the reaction happens faster. Speeding up a reaction by increasing surface area can be dangerous, but it can also be useful. For example, chewing your food breaks it into smaller pieces that your body can digest more easily and quickly.

FLORIDA NGSSS

SC.8.P.9.3 Investigate and describe how temperature influences chemical changes.

LA.8.2.2.3 The student will organize information, such as comparing and contrasting, to show understanding.

do the math!

To find the surface area of a cube with 2-cm-long sides, find the area of each face of the cube.

Area = Length × Width

$$4 \text{ cm}^2 = 2 \text{ cm} \times 2 \text{ cm}$$

Then add them together.

$$4 \text{ cm}^2 + 4 \text{ cm}^2 + 4 \text{ cm}^2 + 4 \text{ cm}^2 + 4 \text{ cm}^2 + 4 \text{ cm}^2 = 24 \text{ cm}^2$$

Imagine cutting the cube in half. Find the surface area of each half. Add the values together to get the total surface area.

_____

_____

_____

_____

_____

MA.8.A.6.4

FIGURE 3 ··

Surface Area and Reaction Rate
Sugar dust can react quickly because it has a greater surface area than a pile of sugar. A chemical reaction that moves quickly can cause an explosion.

apply it!

A chemical reaction takes place in glow sticks. Changing the temperature affects the rate of the reaction.

1 Relate Cause and Effect When the temperature increases, the rate of a chemical reaction (increases/decreases).

2 Predict The brightness of a glow stick's light is affected by temperature. What would happen if the glow stick were placed in boiling water?

_____

_____

3 CHALLENGE The military uses glow sticks for lighting at night. Suggest a method for storing them during the day to maximize their use at night.

_____

_____

_____

_____

Temperature

Changing the temperature of a chemical reaction also affects the reaction rate. When you heat a substance, its particles move faster. Faster-moving particles have more energy, which helps reactants get over the activation energy barrier more quickly. Also, faster-moving particles come in contact more often, giving more chances for a reaction to happen.

In contrast, reducing temperature slows down reaction rates. For example, milk contains bacteria, which carry out thousands of chemical reactions as they live and reproduce. You store milk and other foods in the refrigerator because keeping foods cold slows down those reactions, so your foods stay fresh longer.

Concentration

Another way to increase the rate of a chemical reaction is to increase the concentration of the reactants. **Concentration** is the amount of a substance in a given volume. For example, adding a small spoonful of sugar to a cup of tea will make it sweet. Adding a large spoonful of sugar makes the tea even sweeter. The cup of tea with more sugar has a greater concentration of sugar molecules.

Increasing the concentration of reactants supplies more particles to react. Look at the tower of bubbles in **Figure 4.** This is the product of the decomposition reaction of a 35 percent hydrogen peroxide solution in water. Hydrogen peroxide that you buy at your local drug store is usually between 3 percent and 12 percent. The high concentration of hydrogen peroxide solution used in this reaction will release huge amounts of oxygen gas more quickly than a lower concentration would.

FIGURE 4 ·······

Elephant Toothpaste

This reaction (above right) is nicknamed "elephant toothpaste" because of the enormous amount of bubbles it produces.

Predict How would using a lower concentration of hydrogen peroxide affect the rate of reaction?

_____

_____

_____

_____

Catalysts and Inhibitors Another way to control the rate of a reaction is to change the activation energy needed. A **catalyst** (KAT uh list) increases the reaction rate by lowering the activation energy needed. Although catalysts affect a reaction's rate, they are not permanently changed by a reaction and are not considered reactants.

Many chemical reactions can normally only happen at temperatures that would kill living things. Yet, some of these reactions are necessary for life. The cells in your body contain thousands of biological catalysts called **enzymes** (EN zymz) that help these reactions occur at body temperature. Each one is specific to only one chemical reaction. Enzymes provide a surface on which reactions can take place. Since enzymes bring reactant molecules close together, chemical reactions using enzymes require less activation energy and can happen at lower temperatures.

Sometimes it is more useful to slow down a reaction rather than speed it up. A material used to decrease the rate of a chemical reaction is an **inhibitor**. Inhibitors called preservatives are added to food to prevent spoiling.

FIGURE 5 ·······························
Catalysts
Adding a catalyst speeds up a chemical reaction.

✎ **Graph** Draw and label the energy graph for the same chemical reaction when using a catalyst.

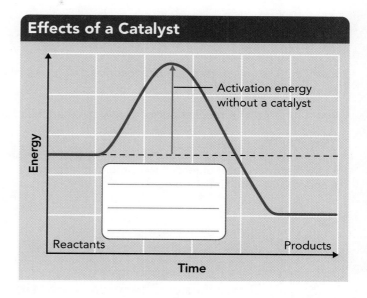

Effects of a Catalyst

Energy

Activation energy without a catalyst

Reactants

Products

Time

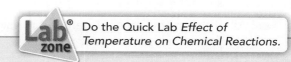
Do the Quick Lab *Effect of Temperature on Chemical Reactions.*

🔑 Assess Your Understanding

1a. Review To slow down a reaction, you can (increase/decrease) the concentration of the reactants.

SC.8.P.9.3

b. Compare and Contrast What would react more quickly in the air, a pile of grain or a cloud of grain dust? Explain.

_____

_____

SC.8.P.9.3, LA.8.2.2.3

c. Describe Explain two ways temperature influences the rate of a chemical reaction.

_____

_____

_____

_____

_____

SC.8.P.9.3

got**it?** ···

○ **I get it!** Now I know that the rate of a chemical reaction can be affected by_____

_____

○ **I need extra help with** _____

Go to MY SCIENCE 🅢 COACH *online for help with this subject.*

SC.8.P.9.3

12 Study Guide

The total mass of reactants before a chemical or physical change equals _____

LESSON 1 Observing Changes in Matter
SC.8.N.2.2, SC.8.P.9.1, SC.8.P.9.2

🔑 Changes in matter can be described in terms of physical and chemical changes.

🔑 During a chemical change, a new substance is formed.

Vocabulary
- physical change • chemical change • reactants • products
- law of conservation of mass • exothermic reaction
- endothermic reaction • precipitate

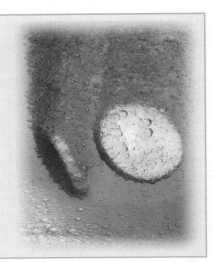

LESSON 2 Describing Chemical Reactions
SC.8.N.3.1, SC.8.P.9.1

🔑 A chemical equation tells you the substances you start with in a reaction and the substances that are formed at the end.

🔑 All of the atoms present before a physical or chemical change are present after the change.

Vocabulary
- chemical equation • coefficient

$2 H_2$ + O_2 → $2 H_2O$

LESSON 3 Controlling Chemical Reactions
SC.8.P.9.3

🔑 All chemical reactions need a certain amount of activation energy to get started.

🔑 Factors that can affect rates of reactions include surface area, temperature, concentration, and the presence of catalysts and inhibitors.

Vocabulary
- activation energy • concentration
- catalyst • enzyme • inhibitor

Review and Assessment

LESSON 1 Observing Changes in Matter

1. Which of the following results in a chemical change in matter?

a. bending a straw **b.** boiling water

c. braiding hair **d.** burning wood

SC.8.P.9.2

2. A solid that forms from liquids in a chemical reaction is called a(n) _____

SC.8.P.9.2

3. Interpret Photos What evidence in this photo tells you that a chemical reaction may have occurred?

_____

_____

SC.8.P.9.2

4. Apply Concepts Suppose you measure the mass of the banana before it rots. You measure the mass again days later after the banana has turned black and find that the mass is less. Use the law of conservation of mass to conclude what happened to the mass of the banana.

_____

_____

_____

_____

SC.8.P.9.1, SC.8.P.9.2

5. Write About It Suppose you have an Internet friend who is studying chemistry just like you are. Your friend claims the change from liquid water to water vapor is a chemical change. Write a brief e-mail that might convince your friend otherwise.

SC.8.P.9.2

LESSON 2 Describing Chemical Reactions

6. How can you balance a chemical equation?

a. Change the coefficients.

b. Change the products.

c. Change the reactants.

d. Change the subscripts.

SC.8.P.9.1

7. The law of conservation of mass states that

_____

_____

_____

_____

SC.8.P.9.1

8. Interpret Diagrams Name the reactants and products for the following chemical equation. Underline the coefficients and circle the subscripts.

$$N_2 + 3\,H_2 \rightarrow 2\,NH_3$$

_____

_____

SC.8.P.9.1

9. Calculate A reaction between lithium (Li) and chlorine (Cl) uses 42 grams of lithium to produce 80 grams of lithium chloride (LiCl). How many grams of chlorine were used?

_____

SC.8.P.9.1

10. math! Demonstrate the law of conservation of mass by balancing the following equations.

$MgO + HBr \rightarrow MgBr_2 + H_2O$

$N_2 + O_2 \rightarrow N_2O_5$

$C_2H_4 + O_2 \rightarrow CO_2 + H_2O$

$Fe + HCl \rightarrow FeCl_2 + H_2$

SC.8.P.9.1

CHAPTER
12

LESSON 3 Controlling
Chemical Reactions

11. In general, what happens when you increase
the temperature of a reaction?

   a. The heat destroys the reactants.

   b. The rate of the reaction decreases.

   c. The rate of the reaction increases.

   d. The rate of the reaction stays the same.

SC.8.P.9.3

Graphs A and B represent the same chemical
reaction under different conditions. Use the
graphs to answer Questions 12 and 13.

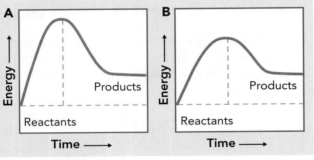

SC.8.P.9.3

12. Interpret Data How does the energy of the
products compare with the energy of the
reactants?

_____

_____

_____

_____

SC.8.P.9.3

13. Apply Concepts What change in condition
might account for the lower activation energy
barrier in the second graph? Explain.

_____

_____

_____

_____

SC.8.P.9.3

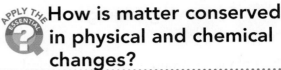

**How is matter conserved
in physical and chemical
changes?**

. . . .

14. Rust forms when iron metal (Fe) reacts with
oxygen (O_2) to produce iron oxide (Fe_2O_3).
Write a balanced equation for this reaction.
Suppose you find the mass of an iron object,
let it rust, and measure the mass again. Predict
whether the mass will increase, decrease, or
stay the same. Explain your answer in terms of
the law of conservation of mass.

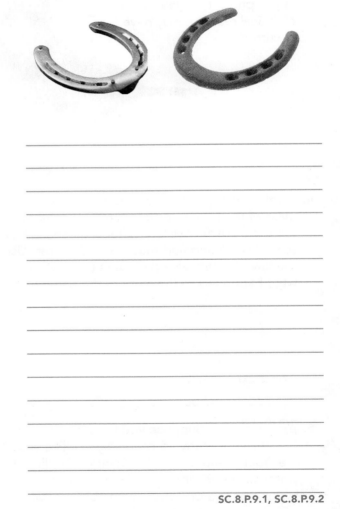

_____

_____

_____

_____

_____

_____

_____

_____

_____

_____

_____

_____

_____

_____

SC.8.P.9.1, SC.8.P.9.2

Florida Benchmarks Review

Circle the letter of the best answer.

1 The diagram below represents molecules of two different elements. The elements react chemically to produce a compound.

The diagram represents an

A endothermic reaction in which energy is absorbed.

B endothermic reaction in which energy is released.

C exothermic reaction in which energy is absorbed.

D exothermic reaction in which energy is released.

SC.8.P.9.2

2 Which of the following is the *best* evidence for a chemical reaction?

A change in temperature

B change of state

C formation of a new substance

D gas bubbles

SC.8.P.9.2

3 Which shows a balanced chemical equation for the decomposition of aluminum oxide (Al_2O_3)?

A $Al_2O_3 \rightarrow 2\,Al + O_2$

B $Al_2O_3 \rightarrow 2\,Al + 3\,O_2$

C $2\,Al_2O_3 \rightarrow 4\,Al + O_2$

D $2\,Al_2O_3 \rightarrow 4\,Al + 3\,O_2$

SC.8.P.9.1

4 Which of the following would increase the rate of reaction?

A remove a catalyst

B increase the temperature

C increase the activation energy

D add an inhibitor

SC.8.P.9.3

5 The fact that matter is neither created nor destroyed in any chemical or physical change is called the

A law of conservation of mass.

B law of chemical change.

C law of exothermic change.

D law of thermal matter.

SC.8.P.9.1

Use the table below and your knowledge of science to help you answer Question 6.

Compound	Formula
Carbon dioxide	CO_2
Methane	CH_4
Oxygen	O_2
Water	H_2O

6 The main compound of natural gas is methane. When methane reacts with oxygen gas, carbon dioxide and water vapor are produced. Write a balanced equation for this reaction.

A $CH_4 \rightarrow O_2 + CO_2 + 2\,H_2O$

B $2\,CH_4 + 2\,O_2 \rightarrow 2\,CO_2 + H_2O$

C $CH_4 + 2\,O_2 \rightarrow CO_2 + 2\,H_2O$

D $CH_4 + 2\,O_2 + CO_2 \rightarrow 2\,H_2O$

SC.8.P.9.1

Waiter there's a soup in my ocean

The oceans are a vast soup of water, salts, dissolved gases, organic compounds, and other chemicals. Marine chemists study ocean water to understand how these chemicals might affect ocean life. One tool used by marine chemists is the mass spectrometer. A mass spectrometer separates and identifies the different types of chemicals in water. This device can also detect the concentrations of each chemical.

Until recently, this kind of analysis could only be done in a lab. Researchers needed to collect water samples, store them, and transport them indoors. This process was expensive, time-consuming, and increased the risk of sample contamination. Fortunately, scientists and engineers at the University of South Florida came up with a better way to analyze ocean water. They invented the world's first underwater mass spectrometer.

An underwater mass spectrometer can collect and analyze water samples while submerged in the ocean. It can remain submerged for days, recording how chemicals change in water. Underwater mass spectrometers can also be attached to vehicles that explore ocean depths. Some researchers hope to send this equipment thousands of meters below the surface to analyze chemicals near hydrothermal vents.

Research It Use reference materials to find out what elements and compounds can be found in seawater. Construct a poster to organize and display the information you find. Be sure to include a list of sources on your poster.

FLORIDA NGSSS

SC.8.P.8.8 Identify basic examples of and compare and classify the properties of compounds, including acids, bases, and salts.

SC.8.P.8.9 Distinguish among mixtures (including solutions) and pure substances.

LA.8.4.2.2 The student will record information related to a topic and include a list of sources used.

Long Ago in a Faraway Land . . .

In an old German tale, a strange little man named Rumpelstiltskin spins straw into gold. Sounds far-fetched, right? It wouldn't have sounded that strange to someone in the fourteenth century. Hundreds of years ago, alchemists searched for a way to turn metals, like lead, into gold. They also tried to make medicines that would cure all diseases and allow people to live for a long time. They thought they needed just one ingredient to do all of this—the philosopher's stone.

Nowadays, we know that a magic ingredient will not change the chemical and physical properties of elements. We have learned that different elements have different properties. But alchemists did make valuable contributions to people's understanding of the physical world. Alchemists discovered alcohol and mineral acids, and recorded their observations of how these acids reacted with other substances. They worked in laboratories heating base metals and observing interactions and changes in color. They recorded their conclusions about these experiments. Even though some of the ideas held by alchemists have been discarded, their research helped build the foundation of chemistry today.

Research It Throughout history, scientists have increased our understanding of the natural world by learning from those before them. Research how the fields of chemistry and medicine have developed from the experiments of alchemists. Write an essay describing the progression. Be sure to list your sources of information.

FLORIDA NGSSS

SC.8.N.2.1 Distinguish between scientific and pseudoscientific ideas.

SC.8.N.3.2 Explain why theories may be modified but are rarely discarded.

SC.8.P.8.5 Recognize that there are a finite number of elements and that their atoms combine in a multitude of ways to produce compounds that make up all of the living and nonliving things that we encounter.

LA.8.4.2.2 The student will record information related to a topic and include a list of sources used.

A fire bomber makes a drop of fire retardant chemicals just above a brush fire.

Summarizing

Physical Science

In this Physical Science unit, you learned about matter and its different states. You learned about the periodic table of elements and that all compounds and mixtures are made of these elements. You also learned how matter can undergo physical and chemical changes.

What states of matter do you see in the photo?

_____

_____

_____

_____

_____

_____

What physical and chemical changes is the fire causing?

_____

_____

_____

_____

_____

_____

_____

_____

_____

As you study this unit, look for answers to these questions.

How do these plants use the SUNLIGHT?

How is water RECYCLED through the environment?

These American lotus plants in Florida's Lake Okeechobee soak up sunlight.

Introducing

Big Ideas and Essential Questions

Life Science

 Florida Big Idea 18

Matter and Energy Transformations

A. Living things all share basic needs for life.

B. Living organisms acquire the energy they need for life processes through various metabolic pathways (photosynthesis and cellular respiration).

C. Matter and energy are recycled through cycles such as the carbon cycle.

 How do energy and matter move through ecosystems?

WHERE DOES FOOD COME FROM?

How do energy and matter move through ecosystems?

Flying around hunting for food, this barn owl spots a mouse for dinner. But what did the mouse eat? Perhaps it nibbled on seeds or a caterpillar. Then you might ask, where did the seeds and caterpillar get their food?

△ **Develop Hypotheses** **Where do living things get their food?**

_____

_____

_____

_____

_____

_____

▷ **UNTAMED SCIENCE** Watch the **Untamed Science** video to learn more about ecosystems and biomes.

Energy, Matter, and Living Things

FLORIDA | Next Generation Sunshine State Standards

Big Idea 2: SC.8.N.2.1, SC.8.N.2.2
Big Idea 18: SC.8.L.18.1, SC.8.L.18.2,
SC.8.L.18.3, SC.8.L.18.4

Language Arts: LA.8.2.2.3
Mathematics: MA.6.A.3.6

13 Getting Started

Check Your Understanding

1. **Background** Read the paragraph below and then answer the question.

> In science class, we looked at both plant and animal cells under the microscope. I could see the nucleus in many cells. In plant cells, we could see green-colored chloroplasts. Both plant and animal cells have mitochondria, but they were too small for us to see with the microscopes that we had.

The nucleus is the organelle that acts as the cell's control center and directs the cell's activities.
Chloroplasts are organelles that capture energy from sunlight and use it to produce food for the cell.
Mitochondria are organelles that convert energy in food to energy the cell can use to carry out its functions.

- Circle the names of the organelles found only in plant cells. Underline the organelles found in both plant and animal cells.

  nucleus   mitochondria   chloroplasts

> MY READING WEB If you had trouble answering the question above, visit **My Reading Web** and type in *Energy, Matter, and Living Things.*

Vocabulary Skill

Greek Word Origins The table below shows the English word parts that have Greek origins. Learning the word parts can help you understand some of the vocabulary in this chapter.

Prefix	Meaning	Example
auto-	self	**autotroph**, *n.* an organism that makes its own food; producer
hetero-	other, different	**heterotroph**, *n.* an organism that cannot make its own food; a consumer

LA.8.1.6.11

2. **Quick Check** The word part *-troph* comes from the Greek word *trophe,* which means "food." Circle the word part in two places in the chart above. How does the Greek word relate to the meaning of these terms?

_____

_____

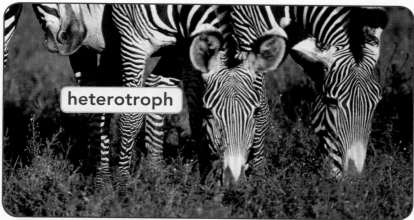

heterotroph

Chapter Preview

LESSON 1
- ecosystem
- photosynthesis
- autotroph
- heterotroph
- chlorophyll
- ↻ **Summarize**
- △ **Classify**

LESSON 2
- cellular respiration
- fermentation
- ↻ **Relate Text and Visuals**
- △ **Control Variables**

LESSON 3
- evaporation
- condensation
- precipitation
- carbon cycle
- nitrogen fixation
- ↻ **Sequence**
- △ **Infer**

fermentation

> **VOCAB FLASH CARDS** For extra help with vocabulary, visit **Vocab Flash Cards** and type in *Energy, Matter, and Living Things.*

precipitation

nitrogen fixation

Photosynthesis

🔑 **How Do Living Things Get Energy From the Sun?**
SC.8.L.18.1, SC.8.N.2.1

🔑 **What Happens During Photosynthesis?**
SC.8.L.18.1, LA.8.2.2.3

my planet diary

MISCONCEPTION

When Is Food Not Food?

Misconception: Some people think that the plant food they give to house and garden plants is food for the plants. It isn't.

Plants make their own food—in the form of sugars—using water, carbon dioxide, and sunlight. So what is the "food" that people add to plants? It's fertilizer. Fertilizer is a mixture of minerals, such as potassium, calcium, and phosphorus. It helps plants grow but doesn't supply them with energy as food does. Farmers add fertilizer to soil to grow better quality crops. People do the same to grow bigger and healthier plants at home.

Communicate Write your answers to the questions below. Then discuss Question 2 with a partner.

1. What is "plant food"?

_____

_____

2. Why do you think people may feed their houseplants more often than farmers fertilize crops?

_____

_____

> **PLANET DIARY** Go to **Planet Diary** to learn more about photosynthesis.

SC.8.N.2.1

Lab zone ® Do the Inquiry Warm-Up *Where Does the Energy Come From?*

Vocabulary

- ecosystem
- autotroph
- chlorophyll
- photosynthesis
- heterotroph

Skills

↻ Reading: Summarize

△ Inquiry: Classify

How Do Living Things Get Energy From the Sun?

On a plain in Africa, a herd of zebras peacefully eats grass. But watch out! A group of lions is about to attack the herd. The lions will kill one of the zebras and eat it.

Both the zebras and the lion you see in **Figure 1** use the food they eat to obtain energy. Every living thing needs energy. All cells need energy to carry out their functions, such as making proteins and transporting substances into and out of the cell. Like the raw materials used within a cell, energy used by living things comes from their environment. Zebra meat supplies the lion's cells with energy. Similarly, grass provides the zebra's cells with energy. But where does the energy in the grass come from? Plants and certain other organisms, such as algae and some bacteria, obtain their energy in a different way. These organisms use the energy in sunlight to make their own food.

FLORIDA NGSSS

SC.8.L.18.1 Describe and investigate the process of photosynthesis, such as the roles of light, carbon dioxide, water, and chlorophyll; production of food; release of oxygen.

SC.8.N.2.1 Distinguish between scientific and pseudoscientific ideas.

FIGURE 1 ••••••••••••••••••••••••••••••

An Energy Chain

All living things need energy.

✎ **Interpret Photos** In the boxes, write the direct source of energy for each organism. Which organism shown does not depend on another organism for food?

_____

The Sun as an Energy Source

The sun is the source of energy in most ecosystems. Recall that an **ecosystem** is a community of organisms that live in a particular area, along with their nonliving environment. The process by which a cell captures energy in sunlight and uses it to make food is called **photosynthesis** (foh toh SIN thuh sis). The term *photosynthesis* comes from the Greek words *photos*, which means "light," and *syntithenai*, which means "putting together."

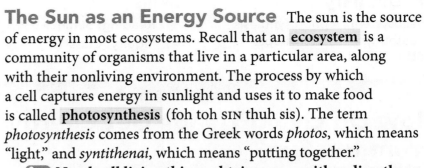 **Nearly all living things obtain energy either directly or indirectly from the energy of sunlight that is captured during photosynthesis.** Grass obtains energy directly from sunlight because grass makes its own food during photosynthesis. The zebra and lion both obtain the sun's energy indirectly. When the zebra eats grass, it gets energy from the sun that has been stored in the grass. Similarly, the lion obtains energy stored in the zebra.

Producers and Consumers

Plants make their own food through the process of photosynthesis. An organism that makes its own food is called a producer, or an **autotroph** (AWT oh trohf). An organism that cannot make its own food is called a consumer, or a **heterotroph** (HET ur oh trohf). Many heterotrophs, such as the zebra and the lion, obtain food by eating other organisms. Some heterotrophs, such as fungi, absorb their food from dead or decaying organisms. This type of heterotroph is called a *decomposer*.

---

apply it!

A spider catches and eats a caterpillar that depends on plant leaves for food.

1 **Sequence** Draw a diagram of your own that tracks how the sun's energy gets to the spider.

2 **Classify** In your diagram, label each organism as a heterotroph or an autotroph.

Do the Quick Lab
Energy From the Sun.

Assess Your Understanding

1a. **Identify** An organism that makes its own food is a(n) (autotroph/heterotroph).

SC.8.L.18.1

b. **Explain** Why do living things need energy?

_____

SC.8.L.18.1

c. **Apply Concepts** Give an example of how energy from the sun gets into your cells.

_____

_____

SC.8.L.18.1

got it? ....

○ **I get it!** Now I know that living things get energy directly from the sun by _____

or indirectly by _____

○ **I need extra help with** _____

Go to **MY SCIENCE** **COACH** online for help with this subject.

SC.8.L.18.1

What Happens During Photosynthesis?

You've just read that plants make their own food. So how do they do that? 🔑 **During photosynthesis, plants and some other organisms absorb energy from the sun and use the energy to convert carbon dioxide and water into sugars and oxygen.** You can think of photosynthesis as taking place in two stages. First, plants capture the sun's energy. Second, plants produce sugars.

Stage 1: Capturing the Sun's Energy In the first stage of photosynthesis, energy from sunlight is captured. In plants, this process occurs mostly in the leaves. Recall that chloroplasts are green organelles inside plant cells. The green color comes from pigments, colored chemical compounds that absorb light. The main pigment for photosynthesis in chloroplasts is **chlorophyll**.

Chlorophyll functions something like the solar cells in a solar-powered calculator. Solar cells capture the energy in light and convert it to a form that powers the calculator. Similarly, chlorophyll captures light energy and converts it to a form that is used in the second stage of photosynthesis.

During Stage 1, water in the chloroplasts is split into hydrogen and oxygen, as shown in **Figure 2**. The oxygen is given off as a waste product. The hydrogen is used in Stage 2.

FLORIDA NGSSS

SC.8.L.18.1 Describe and investigate the process of photosynthesis, such as the roles of light, carbon dioxide, water, and chlorophyll; production of food; release of oxygen.

LA.8.2.2.3 The student will organize information to show understanding or relationships among facts, ideas, and events (e.g., representing main ideas within the text through charting and summarizing).

Vocabulary Greek Word Origins The Greek word part *chloros-* means "pale green." Circle two words in the text that begin with this word part. Which word means "a green compound that absorbs light"?

○ Chloroplast
○ Chlorophyll

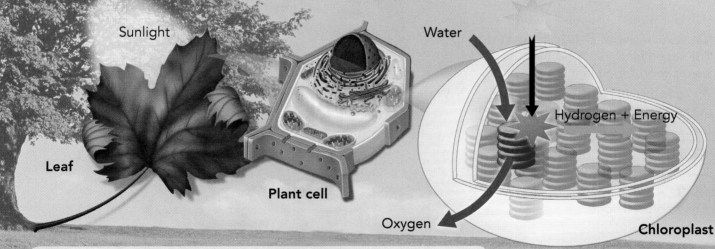

Light energy

Sunlight

Water

Hydrogen + Energy

Leaf

Plant cell

Oxygen

Chloroplast

FIGURE 2 ••••••••••••••••••••••••••••••

First Stage of Photosynthesis

You might say the first stage of photosynthesis powers the "energy engine" of the living world.

✏️ **Make Generalizations** What do you think this sentence means?

_____

_____

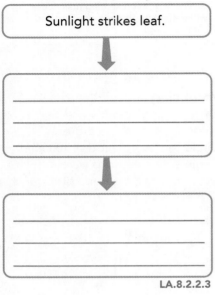

Summarize Complete the flowchart to show the process of photosynthesis.

Photosynthesis

| Sunlight strikes leaf. |

↓

| _____ |
| _____ |
| _____ |

↓

| _____ |
| _____ |
| _____ |

LA.8.2.2.3

Stage 2: Using Energy to Make Food
In the second stage of photosynthesis, cells produce sugars. As shown in **Figure 3,** cells use hydrogen (H) that came from the splitting of water in Stage 1. Cells also use carbon dioxide (CO_2) from the air. Carbon dioxide enters the plant through small openings on the undersides of the leaves and moves into the chloroplasts.

Powered by the energy captured in Stage 1, hydrogen and carbon dioxide undergo a series of reactions that result in sugars. One important sugar produced is glucose. It has the chemical formula $C_6H_{12}O_6$. You may know that sugars are a type of carbohydrate. Cells can use the energy in glucose to carry out vital cell functions.

The other product of photosynthesis is oxygen gas (O_2). Recall that oxygen forms during the first stage when water molecules are split apart. Oxygen gas exits a leaf through the openings on its underside. Almost all the oxygen in Earth's atmosphere is produced by living things through the process of photosynthesis.

FIGURE 3 ················

▶ INTERACTIVE ART **Producing Food**
The second stage of photosynthesis makes food for a plant.

✎ **Identify Fill in the missing terms in the spaces provided.**

Stage 2
The captured light _____
hydrogen, and _____
are used to produce _____

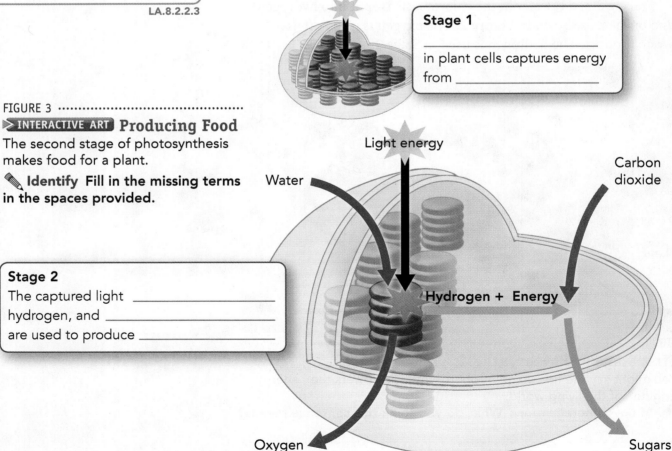

Stage 1
_____
in plant cells captures energy
from _____

Light energy

Water

Carbon dioxide

Hydrogen + Energy

Oxygen

Sugars

The Photosynthesis Equation

The events of photosynthesis that lead to the production of glucose can be summed up by the following chemical equation:

$$\text{light energy} + 6\,CO_2 \text{ (carbon dioxide)} + 6\,H_2O \text{ (water)} \longrightarrow C_6H_{12}O_6 \text{ (glucose)} + 6\,O_2 \text{ (oxygen)}$$

Notice that six molecules of carbon dioxide and six molecules of water are on the left side of the equation. These compounds are raw materials. One molecule of glucose and six molecules of oxygen are on the right side. These compounds are products. An arrow, meaning "yields," points from the raw materials to the products. Energy is not a raw material, but it is written on the left side of the equation to show that it is used in the reaction.

What happens to the sugars produced in photosynthesis? Plant cells use some of the sugars for food. The cells break down these molecules in a process that releases energy. This energy can then be used to carry out the plant's functions, such as growing and making seeds. Some sugar molecules are made into other compounds, such as cellulose for cell walls. Other sugar molecules may be stored in the plant's cells for later use. When you eat food from plants, such as potatoes or carrots, you are eating the plant's stored energy.

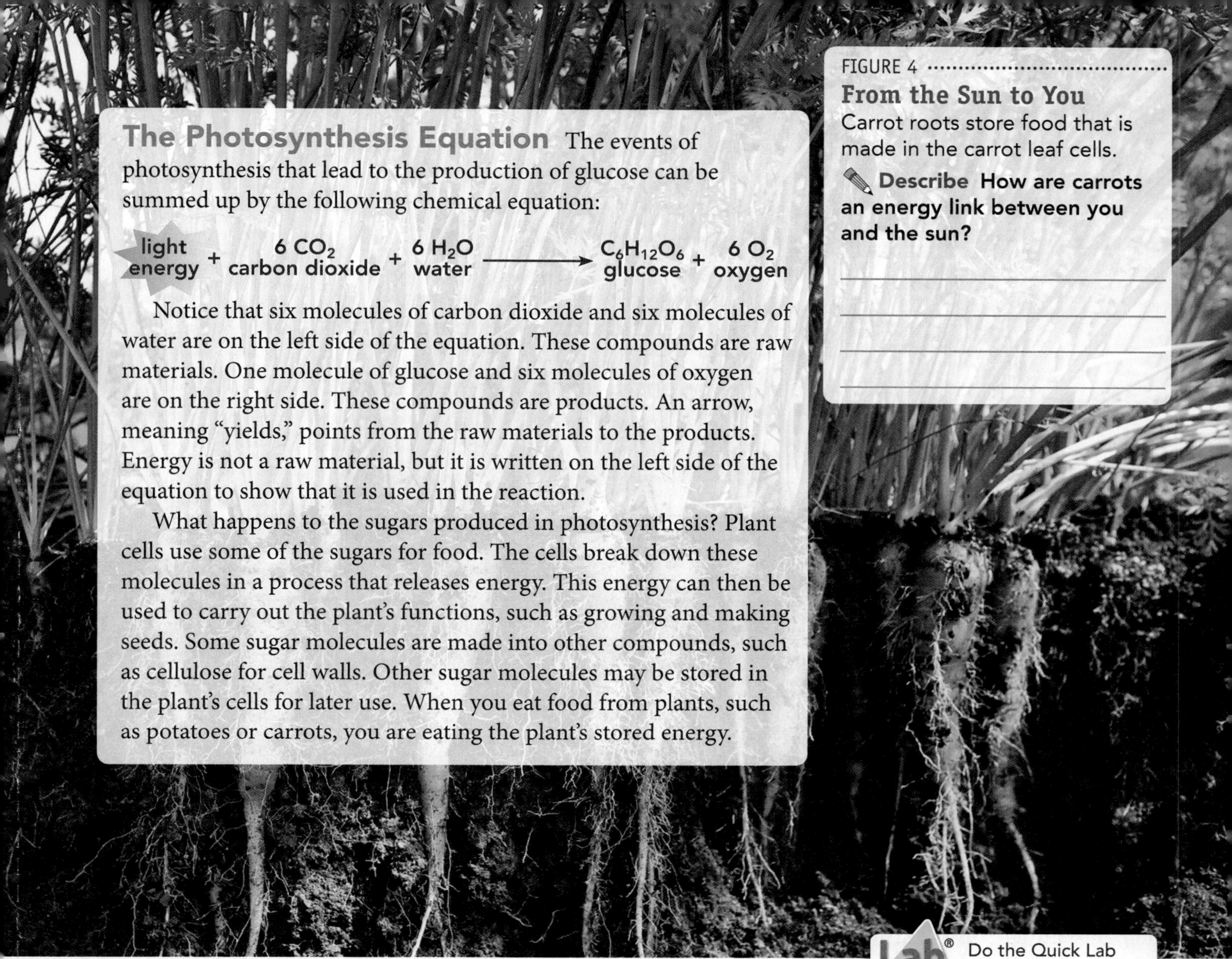

FIGURE 4
From the Sun to You
Carrot roots store food that is made in the carrot leaf cells.

✎ **Describe** How are carrots an energy link between you and the sun?

_____
_____
_____
_____

Lab® zone
Do the Quick Lab
Looking at Pigments.

🔑 Assess Your Understanding

2a. Name Circle two products of photosynthesis.
glucose/carbon dioxide/oxygen/chlorophyll

SC.8.L.18.1

b. Interpret Diagrams Refer to **Figure 3** on the facing page. Where does the hydrogen that is used in Stage 2 of photosynthesis come from?

_____
_____

SC.8.L.18.1

c. CHALLENGE Would you expect a plant to produce more oxygen on a sunny day or a cloudy day? Explain your answer.

_____
_____
_____
_____

SC.8.L.18.1

got it? ....

○ **I get it!** Now I know that during photosynthesis _____

_____

○ **I need extra help with** _____

Go to MY SCIENCE ⓢ COACH *online for help with this subject.*

SC.8.L.18.1

Cellular Respiration

🔑 **What Happens During Cellular Respiration?**
SC.8.L.18.2, LA.8.2.2.3

🔑 **What Happens During Fermentation?**
SC.8.L.18.2

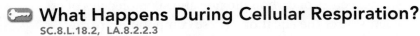

MY PLANET DIARY

FUN FACTS

Going to Extremes

You may not know it, but there are organisms living in rocks deep below Earth's surface. Other organisms hang out in steaming hot lakes, like Grand Prismatic Spring in Yellowstone National Park, shown here. The water in this lake can be as hot as 86°C! Still other organisms nestle inside nuclear waste. All of these organisms are extremophiles, microorganisms that thrive in extreme habitats. These life forms can get energy in strange ways. Some make food from ocean minerals. Others break down compounds in radioactive rocks!

Pose Questions Write a question about something else you would like to learn about extremophiles.

_____

_____

_____

_____

▶ PLANET DIARY Go to **Planet Diary** to learn more about extremophiles.

Lab zone
Do the Inquiry Warm-Up
Cellular Respiration.

🔲 **FLORIDA** NGSSS

SC.8.L.18.2 Describe and investigate how cellular respiration breaks down food to provide energy and releases carbon dioxide.

LA.8.2.2.3 The student will organize information to show understanding or relationships among facts, ideas, and events (e.g., representing main ideas within the text through mapping).

What Happens During Cellular Respiration?

You and your friend have been hiking all morning. You look for a flat rock to sit on, so you can eat the lunch you packed. The steepest part of the trail is ahead. You'll need a lot of energy to get to the top of the mountain! That energy will come from food.

Vocabulary
- cellular respiration
- fermentation

Skills
- Reading: Relate Text and Visuals
- Inquiry: Control Variables

What Is Cellular Respiration? After you eat a meal, your body breaks down the food and releases the sugars in the food. The most common sugar in foods is glucose ($C_6H_{12}O_6$). **Cellular respiration** is the process by which cells obtain energy from glucose. 🔑 **During cellular respiration, cells break down glucose and other molecules from food in the presence of oxygen, releasing energy.** Because living things need a constant supply of energy, the cells of nearly all living things carry out cellular respiration continuously.

Storing and Releasing Energy Imagine you have money in a savings account. If you want to buy something, you withdraw some money. Your body stores and uses energy in a similar way, as shown in **Figure 1**. When you eat a meal, you add to your body's energy savings account by storing glucose. When cells need energy, they "withdraw" it by breaking down glucose through cellular respiration.

Breathing and Respiration You may have already heard of the word *respiration*. It can mean "breathing"—or moving air in and out of your lungs. Breathing brings oxygen into your lungs, which is then carried to cells for cellular respiration. Breathing also removes the waste products of cellular respiration from your body.

FIGURE 1 ·····················
Getting Energy
Your body runs on the energy it gets from food.

✏️ **Complete each task.**

1. **Infer** Color in the last three energy scales to show how the hiker's energy changes.

2. CHALLENGE How do you think the hiker's breathing rate changes as she climbs?

_____

_____

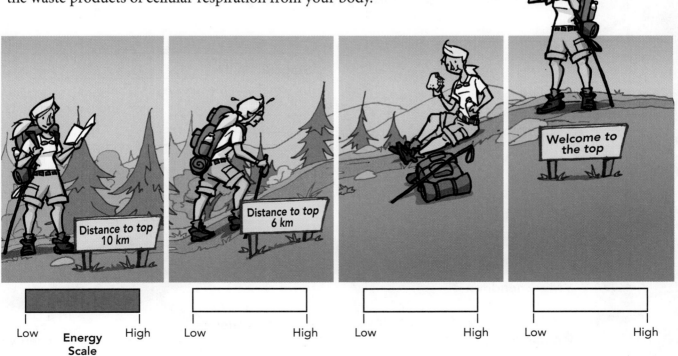

Distance to top
10 km

Distance to top
6 km

Welcome to
the top

Low | Energy Scale | High   Low | High   Low | High   Low | High

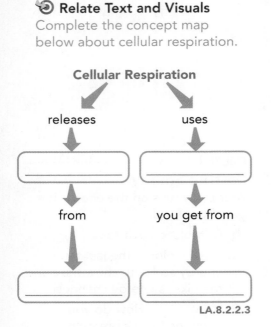
The Two Stages of Cellular Respiration Like photosynthesis, cellular respiration is a two-stage process. See **Figure 2.** The first stage occurs in the cytoplasm of a cell. There, molecules of glucose are broken down into smaller molecules. Oxygen is not involved in this stage, and only a small amount of energy is released.

The second stage takes place in the mitochondria. There, the small molecules are broken down even more. This change requires oxygen and releases a great deal of energy that the cell can use for all its activities. No wonder mitochondria are sometimes called the "powerhouses" of the cell!

The Cellular Respiration Equation Although respiration occurs in a series of complex steps, the overall process can be summarized in the following equation:

$$C_6H_{12}O_6 + 6 O_2 \longrightarrow 6 CO_2 + 6 H_2O + energy$$
glucose + oxygen → carbon dioxide + water + energy

Notice that the raw materials for cellular respiration are glucose and oxygen. Animals get glucose from the foods they consume. Plants and other organisms that carry out photosynthesis are able to produce their own glucose. The oxygen needed for cellular respiration is in the air or water surrounding the organism.

FIGURE 2 ....
▶ **INTERACTIVE ART** **Releasing Energy**
Cellular respiration takes place in two stages.
✎ **Identify** Fill in the missing terms in the spaces provided.

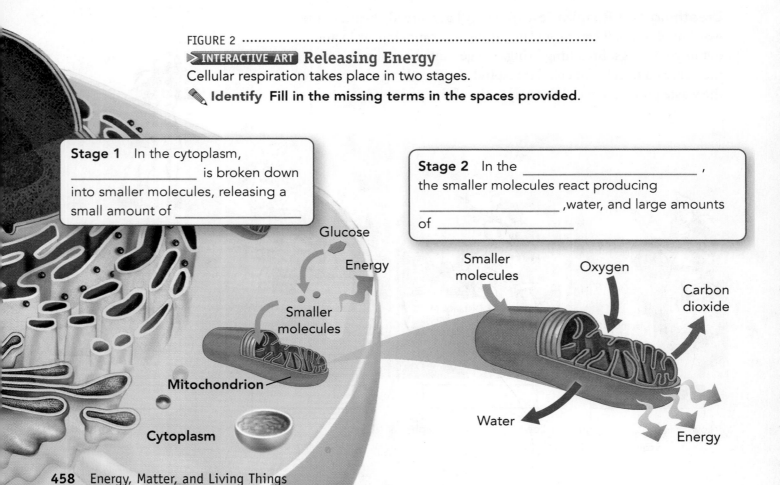

Stage 1 In the cytoplasm, _____ is broken down into smaller molecules, releasing a small amount of _____

Glucose

Energy

Smaller molecules

Mitochondrion

Cytoplasm

Stage 2 In the _____ , the smaller molecules react producing _____ ,water, and large amounts of _____

Smaller molecules

Oxygen

Carbon dioxide

Water

Energy

Comparing Two Energy Processes

If you think the equation for cellular respiration is the opposite of the one for photosynthesis, you're right! Photosynthesis and cellular respiration can be thought of as opposite processes. Together, these two processes form a cycle that keeps the levels of oxygen and carbon dioxide fairly constant in Earth's atmosphere. As you can see from **Figure 3,** living things cycle both gases over and over again.

FIGURE 3 ··································

Opposite Processes

Producers carry out photosynthesis, but producers and consumers both carry out cellular respiration.

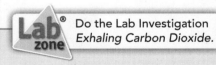 **Name** Use the word bank to fill in the missing terms. Words can be used more than once.

Word Bank	
Oxygen	Energy
Carbon dioxide	Glucose
Water	

Photosynthesis

+

+

Cellular Respiration

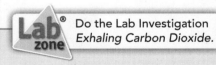 Do the Lab Investigation
Exhaling Carbon Dioxide.

Assess Your Understanding

1a. Describe Why do organisms need to carry out the process of respiration?

_____

_____

_____

SC.8.L.18.2

b. Relate Cause and Effect Why does cellular respiration add carbon dioxide to the atmosphere, but photosynthesis does not?

_____

_____

_____

SC.8.L.18.2

got it? ···

○ **I get it!** Now I know that during cellular respiration, cells _____

○ **I need extra help with** _____

Go to **MY SCIENCE** **COACH** *online for help with this subject.*

SC.8.L.18.2

SC.8.L.18.2 Describe and investigate how cellular respiration breaks down food to provide energy and releases carbon dioxide.

What Happens During Fermentation?

Some organisms can live in the presence or absence of oxygen. If not enough oxygen is present to carry out cellular respiration, these organisms switch to another process. **Fermentation** is an energy-releasing process that does not require oxygen. **During fermentation, cells release energy from food without using oxygen.** One drawback to fermentation is that it releases far less energy than cellular respiration does.

Alcoholic Fermentation Did you know that when you eat a slice of bread, you are eating a product of fermentation? Alcoholic fermentation occurs in yeast and other single-celled organisms. This type of fermentation produces alcohol, carbon dioxide, and a small amount of energy. These products are important to bakers and brewers. Carbon dioxide produced by yeast creates gas pockets in bread dough, causing it to rise. Carbon dioxide is also the source of bubbles in alcoholic drinks such as beer and sparkling wine.

Lactic Acid Fermentation Think of a time when you ran as fast and as long as you could. Your leg muscles were pushing hard against the ground, and you were breathing quickly. But, no matter how quickly you breathed, your muscle cells used up the oxygen faster than it could be replaced. Because your cells lacked oxygen, fermentation occurred. Your muscle cells got energy, but they did so by breaking down glucose without using oxygen. One product of this type of fermentation is a compound known as lactic acid. When lactic acid builds up, you feel a painful sensation in your muscles. Your muscles feel weak and sore. Later, when your cells get more oxygen, the lactic acid breaks down and the pain goes away.

apply it!

A ball of bread dough mixed with yeast is left in a bowl at room temperature. As time passes, the dough increases in size.

❶ Compare and Contrast How does fermentation that causes dough to rise differ from fermentation in muscles?

_____

_____

_____

_____

_____

❷ Control Variables How would you show that yeast was responsible for making the dough rise?

_____

_____

_____

_____

_____

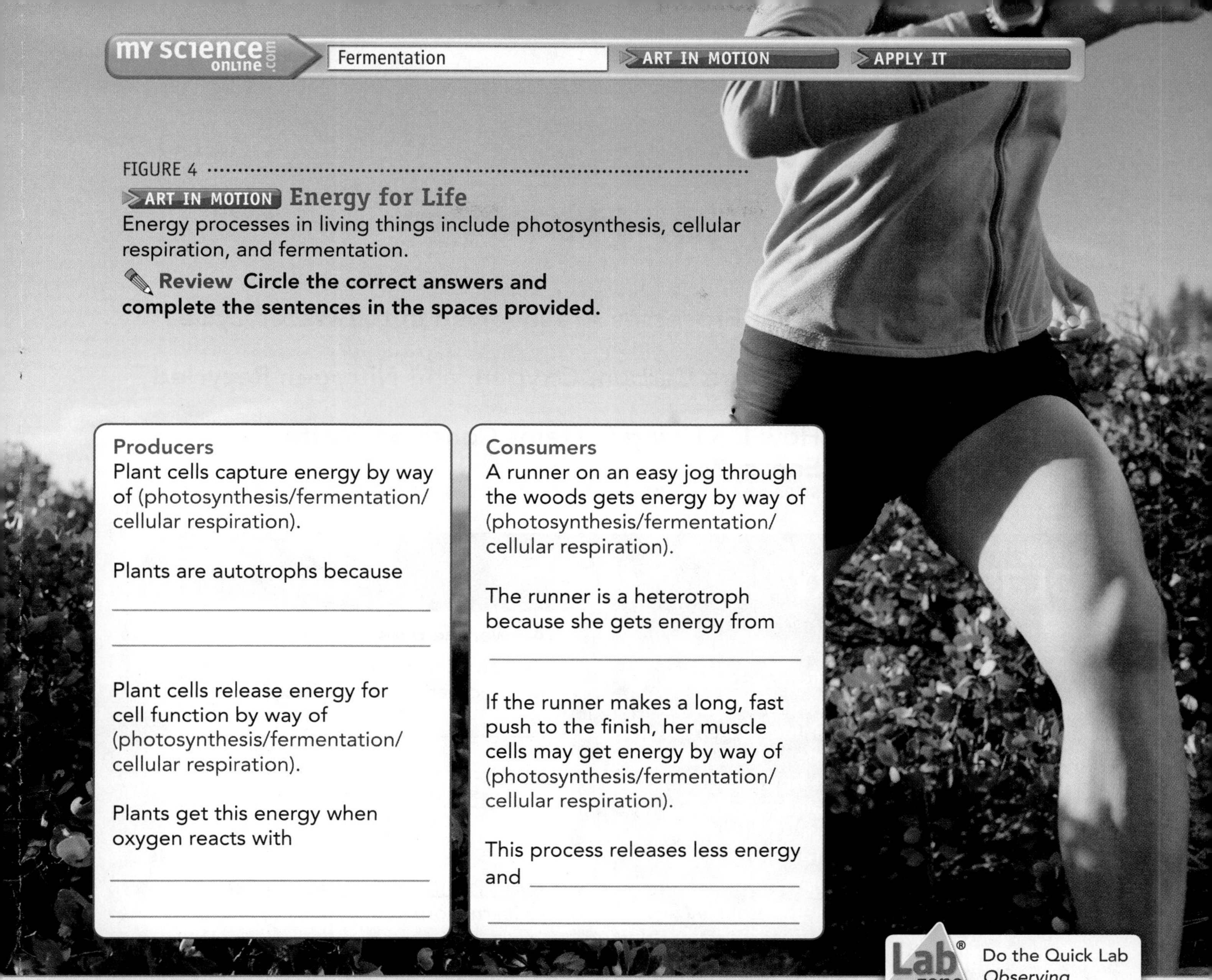

FIGURE 4 ···

 Energy for Life

Energy processes in living things include photosynthesis, cellular respiration, and fermentation.

✎ **Review** Circle the correct answers and complete the sentences in the spaces provided.

Producers

Plant cells capture energy by way of (photosynthesis/fermentation/cellular respiration).

Plants are autotrophs because

_____

_____

Plant cells release energy for cell function by way of (photosynthesis/fermentation/cellular respiration).

Plants get this energy when oxygen reacts with

_____

_____

Consumers

A runner on an easy jog through the woods gets energy by way of (photosynthesis/fermentation/cellular respiration).

The runner is a heterotroph because she gets energy from

_____

If the runner makes a long, fast push to the finish, her muscle cells may get energy by way of (photosynthesis/fermentation/cellular respiration).

This process releases less energy and _____

_____

Lab zone® Do the Quick Lab Observing Fermentation.

🔑 **Assess Your Understanding**

2a. Identify The process in which cells obtain energy without using oxygen is called

_____

SC.8.L.18.2

b. Infer How would athletes be affected if this process could not take place?

_____

_____

_____

_____

_____

SC.8.L.18.2

got it?

○ **I get it!** Now I know fermentation is a way for cells to _____

_____

_____

○ **I need extra help with** _____

_____

_____

Go to my science ⓢ **coach** *online for help with this subject.*

SC.8.L.18.2

461

Cycles of Matter

🔑 **What Processes Are Involved in the Water Cycle?**
SC.8.L.18.3

🔑 **How Are Carbon, Oxygen, and Nitrogen Recycled?**
SC.8.L.18.3, SC.8.N.4.2

🔑 **How Do Living Systems Conserve Matter and Energy?**
SC.8.L.18.4, SC.8.N.2.2, MA.6.A.3.6, LA.8.2.2.3

MY PLANET DIARY

DISASTER

Canaries and Coal

Have you ever stopped to listen to a bird sing? If you were a coal miner in the early 1900s, your life may have depended on it! Sometimes miners stumbled upon pockets of carbon monoxide, a toxic, odorless gas that makes it difficult for the body to get enough oxygen. Without fresh air circulating in the mineshafts, the miners would fall asleep and eventually die. To prevent this disaster from happening, canaries were used to monitor the air quality. A singing canary indicated that all was well. If the canary stopped singing and died, the miners knew to leave the mine right away.

Answer the question below.

Do you think it was ethical, or fair, to use canaries this way? Explain.

_____

_____

_____

_____

▷ **PLANET DIARY** Go to **Planet Diary** to learn more about cycles of matter.

 Do the Inquiry Warm-Up
Are You Part of a Cycle?

🔴 **FLORIDA** NGSSS

SC.8.L.18.3 Construct a scientific model of the carbon cycle to show how matter and energy are continuously transferred within and between organisms and their physical environment.

What Processes Are Involved in the Water Cycle?

Recall that energy moves through an ecosystem as organisms eat other organisms. But how does matter move through an ecosystem? Matter in an ecosystem includes water, carbon, oxygen, nitrogen, and many other substances. Recycling is important for ecosystems because matter is limited. In this lesson, you will learn about some of the cycles of matter.

Water is essential for life. The water cycle is the continuous process by which water moves from Earth's surface to the atmosphere and back. 🔑 **The processes of evaporation, condensation, and precipitation make up the water cycle.**

Vocabulary
- evaporation
- precipitation
- nitrogen fixation
- condensation
- carbon cycle

Skills
↻ **Reading: Sequence**
△ **Inquiry: Infer**

Evaporation
How does water from the ground get into the air? The process by which molecules of liquid water absorb energy and change to a gas is called **evaporation.** The energy for evaporation comes from the heat of the sun. In the water cycle, liquid water evaporates from oceans, lakes, and other sources and forms water vapor, a gas, in the atmosphere. Smaller amounts of water also evaporate from living things. Plants release water vapor from their leaves. You release liquid water in your wastes and water vapor when you exhale.

Condensation
As water vapor rises higher in the atmosphere, it cools down. The cooled vapor then turns back into tiny drops of liquid water. The process by which a gas changes to a liquid is called **condensation.** The water droplets collect around dust particles and form clouds.

Precipitation
As more water vapor condenses, the drops of water in the clouds grow larger. Eventually the heavy drops fall to Earth as **precipitation**—rain, snow, sleet, or hail. Precipitation may fall into oceans, lakes, or rivers. The precipitation that falls on land may soak into the soil and become groundwater, or run off the land, flowing back into a river or ocean.

FIGURE 1 ·····························

⟩ **INTERACTIVE ART** **Water Cycle**
In the water cycle, water moves continuously from Earth's surface to the atmosphere and back.

✎ **Identify** As you read, label the three processes of the water cycle in the diagram.

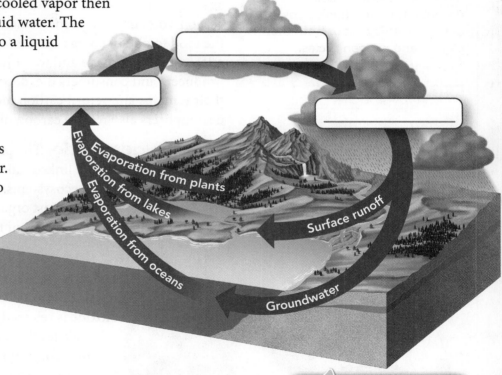

Evaporation from plants

Evaporation from lakes

Evaporation from oceans

Surface runoff

Groundwater

Lab zone Do the Quick Lab *Following Water.*

🔑 Assess Your Understanding

got it? ··

○ **I get it!** Now I know that the processes of the water cycle are _____

_____

○ **I need extra help with** _____

Go to **my science** **COACH** *online for help with this subject.*

SC.8.L.18.3

463

The processes by which carbon and oxygen are recycled are linked.

Infer On the lines below, describe how you think a cow eating grass is part of both the carbon and oxygen cycles.

_____

_____

_____

_____

_____

_____

_____

How Are Carbon, Oxygen, and Nitrogen Recycled?

Carbon, oxygen, and nitrogen are also necessary for life. Carbon and nitrogen are essential building blocks in the bodies of living things. For example, carbon and nitrogen are major components of the proteins that build muscles. Also, most organisms use oxygen for their life processes. **In ecosystems, producers, consumers, and decomposers all play roles in recycling carbon, oxygen, and nitrogen.**

The Carbon Cycle The **carbon cycle** is the process by which carbon moves within and between organisms and their physical environment. Most producers take in carbon dioxide gas from the air during photosynthesis. They use carbon from the carbon dioxide to make food—carbon-containing molecules such as sugars and starches. As consumers eat producers, they take in the carbon-containing food molecules. Consumers then break down the food to obtain energy. As the food is broken down, consumers release carbon dioxide and water into the environment. When producers and consumers die, decomposers break down their remains and return carbon molecules to the soil. Some decomposers also release carbon dioxide into the air.

The Oxygen Cycle The processes by which carbon and oxygen are recycled are linked. Look at **Figure 2.** Like carbon, oxygen cycles through ecosystems. Producers release oxygen as a result of photosynthesis. Most organisms take in oxygen from the air or water and use it to carry out their life processes.

Human Impact Human activities also affect the levels of carbon and oxygen in the atmosphere. When humans burn oil and other plant-based fuels, carbon dioxide is released into the atmosphere. Carbon dioxide levels can also rise when humans clear forests for lumber, fuel, and farmland. Increasing levels of carbon dioxide are a major factor in global warming. When trees are removed from the ecosystem, there are fewer producers to absorb carbon dioxide. There is an even greater effect if trees are burned down to clear a forest. When trees are burned down, additional carbon dioxide is released during the burning process.

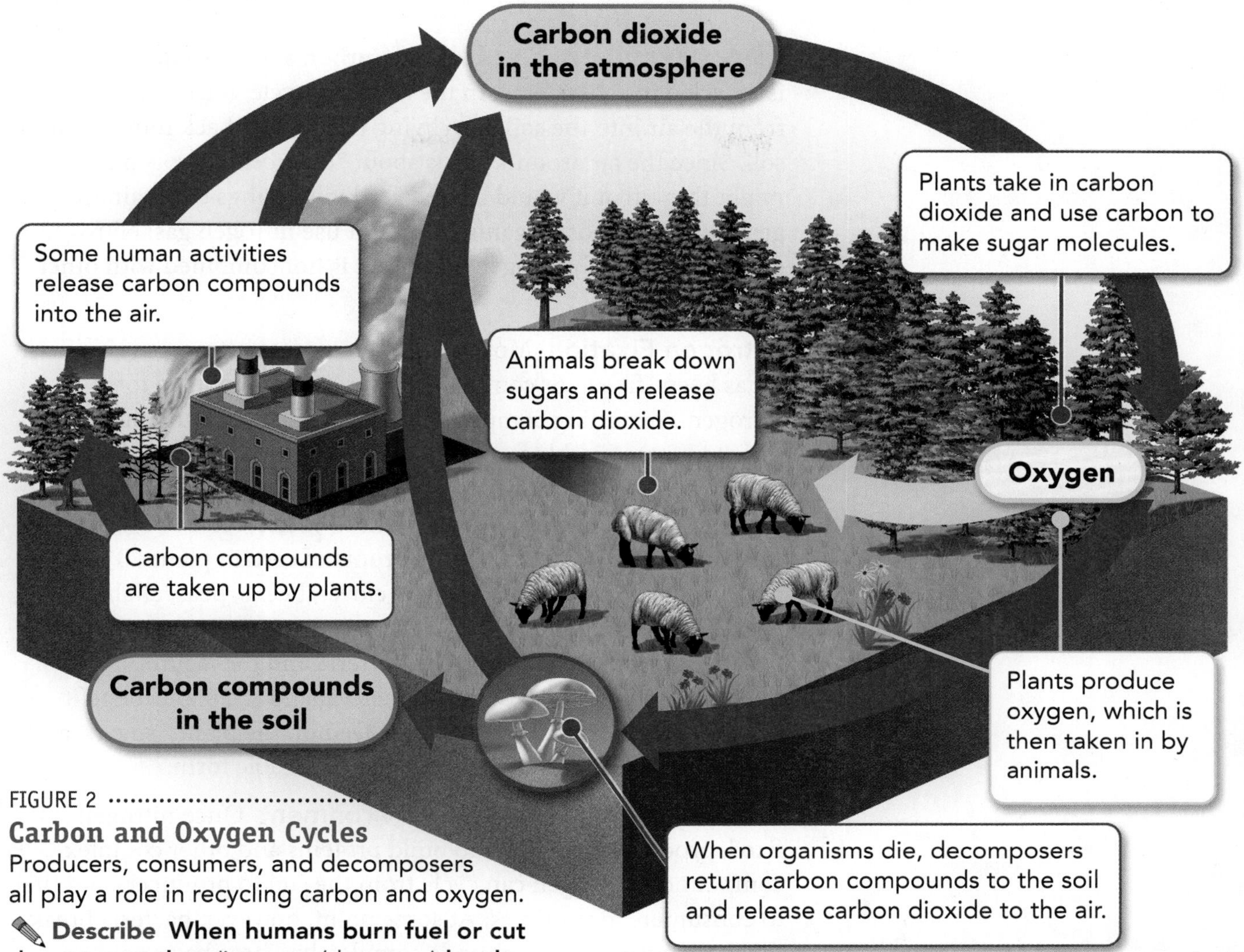

Carbon dioxide in the atmosphere

Some human activities release carbon compounds into the air.

Plants take in carbon dioxide and use carbon to make sugar molecules.

Animals break down sugars and release carbon dioxide.

Oxygen

Carbon compounds are taken up by plants.

Plants produce oxygen, which is then taken in by animals.

Carbon compounds in the soil

When organisms die, decomposers return carbon compounds to the soil and release carbon dioxide to the air.

FIGURE 2 ....

Carbon and Oxygen Cycles
Producers, consumers, and decomposers all play a role in recycling carbon and oxygen.

✎ **Describe** When humans burn fuel or cut down trees, they (increase/decrease) **levels of carbon dioxide in the atmosphere.**

SC.8.N.4.2

⟳ **Sequence** In the frames below, draw a comic strip or describe a situation that shows the order of events in the carbon cycle.

❶

❷

❸

❹

The Nitrogen Cycle

Like carbon and oxygen, nitrogen is recycled in ecosystems. In the nitrogen cycle, nitrogen moves from the air into the soil, into living things, and back into the air or soil. Since the air around you is about 78 percent nitrogen gas, you might think that it would be easy for living things to obtain nitrogen. However, most organisms cannot use nitrogen gas. Nitrogen gas is called "free" nitrogen because it is not combined with other kinds of atoms.

Nitrogen Fixation Most organisms can use nitrogen only after it has been "fixed," or combined with other elements to form nitrogen-containing compounds. The process of changing free nitrogen into a usable form of nitrogen, as shown in **Figure 4,** is called **nitrogen fixation.** Most nitrogen fixation is performed by certain kinds of bacteria. Some of these bacteria live in bumps called nodules (NAHJ oolz) on the roots of certain plants. These plants, known as legumes, include clover, beans, peas, alfalfa, peanuts, and some trees.

The relationship between the bacteria and the legumes is an example of mutualism. Both the bacteria and the plants benefit from this relationship: The bacteria feed on the plants' sugars, and the plants are supplied with nitrogen in a usable form.

Return of Nitrogen to the Environment Once nitrogen is fixed, producers can use it to build proteins and other complex compounds. Nitrogen can cycle from the soil to producers and then to consumers many times. At some point, however, bacteria break down the nitrogen compounds completely. These bacteria then release free nitrogen back into the air, causing the cycle to continue.

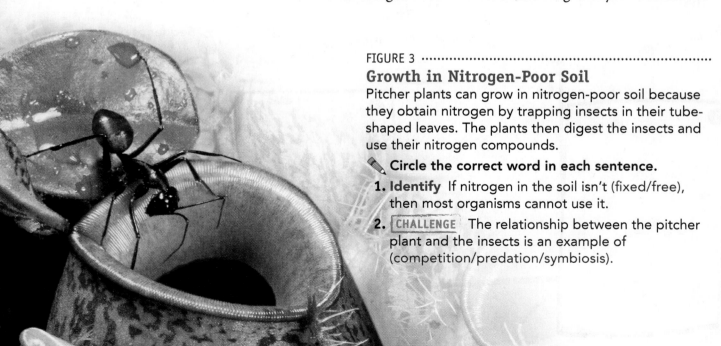

FIGURE 3 ···

Growth in Nitrogen-Poor Soil

Pitcher plants can grow in nitrogen-poor soil because they obtain nitrogen by trapping insects in their tube-shaped leaves. The plants then digest the insects and use their nitrogen compounds.

✎ **Circle the correct word in each sentence.**

1. **Identify** If nitrogen in the soil isn't (fixed/free), then most organisms cannot use it.

2. CHALLENGE The relationship between the pitcher plant and the insects is an example of (competition/predation/symbiosis).

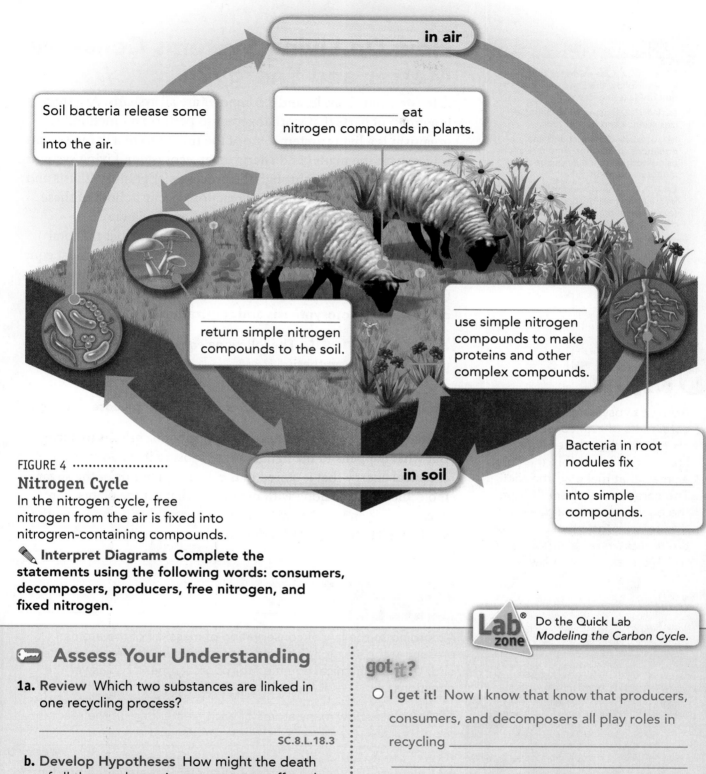

_____ in air

Soil bacteria release some _____ into the air.

_____ eat nitrogen compounds in plants.

_____ return simple nitrogen compounds to the soil.

_____ use simple nitrogen compounds to make proteins and other complex compounds.

Bacteria in root nodules fix _____ into simple compounds.

_____ in soil

FIGURE 4 ·······················

Nitrogen Cycle
In the nitrogen cycle, free nitrogen from the air is fixed into nitrogren-containing compounds.

✎ **Interpret Diagrams Complete the statements using the following words: consumers, decomposers, producers, free nitrogen, and fixed nitrogen.**

Lab
zone®
Do the Quick Lab
Modeling the Carbon Cycle.

🔑 **Assess Your Understanding**

1a. Review Which two substances are linked in one recycling process?

_____

SC.8.L.18.3

b. Develop Hypotheses How might the death of all the producers in an ecosystem affect the carbon, oxygen, and nitrogen cycles?

_____
_____
_____
_____

SC.8.L.18.3

got it?

○ **I get it!** Now I know that know that producers, consumers, and decomposers all play roles in recycling _____

_____

○ **I need extra help with** _____

_____

Go to **MY SCIENCE** 💬 **COACH** *online for help with this subject.*

SC.8.L.18.3

FLORIDA NGSSS

SC.8.L.18.4 Cite evidence that living systems follow the Laws of Conservation of Mass and Energy.

SC.8.N.2.2 Discuss what characterizes science and its methods.

MA.6.A.3.6 Construct and analyze equations to describe simple relations using both common language and algebraic notation.

LA.8.2.2.3 The student will organize information to show understanding (e.g., representing main ideas within the text through summarizing).

Aquatic ecosystems, such as the coral reefs off the coast of Florida, also depend on the energy in sunlight. Algae live within the coral animals that make up the reef. The coral animals benefit from the energy that the algae provide through photosynthesis. In turn, the reef provides a structure on which the algae can grow.

How Do Living Systems Conserve Matter and Energy?

A toaster, your bicycle, and a computer are all systems. A system is a group of parts that work together to perform a function. An organism is a living system. One of the functions of a living system is to recycle the matter and energy in an ecosystem. Living systems perform this function through the processes of photosynthesis and respiration. Recall that chemical reactions occur in both of these processes. And all chemical reactions follow the laws of conservation of mass and energy. These laws state that the total amount of matter and energy before a chemical reaction must equal the total amount of matter and energy after the chemical reaction. **Living systems conserve matter and energy through the processes of photosynthesis and respiration.**

Photosynthesis The following equation summarizes the process of photosynthesis.

$$\text{light energy} + 6\ CO_2 \text{ (carbon dioxide)} + 6\ H_2O \text{ (water)} \longrightarrow C_6H_{12}O_6 \text{ (glucose)} + 6\ O_2 \text{ (oxygen)}$$

Notice that light energy is necessary for photosynthesis to occur. But what happens to the light energy? Most of it is converted to chemical energy that is stored in the chemical bonds of the sugar molecules. Plants, along with organisms that eat the plants, can later use this energy. Matter is also conserved during photosynthesis. Complete the Do the Math to find out how this is so.

do the math!

According to the law of conservation of mass, all of the atoms present at the start of a chemical reaction must be present at the end. Use the chemical equation for photosynthesis to answer the questions.

❶ **Calculate** How many atoms of each element are in the reactants?

_____

❷ **Calculate** How many atoms of each element are in the products?

_____

❸ **Relate Evidence and Explanation** Explain why the chemical equation for photosynthesis shows conservation of mass.

_____

_____

MA.6.A.3.6, SC.8.N.2.2

Respiration

During respiration, the cells in living systems break down chemical bonds and release the energy they contain. The following equation summarizes the process of respiration.

$$C_6H_{12}O_6 + 6\ O_2 \longrightarrow 6\ CO_2 + 6\ H_2O + energy$$

glucose + oxygen ⟶ carbon dioxide + water + energy

Notice that energy is released in this reaction. An organism, such as the white-tailed deer shown in **Figure 5,** uses this energy to move, grow, reproduce, and carry out other life activities. Notice also that all of the atoms present at the start of the reaction are present at the end. As is true with photosynthesis, matter and energy change forms during respiration, but none of it is destroyed.

Conservation Laws and Earth Systems

Recall that Earth is a system made up of the biosphere, geosphere, hydrosphere, and atmosphere. According to the conservation laws, the total amount of matter and energy in the Earth system stays constant. As plants and animals grow, they do not use up matter. Rather, they use energy to transform the raw materials in their environment into living cells. When these organisms die, their matter is returned to the soil, the atmosphere, or other parts of the Earth system. Then the cycle starts again with other organisms.

FIGURE 5 ·······························

Conservation in Florida Ecosystems

White-tailed deer are found in many Florida ecosystems.

Infer Imagine that you are a carbon atom in a molecule of carbon dioxide floating in the air of this photo. Describe how you might move through this ecosystem.

Cycles of Matter

EXPLORE THE ESSENTIAL ?

How do energy and matter move through ecosystems?

FIGURE 6 ·····································

> REAL-WORLD INQUIRY Energy and matter are constantly moving through ecosystems.

✏ **Make Models** Draw and label arrows to represent the following in the figure below: water cycle, carbon cycle, oxygen cycle, nitrogen cycle, and the flow of energy.

Lab® Do the Quick Lab
zone Conservation in
Living Systems.

🔑 Assess Your Understanding

2a. Summarize In your own words, state the meaning of the conservation of energy.

_____

_____

_____

SC.8.L.18.4, LA.8.2.2.3

b. Apply Concepts Suppose a bug eats a plant. Then a frog eats the bug. Does the frog gain the same amount of energy from eating the bug that the bug gained from eating the plant? Explain why in terms of the law of conservation of energy.

_____

_____

_____

_____

_____

_____

SC.8.L.18.4

c. ANSWER THE ESSENTIAL ? How do energy and matter move through ecosystems?

_____

_____

_____

_____

_____

_____

SC.8.L.18.3, SC.8.L.18.4

got it? ....

○ I get it! Now I know that matter and energy are conserved in ecosystems _____

_____

○ I need extra help with _____

_____

Go to MY SCIENCE 🅂 COACH *online for help with this subject.* SC.8.L.18.4

Study Guide

Producers,_____, and _____ help to move matter and energy through ecosystems.

LESSON 1 Photosynthesis

SC.8.L.18.1, SC.8.N.2.1

🔑 Nearly all living things obtain energy either directly or indirectly from the energy of sunlight that is captured during photosynthesis.

🔑 During photosynthesis, plants and some other organisms absorb energy from the sun and use the energy to convert carbon dioxide and water into sugars and oxygen.

Vocabulary
- ecosystem
- photosynthesis
- autotroph
- heterotroph
- chlorophyll

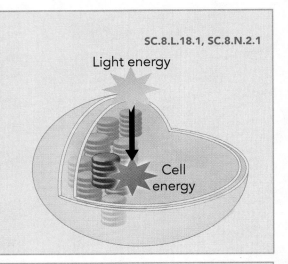

Light energy

Cell energy

LESSON 2 Cellular Respiration

SC.8.L.18.2

🔑 During cellular respiration, cells break down glucose and other molecules from food in the presence of oxygen, releasing energy.

🔑 During fermentation, cells release energy from food without using oxygen.

Vocabulary
- cellular respiration
- fermentation

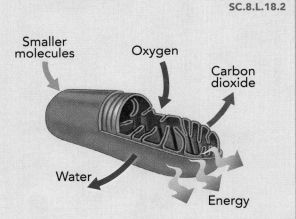

Smaller molecules

Oxygen

Carbon dioxide

Water

Energy

LESSON 3 Cycles of Matter

SC.8.L.18.3, SC.8.L.18.4, SC.8.N.2.2, SC.8.N.4.2

🔑 The processes of evaporation, condensation, and precipitation make up the water cycle.

🔑 In ecosystems, producers, consumers, and decomposers all play roles in recycling carbon, oxygen, and nitrogen.

🔑 Matter and energy are conserved in ecosystems through the processes of photosynthesis and respiration.

Vocabulary
- evaporation
- condensation
- precipitation
- carbon cycle
- nitrogen fixation

Review and Assessment

LESSON 1 Photosynthesis

1. Which of the following organisms are autotrophs?

a. fungi

b. rabbits

c. humans

d. oak trees

SC.8.L.18.1

2. Plants are green because of

_____, the main

photosynthetic pigment in chloroplasts.

SC.8.L.18.1

3. Interpret Diagrams Fill in the missing labels in the diagram below.

SC.8.L.18.1

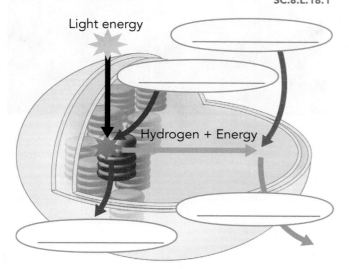

Light energy

Hydrogen + Energy

4. Predict Suppose a volcano threw so much ash into the air that it blocked much of the sunlight. How might this event affect the ability of animals to obtain energy to live?

_____

_____

_____

_____

SC.8.L.18.1

5. [Write About It] How do you get energy? Describe the path of energy from the sun to you, using at least two vocabulary terms you learned in this lesson.

SC.8.L.18.1

LESSON 2 Cellular Respiration

6. In which cell structure does cellular respiration take place?

a. nucleus

b. chloroplast

c. chlorophyll

d. mitochondrion

SC.8.L.18.2

7. _____ is a process that releases energy in cells without using oxygen.

SC.8.L.18.2

8. What is one common food that is made with the help of fermentation?

_____

SC.8.L.18.2

9. Explain Write a word equation for cellular respiration in cells.

_____

_____

_____

_____

SC.8.L.18.2

10. Summarize In one or two sentences, summarize what happens during each of the two stages of cellular respiration.

_____

_____

_____

_____

_____

_____

_____

_____

_____

SC.8.L.18.2

11. Apply Concepts How is breathing related to cellular respiration?

_____

_____

_____

_____

SC.8.L.18.2

473

LESSON 3 Cycles of Matter

12. When drops of water in a cloud become heavy enough, they fall to Earth as

   a. permafrost.   **b.** evaporation.

   c. precipitation.   **d.** condensation.

   SC.8.L.18.3

13. Evaporation, condensation, and precipitation are the three main processes in the

   _____

   SC.8.L.18.3

14. Classify Which group of organisms is the source of oxygen in the oxygen cycle?

   _____

   _____

   SC.8.L.18.3

15. Make Generalizations Describe the roles of producers and consumers in the carbon cycle.

   _____

   _____

   _____

   _____

   _____

   _____

   SC.8.L.18.3

16. Draw Conclusions What would happen if all the nitrogen-fixing bacteria disappeared?

   _____

   _____

   _____

   _____

   SC.8.L.18.3

17. Compare and Contrast How does the mass of the products of respiration compare with the mass of the reactants? How do you know?

   _____

   _____

   _____

   _____

   SC.8.L.18.4

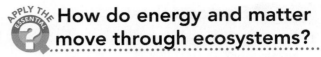

APPLY THE ESSENTIAL ? How do energy and matter move through ecosystems?

18. Many acres of the Amazon rain forest have been destroyed to create farmland. Describe how the movement of energy in this area might be affected. How might the carbon and oxygen cycles also be affected?

   _____

   _____

   _____

   _____

   _____

   _____

   _____

   _____

   _____

   _____

   _____

   _____

   _____

   _____

   _____

   _____

   _____

   _____

   SC.8.L.18.3, SC.8.N.4.2

Florida Benchmarks Review

Circle the letter of the best answer.

1 Choose the name and cellular process that match the cell structure shown below.

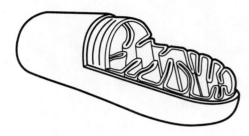

- **A** chloroplast; cellular respiration
- **B** mitochondrion; cellular respiration
- **C** chloroplast; photosynthesis
- **D** mitochondrion; photosynthesis

SC.8.L.18.2

2 What is the source of energy used in photosynthesis?

- **A** glucose
- **B** sunlight
- **C** chlorophyll
- **D** DNA

SC.8.L.18.1

3 Which process produces carbon dioxide?

- **A** photosynthesis
- **B** evaporation
- **C** cellular respiration
- **D** nitrogen fixation

SC.8.L.18.1

4 What is one main difference between fermentation and cellular respiration?

- **A** Fermentation does not require oxygen, while cellular respiration does.
- **B** Fermentation does not release energy, while cellular respiration does.
- **C** Fermentation does not occur in animals, while cellular respiration does.
- **D** Fermentation does not depend on the sun, while cellular respiration does.

SC.8.L.18.2

5 Which two carbon compounds are recycled in the carbon and oxygen cycles?

- **A** carbon dioxide and water
- **B** water and fixed nitrogen
- **C** sugar and water
- **D** carbon dioxide and sugar

SC.8.L.18.3

6 The diagram shows the flow of energy through an ecosystem. Which organisms have the least amount of energy available to them?

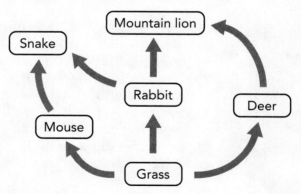

- **A** grass
- **B** mouse, rabbit, and deer
- **C** snake and mountain lion
- **D** grass and mountain lion

SC.8.L.18.4

ARE WE GETTING WARMER?

Explaining Climate Change Most scientists think that an increase in greenhouse gases is warming Earth's climate. The atmosphere contains greenhouse gases, such as carbon dioxide. Greenhouse gases absorb thermal energy radiated from Earth's surface, thus warming the atmosphere. For about 200 years, human activities that release carbon dioxide have been increasing. These activities include burning fossil fuels and cutting down forests. Both fossil fuels and forests are rich in carbon. Look at the graph to see how carbon dioxide in the atmosphere has increased recently.

Earth Systems and the Carbon Cycle
More carbon in the atmosphere affects the carbon cycle. And changes in the carbon cycle affect other Earth systems. For example, as the atmosphere warms, so do the oceans of the hydrosphere. In the cryosphere, glaciers are melting. Melting glaciers are raising sea levels in many parts of the world. Climate change brings warmer temperatures to some regions. Elsewhere, precipitation may increase or decrease.

All these changes affect the biosphere. In many areas, the habitats of plants and animals are changing. Living things that cannot adapt to a new climate may become extinct. Some changes may be beneficial. More carbon dioxide allows plants to carry out photosynthesis at a higher rate. Plants may grow faster and take up more carbon.

Global warming has raised average temperatures in Earth's polar regions. This has caused glaciers to melt and reduced the amount of sea ice during summer. ▲

 FLORIDA NGSSS

SC.8.N.1.5 Analyze the methods used to develop a scientific explanation as seen in different fields of science.

SC.8.N.3.2 Explain why theories are modified but rarely discarded.

SC.8.N.4.2 Explain how political, social, and economic concerns can affect science, and vice versa.

SC.8.L.18.3 Construct a scientific model of the carbon cycle to show how matter and energy are continuously transferred.

LA.8.4.2.2 The student will record information related to a topic and attribute sources of information.

Modifying Climate Theory and Models

Most scientists agree on the theory of climate change and its causes. But it is still hard to predict how much warming will occur and where warming will be greatest. To make these predictions, scientists need data on air and water temperatures worldwide. Some of these data are historic weather statistics. Other data are collected by satellites that monitor the atmosphere, ocean, and land surface. Powerful computers use these data in computer models of climate change. Scientists modify their theory and models as they obtain new data on Earth's changing climate.

Climate Science and Decision Making

Around the world, governments are trying to figure out what to do about climate change. Many people think that countries should agree to limit the use of fossils fuels. Others suggest that people should plant more trees to help remove carbon from the atmosphere. Countries on low-lying islands or coastlines are already threatened by rising sea levels. Climate change may cause droughts in areas where people must raise food to feed themselves. By improving their predictions of how much warming may occur, scientists can help governments plan solutions to the problem of climate change.

▼ Direct measurements of carbon dioxide in the atmosphere over many years show how carbon dioxide has been increasing.

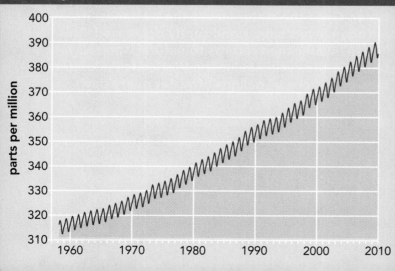

Monthly Carbon Dioxide Concentration

y-axis: parts per million (310, 320, 330, 340, 350, 360, 370, 380, 390, 400)
x-axis: 1960, 1970, 1980, 1990, 2000, 2010

Research It Research a topic related to climate change and write a report about it. How can the science of climate change help decision making in your community and state? Include a list of your information sources.

Everyday Science

HARD WORKING Wetlands

The Orlando Easterly Wetlands Park provides a habitat for many wetland organisms, including this purple gallinule.

Nitrogen is an important nutrient for plants and animals. To help plants grow, nitrogen fertilizers are often added to the soil on farms and in gardens. Plants use much of the nitrogen from the fertilizers, but some of it gets washed away into rivers, streams, lakes, and the ocean.

Although nitrogen is a necessary nutrient, too much nitrogen causes problems in water ecosystems. High levels of nitrogen lead to algae blooms, in which an algae population quickly and dramatically increases. The rapid population explosion causes dissolved oxygen in the water to get used up. Without oxygen, the other plants and animals in the water die off.

To help prevent excess nitrogen from damaging natural water ecosystems, the City of Orlando started the Orlando Easterly Wetlands Park. This wetland habitat was constructed to naturally filter nitrogen out of the water. It works by channeling wastewater containing high levels of nitrogen into the park. As the water moves slowly through the wetlands, plants absorb the nitrogen from the water. Once the water leaves the wetlands, its nitrogen levels have significantly decreased. This "clean" water then returns to natural waterways to begin the cycle again. The Wetlands Park filters tens of millions of gallons of water every day!

Research It Find out more about the water quality in your county. Summarize your findings in a visual presentation to your class. Include information about contaminants found in your local water and ways you can help conserve healthy water.

FLORIDA NGSSS

SC.8.N.4.2 Explain how social concerns can affect science, and vice versa.

SC.8.L.18.4 Cite evidence that living systems follow the Laws of Conservation of Mass and Energy.

LA.8.4.2.2 The student will record information related to a topic and attribute sources of information.

Trees:
Environmental Factories

FLORIDA NGSSS

SC.8.N.4.1 Explain that science can be used for decision making at the community and other levels.

SC.8.L.18.2 Investigate how cellular respiration breaks down food to provide energy and releases carbon dioxide.

Science and Society

Some of the most important members of your community don't volunteer. They consume huge amounts of water and they make a mess. Despite these drawbacks, these long-standing community members do their share. Who are these individuals? They're trees!

Keeping it clean: Trees remove pollutants from the air. Some researchers have calculated the value of the environmental cleaning services that trees provide. One study valued the air-cleaning service that trees in the Chicago area provide at more than $9 million every year.

Keeping it cool: Trees provide shade and lower air temperature by the process of transpiration. Pollutants, like ozone and smog, form more easily when air temperatures are high, so by keeping the air cool, trees also keep it clean.

Acting locally and globally: Trees help fight global environmental problems such as climate change. Trees remove carbon dioxide from the air and store the carbon as they grow. Experts estimate that urban trees in the United States remove more than 700 million tons of carbon from the air every year.

Helping the local economy: Trees are also good for business. One study found that shoppers spend more money in urban areas where trees are planted than they do in similar areas that don't have trees!

Research It Examine a topographical map of the area where you live. Compare it to an aerial photograph from a library or local archive. Identify areas with a lot of trees, and areas that you think could benefit from more trees. Create a proposal to plant trees in one of the areas you identified. What kinds of trees will you plant? What do those trees need in order to grow well?

Schools, clubs, and civic groups all over the United States volunteer to plant trees in their communities. ▶

These American lotus plants in Florida's Lake Okeechobee soak up sunlight.

Summarizing

Life Science

In this Life Science unit, you learned that living things share a basic need for energy. You learned how living things get energy by way of photosynthesis and cellular respiration. You also learned how matter and energy are conserved and recycled in the environment.

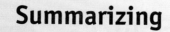 How do these plants use the sunlight?

_____

_____

_____

_____

_____

_____

_____

_____

_____

How is water recycled through the environment?

_____

_____

_____

_____

_____

_____

_____

_____

_____

_____

APPENDIX A

Research Methods and Sources

How do you learn about a scientific discovery, new uses for technology, or how science may apply to issues in your community? You probably gather information from many sources, such as the Internet, newspapers, encyclopedias, or your own observations. These and other sources can also provide details, facts, and information for research papers.

Finding Reliable Sources

To make sure that the sources you use for a research report are reliable, balanced, and accurate, follow these guidelines.

- **Check the copyright date to see how recent the source is.** This step helps ensure that the information you gather from books, science journals, and Web sites is the most current available.

- **Review the author's background and credentials.** An unbiased source is one written by an author who has no special interests in promoting a certain viewpoint on the subject.

- **Avoid personal and commercial (*.com*) Web sites.** For credible and valid information, use the sites of educational institutions (*.edu*), nonprofit groups (*.org*), and government agencies (*.gov*).

- **Evaluate a source to decide if it is relevant to your topic.** Scan the introduction, topic sentences, and conclusion for information related to your topic. Look over footnotes, the source's bibliography, and the index.

- **Use multiple sources to verify information.** If you find discrepancies between two sources, use a third source to check the accuracy of the facts and details. Use information from additional sources to cross-check information from interviews or Internet sites.

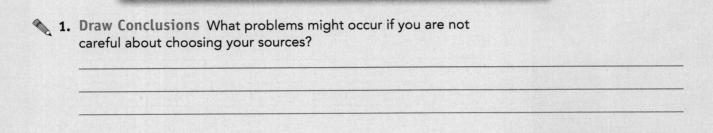

1. **Draw Conclusions** What problems might occur if you are not careful about choosing your sources?

_____

_____

_____

_____

Read the information in the following two sources. Then answer the questions that follow.

http://www.petsinthestates.com

Pets in America

There are now over 73.9 million dogs, 90.5 million cats, and 16.6 million birds owned as pets in America. This can only be seen as an indication that the pet overpopulation crisis is growing. Too many people take on pet ownership without understanding the responsibilities. This hurts both people and pets. Think carefully before adding to this problem by buying a pet you cannot properly care for!

Household Pet Ownership in the United States: 2009
(Based on a sample survey of 50,000 households in 2009)

Type of Pet	Dog	Cat	Bird
Number Owned (in millions)	74.8	88.3	15.0
Number of Households Owning Pets (in millions)	44.8	38.4	6.0

SOURCE: American Pet Products Association, *National Pet Owners Survey, 2009.*

2. Evaluate Which source do you think is more reliable? Explain.

_____

_____

_____

_____

_____

3. Analyze What would be an advantage and a disadvantage of using the table as a source?

_____

_____

_____

_____

APPENDIX B

Safety Symbols

These symbols warn of possible dangers in the laboratory and remind you to work carefully.

 Safety Goggles Wear safety goggles to protect your eyes in any activity involving chemicals, flames or heating, or glassware.

 Lab Apron Wear a laboratory apron to protect your skin and clothing from damage.

 Breakage Handle breakable materials, such as glassware, with care. Do not touch broken glassware.

 Heat-Resistant Gloves Use an oven mitt or other hand protection when handling hot materials such as hot plates or hot glassware.

 Plastic Gloves Wear disposable plastic gloves when working with harmful chemicals and organisms. Keep your hands away from your face, and dispose of the gloves according to your teacher's instructions.

 Heating Use a clamp or tongs to pick up hot glassware. Do not touch hot objects with your bare hands.

 Flames Before you work with flames, tie back loose hair and clothing. Follow instructions from your teacher about lighting and extinguishing flames.

 No Flames When using flammable materials, make sure there are no flames, sparks, or other exposed heat sources present.

 Corrosive Chemical Avoid getting acid or other corrosive chemicals on your skin or clothing or in your eyes. Do not inhale the vapors. Wash your hands after the activity.

 Poison Do not let any poisonous chemical come into contact with your skin, and do not inhale its vapors. Wash your hands when you are finished with the activity.

 Fumes Work in a well-ventilated area when harmful vapors may be involved. Avoid inhaling vapors directly. Only test an odor when directed to do so by your teacher, and use a wafting motion to direct the vapor toward your nose.

 Sharp Object Scissors, scalpels, knives, needles, pins, and tacks can cut your skin. Always direct a sharp edge or point away from yourself and others.

 Animal Safety Treat live or preserved animals or animal parts with care to avoid harming the animals or yourself. Wash your hands when you are finished with the activity.

 Plant Safety Handle plants only as directed by your teacher. If you are allergic to certain plants, tell your teacher; do not do an activity involving those plants. Avoid touching harmful plants such as poison ivy. Wash your hands when you are finished with the activity.

 Electric Shock To avoid electric shock, never use electrical equipment around water, or when the equipment is wet or your hands are wet. Be sure cords are untangled and cannot trip anyone. Unplug equipment not in use.

 Physical Safety When an experiment involves physical activity, avoid injuring yourself or others. Alert your teacher if there is any reason you should not participate.

 Disposal Dispose of chemicals and other laboratory materials safely. Follow the instructions from your teacher.

 Hand Washing Wash your hands thoroughly when finished with an activity. Use soap and warm water. Rinse well.

 General Safety Awareness When this symbol appears, follow the instructions provided. When you are asked to develop your own procedure in a lab, have your teacher approve your plan before you go further.

Using a Laboratory Balance

The laboratory balance is an important tool in scientific investigations. You can use a balance to determine the masses of materials that you study or experiment with in the laboratory.

Different kinds of balances are used in the laboratory. One kind of balance is the triple-beam balance. The balance that you may use in your science class is probably similar to the balance illustrated in this Appendix. **To use the balance properly, you should learn the name, location, and function of each part of the balance you are using. What kind of balance do you have in your science class?**

The Triple-Beam Balance

The triple-beam balance is a single-pan balance with three beams calibrated in grams. The back, or 100-gram, beam is divided into ten units of 10 grams each. The middle, or 500-gram, beam is divided into five units of 100 grams each. The front, or 10-gram, beam is divided into ten units of 1 gram each. Each of the units on the front beam is further divided into units of 0.1 gram. What is the largest mass you could find with a triple-beam balance?

The following procedure can be used to find the mass of an object with a triple-beam balance:
1. Place the object on the pan.
2. Move the rider on the middle beam notch by notch until the horizontal pointer on the right drops below zero. Move the rider back one notch.
3. Move the rider on the back beam notch by notch until the pointer again drops below zero. Move the rider back one notch.
4. Slowly slide the rider along the front beam until the pointer stops at the zero point.
5. The mass of the object is equal to the sum of the readings on the three beams.

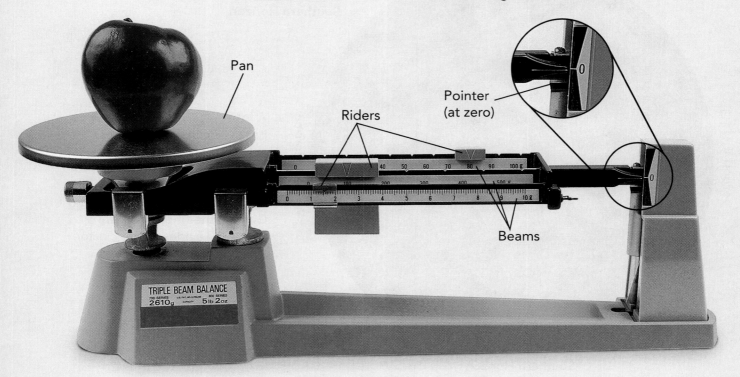

Pan

Riders

Pointer (at zero)

Beams

TRIPLE BEAM BALANCE
700 SERIES   800 SERIES
2610g   CAPACITY 5 lb 2 oz

Star Charts

Use these star charts to locate bright stars and major constellations in the night sky at different times of year. Choose the appropriate star chart for the current season.

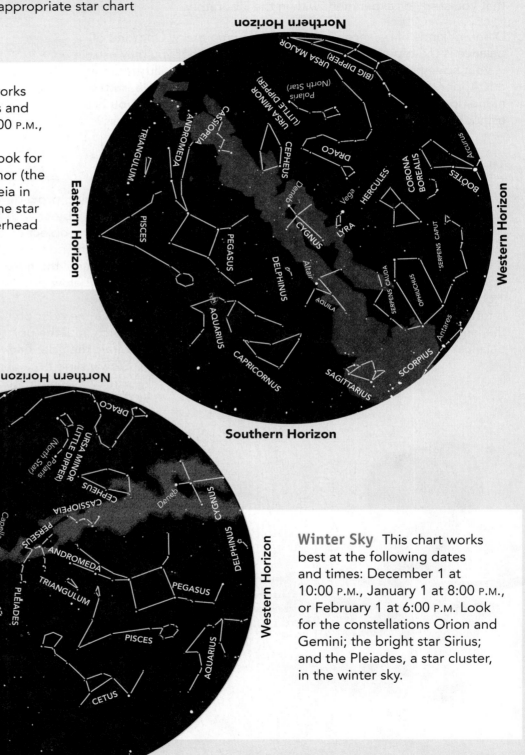

Autumn Sky This chart works best at the following dates and times: September 1 at 10:00 P.M., October 1 at 8:00 P.M., or November 1 at 6:00 P.M. Look for the constellations Ursa Minor (the Little Dipper) and Cassiopeia in the northern sky, and for the star Deneb, which is nearly overhead in autumn.

Winter Sky This chart works best at the following dates and times: December 1 at 10:00 P.M., January 1 at 8:00 P.M., or February 1 at 6:00 P.M. Look for the constellations Orion and Gemini; the bright star Sirius; and the Pleiades, a star cluster, in the winter sky.

How to Use the Star Charts

Using a flashlight and a compass, hold the appropriate chart and turn it so that the direction you are facing is at the bottom of the chart. These star charts work best at 34° north latitude, but can be used at other central latitudes.

Spring Sky This chart works best at the following dates and times: March 1 at 10:00 P.M., March 15 at 9:00 P.M., or April 1 at 8:00 P.M. Look for the constellations Ursa Major (which contains the Big Dipper), Boötes, and Leo in the spring sky. The bright stars Arcturus and Spica can be seen in the east.

Summer Sky This chart works best at the following dates and times: May 15 at 11:00 P.M., June 1 at 10:00 P.M., or June 15 at 9:00 P.M. Look for the bright star Arcturus in the constellation Boötes overhead in early summer. Toward the east, look for the bright stars Vega, Altair, and Deneb, which form a triangle.

APPENDIX E

Periodic Table of the Elements

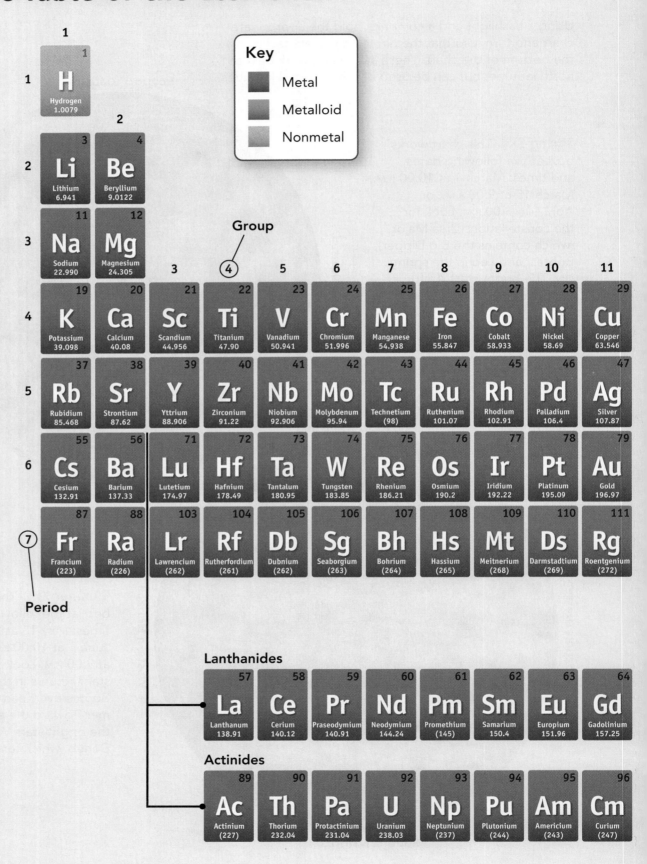

Key

- Metal
- Metalloid
- Nonmetal

Group

Period

1											

1

1 H Hydrogen 1.0079

2

2 3 Li Lithium 6.941 | 4 Be Beryllium 9.0122

3 11 Na Sodium 22.990 | 12 Mg Magnesium 24.305

| | | 3 | 4 | 5 | 6 | 7 | 8 | 9 | 10 | 11 |

4 19 K Potassium 39.098 | 20 Ca Calcium 40.08 | 21 Sc Scandium 44.956 | 22 Ti Titanium 47.90 | 23 V Vanadium 50.941 | 24 Cr Chromium 51.996 | 25 Mn Manganese 54.938 | 26 Fe Iron 55.847 | 27 Co Cobalt 58.933 | 28 Ni Nickel 58.69 | 29 Cu Copper 63.546

5 37 Rb Rubidium 85.468 | 38 Sr Strontium 87.62 | 39 Y Yttrium 88.906 | 40 Zr Zirconium 91.22 | 41 Nb Niobium 92.906 | 42 Mo Molybdenum 95.94 | 43 Tc Technetium (98) | 44 Ru Ruthenium 101.07 | 45 Rh Rhodium 102.91 | 46 Pd Palladium 106.4 | 47 Ag Silver 107.87

6 55 Cs Cesium 132.91 | 56 Ba Barium 137.33 | 71 Lu Lutetium 174.97 | 72 Hf Hafnium 178.49 | 73 Ta Tantalum 180.95 | 74 W Tungsten 183.85 | 75 Re Rhenium 186.21 | 76 Os Osmium 190.2 | 77 Ir Iridium 192.22 | 78 Pt Platinum 195.09 | 79 Au Gold 196.97

7 87 Fr Francium (223) | 88 Ra Radium (226) | 103 Lr Lawrencium (262) | 104 Rf Rutherfordium (261) | 105 Db Dubnium (262) | 106 Sg Seaborgium (263) | 107 Bh Bohrium (264) | 108 Hs Hassium (265) | 109 Mt Meitnerium (268) | 110 Ds Darmstadtium (269) | 111 Rg Roentgenium (272)

Lanthanides

57 La Lanthanum 138.91 | 58 Ce Cerium 140.12 | 59 Pr Praseodymium 140.91 | 60 Nd Neodymium 144.24 | 61 Pm Promethium (145) | 62 Sm Samarium 150.4 | 63 Eu Europium 151.96 | 64 Gd Gadolinium 157.25

Actinides

89 Ac Actinium (227) | 90 Th Thorium 232.04 | 91 Pa Protactinium 231.04 | 92 U Uranium 238.03 | 93 Np Neptunium (237) | 94 Pu Plutonium (244) | 95 Am Americium (243) | 96 Cm Curium (247)

Many periodic tables include a zigzag line that separates the metals from the nonmetals. Metalloids, found on either side of the line, share properties of both metals and nonmetals.

18

2
He
Helium
4.0026

13	**14**	**15**	**16**	**17**

5	**6**	**7**	**8**	**9**	**10**
B	**C**	**N**	**O**	**F**	**Ne**
Boron	Carbon	Nitrogen	Oxygen	Fluorine	Neon
10.81	12.011	14.007	15.999	18.998	20.179

13	**14**	**15**	**16**	**17**	**18**
Al	**Si**	**P**	**S**	**Cl**	**Ar**
Aluminum	Silicon	Phosphorus	Sulfur	Chlorine	Argon
26.982	28.086	30.974	32.06	35.453	39.948

12

30	**31**	**32**	**33**	**34**	**35**	**36**
Zn	**Ga**	**Ge**	**As**	**Se**	**Br**	**Kr**
Zinc	Gallium	Germanium	Arsenic	Selenium	Bromine	Krypton
65.38	69.72	72.59	74.922	78.96	79.904	83.80

48	**49**	**50**	**51**	**52**	**53**	**54**
Cd	**In**	**Sn**	**Sb**	**Te**	**I**	**Xe**
Cadmium	Indium	Tin	Antimony	Tellurium	Iodine	Xenon
112.41	114.82	118.69	121.75	127.60	126.90	131.30

80	**81**	**82**	**83**	**84**	**85**	**86**
Hg	**Tl**	**Pb**	**Bi**	**Po**	**At**	**Rn**
Mercury	Thallium	Lead	Bismuth	Polonium	Astatine	Radon
200.59	204.37	207.2	208.98	(209)	(210)	(222)

112	**113**	**114**	**115**	**116**		**118**
Cn						
Copernicium						
(277)	(284)	(289)	(288)	(292)		(294)

The discoveries of elements 113 and above have not yet been officially confirmed.

Atomic masses in parentheses are those of the most stable isotopes.

65	**66**	**67**	**68**	**69**	**70**
Tb	**Dy**	**Ho**	**Er**	**Tm**	**Yb**
Terbium	Dysprosium	Holmium	Erbium	Thulium	Ytterbium
158.93	162.50	164.93	167.26	168.93	173.04

97	**98**	**99**	**100**	**101**	**102**
Bk	**Cf**	**Es**	**Fm**	**Md**	**No**
Berkelium	Californium	Einsteinium	Fermium	Mendelevium	Nobelium
(247)	(251)	(252)	(257)	(258)	(259)

GLOSSARY

A

absolute brightness The brightness a star would have if it were at a standard distance from Earth. (113)
magnitud absoluta Brillo que tendría una estrella si estuviera a una distancia estándar de la Tierra.

accretion The process of building something up gradually by the gathering together of smaller pieces. (108)
acreción Crecimiento gradual por adición de trozos pequeños.

accuracy How close a measurement is to the true or accepted value. (24)
exactitud Cuán cerca está una medida del valor verdadero o aceptado.

acid A substance that tastes sour, reacts with metals and carbonates, and turns blue litmus red. (378)
ácido Sustancia de sabor agrio que reacciona con metales y carbonatos, y que vuelve rojo el papel de tornasol azul.

activation energy The minimum amount of energy needed to start a chemical reaction. (431)
energía de activación Cantidad mínima de energía que se necesita para iniciar una reacción química.

alkali metal An element in Group 1 of the periodic table. (328)
metal alcalino Elemento en el Grupo 1 de la tabla periódica.

alkaline earth metal An element in Group 2 of the periodic table. (328)
metal alcalinotérreo Elemento en el Grupo 2 de la tabla periódica.

amorphous solid A solid made up of particles that are not arranged in a regular pattern. (266)
sólido amorfo Sólido constituido por partículas que no están dispuestas en un patrón regular.

analyzing Evaluating data to reach a conclusion about an experiment. (10)
analizar Evaluar datos para llegar a una conclusión acerca de un experimento.

anomalous data Data that do not fit with the rest of a data set. (28)
datos anómalos Información que no encaja con los otros datos de un conjunto de datos.

apparent brightness The brightness of a star as seen from Earth. (113)
magnitud aparente Brillo de una estrella vista desde la Tierra.

asteroid One of the rocky objects revolving around the sun that are too small and numerous to be considered planets. (166)
asteroide Uno de los cuerpos rocosos que se mueven alrededor del Sol y que son demasiado pequeños y numerosos como para ser considerados planetas.

asteroid belt The region of the solar system between the orbits of Mars and Jupiter, where many asteroids are found. (163)
cinturón de asteroides Región del sistema solar entre las órbitas de Marte y Júpiter, donde se encuentran muchos asteroides.

astronomical unit A unit of distance equal to the average distance between Earth and the sun, about 150 million kilometers. (137)
unidad astronómica Unidad de medida equivalente a la distancia media entre la Tierra y el Sol, aproximadamente 150 millones de kilómetros.

atom The basic particle from which all elements are made; the smallest particle of an element that has the properties of that element. (261)
átomo Partícula básica de la que todos los elementos están formados; partícula más pequeña de un elemento, que tiene las propiedades de ese elemento.

atomic mass The average mass of all the isotopes of an element. (31)
masa atómica Promedio de la masa de todos los isótopos de un elemento.

atomic number The number of protons in the nucleus of an atom. (318)
número atómico Número de protones en el núcleo de un átomo.

autotroph An organism that is able to capture energy from sunlight or chemicals and use it to produce its own food. (452)
autótrofo Organismo que capta energía de la luz del Sol o de sustancias químicas y la usa para producir sus propios alimentos.

axis An imaginary line that passes through a planet's center and its north and south poles, about which the planet rotates. (183)
eje Línea imaginaria alrededor de la cual gira un planeta, y que atraviesa su centro y sus dos polos, norte y sur.

B

base A substance that tastes bitter, feels slippery, and turns red litmus paper blue. (379)
base Sustancia de sabor amargo, escurridiza y que vuelve azul el papel de tornasol rojo.

benefit A good consequence of taking an action. (74)
beneficio Buena consecuencia de una acción.

bias A subjective belief that affects a person's attitude toward something; an error in the design of an experiment that affects the results of the experiment. (38)
predisposición Creencia subjetiva que afecta la actitud de una persona acerca de algo; un error en el diseño de un experimento que afecta los resultados del experimento.

binary star A star system with two stars. (100)
estrella binaria Sistema estelar de dos estrellas.

black hole An object whose gravity is so strong that nothing, not even light, can escape. (121)
agujero negro Cuerpo cuya gravedad es tan fuerte que nada, ni siquiera la luz, puede escapar.

boiling Vaporization that occurs at and below the surface of a liquid. (277)
ebullición Evaporación que ocurre en y bajo la superficie de un líquido.

boiling point The temperature at which a liquid boils. (277)
punto de ebullición Temperatura a la cual hierve un líquido.

C

calendar A system of organizing time that defines the beginning, length, and divisions of a year. (184)
calendario Sistema de organización del tiempo que define el principio, la duración y las divisiones de un año.

catalyst A material that increases the rate of a reaction by lowering the activation energy. (435)
catalizador Material que aumenta la velocidad de una reacción al disminuir la energía de activación.

cellular respiration The process in which oxygen and glucose undergo a complex series of chemical reactions inside cells, releasing energy. (457)
respiración celular Proceso en el cual el oxígeno y la glucosa pasan por una serie compleja de reacciones químicas dentro de las células y así liberan energía.

chemical bond The force of attraction that holds two atoms together. (261, 359)
enlace químico Fuerza de atracción que mantiene juntos a dos átomos.

chemical change A change in which one or more substances combine or break apart to form new substances. (304, 417)
cambio químico Cambio en el cual una o más sustancias se combinan o se descomponen para formar sustancias nuevas.

chemical equation A short, easy way to show a chemical reaction, using symbols. (422)
ecuación química Forma corta y sencilla de mostrar una reacción química usando símbolos.

chemical formula Symbols that show the elements in a compound and the ratio of atoms. (262, 367)
fórmula química Símbolos que muestran los elementos de un compuesto y la cantidad de átomos.

chemical property A characteristic of a substance that describes its ability to change into different substances. (299)
propiedad química Característica de una sustancia que describe su capacidad de convertirse en sustancias diferentes.

chemical symbol A one- or two-letter representation of an element. (319)
símbolo químico Representación con una o dos letras de un elemento.

chemistry The study of the properties of matter and how matter changes. (259)
química Estudio de las propiedades de la materia y de sus cambios.

chlorophyll A green photosynthetic pigment found in the chloroplasts of plants, algae, and some bacteria. (453)
clorofila Pigmento verde fotosintético de los cloroplastos de las plantas, algas y algunas bacterias.

chromosphere The middle layer of the sun's atmosphere. (124)
cromósfera Capa central de la atmósfera solar.

GLOSSARY

classifying The process of grouping together items that are alike in some way. (8)
clasificar Proceso de agrupar objetos con algún tipo de semejanza.

coefficient A number in front of a chemical formula in an equation that indicates how many molecules or atoms of each reactant and product are involved in a reaction. (427)
coeficiente En un ecuación, número delante de una fórmula química que indica cuántas moléculas o átomos de cada reactante y producto intervienen en una reacción.

colloid A mixture containing small, undissolved particles that do not settle out. (399)
coloide Mezcla que contiene partículas pequeñas y sin disolver que no se depositan.

coma The fuzzy outer layer of a comet. (165)
coma Capa exterior y difusa de un cometa.

comet A loose collection of ice and dust that orbits the sun, typically in a long, narrow orbit. (165)
cometa Conjunto poco denso de hielo y partículas que orbitan alrededor del Sol. Generalmente su órbita es larga y estrecha.

compound A substance made of two or more elements chemically combined in a specific ratio, or proportion. (262)
compuesto Sustancia compuesta de dos o más elementos combinados químicamente en una razón o proporción específica.

concentrated solution A mixture that has a lot of solute dissolved in it. (403)
solución concentrada Mezcla que tiene muchos solutos disueltos en ella.

concentration The amount of one material in a certain volume of another material. (434)
concentración Cantidad de un material en cierto volumen de otro material.

condensation The change in state from a gas to a liquid. (278, 463)
condensación Cambio del estado gaseoso al estado líquido.

controlled experiment An experiment in which only one variable is manipulated at a time. (38)
experimento controlado Experimento en el cual sólo se manipula una variable a la vez.

convection zone The outermost layer of the sun's interior. (123)
zona de convección Capa más superficial del interior del Sol.

core The central region of the sun, where nuclear fusion takes place. (123)
núcleo Región central del Sol, donde ocurre la fusión nuclear.

corrosion The gradual wearing away of a metal element due to a chemical reaction. (327)
corrosión Desgaste progresivo de un elemento metal debido a una reacción química.

cost A negative result of either taking or not taking an action. (74)
costo Resultado negativo de una acción o de la falta de acción.

covalent bond A chemical bond formed when two atoms share electrons. (369)
enlace covalente Enlace químico que se forma cuando dos átomos comparten electrones.

crater 1. A large round pit caused by the impact of a meteoroid. 2. A bowl-shaped area that forms around a volcano's central opening. (143)
cráter 1. Gran hoyo redondo que se forma por el impacto de un meteorito. 2. Área en forma de tazón que se forma en la abertura central de un volcán.

crystal A solid in which the atoms are arranged in a pattern that repeats again and again. (375)
cristal Cuerpo sólido en el que los átomos siguen un patrón que se repite una y otra vez.

crystalline solid A solid that is made up of crystals in which particles are arranged in a regular, repeating pattern. (266)
sólido cristalino Sólido constituido por cristales en los que las partículas están colocadas en un patrón regular repetitivo.

D

data Facts, figures, and other evidence gathered through observations. (54)
dato Hechos, cifras u otra evidencia reunida por medio de observaciones.

density The measurement of how much mass of a substance is contained in a given volume. (18, 294)
densidad Medida de la masa de una sustancia que tiene un volumen dado.

dependent variable The factor that changes as a result of changes to the independent variable in an experiment; also called responding variable. (37)
variable dependiente Factor que cambia a causa de los cambios de la variable independiente de un experimento; también se denomina variable de respuesta.

diatomic molecule A molecule consisting of two atoms. (336)
molécula diatómica Molécula que tiene dos átomos.

dilute solution A mixture that has only a little solute dissolved in it. (403)
solución diluida Mezcla que sólo tiene un poco de soluto disuelto en ella.

ductile A term used to describe a material that can be pulled out into a long wire. (326)
dúctil Término usado para describir un material que se puede estirar hasta crear un alambre largo.

dwarf planet An object that orbits the sun and is spherical, but has not cleared the area of its orbit. (138)
planeta enano Un cuerpo esférico que orbita alrededor del Sol, pero que no ha despejado las proximidades de su órbita.

E

eclipse The partial or total blocking of one object in space by another. (193)
eclipse Bloqueo parcial o total de un cuerpo en el espacio por otro.

ecosystem The community of organisms that live in a particular area, along with their nonliving environment. (452)
ecosistema Comunidad de organismos que viven en un área específica, y el medio ambiente que los rodea.

electrical conductivity The ability of an object to carry electric current. (326)
conductividad eléctrica Capacidad de un objeto para cargar corriente eléctrica.

electromagnetic radiation The energy transferred through space by electromagnetic waves. (232)
radiación electromagnética Energía transferida a través del espacio por ondas electromagnéticas.

electron A tiny, negatively charged particle that moves around the outside of the nucleus of an atom. (318)
electrón Partícula pequeña de carga negativa que se mueve alrededor del núcleo de un átomo.

electron dot diagram A representation of the valence electrons in an atom, using dots. (359)
esquema de puntos por electrones Representación del número de electrones de valencia de un átomo, usando puntos.

element A substance that cannot be broken down into any other substances by chemical or physical means. (260)
elemento Sustancia que no se puede descomponer en otras sustancias por medios químicos o físicos.

ellipse An oval shape, which may be elongated or nearly circular; the shape of the planets' orbits. (171)
elipse Forma ovalada que puede ser alargada o casi circular; la forma de la órbita de los planetas.

elliptical galaxy A galaxy shaped like a round or flattened ball, generally containing only old stars. (102)
galaxia elíptica Galaxia de forma redonda o semejante a una pelota desinflada, que generalmente sólo contiene estrellas viejas.

empirical evidence Data and observations that are collected through scientific processes and that explain a particular observation. (54)
evidencia empírica Datos y observaciones que se recopilan a través de procesos científicos y que explican una observación particular.

endothermic reaction A reaction that absorbs energy. (419)
reacción endotérmica Reacción que absorbe energía.

energy level A region of an atom in which electrons of the same energy are likely to be found. (346)
nivel de energía Región de un átomo en la que es probable que se encuentren electrones con la misma energía.

enzyme 1. A type of protein that speeds up a chemical reaction in a living thing. 2. A biological catalyst that lowers the activation energy or reactions in cells. (435)
enzima 1. Tipo de proteína que acelera una reacción química en un ser vivo. 2. Catalizador biológico que reduce la energía de activación o la reacción de las células.

equinox Either of the two days of the year on which neither hemisphere is tilted toward or away from the sun. (188)
equinoccio Cualquiera de los de dos días del año en el que ningún hemisferio se retrae o inclina hacia el Sol.

escape velocity The velocity an object must reach to fly beyond a planet's or moon's gravitational pull. (211)
velocidad de escape Velocidad que debe alcanzar un cohete para salir del empuje gravitacional de un planeta o luna.

estimate An approximation of a number based on reasonable assumptions. (23)
estimación Aproximación de un número basada en conjeturas razonables.

evaporation The process by which molecules at the surface of a liquid absorb enough energy to change to a gas. (277, 461)
evaporación Proceso mediante el cual las moléculas en la superficie de un líquido absorben suficiente energía para pasar al estado gaseoso.

exothermic reaction A reaction that releases energy, usually in the form of heat. (419)
reacción exotérmica Reacción que libera energía generalmente en forma de calor.

——————— F ———————

feedback Output that changes a system or allows the system to adjust itself. (63)
retroalimentación Salida que cambia un sistema o permite que éste se ajuste.

fermentation The process by which cells release energy by breaking down food molecules without using oxygen. (460)
fermentación Proceso en el que las células liberan energía al descomponer las moléculas de alimento sin usar oxígeno.

fluid Any substance that can flow. (267)
fluido Cualquier sustancia que puede fluir.

force A push or pull exerted on an object. (104)
fuerza Empuje o atracción que se ejerce sobre un cuerpo.

freezing The change in state from a liquid to a solid. (276)
congelación Cambio del estado líquido al sólido.

frequency The number of complete waves that pass a given point in a certain amount of time. (233)
frecuencia Número de ondas completas que pasan por un punto dado en cierto tiempo.

——————— G ———————

galaxy A huge group of single stars, star systems, star clusters, dust, and gas bound together by gravity. (100)
galaxia Enorme grupo de estrellas individuales, sistemas estelares, cúmulos de estrellas, polvo y gases unidos por la gravedad.

gas A state of matter with no definite shape or volume. (269)
gas Estado de la materia sin forma ni volumen definidos.

gas giant The name often given to the outer planets: Jupiter, Saturn, Uranus, and Neptune. (154)
gigantes gaseosos Nombre que normalmente se da a los cuatro planetas exteriores: Júpiter, Saturno, Urano y Neptuno.

geocentric Term describing a model of the universe in which Earth is at the center of the revolving planets and stars. (169)
geocéntrico Término que describe un modelo del universo en el cual la Tierra se encuentra al centro de los planetas y estrellas que circulan a su alrededor.

geostationary orbit An orbit in which a satellite orbits Earth at the same rate as Earth rotates and thus stays over the same place all the time. (230)
órbita geoestacionaria Órbita en la que un satélite orbita alrededor de la Tierra a la misma velocidad que rota la Tierra y que, por lo tanto, permanece en el mismo lugar todo el tiempo.

graph A picture of information from a data table; shows the relationship between variables. (30)
gráfica Representación visual de la información de una tabla de datos; muestra la relación entre las variables.

gravity The attractive force between objects; the force that moves objects downhill. (105)
gravedad Fuerza que atrae a los cuerpos entre sí; fuerza que mueve un cuerpo cuesta abajo.

greenhouse effect The trapping of heat near a planet's surface by certain gases in the planet's atmosphere. (150)
efecto invernadero Retención de calor cerca de la superficie de un planeta debido a la presencia de ciertos gases en la atmósfera.

group Elements in the same vertical column of the periodic table; also called family. (323)
grupo Elementos en la misma columna vertical de la tabla periódica; también llamado familia.

——————— H ———————

halogen An element found in Group 17 of the periodic table. (337)
halógeno Elemento del Grupo 17 de la tabla periódica.

heat The transfer of thermal energy from a warmer object to a cooler object. (273)
calor Transferencia de energía térmica de un cuerpo más cálido a uno menos cálido.

heliocentric Term describing a model of the solar system in which Earth and the other planets revolve around the sun. (170)
heliocéntrico Término que describe un modelo del universo en el cual la Tierra y los otros planetas giran alrededor del Sol.

Hertzsprung-Russell diagram A graph relating the surface temperatures and absolute brightnesses of stars. (114)
diagrama Hertzsprung-Russell Gráfica que muestra la relación entre la temperatura de la superficie de una estrella y su magnitud absoluta.

heterogeneous mixture A mixture in which the different parts can be seen and easily separated out. (393)
mezcla heterogénea Mezcla en la cual las distintas partes se pueden distinguir y separar fácilmente.

homogeneous mixture A mixture that is so evenly mixed that the different parts cannot be differentiated simply by looking at them. (393)
mezcla homogénea Mezcla en la cual las distintas partes están uniformemente mezcladas y no se pueden diferenciar a la vista.

hypothesis A possible explanation for a set of observations or answer to a scientific question; must be testable. (36)
hipótesis Explicación posible de un conjunto de observaciones o respuesta a una pregunta científica; se debe poder poner a prueba.

I

independent variable The one factor that a scientist changes during an experiment; also called manipulated variable. (37)
variable independiente El único factor que un científico altera durante un experimento; también se denomina variable manipulada.

indicator A compound that changes color in the presence of an acid or a base. (378)
indicador Compuesto que cambia de color en presencia de un ácido o una base.

inertia The tendency of an object to resist a change in motion. (106)
inercia Tendencia de un cuerpo de resistirse a cambios de movimiento.

inferring The process of making an inference, an interpretation based on observations and prior knowledge. (8, 55)
inferir Proceso de hacer una inferencia; interpretación basada en observaciones y conocimientos previos.

inhibitor A material that decreases the rate of a reaction. (435)
inhibidor Material que disminuye la velocidad de una reacción.

input Material, energy, or information that goes into a system. (62)
entrada Material, energía o informacion que se agrega a un sistema.

International System of Units (SI) A system of units used by scientists to measure the properties of matter. (13, 292)
Sistema Internacional de Unidades (SI) Sistema de unidades que los científicos usan para medir las propiedades de la materia.

ion An atom or group of atoms that has become electrically charged. (365)
ión Átomo o grupo de átomos que está cargado eléctricamente.

ionic bond The attraction between oppositely charged ions. (366)
enlace iónico Atracción entre iones con cargas opuestas.

ionic compound A compound that consists of positive and negative ions. (366)
compuesto iónico Compuesto que tiene iones positivos y negativos.

irregular galaxy A galaxy that does not have a regular shape. (102)
galaxia irregular Galaxia que no tiene una forma regular.

isotope An atom with the same number of protons and a different number of neutrons from other atoms of the same element. (349)
isótopo Átomo con el mismo número de protones y un número diferente de neutrones que otros átomos del mismo elemento.

GLOSSARY

K

Kuiper belt A region where many small objects orbit the sun and that stretches from beyond the orbit of Neptune to about 100 times Earth's distance from the sun. (163)
cinturón de Kuiper Región en la cual muchos cuerpos pequeños giran alrededor del Sol y que se extiende desde más allá de la órbita de Neptuno hasta aproximadamente cien veces la distancia entre la Tierra y el Sol.

L

law of conservation of mass The principle that the total amount of matter is neither created nor destroyed during any chemical or physical change. (418)
ley de conservación de la masa Principio que establece que la cantidad total de materia no se crea ni se destruye durante cambios químicos o físicos.

law of universal gravitation The scientific law that states that every object in the universe attracts every other object. (105)
ley de gravitación universal Ley científica que establece que todos los cuerpos del universo se atraen entre sí.

light-year The distance that light travels in one year, about 9.5 million million kilometers. (96)
año luz Distancia a la que viaja la luz en un año; aproximadamente 9.5 millones de millones de kilómetros.

linear graph A line graph in which the data points yield a straight line. (32)
gráfica lineal Gráfica en la cual los puntos de los datos forman una línea recta.

liquid A state of matter that has no definite shape but has a definite volume. (267)
líquido Estado de la materia que no tiene forma definida pero sí volumen definido.

lunar eclipse The blocking of sunlight to the moon that occurs when Earth is directly between the sun and the moon. (194)
eclipse lunar Bloqueo de la luz solar que ilumina la Luna que ocurre cuando la Tierra se interpone entre el Sol y la Luna.

luster The way a mineral reflects light from its surface. (326)
brillo Manera en la que un mineral refleja la luz en su superficie.

M

main sequence A diagonal area on an Hertzsprung-Russell diagram that includes more than 90 percent of all stars. (115)
secuencia principal Área diagonal en un diagrama de Hertzsprung-Russell que incluye más del 90 por ciento de todas las estrellas.

malleable A term used to describe material that can be hammered or rolled into flat sheets. (326)
maleable Término usado para describir materiales que se pueden convertir en láminas planas por medio de martillazos o con un rodillo.

maria Dark, flat areas on the moon's surface formed from huge ancient lava flows. (143)
maria Áreas oscuras y llanas de la superficie lunar formadas por enormes flujos de lava antiguos.

mass number The sum of protons and neutrons in the nucleus of an atom. (349)
número de masa Suma de los protones y neutrones en el núcleo de un átomo.

mass A measure of how much matter is in an object. (16, 105, 292)
masa Medida de cuánta materia hay en un cuerpo.

matter Anything that has mass and takes up space. (259)
materia Cualquier cosa que tiene masa y ocupa un espacio.

mean The numerical average of a set of data. (27)
media Promedio numérico de un conjunto de datos.

median The middle number in a set of data. (27)
mediana Número del medio de un conjunto de datos.

melting The change in state from a solid to a liquid. (275)
fusión Cambio del estado sólido a líquido.

melting point The temperature at which a substance changes from a solid to a liquid; the same as the freezing point, or temperature at which a liquid changes to a solid. (275)
punto de fusión Temperatura a la que una sustancia cambia de estado sólido a líquido; es lo mismo que el punto de congelación (la temperatura a la que un líquido se vuelve sólido).

meniscus The curved upper surface of a liquid in a column of liquid. (17)
menisco Superficie superior curva de un líquido en una columna de líquido.

metal A class of elements characterized by physical properties that include shininess, malleability, ductility, and conductivity. (325)
metal Clase de elementos caracterizados por propiedades físicas que incluyen brillo, maleabilidad, ductilidad y conductividad.

metallic bond An attraction between a positive metal ion and the electrons surrounding it. (372)
enlace metálico Atracción entre un ión metálico positivo y los electrones que lo rodean.

metalloid An element that has some characteristics of both metals and nonmetals. (339)
metaloide Elemento que tiene algunas características de los metales y de los no metales.

meteor A streak of light in the sky produced by the burning of a meteoroid in Earth's atmosphere. (167)
meteoro Rayo de luz en el cielo producido por el incendio de un meteoroide en la atmósfera terrestre.

meteorite A meteoroid that passes through the atmosphere and hits Earth's surface. (167)
meteorito Meteoroide que pasa por la atmósfera y toca la superficie terrestre.

meteoroid A chunk of rock or dust in space, generally smaller than an asteroid. (143)
meteoroide Un trozo de roca o polvo, generalmente más pequeño que un asteroide, que existe en el espacio.

metric system A system of measurement based on the number 10. (13)
sistema métrico Sistema de medidas basado en el número 10.

microgravity The condition of experiencing weightlessness in orbit. (225)
microgravedad Manifestación de la falta de pesadez al estar en órbita.

mixture Two or more substances that are together in the same place but their atoms are not chemically bonded. (263, 391)
mezcla Dos o más sustancias que están en el mismo lugar pero cuyos átomos no están químicamente enlazados.

mode The number that appears most often in a list of numbers. (27)
moda Número que aparece con más frecuencia en una lista de números.

model A representation of a complex object or process, used to help people understand a concept that they cannot observe directly. (61)
modelo Representación de un objeto o proceso complejo que se usa para explicar un concepto que no se puede observar directamente.

molecular compound A compound that is composed of molecules. (369)
compuesto molecular Compuesto que tiene moléculas.

molecule A neutral group of two or more atoms held together by covalent bonds. (261, 369)
molécula Grupo neutral de dos o más átomos unidos por medio de enlaces covalentes.

N

neap tide The tide with the least difference between consecutive low and high tides. (198)
marea muerta Marea con la mínima diferencia entre las mareas altas y bajas consecutivas.

nebula A large cloud of gas and dust in space. (117)
nebulosa Gran nube de gas y polvo en el espacio.

neutralization A reaction of an acid with a base, yielding a solution that is not as acidic or basic as the starting solutions were. (380)
neutralización Reacción de un ácido con una base, que produce una solución que no es ácida ni básica, como lo eran las soluciones originales.

neutron A small particle in the nucleus of the atom, with no electrical charge. (318)
neutrón Partícula pequeña en el núcleo del átomo, que no tiene carga eléctrica.

neutron star The small, dense remains of a high-mass star after a supernova. (120)
estrella de neutrones Restos pequeños y densos de una estrella de gran masa tras ocurrir una supernova.

Newton's first law of motion The scientific law that states that an object at rest will stay at rest and an object in motion will stay in motion with a constant speed and direction unless acted on by a force. (106)
Primera ley de movimiento de Newton Ley científica que establece que un cuerpo en reposo se mantendrá en reposo y un cuerpo en movimiento se mantendrá en movimiento con una velocidad y dirección constantes a menos que se ejerza una fuerza sobre él.

GLOSSARY

nitrogen fixation The process of changing free nitrogen gas into nitrogen compounds that plants can absorb and use. (466)
fijación del nitrógeno Proceso que consiste en transformar el gas de nitrógeno libre en compuestos de nitrógeno que las plantas pueden absorber y usar.

noble gas An element in Group 18 of the periodic table. (338)
gas noble Elemento del Grupo 18 de la tabla periódica.

nonlinear graph A line graph in which the data points do not fall along a straight line. (32)
gráfica no lineal Gráfica lineal en la que los puntos de datos no forman una línea recta.

nonmetal An element that lacks most of the properties of a metal. (333)
no metal Elemento que carece de la mayoría de las propiedades de un metal.

nonpolar bond A covalent bond in which electrons are shared equally. (370)
enlace no polar Enlace covalente en el que los electrones se comparten por igual.

nuclear fusion The process in which two atomic nuclei combine to form a larger nucleus, forming a heavier element and releasing huge amounts of energy; the process by which energy is produced in stars. (123)
fusión nuclear Unión de dos núcleos atómicos que produce un elemento con una mayor masa atómica y que libera una gran cantidad de energía; el proceso mediante el cual las estrellas producen energía.

nucleus 1. In cells, a large oval organelle that contains the cell's genetic material in the form of DNA and controls many of the cell's activities. **2.** The central core of an atom which contains protons and neutrons. **3.** The solid inner core of a comet. (165, 318)
núcleo 1. Orgánulo ovalado de una célula que contiene el material genético en forma de ADN y controla las distintas funciones celulares. **2.** Parte central de un átomo que contiene los protones y los neutrones. **3.** Centro denso e interior de un cometa.

O

objective reasoning Reasoning based on evidence. (56)
razonamiento objetivo Razonamiento basado en la evidencia.

observing The process of using one or more of your senses to gather information. (7, 53)
observar Proceso de usar uno o más de tus sentidos para reunir información.

Oort cloud A spherical region of comets that surrounds the solar system. (163)
nube de Oort Región esférica de cometas que rodea al sistema solar.

opinion An idea about a situation that is not supported by evidence. (56)
opinión Idea sobre una situación que la evidencia no sustenta.

orbit The path of an object as it revolves around another object in space. (104)
órbita Trayectoria de un cuerpo a medida que gira alrededor de otro en el espacio.

orbital velocity The velocity a rocket must achieve to establish an orbit around a body in space. (211)
velocidad orbital Velocidad que un cohete debe alcanzar para establecer una órbita alrededor de un cuerpo en el espacio.

outlier An abnormal or irregular data point; a point on a graph that is clearly not part of the trend. (32)
valor atípico Punto de datos anormal o irregular; punto en una gráfica que se aleja demasiado de los valores esperados.

output Material, energy, result, or product that comes out of a system. (62)
salida Material, energía, resultado o producto que un sistema produce.

P

parallax The apparent change in position of an object when seen from different places. (94)
paralaje Cambio aparente en la posición de un cuerpo cuando es visto desde distintos lugares.

penumbra The part of a shadow surrounding the darkest part. (193)
penumbra Parte de la sombra que rodea su parte más oscura.

percent error A calculation used to determine how accurate, or close to the true value, an experimental value really is. (29)
error porcentual Cálculo usado para determinar cuán exacto, o cercano al valor verdadero, es realmente un valor experimental.

period 1. A horizontal row of elements in the periodic table. **2.** One of the units of geologic time into which geologists divide eras. (322)
período 1. Fila horizontal de los elementos de la tabla periódica. **2.** Una de las unidades del tiempo geológico en las que los geólogos dividen las eras.

periodic table An arrangement of the elements showing the repeating pattern of their properties. (316)
tabla periódica Configuración de los elementos que muestra el patrón repetido de sus propiedades.

pH scale A range of values used to indicate how acidic or basic a substance is; expresses the concentration of hydrogen ions in a solution. (381)
escala pH Rango de valores que se usa para indicar cuán ácida o básica es una sustancia; expresa la concentración de iones hidrógeno de una solución.

phase One of the different apparent shapes of the moon as seen from Earth. (190)
fase Una de las distintas formas aparentes de la Luna vistas desde la Tierra.

photosphere The inner layer of the sun's atmosphere that gives off its visible light; the sun's surface. (124)
fotósfera Capa más interna de la atmósfera solar que provoca la luz que vemos; superficie del Sol.

photosynthesis The process by which plants and other autotrophs capture and use light energy to make food from carbon dioxide and water. (452)
fotosíntesis Proceso por el cual las plantas y otros autótrofos absorben la energía de la luz para producir alimentos a partir del dióxido de carbono y el agua.

physical change A change that alters the form or appearance of a material but does not make the material into another substance. (303, 417)
cambio físico Cambio que altera la forma o apariencia de un material, pero que no convierte el material en otra sustancia.

physical property A characteristic of a pure substance that can be observed without changing it into another substance. (274, 298)
propiedad física Característica de una sustancia pura que se puede observar sin convertirla en otra sustancia.

pixel One bit of a digitized image, often appearing as a small square or dot. (238)
pixel Trozo pequeño de una imagen digital que a menudo aparece como un cuadrado o punto pequeño.

planet An object that orbits a star, is large enough to have become rounded by its own gravity, and has cleared the area of its orbit. (99, 138)
planeta Cuerpo que orbita alrededor de una estrella, que tiene suficiente masa como para permitir que su propia gravedad le dé una forma casi redonda, y que además ha despejado las proximidades de su órbita.

planetary image A picture of a planet taken in visible light or in another form of electromagnetic radiation. (239)
imagen planetaria Imagen de un planeta que se obtiene usando luz visible u otro tipo de radiación electromagnética.

planetesimal One of the small asteroid-like bodies that formed the building blocks of the planets. (140)
planetesimal Uno de los cuerpos pequeños parecidos a asteroides que dieron origen a los planetas.

polar bond A covalent bond in which electrons are shared unequally. (370)
enlace polar Enlace covalente en el que los electrones se comparten de forma desigual.

precipitate A solid that forms from a solution during a chemical reaction. (420)
precipitado Sólido que se forma de una solución durante una reacción química.

precipitation Any form of water that falls from clouds and reaches Earth's surface as rain, snow, sleet, or hail. (463)
precipitación Cualquier forma del agua que cae de las nubes y llega a la superficie de la tierra como lluvia, nieve, aguanieve o granizo.

precision How close a group of measurements are to each other. (24)
precisión Cuán cerca se encuentran un grupo de medidas.

predicting The process of forecasting what will happen in the future based on past experience or evidence. (9)
predecir Proceso de pronosticar lo que va a suceder en el futuro, basándose en evidencia o experiencias previas.

pressure The force pushing on a surface divided by the area of that surface. (270)
presión Fuerza que actúa contra una superficie, dividida entre el área de esa superficie.

process A sequence of actions in a system. (62)
proceso Secuencia de acciones en un sistema.

product A substance formed as a result of a chemical reaction. (417)
producto Sustancia formada como resultado de una reacción química.

GLOSSARY

prominence A huge, reddish loop of gas that protrudes from the sun's surface, linking parts of sunspot regions. (126)
prominencia Enorme burbuja de gas rojiza que sobresale de la superfice solar, y conecta partes de las manchas solares.

protons Small, positively charged particles that are found in the nucleus of an atom. (318)
protones Partículas pequeñas de carga positiva que se encuentran en el núcleo de un átomo.

protostar A contracting cloud of gas and dust with enough mass to form a star. (117)
protoestrella Nube de gas y polvo que se contrae, con suficiente masa como para formar una estrella.

pseudoscience A set of beliefs that may make use of science but whose conclusions and predictions are not based on observation, objective reasoning, or scientific evidence. (57)
pseudociencia Conjunto de creencias que pueden basarse en la ciencia, pero cuyas conclusiones no se derivan de la observación, el razonamiento objetivo o la evidencia científica.

pulsar A rapidly spinning neutron star that produces radio waves. (120)
pulsar Estrella de neutrones que gira rápidamente y produce ondas de radio.

pure substance A single kind of matter that has a specific makeup, or composition. (391)
sustancia pura Tipo singular de materia que tiene una composición específica.

Q

qualitative observation An observation that deals with characteristics that cannot be expressed in numbers. (7)
observación cualitativa Observación que se centra en las características que no se pueden expresar con números.

quantitative observation An observation that deals with a number or amount. (7)
observación cuantitativa Observación que se centra en un número o cantidad.

quasar An enormously bright, distant galaxy with a giant black hole at its center. (102)
quásar Galaxia extraordinariamente luminosa y distante con un agujero negro gigante en el centro.

R

radiation zone A region of very tightly packed gas in the sun's interior where energy is transferred mainly in the form of electromagnetic radiation. (123)
zona radioactiva Región al interior del Sol de gases densamente acumulados y donde se transmite energía principalmente en la forma de radiación electromagnética.

range The difference between the greatest value and the least value in a set of data. (27)
rango Diferencia entre el mayor y el menor valor de un conjunto de datos.

reactant A substance that enters into a chemical reaction. (417)
reactante Sustancia que interviene en una reacción química.

reactivity The ease and speed with which an element combines, or reacts, with other elements and compounds. (327)
reactividad Facilidad y rapidez con las que un elemento se combina, o reacciona, con otros elementos y compuestos.

reflecting telescope A telescope that uses a curved mirror to collect and focus light. (235)
telescopio de reflexión Telescopio que usa un espejo curvado para captar y enfocar la luz.

refracting telescope A telescope that uses convex lenses to gather and focus light. (235)
telescopio de refracción Telescopio que usa lentes convexas para captar y enfocar la luz.

remote sensing The collection of information about Earth and other objects in space using satellites or probes. (221)
percepción remota Recolección de información sobre la Tierra y otros cuerpos del espacio usando satélites o sondas.

repeated trial A repetition of an experiment to gather additional data and determine whether the experiment's results support the hypothesis. (40)
prueba repetida Repetición de un experimento para recopilar datos adicionales y determinar si los resultados de un experimento sustentan la hipótesis.

replication An attempt to repeat a scientist's experiment by a different scientist or group of scientists. (41)
replicación Intento, por parte de un científico o grupo de científicos, de repetir el experimento de otro científico.

revolution The movement of an object around another object. (184)

revolución Movimiento de un cuerpo alrededor de otro.

ring A thin disk of small ice and rock particles surrounding a planet. (155)

anillo Disco fino de pequeñas partículas de hielo y roca que rodea un planeta.

rocket A device that expels gas in one direction to move in the opposite direction. (208)

cohete Aparato que expulsa gases en una dirección para moverse en la dirección opuesta.

rotation The spinning motion of a planet on its axis. (183)

rotación Movimiento giratorio de un planeta sobre su eje.

rover A small robotic space probe that can move about the surface of a planet or moon. (221)

rover Pequeña sonda espacial robótica que puede desplazarse sobre la superficie de un planeta o sobre la Luna.

—————————— S ——————————

salt An ionic compound made from the neutralization of an acid with a base. (380)

sal Compuesto iónico formado por la neutralización de un ácido con una base.

satellite 1. An object that orbits a planet. 2. Any object that orbits around another object in space. (215)

satélite 1. Cuerpo que orbita alrededor de un planeta. 2. Cualquier cuerpo que orbita alrededor de otro cuerpo en el espacio.

satellite photograph A picture of the land surface based on computer data collected from satellites. (238)

fotografía satelital Representación visual de la superficie terrestre basada en la colección de datos de un satélite.

saturated solution A mixture that contains as much dissolved solute as is possible at a given temperature. (403)

solución saturada Mezcla que contiene la mayor cantidad posible de soluto disuelto a una temperatura determinada.

science A way of learning about the natural world through observations and logical reasoning; leads to a body of knowledge. (7)

ciencia Estudio del mundo natural a través de observaciones y del razonamiento lógico; conduce a un conjunto de conocimientos.

scientific explanation A generalization that makes sense of observations by using logical reasoning. (42)

explicación científica Generalización que usa el razonamiento lógico para darle sentido a las observaciones.

scientific inquiry The ongoing process of discovery in science; the diverse ways in which scientists study the natural world and propose explanations based on evidence they gather. (35)

indagación científica Proceso continuo de descubrimiento en la ciencia; diversidad de métodos con los que los científicos estudian el mundo natural y proponen explicaciones del mismo basadas en la evidencia que reúnen.

scientific law A statement that describes what scientists expect to happen every time under a particular set of conditions. (70)

ley científica Enunciado que describe lo que los científicos esperan que suceda cada vez que se da una serie de condiciones determinadas.

scientific notation A mathematical method of writing numbers using powers of ten. (96)

notación científica Método matemático de escritura de números que usa la potencia de diez.

scientific theory A well-tested explanation for a wide range of observations or experimental results. (69)

teoría científica Explicación comprobada de una gran variedad de observaciones o resultados de experimentos.

semiconductor A substance that can conduct electric current under some conditions. (339)

semiconductor Sustancia que puede conducir una corriente eléctrica bajo ciertas condiciones.

significant figures All the digits in a measurement that have been measured exactly, plus one digit whose value has been estimated. (25)

cifras significativas En una medida, todos los dígitos que se han medido con exactitud, más un dígito cuyo valor se ha estimado.

solar eclipse The blocking of sunlight to Earth that occurs when the moon is directly between the sun and Earth. (193)

eclipse solar Bloqueo de la luz solar que ilumina la Tierra que ocurre cuando la Luna se interpone entre el Sol y la Tierra.

GLOSSARY

solar flare An eruption of gas from the sun's surface that occurs when the loops in sunspot regions suddenly connect. (126)
destello solar Erupción de los gases de la superficie solar que ocurre cuando las burbujas de las manchas solares se conectan repentinamente.

solar system The system consisting of the sun and the planets and other objects that revolve around it. (99, 137)
sistema solar Sistema formado por el Sol, los planetas y otros cuerpos que giran alrededor de él.

solar wind A stream of electrically charged particles that emanate from the sun's corona. (125)
viento solar Flujo de partículas cargadas que emanan de la corona del Sol.

solid A state of matter that has a definite shape and a definite volume. (265)
sólido Estado en el que la materia tiene forma y volumen definidos.

solstice Either of the two days of the year on which the sun reaches its greatest distance north or south of the equator. (188)
solsticio Uno de los dos días del año en el que el Sol alcanza la mayor distancia al norte o al sur del ecuador.

solubility A measure of how much solute can dissolve in a given solvent at a given temperature. (403)
solubilidad Medida de cuánto soluto se puede disolver en un solvente a una temperatura dada.

solute The part of a solution that is dissolved by a solvent. (397)
soluto Parte de una solución que se disuelve en un solvente.

solution A mixture containing a solvent and at least one solute that has the same properties throughout; a mixture in which one substance is dissolved in another. (397)
solución Mezcla que contiene un solvente y al menos un soluto, y que tiene las mismas propiedades en toda la solución; mezcla en la que una sustancia se disuelve en otra.

solvent The part of a solution that is usually present in the largest amount and dissolves a solute. (397)
solvente Parte de una solución que, por lo general, está presente en la mayor cantidad y que disuelve a un soluto.

Space Coast An area of Florida's Brevard County noted for the presence of the Kennedy Space Center. (242)
costa espacial Área del condado de Brevard, en la Florida, famoso por la presencia del centro espacial Kennedy.

space port A site for launching or receiving spacecraft. (241)
puerto espacial Lugar de despegue y aterrizaje para naves espaciales.

space probe A spacecraft that has various scientific instruments that can collect data, including visual images, but has no human crew. (221)
sonda espacial Nave espacial que tiene varios instrumentos científicos que pueden reunir datos e imágenes, pero que no tiene una tripulación.

space shuttle A spacecraft that can carry a crew into space, return to Earth, and then be reused for the same purpose. (219)
transbordador espacial Nave espacial que puede llevar a una tripulación al espacio, volver a la Tierra, y luego volver a ser usada para el mismo propósito.

space spinoff An item that has uses on Earth but was originally developed for use in space. (228)
derivación espacial Objeto que se puede usar en la Tierra, pero que originalmente se construyó para ser usado en el espacio.

space station A large artificial satellite on which people can live and work for long periods. (220)
estación espacial Enorme satélite artificial en el que la gente puede vivir y trabajar durante largos períodos.

spectrograph An instrument that separates light into colors and makes an image of the resulting spectrum. (112)
espectrógrafo Instrumento que separa la luz en colores y crea una imagen del espectro resultante.

spectrum The range of wavelengths of electromagnetic waves. (233)
espectro Gama de las longitudes de ondas electromagnéticas.

spiral galaxy A galaxy with a bulge in the middle and arms that spiral outward in a pinwheel pattern. (102)
galaxia espiral Galaxia con una protuberancia en el centro y brazos que giran en espiral hacia el exterior, como un remolino.

spring tide The tide with the greatest difference between consecutive low and high tides. (198)
marea viva Marea con la mayor diferencia entre las mareas altas y bajas consecutivas.

star A ball of hot gas, primarily hydrogen and helium, that undergoes nuclear fusion. (99)
estrella Bola de gases calientes, principalmente hidrógeno y helio, en cuyo interior se produce una fusión nuclear.

subjective reasoning Reasoning based on personal feelings or values. (56)
razonamiento subjetivo Razonamiento basado en los sentimientos o los valores personales.

sublimation The change in state from a solid directly to a gas without passing through the liquid state. (279)
sublimación Cambio del estado sólido directamente a gas, sin pasar por el estado líquido.

subscript A number in a chemical formula that tells the number of atoms in a molecule or the ratio of elements in a compound. (367)
subíndice Número en una fórmula química que indica el número de átomos que tiene una molécula o la razón de elementos en un compuesto.

substance A single kind of matter that is pure and has a specific set of properties. (259)
sustancia Tipo único de materia que es pura y tiene propiedades específicas.

sunspot 1. A dark area of gas on the sun's surface that is cooler than surrounding gases. **2.** Relatively dark, cool region on the surface of the sun. (126)
mancha solar 1. Área gaseosa oscura de la superficie solar, que es más fría que los gases que la rodean. **2.** Región relativamente fría y oscura de la superficie solar.

supernova The brilliant explosion of a dying supergiant star. (119)
supernova Explosión brillante de una estrella supergigante en extinción.

surface tension The result of an inward pull among the molecules of a liquid that brings the molecules on the surface closer together; causes the surface to act as if it has a thin skin. (268)
tensión superficial Resultado de la atracción hacia el centro entre las moléculas de un líquido, que hace que las moléculas de la superficie se acerquen mucho, y que la superficie actúe como si tuviera una piel delgada.

suspension A mixture in which particles can be seen and easily separated by settling or filtration. (399)
suspensión Mezcla en la cual las partículas se pueden ver y separar fácilmente por fijación o por filtración.

system 1. A group of parts that work together as a whole. **2.** A group of related parts that work together to perform a function or produce a result. (62)
sistema 1. Partes de un grupo que trabajan en conjunto. **2.** Grupo de partes relacionadas que trabajan conjuntamente para realizar una función o producir un resultado.

T

temperature How hot or cold something is; a measure of the average energy of motion of the particles of a substance; the measure of the average kinetic energy of the particles of a substance. (271)
temperatura Cuán caliente o frío es algo; medida de la energía de movimiento promedio de las partículas de una sustancia; medida de la energía cinética promedio de las partículas de una sustancia.

terrestrial planets The name often given to the four inner planets: Mercury, Venus, Earth, and Mars. (147)
planetas telúricos Nombre dado normalmente a los cuatro planetas interiores: Mercurio, Venus, Tierra y Marte.

thermal conductivity The ability of an object to transfer heat. (326)
conductividad térmica Capacidad de un objeto para transferir calor.

thermal energy The total kinetic and potential energy of all the particles of an object. (273)
energía térmica Energía cinética y potencial total de las partículas de un cuerpo.

thrust The reaction force that propels a rocket forward. (210)
empuje Fuerza de reacción que propulsa un cohete hacia delante.

tide The periodic rise and fall of the level of water in the ocean. (197)
marea La subida y bajada periódica del nivel de agua del océano.

transition metal One of the elements in Groups 3 through 12 of the periodic table. (329)
metal de transición Uno de los elementos de los Grupos 3 a 12 de la tabla periódica.

U

umbra The darkest part of a shadow. (193)
umbra La parte más oscura de una sombra.

universe All of space and everything in it. (96)
universo Todo el espacio y todo lo que hay en él.

GLOSSARY

V

vacuum A place that is empty of all matter. (225)
vacío Lugar en donde no existe materia.

valence electrons The electrons that are in the highest energy level of an atom and that are involved in chemical bonding. (359)
electrones de valencia Electrones que tienen el nivel más alto de energía de un átomo y que intervienen en los enlaces químicos.

vaporization The change of state from a liquid to a gas. (277)
vaporización Cambio del estado de líquido a gas.

velocity Speed in a given direction. (210)
velocidad Rapidez en una dirección dada.

viscosity A liquid's resistance to flowing. (268)
viscosidad Resistencia a fluir que presenta un líquido.

visible light Electromagnetic radiation that can be seen with the unaided eye. (232)
luz visible Radiación electromagnética que se puede ver a simple vista.

volume The amount of space that matter occupies. (17, 293)
volumen Cantidad de espacio que ocupa la materia.

W

wavelength The distance between two corresponding parts of a wave, such as the distance between two crests. (232)
longitud de onda Distancia entre dos partes correspondientes de una onda, por ejemplo la distancia entre dos crestas.

weight A measure of the force of gravity acting on an object. (16, 105, 291)
peso Medida de la fuerza de gravedad que actúa sobre un cuerpo.

white dwarf The blue-white hot core of a star that is left behind after its outer layers have expanded and drifted out into space. (119)
enana blanca Núcleo caliente y azul blanquecino de una estrella que queda después de que sus capas externas se han expandido y esparcido por el espacio.

INDEX
Page numbers for key terms are printed in **boldface** type.
Page numbers for illustrations, maps, and charts are printed in *italics*.

INDEX

Page numbers for key terms are printed in **boldface** type.
Page numbers for illustrations, maps, and charts are printed in *italics*.

INDEX

Page numbers for key terms are printed in **boldface** type.
Page numbers for illustrations, maps, and charts are printed in *italics*.

INDEX

Page numbers for key terms are printed in **boldface** type.
Page numbers for illustrations, maps, and charts are printed in *italics*.

INDEX

Page numbers for key terms are printed in **boldface** type.
Page numbers for illustrations, maps, and charts are printed in *italics*.

T

U

V

INDEX

Page numbers for key terms are printed in **boldface** type.
Page numbers for illustrations, maps, and charts are printed in *italics*.

ACKNOWLEDGMENTS

Staff Credits

The people who made up the *Interactive Science* team—representing composition services, core design digital and multimedia production services, digital product development, editorial, editorial services, manufacturing, and production—are listed below:

Jan Van Aarsen, Samah Abadir, Ernie Albanese, Chris Anton, Zareh Artinian, Bridget Binstock, Suzanne Biron, Niki Birbilis, MJ Black, Nancy Bolsover, Stacy Boyd, Jim Brady, Katherine Bryant, Michael Burstein, Pradeep Byram, Jessica Chase, Jonathan Cheney, Arthur Ciccone, Allison Cook-Bellistri, Rebecca Cottingham, AnnMarie Coyne, Bob Craton, Chris Deliee, Paul Delsignore, Michael Di Maria, Diane Dougherty, Kristen Ellis, Kelly Engel, Theresa Eugenio, Amanda Ferguson, Jorgensen Fernandez, Kathryn Fobert, Alicia Franke, Julia Gecha, Mark Geyer, Steve Gobbell, Paula Gogan-Porter, Jeffrey Gong, Sandra Graff, Robert M. Graham, Adam Groffman, Lynette Haggard, Christian Henry, Karen Holtzman, Susan Hutchinson, Sharon Inglis, Marian Jones, Sumy Joy, Sheila Kanitsch, Courtenay Kelley, Chris Kennedy, Toby Klang, Greg Lam, Russ Lappa, Margaret LaRaia, Ben Leveillee, Thea Limpus, Charles Luey, Dotti Marshall, Kathy Martin, Robyn Matzke, John McClure, Mary Beth McDaniel, Krista McDonald, Tim McDonald, Rich McMahon, Cara McNally, Bernadette McQuilkin, Melinda Medina, Angelina Mendez, Maria Milczarek, Claudi Mimo, Mike Napieralski, Deborah Nicholls, Dave Nichols, William Oppenheimer, Jodi O'Rourke, Ameer Padshah, Lorie Park, Celio Pedrosa, Jonathan Penyack, Linda Zust Reddy, Jennifer Reichlin, Stephen Rider, Charlene Rimsa, Walter Rodriguez, Stephanie Rogers, Marcy Rose, Rashid Ross, Anne Rowsey, Logan Schmidt, Amanda Seldera, Laurel Smith, Nancy Smith, Ted Smykal, Emily Soltanoff, Cindy Strowman, Dee Sunday, Barry Tomack, Elizabeth Tustian, Patricia Valencia, Ana Sofia Villaveces, Stephanie Wallace, Amanda Watters, Christine Whitney, Brad Wiatr, Heidi Wilson, Heather Wright, Rachel Youdelman.

Photography

All otherwise unacknowledged photos are copyright © 2011 Pearson Education.

Cover, Front and Back
NASA.

Front Matter
Page vi palm tree l, Fotomak/Shutterstock; **vi palm tree r,** Albo/Shutterstock; **vi roller coaster,** Jeffrey Greenberg/Photo Researchers, Inc.; **vi Florida Keys,** Thomas Barrat/Shutterstock; **vii coral,** Doug Perrine/Minden Pictures; **vii manatees,** Jeff Mondragon/Alamy; **vi-vii sky bkgrnd,** Serg64/Shutterstock; **viii,** Daniel Cox/Photolibrary New York; **ix,** Christian Darkin/Photo Researchers, Inc.; **x,** JPL/CalTech/STScI/Vassar/NASA/Photo Researchers, Inc.; **xi,** ESA/J. Clarke (Boston University)/Z. Levay (STScI)/NASA; **xii,** Tom Fox/Dallas Morning News/Corbis; **xiii,** Donald Miralle/Getty Images; **xiv,** Michael C. York/AP Images; **xv,** Nordic Photos/Photolibrary New York; **xvi,** Photolibrary New York; **xvii,** Javier Trueba/Madrid Scientific Films; **xviii,** David Doubilet/National Geographic Stock; **xix,** Cyril Ruoso/JH Editorial/Minden Pictures; **xx,** Rolf Nussbaumer/Minden Pictures, **xxi laptop,** iStockphoto; **xxi TV,** iStockphoto; **xxiii laptop,** iStockphoto; **xxv br,** JupiterImages/Getty Images; **xxviii laptop,** iStockphoto.

Unit 1 Big Idea Opener
Pages xxx–1, Photo by James Gathany/Susan McClure, Content Provider/Centers for Disease Control (CDC).

Chapter 1
Pages 2–3 spread, Daniel Cox/Photolibrary New York; **5 m1,** Paul Burns/Getty Images; **5 m2,** Paul Sutherland/National Geographic Stock; **5 t,** Mark Humphrey/AP Images; **6 l,** Copyright © 2006 by The National Academy of Sciences of the USA; **6 r,** Science Source/Photo Researchers, Inc.; **7 inset,** Inga Spence/Getty Images; **7 bkgrnd,** Tom & Pat Leeson/Photo Researchers, Inc.; **8,** W.D. Brush/USDA-NRCS PLANTS Database; **9,** Thomas Mangelsen/Minden Pictures; **10–11 spread,** Mark Humphrey/AP Images; **13,** Zhao Jianwei/ImagineChina/AP Images; **14,** Image Source/Getty Images; **15 bkgrnd,** Barry Mansell/Nature Picture Library; **15 butterfly,** Stephen Dalton/Minden Pictures; **16 l,** Paul Burns/Getty Images; **17,** Image100/Superstock; **19,** Kenneth Morris/ASP-Covered Images/Zuma Press; **20 b,** Tue Nam Ton/Contra Costa Newspapers/Zuma Press; **20 t,** Olga Lipatova/Shutterstock; **22 bkgrnd,** Image Source/Getty Images; **23,** Stem Jems/Photo Researchers, Inc.; **25,** Tomas Rodriguez/Photolibrary New York; **26,** Paul Sutherland/National Geographic Stock; **26–27 bkgrnd,** Craig Lenihan/AP Images; **28,** Mark Conlin/Alamy; **29,** Science & Society Picture Library/Getty Images; **30,** Mark Conlin/Alamy; **31,** Ho New/Reuters; **32,** Bill Curtsinger/National Geographic Stock; **33,** Mike Theiss/National Geographic Stock; **34,** NASA; **35,** Navnit/Shutterstock; **36,** Radius Images/Photolibrary New York; **37,** Sam Yu/The Frederick News-Post/AP Images; **40,** Patrick LaRoque/First Light Associated Photographers/Photolibrary New York; **42,** Tim Fitzharris/Minden Pictures; **43,** John Dominis/Index Stock Imagery/Photolibrary New York; **44 t,** Science Source/Photo Researchers, Inc.; **44 b,** Navnit/Shutterstock; **45,** Charlie Neuman/San Diego Union-Tribune/Zuma Press.

Chapter 2
Pages 48–49 spread, Christian Darkin/Photo Researchers, Inc.; **51 b,** Heribert Proepper/AP Images; **51 m1,** J. I. Alvarez-Hamelin, M. Beiró, L. Dall'Asta, A. Barrat, A. Vespignani, http://xavier.informatics.indiana.edu/lanet-vi/, http://sourceforge.net/projects/lanet-vi/; **51 m2,** Sergiy N./Shutterstock; **52,** Frank Greenaway/Dorling Kindersley; **56** Edgewater Media/Shutterstock; **057,** Babak Tafreshi/Photo Researchers, Inc.; **58,** *Untitled* (1920), George Grosz. Oil on canvas. Collection Kunstsammlung Nordrhein-Westfalen, Duesseldorf, Germany/Photo by Erich Lessing/Art Resource, New York/Copyright © 2009 VAGA; **59,** Walter C. Jaap/Sustainable Seas/R. Halley/Courtesy of USGS; **60 l,** Steve A. Munsinger/Photo Researchers, Inc.; **60 tr,** NASA; **61,** J. I. Alvarez-Hamelin, M. Beiró, L. Dall'Asta, A. Barrat, A. Vespignani, http://xavier.informatics.indiana.edu/lanet-vi/, http://sourceforge.net/projects/lanet-vi/; **62–63 spread,** Agence Zoom/Getty Images; **64,** Brian E. Small/VIREO; **66 inset,** Tony Heald/Minden Pictures; **66–67 spread,** Suzi Eszterhas/Minden Pictures; **68,** Michael & Patricia Fogden/Minden Pictures; **69,** Judy Kennamer/Shutterstock;

ACKNOWLEDGMENTS

70 l, NASA; **70 m,** Sergiy N./Shutterstock; **70 r,** Michael Abbey/Photo Researchers, Inc.; **71,** Jon Hughes/Bedrock Studios/Dorling Kindersley; **72,** Denis Farrell/AP Images; **73,** Merritt Vincent/PhotoEdit; **74–75 spread,** Heribert Proepper/AP Images; **75 inset,** Joel Sartore/National Geographic Stock; **76,** CERN/Photo Researchers, Inc.; **78 tl,** Bell Labs/Lucent Technologies/AP Images; **78 tr,** Science Source/Photo Researchers, Inc.; **78–79,** Harvey Georges/AP Images; **78–79 bkgrnd,** Dgrilla/Shutterstock; **79 b,** Kyodo/AP Images; **79 tl,** Kyodo/AP Images; **79 tr,** AmanaImages/Photolibrary New York; **80 b,** AmanaImages/Photolibrary New York; **80 t,** Walter C. Jaap/Sustainable Seas/R. Halley/Courtesy of USGS; **81 b,** Reha Mark/Shutterstock; **82,** Dr. Ken MacDonald/Photo Researchers, Inc.

Unit 1 Feature
Page 84 bkgrnd, Richard Broadwell/Alamy; **85,** Academie des Sciences, Paris/Archives Charmet/The Bridgeman Art Library.

Unit 1 Big Idea Review
Pages 86–87, Photo by James Gathany/Susan McClure, Content Provider/Centers for Disease Control (CDC).

Unit 2 Big Idea Opener
Pages 88–89, Hubble Space Telescope Collection/NASA.

Chapter 3
Pages 90–91 spread, JPL-CalTech/STScI/Vassar/NASA/Photo Researchers, Inc.; **93 b,** SOHO-EIT Consortium/ESA/NASA; **93 m1,** CXC/MIT/UMass Amherst/M.D.Stage/NASA Chandra Space Telescope Collection; **93 t,** Ames Research Center Image Library/NASA; **93 m2,** Photograph by David Malin/Copyright © 1980–2002, Anglo-Australian Observatory; **94,** Science Source/Photo Researchers, Inc.; **97 bl,** NASA; **97 bm,** SOHO/ESA/NASA; **97, br,** Photograph by David Malin/Copyright © 1980–2002, Anglo-Australian Observatory; **97 tr,** Tom Stack & Associates; **99,** NASA; **100–101 bkgrnd,** NASA; **101 b,** Spitzer Space Telescope Collection/NASA; **101 m2,** NASA; **101 m1,** Ames Research Center Image Library/NASA; **101 t,** ESA, R. O'Connell (University of Virginia), B. Whitmore (Space Telescope Science Institute), M. Dopita (Australian National University), and the Wide Field Camera 3 Science Oversight Committee/NASA; **102,** Photograph by David Malin/Copyright © 1980–2002, Anglo-Australian Observatory; **103 tl,** Photograph by David Malin/Copyright © 1980–2002, Anglo-Australian Observatory; **103 b,** JPL-CalTech/T. Pyle (SSC)/NASA; **103 tr,** Science Source/Photo Researchers, Inc.; **105,** Paul & Lindamarie Ambrose/Getty Images; **108–109 spread,** Malcolm Park/Oxford Scientific/Photolibrary New York; **110,** NASA/CXC/M.Weiss; Spectra: NASA/CXC/SAO/J. Miller, et al./NASA Chandra Space Telescope Collection; **112–113,** ESA/ESO/NASA FITS Liberator/NASA Digitized Sky Survey; **115,** Larry Landolfi/Photo Researchers, Inc.; **116,** ESA/CXC/JPL-CalTech/J. Hester and A. Loll (Arizona State Univ.)/R. Gehrz (Univ. Minn.)/STScI/NASA; **117,** ESA/The Hubble Heritage Team/NASA; **119,** CXC/MIT/UMass Amherst/M.D.Stage/NASA Chandra Space Telescope Collection; **119 bkgrnd,** European Space Agency and Justyn R. Maund (University of Cambridge)/NASA; **122,** LOOK Die Bildagentur der Fotografen GmbH/Alamy; **124–125 spread,** SOHO/ESA/NASA; **126 l,** SOHO-EIT Consortium/ESA/NASA; **126 r,** SOHO/ESA/NASA.

Chapter 4
Pages 132–133 spread, ESA/J. Clarke (Boston University)/Z. Levay (STScI)/NASA; **135 b,** JPL/Caltech/T. Pyle (SSC)/NASA; **135 t,** JPL/NIX/NASA; **136 b,** Johns Hopkins University Applied Physics Laboratory/NASA; **138 b,** Friedrich Saurer/Alamy; **139 m,** NASA Lunar and Planetary Laboratory; **141,** NASA Lunar and Planetary Laboratory; **142 inset,** Omikron/Photo Researchers, Inc.; **142–143 spread,** JPL/USGS/NASA; **144 Earth,** NASA Langley Research Center (NASA-LaRC); **144 moon,** JPL/USGS/NASA; **144–145 spread,** Apollo 11 Image Library/NASA; **146 l,** Magellan Project/JPL/NASA; **146 m1,** Bettmann/Corbis; **146 m,** Bettmann/Corbis; **146 r,** Library of Congress Department of Prints and Photographs [LC-USZ62-119343]; **148 tl,** NASA Lunar and Planetary Laboratory; **148 bl,** Messenger Teams/Johns Hopkins University Applied Physics Laboratory/NASA; **149 bl,** Apollo 17 Crew/NASA; **149 br,** NASA; **149 tl,** JPL/USGS/NASA; **149 tr,** NASA; **152–153 spread,** Mars Exploration Rover Mission/JPL/NASA; **153 inset,** Goddard Space Flight Center Scientific Visualization Studio, and Virginia Butcher (SSAI)/NASA; **154,** Judy Dole/The Image Bank/Getty Images; **155 m1,** NASA Lunar and Planetary Laboratory; **155 m2,** ESA/L. Sromovsky (University of Wisconsin, Madison)/H. Hammel (Space Science Institute)/K. Rages (SETI)/NASA; **155 r,** NASA; **155 l,** JPL/NIX/NASA; **156 l,** JPL/NIX/NASA; **156 Earth,** Apollo 17 Crew/NASA; **156 r,** JPL/NASA; **157 bkgrnd,** NASA; **158 b,** JPL/Space Science Institute/NASA; **158 m1,** JPL/NASA; **158 m2,** JPL/NASA; **159 t,** JPL/NASA; **158 t,** JPL/University of Arizona/NASA; **159 bl,** Science Source/Photo Researchers Inc.; **159 br,** JPL/Space Science Institute/NASA; **159 Earth,** Apollo 17 Crew/NASA; **160 Earth,** Apollo 17 Crew/NASA; **161 Earth,** Apollo 17 Crew/NASA; **160 tl,** ESA/L. Sromovsky (University of Wisconsin, Madison)/H. Hammel (Space Science Institute)/K. Rages (SETI)/NASA; **161 tr,** NASA; **161 m,** L. Sromovsky/P. Fry (University of Wisconsin-Madison)/NASA; **162 bkgrnd,** Alan Sirulnikoff/Getty Images; **165 bkgrnd,** Jerry Lodriguss/Photo Researchers, Inc.; **166 inset,** JPL/NASA; **167,** Paolo Koch/Photo Researchers, Inc.; **168 l,** Walter Myers; **168 r,** Walter Myers; **170 l inset,** Crawford Library/Royal Observatory, Edinburgh/Photo Researchers, Inc.; **170 r,** Detlev van Ravenswaay/Photo Researchers, Inc.; **170–171 quill pen & ink,** Furabolo/iStockphoto; **171 tl inset,** SPL/Photo Researchers, Inc.; **171 r,** Pictorial Press Ltd/Alamy; **172 l,** NASA; **174 b,** Jerry Lodriguss/Photo Researchers, Inc.; **174 m,** JPL/NIX/NASA; **174 t,** Omikron/Photo Researchers, Inc.

Chapter 5
Pages 178–179 spread, Tom Fox/Dallas Morning News/Corbis; **181 m1,** John W. Bova/Photo Researchers, Inc.; **181 m2,** Roger Ressmeyer/Corbis; **182 b,** John White Photos/Alamy; **182 t,** Robert Harding Picture Library Ltd/Alamy; **185 b,** Science Museum Pictorial/SSPL; **185 m,** Dea/A. Dagli Orti/Getty Images; **185 t,** Ragab Papyrus Institute Cairo/Gianni Dagli Orti/The Art Archive/The Picture Desk; **188,** Philippe Clement/Nature Picture Library; **189,** Elan Fleisher/

Look/AGE Fotostock; **190 bkrnd,** UV Images/Amana Images/ Corbis; **190 t,** Fred Espenak/Photo Researchers, Inc.; **192 l,** John W. Bova/Photo Researchers, Inc.; **192 m1,** John W. Bova/Photo Researchers, Inc.; **192 m2,** Eckhard Slawik/Photo Researchers, Inc.; **192 m3,** John W. Bova/Photo Researchers, Inc.; **192 r,** John W. Bova/Photo Researchers, Inc.; **193,** Roger Ressmeyer/Corbis; **194,** Jeff Vanuga/Corbis; **196 l,** Everett C. Johnson/Stock Connection/Science Faction/Corbis; **196 R,** Everett C. Johnson/Stock Connection/Science Faction/ Corbis; **199,** David Chapman/Photolibrary New York; **200 m,** Jeff Vanuga/Corbis; **201,** Jeff Vanuga/Corbis; **202 l,** Roger Ressmeyer/Corbis; **202 l,** Roger Ressmeyer/Corbis; **202 r,** Jeff Vanuga/Corbis.

Chapter 6
Pages 204–205 spread, Donald Miralle/Getty Images; **207 m2,** NASA; **208,** Yesikka Vivancos/epa/Corbis; **209,** US Civil Air Patrol/NASA; **211,** Mark Scheuern/Alamy; **214,** David Seal/NASA; **215 bl,** Sovfoto/Eastfoto; **215 br,** Detlev van Ravenswaay/Science Photo Library; **215 cl,** Ria Novosti/ Science Photo Library; **215 cr,** NASA; **215 tr,** NASA/Science Photo Library; **216 bl,** Hulton Archive/Getty Images; **216 tl,** Corbis; **216–217 bkgrnd,** NASA; **216–217 footprints,** NASA; **217 bl,** Corbis; **217 tl,** Roger Ressmeyer/Corbis; **218,** John Frassanito & Associates, Inc.; **222 b,** Roger Arno/ NASA; **222–223 t,** NASA/Johns Hopkins University Applied Physics Laboratory/Southwest Research Institute/Photo Researchers, Inc.; **223 b,** JPL/NASA; **223 tr,** David Ducros/ Science Photo Library/Photo Researchers, Inc.; **224,** NASA/ Science Photo Library; **225,** NASA/Roger Ressmeyer/Corbis; **226 l,** JSC/Stanford University/NASA; **226 t,** Steven Hobbs/ NASA; **226–227 bkgrnd,** Viktoriya/Shutterstock; **227 b,** Larry Lee/Photolibrary New York; **227 m,** Hank Morgan/ Photo Researchers, Inc.; **227 t,** Kennedy Space Center/NASA; **228 astronaut,** NASA/Roger Ressmeyer/Corbis; **228 bl,** Mark Andersen/Rubberball; **228 satelite,** Mark Evans/iStockphoto; **228 tl,** William King/Getty Images; **228 br,** iStockphoto; **229 headphones,** Photomorgana/Corbis/Photolibrary New York; **229 m,** Mehau Kulyk/Photo Researchers, Inc.; **229 shoes,** NASA Human Spaceflight Collection; **229 tr,** Terry Vine/Getty Images; **230 bkgrnd,** Frans Lanting/ Corbis; **230 inset,** Joe Raedle/Getty Images; **231 b,** Robert Nickelsberg/Getty Images; **231 helmet,** Colin Anderson/Blend Images/Corbis; **231 inset,** Steven Puetzer/Getty Images; **231 t,** John Tomaselli/Alamy; **232,** Chip Simons/Getty Images; **233 l,** John B. Free/Minden Pictures; **233 m,** Bjorn Rorslett/Science Photo Library/Photo Researchers, Inc.; **233 r,** Bjorn Rorslett/Science Photo Library/Photo Researchers, Inc.; **234 fifth from top left,** Biophoto Associates/Photo Researchers, Inc.; **234 first from top left,** Mehau Kulyk/Photo Researchers, Inc.; **234 fourth from top left,** Triff/iStockphoto; **234 second from top left,** Tek Image/Photo Researchers, Inc.; **234 seventh from top left,** Science Source/Photo Researchers, Inc.; **234 sixth from top left,** Gustoimages/ Photo Researchers, Inc.; **234 third from top left,** Ted Kinsman/Photo Researchers, Inc.; **236 b,** David Parker/Photo Researchers, Inc.; **236 t,** Jim Richardson/National Geographic Stock; **238,** GSFC/LaRC/JPL, MISR Team/NASA; **239,** NASA and E. Karkoschka (University of Arizona); **240–241 bkgrnd,** Kennedy Space Center/NASA; **241 l,** John Raoux/AP Images; **241 r,** Lynne Sladky/AP Images; **242 bl,** Terry Renna/AP

Images; **242 t,** St. Petersburg Times/ZUMA Press; **242–243 bkgrnd,** S.Borisov/Shutterstock; **243 b,** Scott Audette/ AP Images; **243 t,** Chris O'Meara/AP Images; **244,** Mark Scheuern/Alamy.

Unit 2 Feature
Page 248 bkgrnd, Tony McConnell/Photo Researchers, Inc.; **249 moon,** iStockphoto; **249 Aztec calendar,** Andy Crawford/ University Museum of Archaeology and Anthropology, Cambridge/Dorling Kindersley; **249 Earth,** iStockphoto.

Unit 2 Big Idea Review
Pages 250–251, Hubble Space Telescope Collection/NASA.

Unit 3 Big Idea Opener
Pages 252–253, Reuters.

Chapter 7
Pages 254–255 spread, AP Photo/Michael C. York; **257 b,** Charles D. Winters/Photo Researchers, Inc.; **257 m1,** BC Photography/Alamy; **257 m2,** SuperStock; **258 b,** *The Head of Medusa* (ca 1590), Michelangelo Merisi da Caravaggio. Oil on canvas glued to wood. Diameter: 21 5/8 in (55 cm). Restored 2005. Uffizi Gallery, Florence, Italy/Photograph copyright © Scala/Ministero per i Beni e le Attività culturali/Art Resource NY; **258 t,** *The Head of Medusa* (ca 1590), Michelangelo Merisi da Caravaggio. Oil on canvas glued to wood. Diameter: 21 5/8 in (55 cm). Pre-restoration. Uffizi Gallery, Florence, Italy/Photograph copyright © Nicolo Orsi Battaglini/ Art Resource NY; **259 l,** Nigel Hicks/Dorling Kindersley; **259 r,** Katy Williamson/Dorling Kindersley; **260 balloon,** Ashok Rodrigues/iStockphoto; **260 jewelry,** iStockphoto; **260 kettle,** Dorling Kindersley; **260 pan,** PhotoObjects/ JupiterUnlimited; **261 bkgrnd,** Max Blain/Shutterstock; **262 copper,** Albert J. Copley/AGE Fotostock/Photolibrary New York; **262 sulfur,** Mark A. Schneider/Photo Researchers, Inc.; **262 copper sulfide,** Steve Gorton/Dorling Kindersley; **263,** Fresh Food Images/Philip Wilkins/Photolibrary New York; **264 b,** Ryan Pyle/Corbis; **264 bkgrnd,** James M. Bell/Photo Researchers, Inc.; **265 rock,** Joel Arem/Photo Researchers, Inc.; **266 l,** Sue Atkinson/Fresh Food Images/Photolibrary New York; **266 r,** Mark A. Schneider/Photo Researchers, Inc.; **268,** BC Photography/Alamy; **269,** Charles D. Winters/ Photo Researchers, Inc.; **271,** Frits Meyst/Adventure4ever. com; **272,** Simon Butcher/Imagestate/Photolibrary New York; **274 l,** B. G. Thomson/Photo Researchers, Inc.; **274 r,** Mazzzur/Shutterstock; **275 b,** SuperStock; **275 t,** The Granger Collection, New York; **276,** Winfield Parks/National Geographic Society; **279 bkgrnd,** Neal Preston/Corbis; **279 inset,** Charles D. Winters/Photo Researchers, Inc.; **279 t,** Frank Greenaway/Dorling Kindersley; **280 l,** Michael S. Quinton/ National Geographic Stock; **280 r,** AlaskaStock/Photolibrary New York; **281 b,** Mark Gibson, **281 t,** Photolibrary New York; **282 b,** Mark Gibson; **282 t,** Mark A. Schneider/Photo Researchers, Inc.; **284,** David Branch/AP Images.

Chapter 8
Pages 286–287 spread, Nordic Photos/Photolibrary New York; **289 m2,** Andy Crawford/Dorling Kindersley; **289 m1,** Rita Januskeviciute/Shutterstock; **289 b crime-scene tape,** iStockphoto; **290 bkgrnd,** Patrick Robert/Corbis; **290 inset,**

ACKNOWLEDGMENTS

Juergen Hasenkopf/Alamy; **292 tl,** NASA; **292–293 spread,** Mark Lennihan/AP Images; **295 figure 4a,** Steve Gorton/Dorling Kindersley; **295 figure 4b,** Charles D. Winters/Photo Researchers, Inc.; **295 figure 4c,** Dorling Kindersley; **295 miners,** The Granger Collection, New York; **296,** Jennifer Davis/St. Petersburg Times/Zuma Press; **296 inset,** Mark Bowler/Photo Researchers, Inc.; **297 b,** Rita Januskeviciute/Shutterstock; **297 inset,** Stephen Coburn/Shutterstock; **298 b inset,** Yury Kosourov/Shutterstock; **298 bkgrnd,** Xiang Mei/Zuma Press; **298 m inset,** Jonathan Kitchen/White/Photolibrary New York; **298 t inset,** Olga Utlyakova/Shutterstock; **299 b,** Andy Crawford/Dorling Kindersley; **299 t,** iStockphoto; **300 arrowhead,** Matthew J. Sroka/Reading Eagle/AP Images; **300 single coin,** iStockphoto; **300–301 mummy,** Amr Nabil/AP Images; **300–301 t,** Jakub Semeniuk/iStockphoto; **301 pot inset,** Alex Wilson/Dorling Kindersley/Getty Images; **302 bkgrnd,** iStockphoto; **303,** iStockphoto; **304 fingerprint,** Courtesy of North Carolina State Bureau of Investigation, Raleigh NC; **304 crime-scene tape,** iStockphoto; **305 l,** *Erasmus Weathervane* (2008), Rodney Graham. Copper and steel. Whitechapel Gallery, London. Reproduced by permission of artist. Photo: Anthony Upton/AP Images; **306 t,** Nigel Hicks/Dorling Kindersley; **306 b,** Courtesy of North Carolina State Bureau of Investigation, Raleigh NC; **308,** Erasmus Weathervane (2008), Rodney Graham. Copper and steel. Whitechapel Gallery, London. Reproduced by permission of artist. Photo: Anthony Upton/AP Images.

Chapter 9
Pages 310–311 spread, Photolibrary New York; **313 m1,** Tom Schierlitz/Getty Images; **313 m2,** NASA/Photo Researchers, Inc.; **314 inset,** Portrait of Dmitry Ivanovich Mendeleyev (ca. 1865). Archives Larousse, Paris, France/The Bridgeman Art Library International; **315,** Copyright © 2008 Richard Megna/Fundamental Photographs; **317,** Photo by Gary Shulfer/Collection of C. Marvin Lang/University of Wisconsin, Stevens Point; **319,** Dorling Kindersley; **322 l,** Charles D. Winters/Photo Researchers, Inc.; **322 m,** Charles D. Winters/Photo Researchers, Inc.; **322 r,** Charles D. Winters/Photo Researchers, Inc.; **323 bl,** Charles D. Winters/Photo Researchers, Inc.; **323 br,** Kim Kyung Hoon/Reuters; **323 t,** PjrFoto/Studio/Alamy; **324 b,** Lucato/iStockphoto; **324 t,** Douglas Whyte/Corbis; **326 bl,** Myotis/Shutterstock; **326 tl,** Joel Arem/Photo Researchers, Inc.; **326 tm,** László Rákoskerti/iStockphoto; **326 tr,** Charles D. Winters/Photo Researchers, Inc.; **326–327 chain,** Tom Schierlitz/Getty Images; **327 forks,** Kai Schwabe/Photolibrary New York; **328 bl,** Living Art Enterprises, LLC/Photo Researchers, Inc.; **328 fireworks,** Corey Bill Ross/Flirt Collection/Photolibrary New York; **329 br,** Science Source/Photo Researchers, Inc.; **330 b,** Bullit Marquez/AP Images; **330 t,** Juerg Mueller/Keystone/AP Images; **331,** Salvatore Di Nolfi/Keystone/AP Images; **332,** Rene Tillmann/AP Images; **333,** Michael Freeman/Phototake Inc/Oxford Scientific/Photolibrary New York; **334,** Charles D. Winters/Photo Researchers, Inc.; **335,** Lawrence Lawry/Photo Researchers, Inc.; **336 bkgrnd,** Jim W. Grace/Photo Researchers, Inc.; **336 tl inset,** Tatiana Popova/Shutterstock; **337 b,** Stockbyte/Photolibrary; **337 t,** LWA/Dann Tardif/Photolibrary New York; **338 sun,** Julian Baum/Photo Researchers, Inc.; **339 l,** Rosenfeld Images Ltd/Photo Researchers, Inc.; **339 r,** NASA/Photo Researchers,

Inc.; **340 green man,** Peter Galbraith/iStockphoto; **342 l,** Courtesy of Nano-Tex, Inc.; **342 r,** Courtesy of Nano-Tex, Inc.; **343,** Novastock/Photolibrary New York; **344,** Paul Blundell Photography/Fresh Food Images/Photolibrary New York; **345 b,** Martin Bond/Photo Researchers, Inc.; **345 t,** Lynx/Iconotec/Photolibrary New York; **346 b,** Corey Radlund/Brand X Pictures/Photolibrary New York; **346 ml,** Steve Gorton and Gary Ombler/Dorling Kindersley; **346 mr,** Steve Gorton/Dorling Kindersley; **346 t,** Milton Wordley/Photolibrary New York; **348 cat,** Copyright © 2008 William Steinecker; **348 elephant,** DLILLC/Corbis; **350 t,** Kim Kyung Hoon/Reuters; **350 b,** Paul Blundell Photography/Fresh Food Images/Photolibrary New York; **350 ml,** Myotis/Shutterstock New York; **350 mr,** Lawrence Lawry/Photo Researchers, Inc.

Chapter 10
Pages 354–355 spread, Javier Trueba/Madrid Scientific Films; **357 b,** iStockphoto; **357 m2,** M. Claye/Photo Researchers, Inc.; **357 t,** Jerry Lampen/Reuters; **358,** Panorama Stock/Photolibrary New York; **359,** Andy Crawford/Dorling Kindersley; **361,** Ed Reinke/AP Images; **362–363 spread,** Charles D. Winters/Photo Researchers, Inc.; **363 t,** Edward Kinsman/Photo Researchers, Inc.; **364,** Chris Newbert/Minden Pictures; **366 m,** Andrew Lambert Photography/Photo Researchers, Inc.; **366 r,** Charles D. Winters/Photo Researchers, Inc.; **367 b,** Jerry Lampen/Reuters; **367 t,** Geoffrey Holman/iStockphoto; **368,** Fedorov Oleksiy/Shutterstock; **370–371 spread,** Peter Weber/Getty Images; **372–373 spread,** Damian Dovarganes/AP Images; **374 b inset,** Richard Ashworth/Robert Harding World Imagery; **374 bkgrnd,** Artur Tabor/Minden Pictures; **374 t inset,** Niedersächsisches Landesamt für Denkmalpflege/AP Images; **375,** M. Claye/Photo Researchers, Inc.; **378 l,** Jules Selmes and Debi Treloar/Dorling Kindersley; **378 b,** Cristina Pedrazzini/Photo Researchers, Inc.; **379 dish soap,** Shutterstock; **379 lime,** iStockphoto; **379 tr,** Dorling Kindersley; **379 window cleaner,** Shutterstock; **380 l salt close up,** Tom Pepeira/Photolibrary New York; **380–381 spread,** Eric Martin/Icontec/Photolibrary New York; **382 b,** Eric Martin/Icontec/Photolibrary New York; **382 t,** Ed Reinke/AP Images.

Chapter 11
Pages 386–387 spread, David Doubilet/National Geographic Stock; **389 m1,** Stew Milne/AP Images; **389 m2,** Eric Risberg/AP Images; **390 b,** Keller & Keller Photography/StockFood Creative/Getty Images; **391,** Jim Schwabel/Index Stock/Photolibrary New York; **392,** Skip O'Rourke/St Petersburg Times/Zuma Press; **394,** St. Petersburg Times/Zuma Press; **395 tr,** Charles D. Winters/Photo Researchers, Inc.; **396,** Marshville Productions/The Kobal Collection; **398,** Joe Scherschel/National Geographic Society; **399,** Eric Risberg/AP Images; **400–401 spread,** Stew Milne/AP Images; **402,** Tui De Roy/Minden Pictures; **403,** Jacqueline Larma/AP Images; **404 bkgrnd,** Patrick Byrd/Science Faction; **404 t inset,** Sergei Kozak/Getty Images; **408 t,** Jim Schwabel/Index Stock/Photolibrary New York.

Chapter 12
Pages 412–413 spread, Cyril Ruoso/JH Editorial/Minden Pictures; **415 m2,** Martyn F. Chillmaid/Photo Researchers, Inc.;

416 cookies, Zef/Shutterstock; **417 b,** Efiplus/Shutterstock; **417 m,** Christopher Pattberg/iStockphoto; **417 t,** Drew Hadley/iStockphoto; **420 l,** Martyn F. Chillmaid/Photo Researchers, Inc.; **420–421 effervescent tablets,** Gandee Vasan/Getty Images; **420–421 spread,** Kevin Summers/Getty Images; **421 tr,** Olivier Blondeau/iStockphoto; **422,** Ho New/ Reuters; **425 t,** Rue des Archives/Tal/The Granger Collection, New York; **426–427 spread,** Kaminskiy/Shutterstock; **428–429 spread m,** Morgan/AP Images; **429 b,** Peter Bennett/Ambient Images/Alamy; **429 t inset,** Steven Raniszewski/Design Pics Inc./Photolibrary New York; **430,** NASA/AP Images; **433,** Stephen Morton/AP Images; **436 t,** Gandee Vasan/Getty Images; **437,** James Harrop/iStockphoto; **438 l,** iStockphoto; **438 r,** Amanda Rohde/iStockphoto.

Unit 3 Feature
Page 440 bkgrnd, Joe Belanger /Shutterstock; **441,** *The Alchemist* (ca. 1640), Hendrick Heerschon. Oil on canvas. The Fisher Collection, Pittsburgh PA/Alamy.

Unit 3 Big Idea Review
Pages 442–443, Reuters.

Unit 4 Big Idea Opener
Pages 444–445, Wendell Metzen/Index Stock Imagery/ Photolibrary New York.

Chapter 13
Pages 446–447 spread, Rolf Nussbaumer/Minden Pictures; **449 m1,** Vincenzo Lombardo/Getty Images; **449 t,** AGE Fotostock/SuperStock; **450,** David Cook/Blueshiftstudios/ Alamy; **451 bkgrnd,** Robbert Koene/Getty Images; **451 l inset,** Adrian Bailey/Aurora Photos; **451 r inset,** AGE Fotostock/SuperStock; **453 bkgrnd,** Rich Iwasaki/Getty Images; **455,** Yuji Sakai/Getty Images; **456,** Pete Saloutos/ Corbis; **460,** Vincenzo Lombardo/Getty Images; **461,** Noah Clayton/Getty Images; **462,** Juniors Bildarchiv/Alamy; **464,** Emma Firth/Dorling Kindersley; **466,** Dr. Paul A. Zahl/Photo Researchers, Inc.; **468,** Christian Wheatley/Shutterstock; **469,** Scott Leslie/Minden Pictures; **472,** Scott Leslie/Minden Pictures; **474,** Rickey Rogers/Reuters.

Unit 4 Feature
Pages 476–477, XYZ/Shutterstock; **478 bkgrnd,** Carrie Garcia/Alamy; **478 inset,** FloridaStock/Shutterstock; **479 inset,** Jupiter Images/Creatas/Alamy; **479 bkgrnd,** Brent Waltermire/Alamy.

Unit 4 Big Idea Review
Pages 480–481, Wendell Metzen/Index Stock Imagery/ Photolibrary New York.

Appendix
Page 482, Moodboard/SuperStock; **483 all,** Eric Isselée/ Shutterstock.

this is your book

you can write in it

take note

this space is yours—great for drawing diagrams and making notes

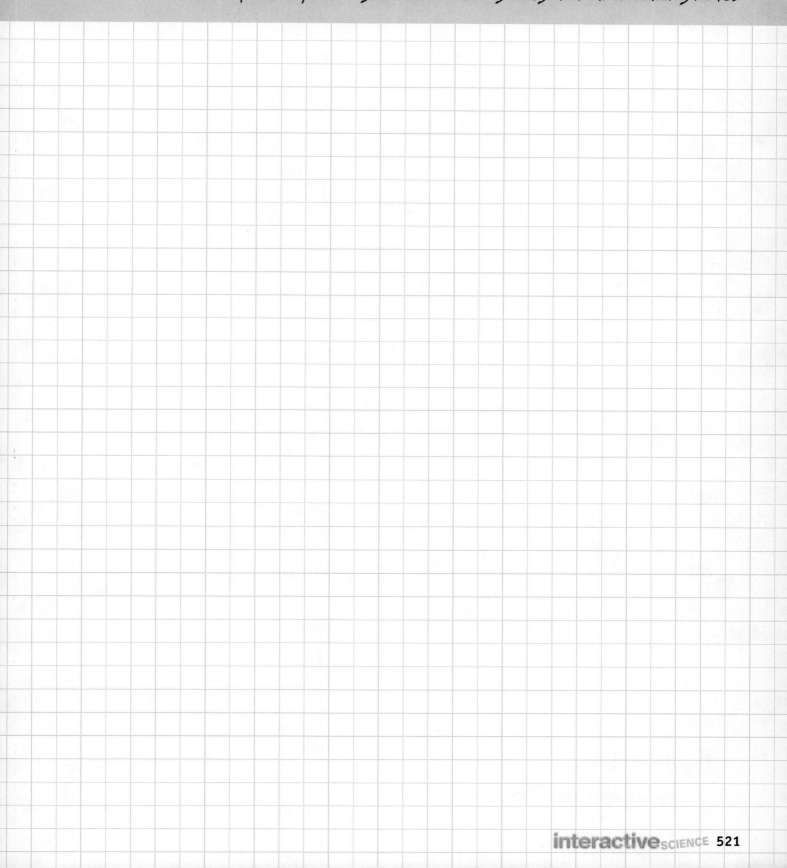

this is your book

you can write in it

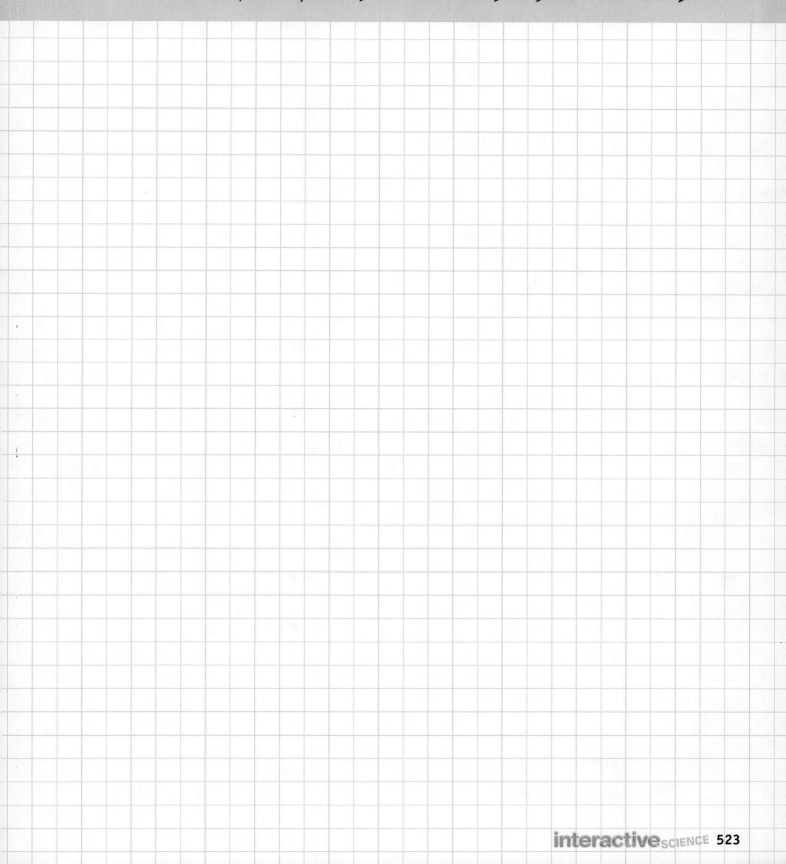

this is your book

you can write in it

this is your book

you can write in it

take note

this space is yours—great for drawing diagrams and making notes

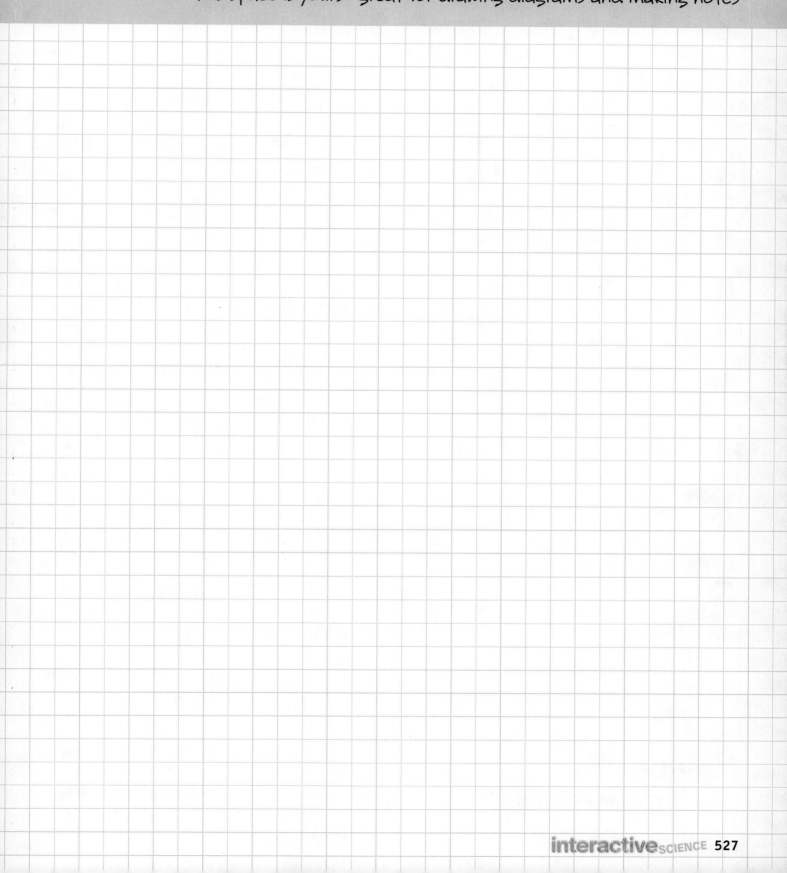

this is your book

you can write in it

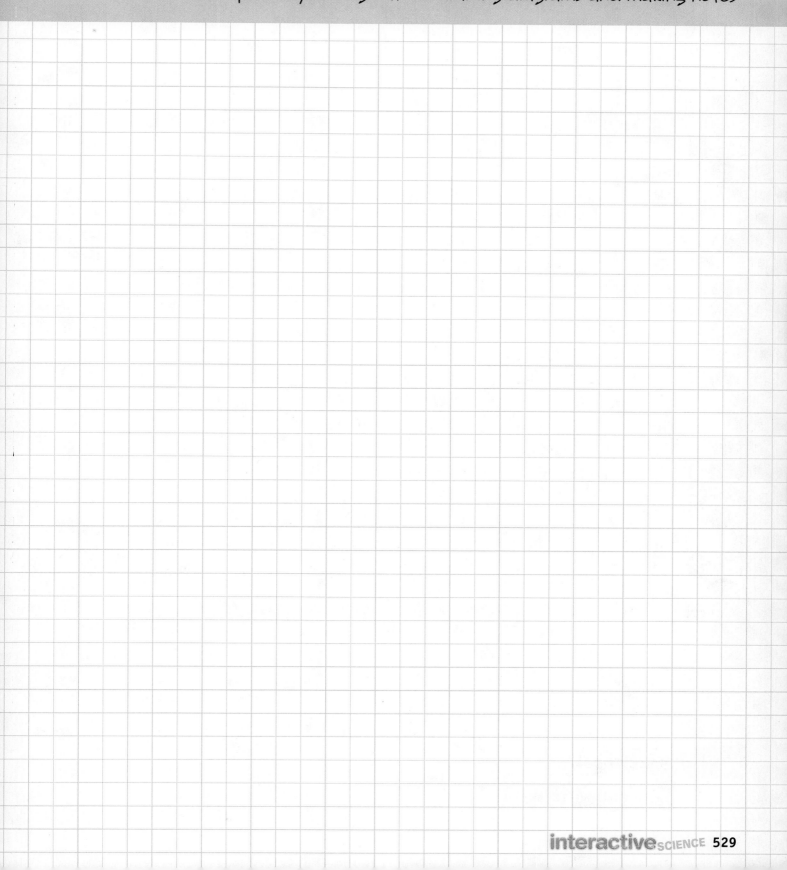

this is your book

you can write in it

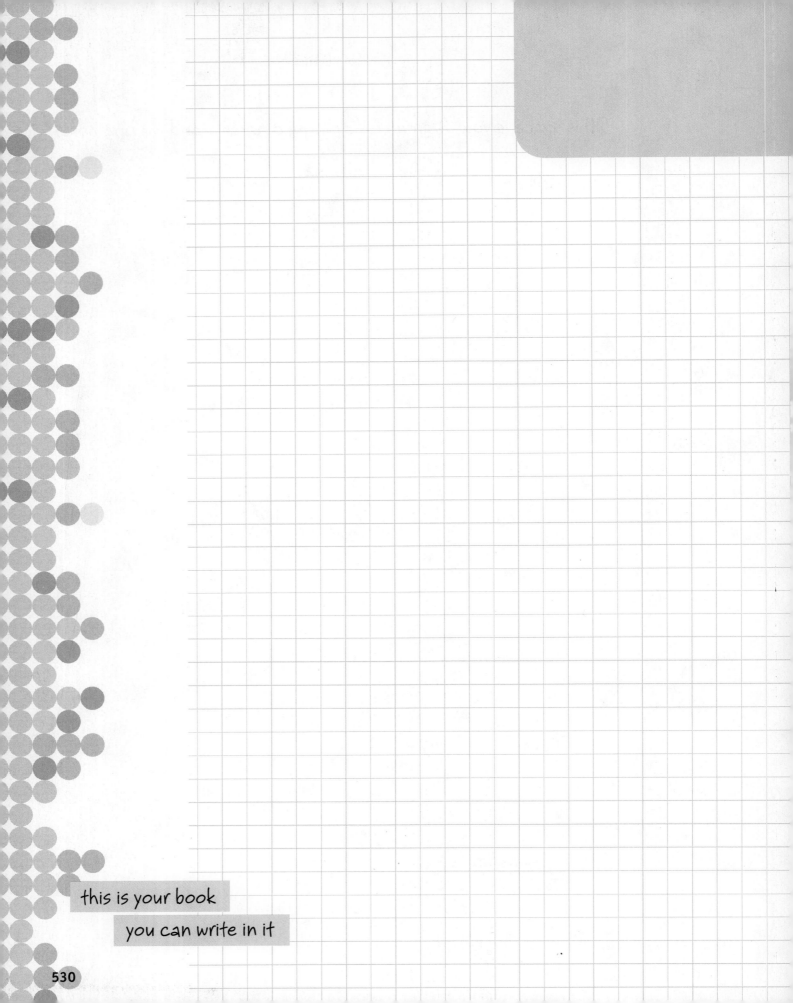